Style Guide

Lawrence H. Freeman, PhD
Terry R. Bacon, PhD

Contributors: **Sidney L. Jenson, PhD**
R. Breck England, PhD

*Shipley*Associates®

Writing in the World of Work

***Shipley**Associates*®
P.O. Box 460
Bountiful, Utah 84011

(801) 295-2386

Bethesda, MD	Dallas, TX	Chicago, IL	Burbank, CA
(301) 564-4301	(214) 637-7788	(708) 240-5111	(818) 842-4447

International Standard Book Number: 0-933427-00-X

Printed in the United States of America

About Shipley Associates

Customized Training Programs and Professional Services

Shipley Associates has served business, industry, and state and Federal Government agencies with excellent, customized communication programs and professional services since the early 1970s. Instead of the usual "off-the-shelf" programs and services, we customize our work to fulfill individual client and participant needs, thus ensuring increased productivity.

Benefits of Shipley Training and Services

Participants in Shipley Associates training:

- Identify their individual communication needs.
- Develop practical skills to solve real-world problems, with a minimum of theoretical discussion.
- Practice these skills for easy transfer from the workshop to the work environment.
- Receive workshop materials that can be used later as a guide and as a reference.
- Learn a common terminology with their peers and superiors about writing and speaking skills so that they can continue to help each other after completing the training.
- Develop a positive attitude about their abilities to write, edit, and speak that translates into increased productivity and profitability.

Professional Services

Communications Audits
Proposal Consultation Services
Proposal Process Audits
Document Management and Review
Coaching Presentations

Training Programs

Writing

Technical Writing
Effective Business Writing
Effective Business Writing/Interactive Videodisc
Executive Writing
Proofreading, Editing, and Writing
Audit Report Writing
Investigative Report Writing
Scientific Writing
Writing Effective NEPA Documents
Applying the NEPA Process
NEPA Executive Overview
Construction Specifications Writing
Equipment Specifications Writing
Military Specifications Writing
Managing Written Communication
Mastering Business Grammar

Presentations

Professional Presentations
Sales Presentations
Technical Presentations
Interactive Teaching Skills
Appraisal Process
Effective Meeting Management

Proposal

Managing Winning Proposals
Writing Commercial Proposals
Writing Winning Proposals
Developing Cost Volumes

Clientele

Private Sector Clients

Advanced Micro Devices, Inc.
Advanced Nuclear Fuels
Aerojet Electrosystems
Aerojet Techsystems
Allen-Bradley Company
Allied-Signal Aerospace
Amdahl Corporation
Amerada Hess Corporation
American Cyanamid Company
American Stores Company
Ameritech
Amoco Corporation
AMP Incorporated
ANG Coal Gasification Company
Apple Computer, Inc.
Applied Materials, Inc.
ARCO Oil & Gas Co.
ARINC Inc.
Arizona Nuclear
Armstrong World Industries, Inc.
Associated Field Engineers
AT&T
Avery International Corporation
Baltimore Aircoil Company
Baltimore Gas and Electric Company
Bank South Corporation
BASF Corporation
Baxter Healthcare Corporation
BBN, Inc.
Bechtel Group, Inc.
Beech Aircraft Corp.
Bell Helicopter Textron
The B. F. Goodrich Company
Blue Cross and Blue Shield Association
Boeing
BP Canada
C&S Bank
Cessna Aircraft
CH2M HILL
Chemical Waste Management, Inc.
Chevron Corporation
Chrysler Corporation
The Clorox Company
Comerica Incorporated
Computer Data Systems, Inc.
Comsat
Corning Inc.
Davy McKee Corporation
Detroit Edison Company
Digital Equipment Corporation
Douglas Aircraft Co.
DynCorp
Earth Technology Corporation
Eastman Kodak Company
EDS
EG&G, Inc.
E.I. Du Pont de Nemours & Co.
ENATOR, Sweden
ENSR
Ericsson Information Systems
E-Systems, Inc.
Esso
Exxon Corporation
Federal Reserve Bank
Fluor Daniel Inc.
FMC Corporation
Ford Aerospace
Ford Motor Company
Garrett Turbine Engine Company
General Dynamics Corporation
General Electric Company
General Instrument Corp.
General Motors Corporation
Georgia-Pacific Corporation
Gerber Products Company
Glaxo, Inc.
Grumman Corporation
GTE Corporation
Harris Corporation
Hercules Aerospace Company
Hewlett-Packard Company
Hoechst Celanese Corporation
Honeywell Inc.
Houston Lighting & Power Co.
Hughes Aircraft Company
IBM Corporation
Institute of Internal Auditors
Impell Corporation
Information Systems & Networks Corp.
Intel Corporation
Interstate Electronics Corp.
JHU Applied Physics Lab
J.M. Huber Corporation
J. Walter Thompson
Johnson & Johnson
Kaiser Engineers Hanford
Kerr-McGee Corporation
Kiewit Construction Group
Kimberly-Clark Corporation
Kraft Inc.
Link Flight Simulations
Litton Industries, Inc.
Lockheed Corporation
Loral
Los Angeles Times
Magnavox Electronic Systems Co.
Marion Merrell Dow
Martin Marietta Corporation
MCI Communications Corp.
McDonnell Douglas Corporation
McNeil Pharmaceutical
Meridian Oil Inc.
Michigan Bell
Milliman & Robertson
Mobil Corporation
Motorola, Inc.
National Bank of Detroit
NCNB Corporation
Newmont Gold Company
Newport Corporation
Newport News
Northrop Corporation
Novell, Inc.
Occidental Petroleum Corp.
Ohio Bell
Oryx Energy
Pacific Bell
Pacific Telesis Group
Parke-Davis Group
Phillips Petroleum Company
Planning Research Corporation
Power Technologies, Inc.
Raytheon Company
Rockwell International Corporation
Scott Paper Company
Security Pacific Corporation
Shell Oil Company
Sierra Pacific Industries
Sonat Inc.
Space Industries
Square D Company
Stewart & Stevenson Services, Inc.
Taco Bell
Telenet Communications Corp.
Texaco Inc.
Textron Inc.
TRW Inc.
Union Carbide Corporation
Unisys Corporation
United Technologies Corporation
Unocal Corporation
US West Communications
U.T.L. Corporation
Volkswagen of America, Inc.
Warner-Lambert Company
Waste Management, Inc.
Westinghouse Electric Corporation
The Wyatt Company
Xerox Corporation

Public Sector Clients

Air Force
Army
Bureau of Indian Affairs
Bureau of Land Management
Bureau of Mines
Bureau of Reclamation
CIA
Coast Guard
Corps of Engineers
DCAA
Defense Logistics Agency
Department of Energy
Environmental Protection Agency
Federal Aviation Agency
Federal Energy Regulatory Comm.
Fish and Wildlife Service
Forest Service
General Directorate of Posts, Sweden
General Services Administration
Geological Survey
Los Angeles Water and Power
Marine Corps
Minerals Management Service
NAS/Naval Air Depots
NASA
National Park Service
NAVAIR
NAVFAC
NAVSEA
Navy
Office of Surface Mining
Soil Conservation Service
SPAWAR
State of Alaska
State of Arizona
State of California
State of Maryland
State of Michigan
State of Montana
State of Utah
Voice of America
Western Area Power Administration

Contents

Reference Glossary (Section 1)

Model Documents Contents (Section 2)

Letters

Memos

Others

Reports

Surveying the Sections of the Style Guide

Use the chart below and the illustrations on the following pages when you have questions about using the *Style Guide*. As the chart indicates, you can locate information on writing style and the conventions of English either in the Reference Glossary (Section 1, pp. 1-288) or in the Model Documents (Section 2, pp. 1-70). The *Style Guide* also has a table of contents (pp. v-vi) and two indexes: Reference Glossary Index (Section 1, pp. 289-301) and Model Documents Index (Section 2, pp. 71-72).

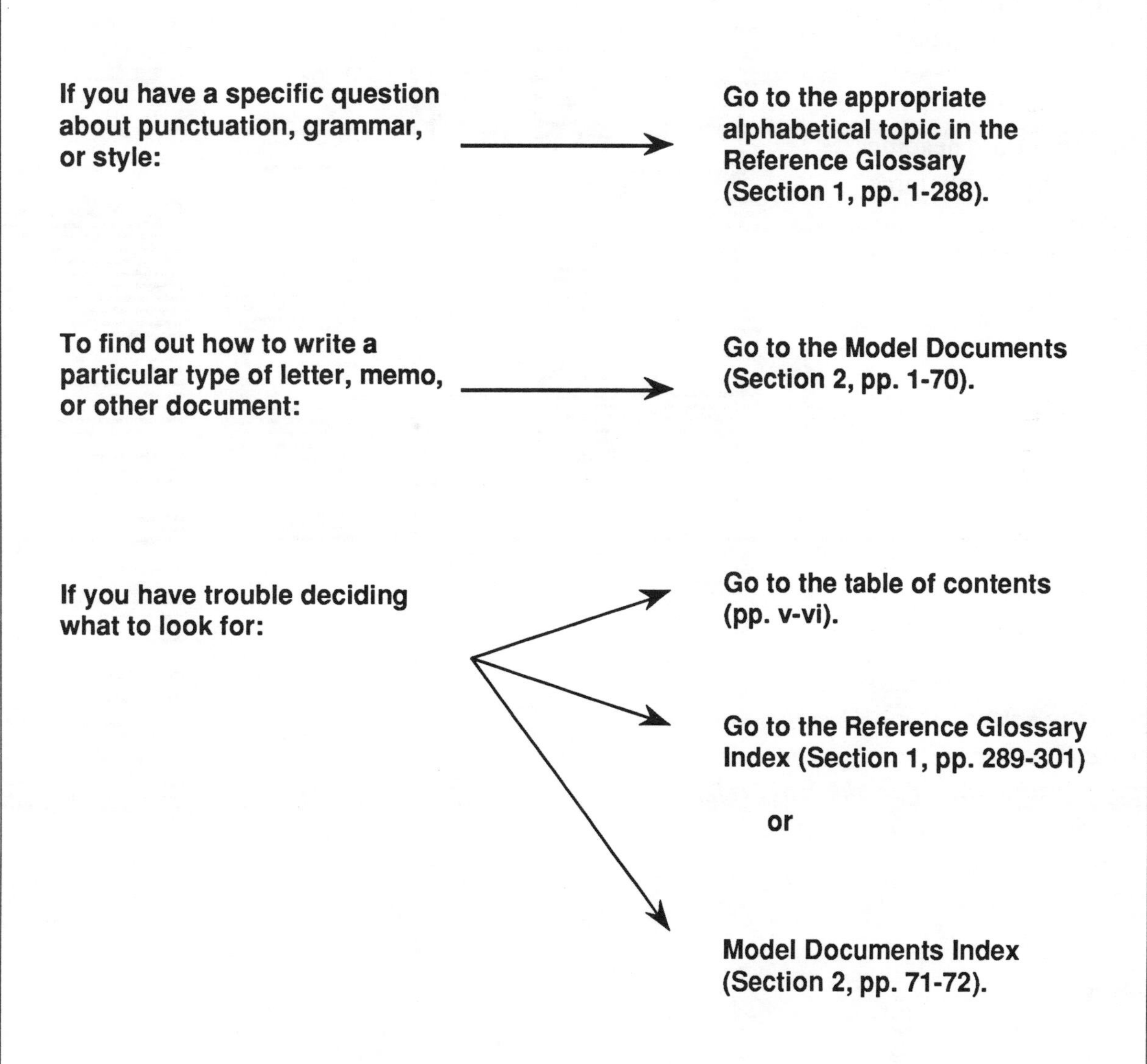

How to Use the Shipley Associates Style Guide

If you have a specific question about punctuation, grammar, or style—go to the appropriate alphabetical topic in the Reference Glossary (Section 1, pp. 1-288).

Sample Questions

- Should I use a comma or a semicolon to separate items in a series?
- Should I use a pie chart or a bar chart to illustrate my data?
- Should I use headings in a report only three pages long?

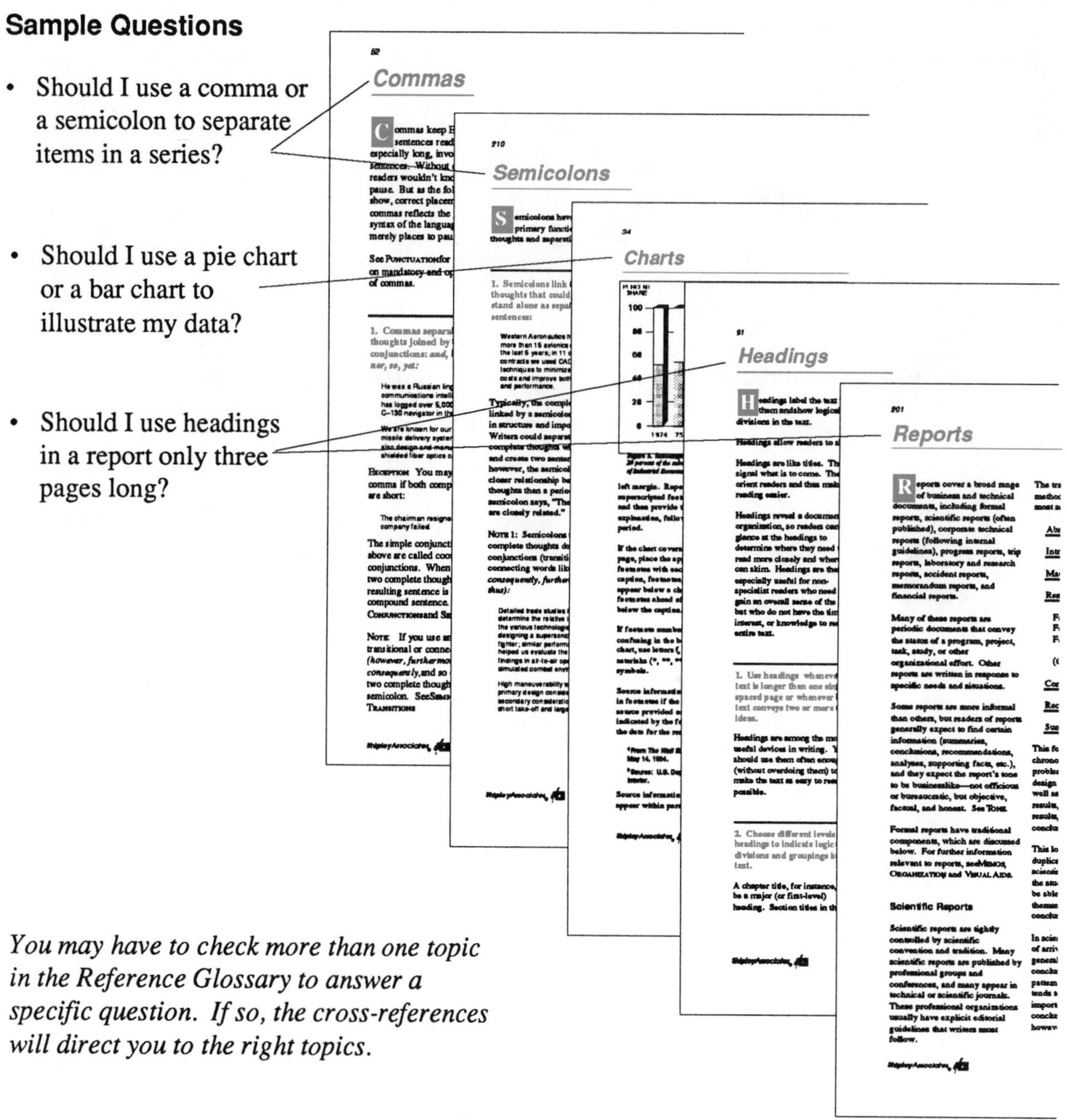

You may have to check more than one topic in the Reference Glossary to answer a specific question. If so, the cross-references will direct you to the right topics.

How to Use the Shipley Associates Style Guide

What should you look for once you find a topic that addresses your question?

Sample Question

- Should I use a comma or a semicolon to separate items in a series?

Step 1: Scan the topic for the pertinent rule. (Rules are numbered and printed in blue.)

Step 2: Look through the examples for one like your sentence or paragraph.

Step 3: Check the notes for exceptions or additional examples that might be helpful.

Step 4: Look up the cross-references (in small capital letters) if you need further information.

9

Commas

Commas keep English sentences readable, especially long, involved sentences. Without commas, readers wouldn't know when to pause. But as the following rules show, correct placement of commas reflects the grammar and syntax of the language, not merely places to pause.

See PUNCTUATION for information on mandatory and optional uses of commas.

1. Commas separate complete thoughts joined by these simple conjunctions: *and, but, or, for, nor, so, yet:*

> He was a Russian linguist in communications intelligence, and he has logged over 5,000 hours as a C–130 navigator in the Air Force.
>
> We are known for our land-based missile delivery systems, but we also design and manufacture shielded fiber optics cables.

EXCEPTION: You may omit this comma if both complete thoughts are short:

> The chairman resigned and the company failed.

The simple conjunctions cited above are called coordinate conjunctions. When they link two complete thoughts, the resulting sentence is called a compound sentence. See CONJUNCTIONS and SENTENCES.

NOTE: If you use any other transitional or connecting word (*however, furthermore, consequently,* and so on) to join two complete thoughts, use a semicolon. See SEMICOLONS and TRANSITIONS.

2. Commas separate items in a series consisting of three or more words, phrases, or even whole clauses:

> Control Data's Integrated Support Software System provides compatibility between tools and workers, consistent tool interfaces, ease of learning, user friendliness, and expandability.
>
> The user may also return to control program to perform such other functions as database editing, special report generation, and statistical analyses.
>
> The Carthage-Hines agreement contained provisions for testing the Pennsylvania sands, developing local permeability pinchouts, and exploring for undeveloped oil reserves in subthrust traps.

NOTE 1: A comma separates the last two items in a series although these items are linked by a conjunction (*and* in the above examples, but the rule applies for any conjunction). This comma was once considered optional, but the trend is to make it mandatory, especially in technical and business English. Leaving it out can cause confusion and misinterpretation. See PUNCTUATION.

NOTE 2: If all of the items in the series are linked by a simple conjunction, do not use commas:

> The user may also return to control program to perform such other functions as database editing and special report generation and statistical analyses.

NOTE 3: In sentences containing a series of phrases or clauses that already have commas, use semicolons to separate each phrase or clause:

> Our legal staff prepared analyses of the Drury-Engels agreement, which we hoped to discontinue; the Hopkinson contract; and the joint leasing proposal from Shell, Mobil, and Amoco.

See CONJUNCTIONS and SEMICOLONS.

3. Commas separate long introductory phrases and clauses from the main body of a sentence:

> Although we are new to particle scan technology, our work with split-beam lasers gives us a solid experiential base from which to undertake this study.
>
> For the purposes of this investigation, the weapon will be synthesized by a computer program called RATS (Rapid Approach to Transfer Systems).
>
> Oil production was down during the first quarter, but when we analyzed the figures, we discovered that the production decline was due to only two of our eight wells.

NOTE: In the last example, the *when we analyzed* clause does not open the sentence, but it must still be separated from the main clause following it. It introduces the main thought of the last half of the sentence.

EXCEPTION: If the introductory thought is short and no confusion will result, you can omit this comma:

How to Use the Shipley Associates Style Guide

To find out how to write a particular type of letter, memo, or other document—go to the Model Documents (Section 2, pp. 1-70). To see what models are available, check page vi of the table of contents or the duplicate table of contents on the divider page for the Model Documents.

Sample Questions

- How should I write a letter complaining about a product?
- How should I summarize information for executive bodies?
- How should I set up and organize a procedure for a procedure manual?

You may find more than one useful model.

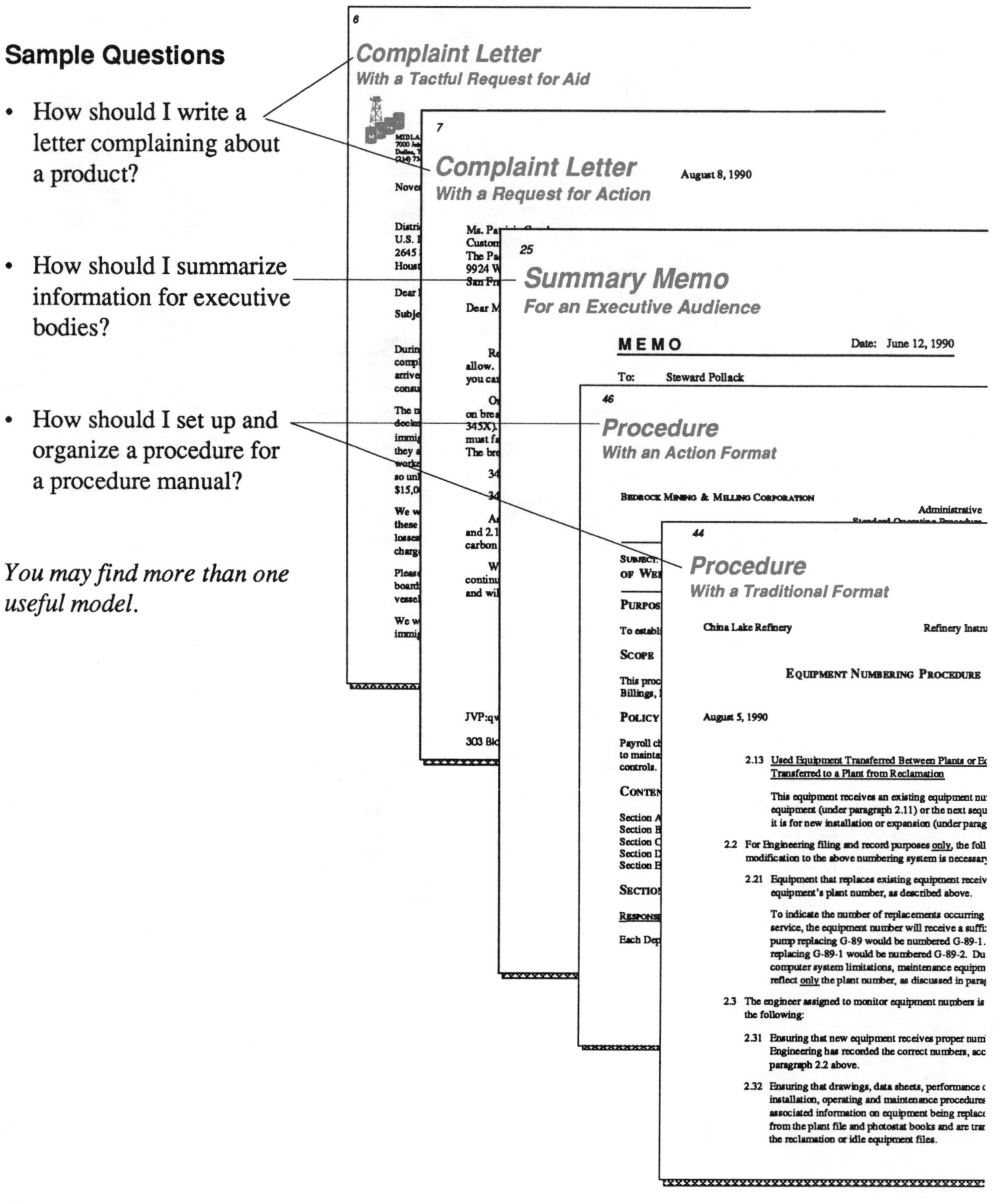

What should you look for once you locate a model similar to the letter, memo, or document you want to write?

8

Complaint Letter

With a Request for Action

Sample Question

- How should I write a letter complaining about a product?

Step 1: Read the model, noting its organization, format, style, and tone.

Step 2: Study the marginal comments for important notes, suggestions, and options.

Step 3: Read the bottom comment for general guidance on writing the letter, memo, or document.

Step 4: For further information or clarification, check one or more of the cross-references, usually to entries in the Reference Glossary (Section 1).

The lead sentence sets up the problem, and the second sentence asks for a solution. See LETTERS and ORGANIZATION.

The test results are highlighted by the additional space around them. See EMPHASIS.

The closing paragraph establishes how serious the writer considers the problem to be and applies some pressure; yet the tone is not blunt or negative. See TONE.

August 8, 1990

Ms. Patricia Goodway
Customer Support Manager
The Pacific Baking Company
9924 West Pacific Way
San Francisco, CA 97521

Dear Ms. Goodway:

Request for Adherence to Breader Specifications

Recent samples of your breader contain more fines than our specifications allow. Please investigate the problem and let me know as soon as possible what you can do to solve it.

On August 5, our Medford plant inspectors noticed excessive carbon specks on breaded products, so they checked the breader lots on hand (codes 341X and 345X). According to our specification, fines through a U.S. Standard Sieve No. 80 must fall within these limits: 1 percent ± 1 percent (or a maximum of 2 percent). The breader lots on hand gave these results:

341X—3.30%

345X—4.10%

As you can see, the fines in these two lots exceeded our specification by 1.3 and 2.1 percent. These levels are not yet serious, but they do cause excessive carbon specks in the frying oil and on the finished product.

We have enjoyed a long relationship with Pacific Baking and hope to continue doing business with you. We are therefore anxious to solve this problem and will appreciate your prompt action.

Sincerely,

James Van Prooven

James Van Prooven
Plant Manager

JVP:qw

303 Blossom Avenue   Des Moines, Iowa 50321   (515) 521-4911

Complaint letters, even if written in anger, should not sound angry. The tone should be positive and constructive. The writer should present clear evidence of dissatisfaction but should strive to balance the complaint with positive solutions. See TONES and LETTERS.

As in this letter, complaint letters usually start with a concise statement of the problem followed by a request for action or resolution. The problem statement should be as brief as possible but long enough to make the request understandable. See the discussion of set-ups in ORGANIZATION.

This letter illustrates the semiblock format with standard punctuation. See LETTERS.

How to Use the Shipley Associates Style Guide

If you have trouble deciding what to look for—go to the table of contents (pp. v-vi) or one of the indexes:

Reference Glossary Index (Section 1, pp. 289-301)
Model Documents Index (Section 2, pp. 71-72)

Sample Question

- How should I begin a response letter?

Step 1: Check the table of contents for topics that might help you with your problem.

Step 2: Turn to the most promising topic in the Reference Glossary or model in the Model Documents.

Step 3: If your first topic or model doesn't help you, go to another one.

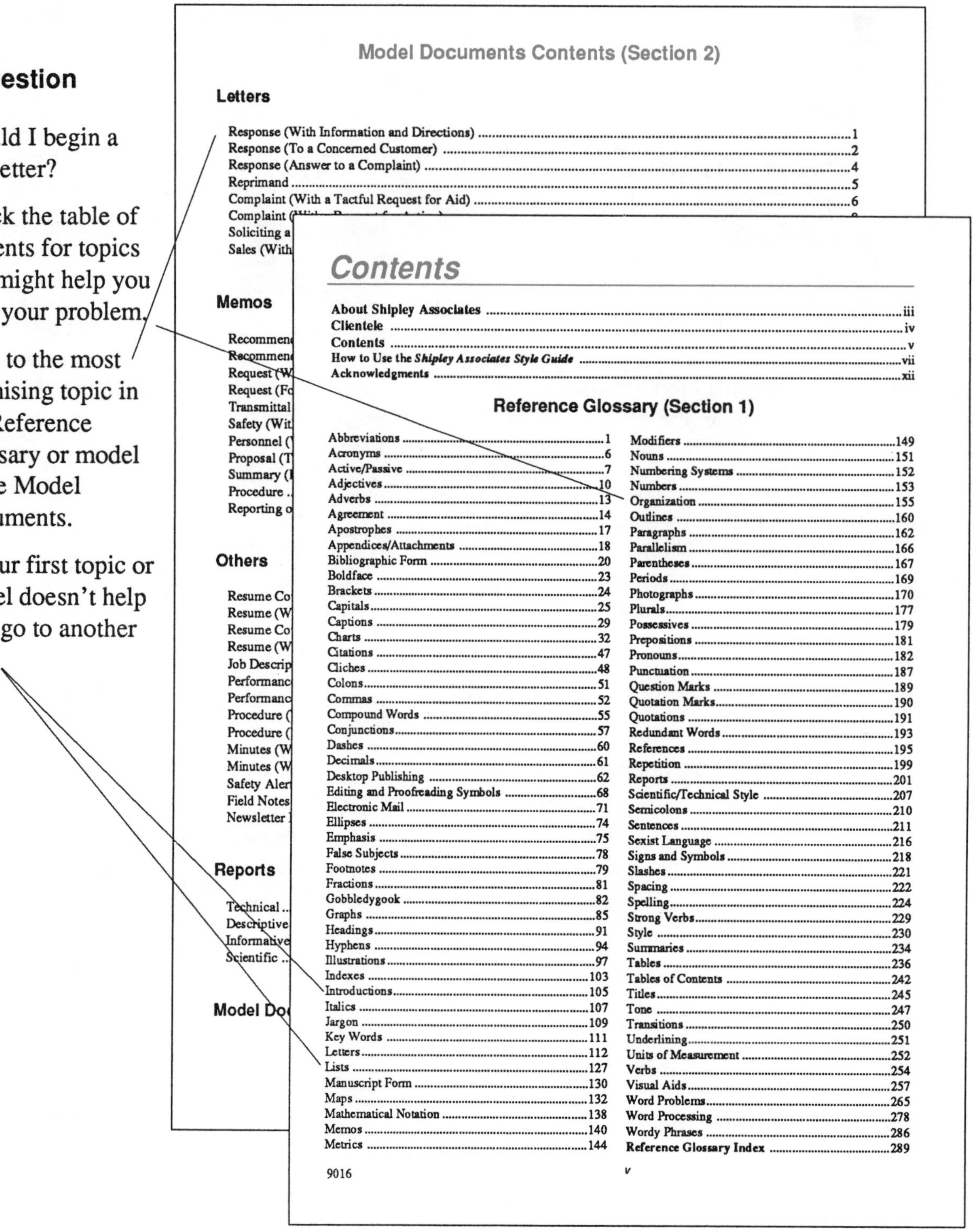

Model Documents Contents (Section 2)

Letters

Memos

Others

Reports

Model Do

Contents

Reference Glossary (Section 1)

9016 v

How to Use the Shipley Associates Style Guide

Sample Question

- How should I begin a response letter?

Step 1: Survey either of the two indexes for topics that might help you with your problem.

Step 2: Check any cross-references to other topics in the index.

Step 3: Look up the most promising topic in the Reference Glossary or model in the Model Documents.

Step 4: If your first topic or model doesn't help you, go to another one.

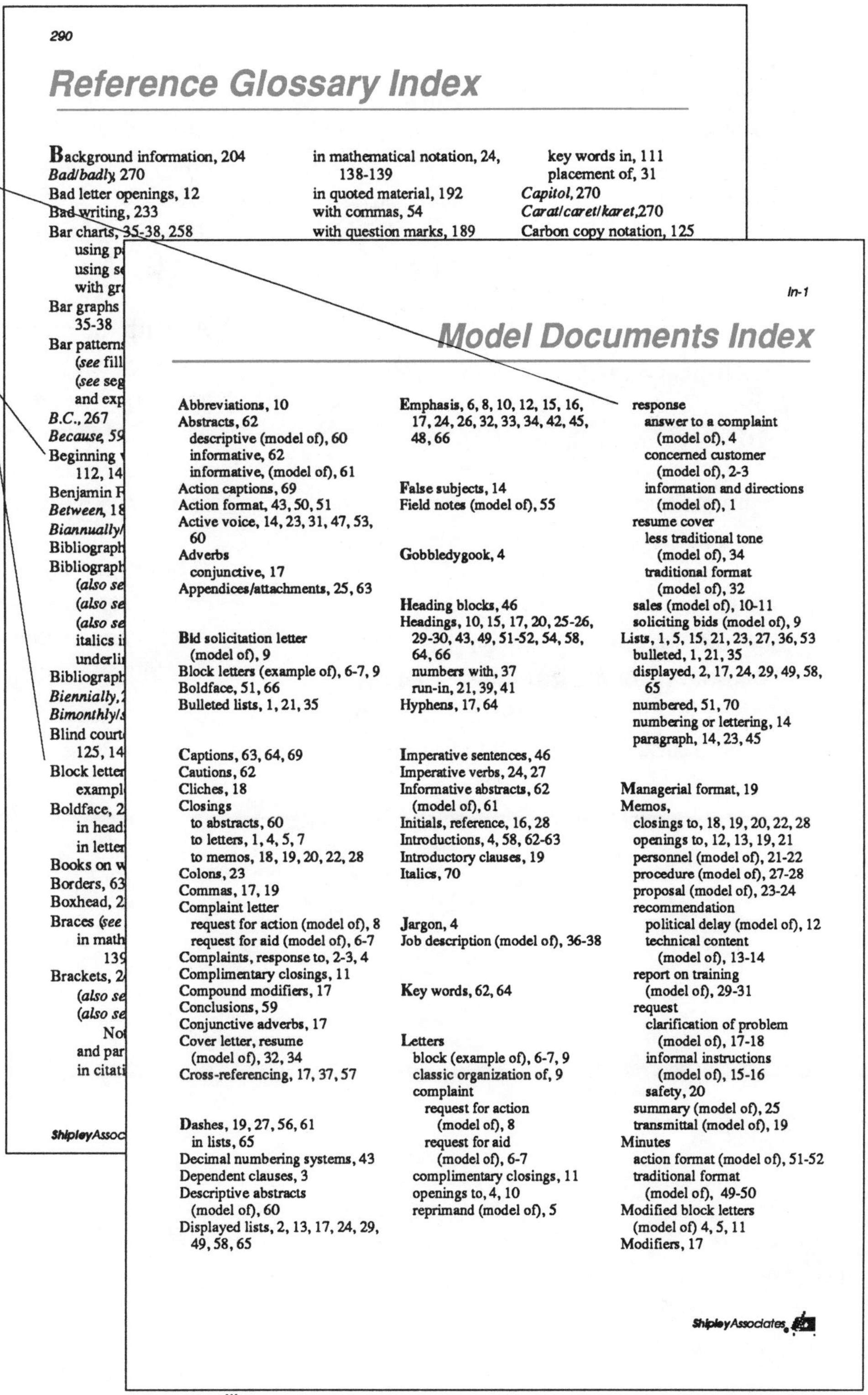

290

Reference Glossary Index

ShipleyAssoc

In-1

Model Documents Index

ShipleyAssociates

Acknowledgments

Before acknowledging those people who actively contributed to this revised edition of the *Shipley Associates Style Guide*, we wish to thank the tens of thousands of engineers, geologists, proposal managers, chemists, technicians, biologists, environmental specialists, lawyers, geophysicists, secretaries, editors, accountants, auditors, managers, supervisors, and others who have participated in Shipley Associates workshops. Without their questions, concerns, problems, uncertainties, challenges, and insights, we would not have been able to produce either the original *Style Guide* or this revised edition. In teaching them, we have learned; in learning from us, they have taught.

Many professionals at Shipley Associates have contributed to the revised edition of the *Shipley Associates Style Guide*. In particular, Jeff Butler, William Stringham, Breck England, and Sidney Jenson participated in the initial planning meetings, which were chaired by George Knight, the Director of our Research and Development Division.

Many other Shipley Associates consultants and professionals have made informal comments and suggestions. We have tried to incorporate all such suggestions into this revised edition.

Judy Olson, the project leader, has supervised and coordinated all professional and support activities. Her attention to detail and her dedication to the project have been outstanding.

As with the original edition, we acknowledge an excellent staff: Deanna Metcalf (editor and proofreader), Barbara Petersen (word processing), and Fred Boyd (graphics). We also wish to acknowledge June Freeman's assistance with proofreading.

Without the labor, intelligence, and dedication of these many fine Shipley Associates professionals, this revised edition would not exist.

Lawrence H. Freeman
Terry R. Bacon
April 1990

Reference Glossary

Contents (Section 1)

English and Current Style

Like all languages, English is a set of conventions: sounds and ways to spell these sounds, words and ways to combine them, sentence structures, punctuation symbols, and word meanings that range from the concrete to the abstract.

These conventions change over time. Words are born, grow, and change in meaning; they evolve through usage and die from disuse when writers and speakers no longer need them. Similarly, punctuation, spelling, and stylistic conventions change. They evolve as the language adapts to printing presses, computers, space shuttles, television, new industries, changing social concerns and political issues, new perspectives on history, new economic theories—in short, to everything in a constantly changing world.

English has changed dramatically since eighth-century *Beowulf,* one of the earliest English texts. Today, the original text of *Beowulf* looks as though it is written in a foreign language. English has even changed since Shakespeare was writing—only 400 years ago. The original language in Shakespeare's plays is often incomprehensible to modern readers. And 400 years from now, readers of English will likely consider today's English just as incomprehensible.

Living languages like English constantly change. (Dead languages like Latin do not change.) If English were static, we could give precise rules for style and usage. We could ensure that those rules followed logic, were consistent, and had no unruly exceptions. But English is dynamic, and over time its conventions have evolved—often in unpredictable and seemingly nonsensical ways. So its rules are not always logical; they are rarely consistent; and they have many, many exceptions.

However, with a little diligence and the right tools, you can use English well. This *Style Guide* is one of the right tools. **You** have to supply the diligence.

In this book, we have recorded the *currently* accepted stylistic conventions of English. We have labeled those conventions *rules*, but you should understand that these rules merely describe current stylistic conventions, especially as they apply to business and technical documents. The rules are not laws, and over time they will surely change. If you compare this *Style Guide* to other style guides, you will probably find disagreements. As we wrote this book, we often had to make decisions about stylistic preferences. Where authorities disagreed with each other, we chose the style most in harmony with the needs of technical and business writers and readers, and where an academic authority's stylistic preference conflicted with common and accepted usage in today's business and technical community, we chose common usage.

We have simplified some discussions and descriptions to make them more useful to writers who are not experts in grammar and punctuation. Our simplifications do not misrepresent the current conventions of English grammar, but they may overlook certain exceptions and complexities (often of value only to university scholars).

Abbreviations

Abbreviations allow writers to avoid cumbersome repetition of lengthy words and phrases. They are a form of shorthand and are appropriate in technical and business writing, particularly in lists, tables, charts, graphs, and other visual aids where space is limited.

See ACRONYMS.

1. Eliminate periods in and after most abbreviations.

Formerly, most abbreviations required periods. Today, the trend is to eliminate periods in and after abbreviations, especially in the abbreviated names of governmental agencies, companies, private organizations, and other groups:

AFL-CIO	AMA	CBS	DOE
FTC	IOOF	NFL	NLRB
OPEC	TVA	TWA	YWCA

NOTE 1: The abbreviations covered by this rule do not include informal ones such as Dept. and Mgt., which use a final period but no periods between letters.

NOTE 2: By convention some abbreviations still require periods:

A.D.	a.m.	B.C.	Dr.
e.g.	etc.	i.e.	Mr.
Mrs.	Ms.	p.m.	pp.
U.K.	U.S.A.	U.S.S.R.	

Retain the period, too, in abbreviations that spell normal words:

in., inches (*not* in)

no., number (*not* no)

A recent dictionary, such as *Webster's New Collegiate Dictionary,* is the best resource for determining if an abbreviation requires periods. See REFERENCES.

NOTE 3: Abbreviations with periods should be typed without spaces between letters and periods:

e.g. (*not* e. g.)

U.K. (*not* U. K.)

2. Use the same abbreviation for both singular and plural units of measurement.

When you abbreviate a unit of measurement, use the same symbol for both the singular and the plural forms:

6 lb and 1 lb
3 m and 1 m
20 ft and 1 ft
23.5 cm and 1.0 cm

If you spell out the abbreviated word, retain the plural when the number is greater than one:

15 kilometers and 1 kilometer
6.8 meters and 1 meter

3. Clarify an unfamiliar abbreviation by enclosing its unabbreviated form within parentheses following its first use in a document:

The applicant had insurance through CHAMPUS (Civilian Health and Medical Program of the Uniformed Services).

The alloy is hardened with 0.2 percent Np (neptunium). Adding Np before cooling alters the crystalline structure of manganese host alloys.

NOTE 1: Some authorities prefer to cite the unabbreviated form of the word before its abbreviation. We believe that this practice can inhibit, rather than enhance, the reader's comprehension of the abbreviation:

The applicant had insurance through the Civilian Health and Medical Program of the Uniformed Services (CHAMPUS).

The alloy is hardened with 0.2 percent neptunium (Np). Adding Np before cooling alters the crystalline structure of manganese host alloys.

NOTE 2: Do not use an unfamiliar abbreviation unless you plan to use it more than once in the same document.

4. Do not abbreviate a unit of measurement unless it is used in conjunction with a number:

Pipe diameters will be measured in inches.

but

Standard pipe diameter is 3 in.

The dimensions of the property were recorded in both meters and feet.

but

The property is 88 ft by 130 ft.

The southern property line is 45.3 m.

5. Do not abbreviate a title unless it precedes a name:

The cardiac research unit comprises five experienced doctors.

but

Our program director is Dr. Royce Smith.

Abbreviations

6. Spell out abbreviations that begin a sentence (except for abbreviated words that, by convention, are never spelled out, like *Mr.* and *Mrs.*):

Oxygen extraction will be accomplished at high temperatures.

not

O_2 extraction will be accomplished at high temperatures.

except

Ms. Jean MacIntyre will be responsible for modifying our subsea sensors.

7. Spell out abbreviated words that are connected to other words by hyphens:

6-foot gap *(not* 6-ft)
12-meter cargo bay *(not* 12-m)
3.25-inch pipe *(not* 3.25-in.)

NOTE: The spelled-out form is preferred. The abbreviated form (as in 6-ft) is common in some engineering documents, especially those with many numerical values. The hyphen is retained in the abbreviated form. See HYPHENS.

Other Conventions

8. Do not abbreviate the names of months and days within normal text. Use the abbreviations in chronologies, notes, tables, and charts:

The facilities modernization plan is due January 1985. *(not* Jan 1985 *or* 1/85)

9. Avoid the symbol form of abbreviations except in charts, graphs, illustrations, and other visual aids:

55 percent *(not* 55%)
15 ft *(not* 15')
32.73 in. *(not* 32.73")

10. Use a single period when an abbreviation ends a sentence:

To head our laser redesign effort, we have hired the 1990 Nobel prize winner from the U.S.A. *(not* U.S.A..)

NOTE: If the clause or sentence ends with something other than a period, (e.g., commas, semicolons, colons, question marks, exclamation points), then the other mark of punctuation follows the period at the end of the abbreviation:

Have we hired the 1990 Nobel prize winner from the U.S.A.?

If you plan to arrive by 6 p.m., you will not need to guarantee your reservation.

List of Abbreviations

Following is a list of many common abbreviations for words and common measurements.

In this listing, some abbreviations appear with periods, although the trend is to eliminate the periods (see rule 1). For example, *Ph.D.* appears with periods to assist writers and typists who wish to retain the periods, although many writers today prefer the increasingly more common *PhD* without periods.

In this listing, abbreviations printed without periods are ones that customarily appear without periods—e.g., *HF* or *log*.

Also refer to *The Chicago Manual of Style,* 13th edition, and to *Webster's New Collegiate Dictionary*. See REFERENCES.

Abbreviations of Words and Phrases

AA, Alcoholics Anonymous
A.B. or B.A., bachelor of arts
abbr., abbreviation
abs., abstract
acct., account
A.D. *(anno Domini),* in the year of the Lord
ADP, automated data processing
a.k.a., also known as
A.M. *(anno mundi),* in the year of the world
A.M. or M.A., master of arts
a.m. *(ante meridiem),* before noon
approx., approximately
Ave., avenue
a.w.l., absent with leave
a.w.o.l., absent without official leave

B.C., before Christ
bf., boldface
Bldg., building
B.Lit(t). or Lit(t).B., bachelor of literature
Blvd., boulevard
b.o., buyer's option
B.S. or B.Sc., bachelor of science

Ca. *(circa),* about
ca, centiare
c. and s.c., caps and small caps
c.b.d., cash before delivery
cf. *(confer),* compare or see
Co., company
c.o.d., cash on delivery
COLA, cost of living adjustment
con., continued
Conus., continental United States
Corp., corporation
c.p., chemically pure
C.P.A., certified public accountant
cr., credit; creditor
Ct., court

d.b.a., doing business as
D.D., doctor of divinity
D.D.S., doctor of dental surgery
Dist. Ct., District Court
D.Lit(t). or Lit(t).D., doctor of literature
do. (ditto), the same

Abbreviations

DP, displaced person
D.P.H., doctor of public health
D.P.Hy., doctor of public hygiene
dr., debit; debtor
Dr., doctor; drive
D.V.M., doctor of veterinary medicine

E., east
e.g. *(exempli gratia)*, for example
emcee, master of ceremony
e.o.m., end of month
et al. *(et alii)*, and others
et seq. *(et sequentia)*, and the following
etc. *(et cetera)*, and others

f., ff., and following page (pages)
f°, folio
f.o.b., free on board
4°, quarto

GI, general issue; government issue
G.M.&S., general, medical, and surgical
GNP, gross national product
Gov., governor
Govt., government
gr. wt., gross weight

HE, high explosive
HF, high frequency

ibid. *(ibidem)*, in the same place
id. *(idem)*, the same
i.e. *(id est)*, that is
IF, intermediate frequency
Insp. Gen., Inspector General
IOU, I owe you
IQ, intelligence quotient

J.D. *(jurum doctor)*, doctor of laws
Jr., junior

lat., latitude
LC, Library of Congress
lc., lowercase
liq., liquid
lf., lightface
LF, low frequency
LL.B., bachelor of laws
LL.D., doctor of laws
loc. cit. *(loco citato)*, in the place cited
log, logarithm
long., longitude
Ltd., limited
Lt. Gov., lieutenant governor

M, money supply: M_1; M_{1B}; M_2
M., monsieur; MM., messieurs
m. *(meridies)*, noon
M.D., doctor of medicine
memo, memorandum
MF, medium frequency
MIA, missing in action *(plural,* MIAs)
Mlle., mademoiselle
Mme., madam; Mmes., mesdames
mo., month
Mr., mister *(plural,* Messrs.)
Mrs., mistress
Ms., coined feminine title *(plural,* Mses.)
M.S., master of science
MS., MSS., manuscript, manuscripts
Msgr., monsignor
m.s.l., mean sea level

N., north
NA., not available; not applicable
NE., northeast
n.e.c., not elsewhere classified
n.e.s., not elsewhere specified
net wt., net weight
No., Nos., number, numbers
n.o.i.b.n., not otherwise indexed by name
n.o.p., not otherwise provided (for)
n.o.s., not otherwise specified
n.s.k., not specified by kind
n.s.p.f., not specifically provided for
NW., northwest

OK, OK'd, OK'ing, OK's
op. cit. *(opere citato)*, in the work cited

PA, public address system
PAC, political action committee *(plural,* PACs)
Ph.B. or B.Ph., bachelor of philosophy
Ph.D. or D.Ph., doctor of philosophy
Ph.G., graduate in pharmacy
PIN, personal identification number
Pl., place
p.m. *(post meridiem)*, afternoon
P.O. Box *(with number), but* post office box *(in general sense)*
POW, prisoner of war *(plural,* POWs)
Prof., professor
pro tem *(pro tempore)*, temporarily
P.S. *(post scriptum)*, postscript; public school *(with number)*

QT, on the quiet

RAM, random access memory
R&D, research and development
Rd., road
RDT&E, research, development, testing, and evaluation
Rev., reverend
RF, radio frequency
R.F.D., rural free delivery
RIF, reduction(s) in force; RIF'd, RIF'ing, RIF's
R.N., registered nurse
RR., railroad
Rt. Rev., right reverend
Ry., railway

S., south; Senate bill *(with number)*
S&L(s), savings and loan(s)
sc. *(scilicet)*, namely *(see also* ss)
s.c., small caps
s.d. *(sine die)*, without date
SE., southeast
2d, 3d, second, third
SHF, superhigh frequency
sic, thus
SOP, standard operating procedure
SOS, wireless distress signal
sp. gr., specific gravity
Sq., square *(street)*
Sr., senior
SS, steamship
ss *(scilicet)*, namely *(in law) (see also* sc.)
St., Ste., SS., Saint, Sainte, Saints
St., street
STP, standard temperature and pressure
Supt., superintendent
Surg., surgeon
SW., southwest

T., Tps., township, townships
Ter., terrace
t.m., true mean
TV, television

uc., uppercase
UHF, ultrahigh frequency
U.S.A., United States of America
USA, U.S. Army
U.S. 40, U.S. No. 40, U.S. Highway No. 40

v. or vs. *(versus)*, against
VAT, value added tax
VCR, videocassette recorder
VHF, very high frequency
VIP, very important person
viz *(videlicet)*, namely
VLF, very low frequency
VTR, videotape recording

W., west
w.a.e., when actually employed
wf, wrong font
w.o.p., without pay

ZIP Code, Zone Improvement Plan Code *(Postal Service)*
ZIP+4, 9-digit ZIP Code

Abbreviations of Units of Measurement

A, ampere
Å, angstrom
a, are
a, atto *(prefix,* one-quintillionth)
aA, attoampere
abs, absolute *(temperature and gravity)*
ac, alternating current
AF, audiofrequency
Ah, ampere-hour
A/m, ampere per meter
AM, amplitude modulation
asb, apostilb
At, ampere-turn
at, atmosphere
atm, atmosphere *(infrequently,* As)
at wt, atomic weight

Abbreviations

au, astronomical units
avdp, avoirdupois

b, barn
B, bel
b, bit
bbl, barrel
bbl/d, barrel per day
Bd, baud
bd. ft., board foot *(obsolete); use* fbm
Bé, Baumé,
Bev *(obsolete); see* GeV
Bhn, Brinell hardness number
bhp, brake horsepower
bm, board measure
bp, boiling point
Btu, British thermal unit
bu, bushel

c, ¢, ct; cent(s)
c, centi *(prefix,* one-hundredth)
C, coulomb
c, cycle *(radio)*
°C, degree Celsius
cal, calorie *(also*: cal_{IT}, International Table; cal_{th}, thermochemical)
cc. *(obsolete), use* cm^3
cd, candela *(obsolete:* candle)
cd/in², candela per square inch
cd/m², candela per square meter
c.f.m. *(obsolete),* use ft³/min
c.f.s. *(obsolete), use* ft³/s
cg, centigram
c·h, candela-hour
Ci, curie
cL, centiliter
cm, centimeter
c/m, cycles per minute
cm², square centimeter
cm³, cubic centimeter
cmil, circular mil
cp, candlepower
cP, centipoise
cSt, centistokes
cu ft *(obsolete),* use ft³
cu in *(obsolete),* use in³
cwt, hundredweight

D, darcy
d, day
d, deci *(prefix,* one-tenth)
d, pence
da, deka *(prefix,* 10)
dag, dekagram
daL, dekaliter
dam, dekameter
dam², square dekameter
dam³, cubic dekameter
dB, decibel
dBu, decibel unit
dc, direct current
dg, decigram
dL, deciliter
dm, decimeter
dm², square decimeter
dm³, cubic decimeter

dol, dollar
doz, dozen
dr, dram
dwt, deadweight tons
dwt, pennyweight
dyn, dyne

EHF, extremely high frequency
emf, electromotive force
emu, electromagnetic unit
erg, erg
esu, electrostatic unit
eV, electronvolt

°F, degree Fahrenheit
F, farad
f, femto *(prefix,* one-quadrillionth)
F, fermi *(obsolete); use* fm, femtometer
fbm, board foot; board foot measure
fc, footcandle
fL, footlambert
fm, femtometer
FM, frequency modulation
ft, foot
ft², square foot
ft³, cubic foot
ftH_2O, conventional foot of water
ft·lb, foot-pound
ft·lbf, foot pound-force
ft/min, foot per minute
ft²/min, square foot per minute
ft³/min, cubic foot per minute
ft-pdl, foot poundal
ft/s, foot per second
ft²/s, square foot per second
ft³/s, cubic foot per second
ft/s², foot per second squared
ft/s³, foot per second cubed

G, gauss
G, giga *(prefix,* one billion)
g, gram; acceleration of gravity
Gal, gal cm/s²
gal, gallon
gal/min, gallons per minute
gal/s, gallons per second
Gb, gilbert
g/cm³, gram per cubic centimeter
GeV, gigaelectronvolt
GHz, gigahertz (gigacycle per second)
gr, grain; gross

h, hecto *(prefix,* 100)
H, henry
h, hour
ha, hectare
HF, high frequency
hg, hectogram
hL, hectoliter
hm, hectometer
hm², square hectometer
hm³, cubic hectometer
hp, horsepower
hph, horsepower-hour
Hz, hertz (cycles per second)

Id, inside diameter
ihp, indicated horsepower
in., inch
in², square inch
in³, cubic inch
in/h, inch per hour
inH_2O, conventional inch of water
inHg, conventional inch of mercury
in-lb, inch-pound
in/s, inch per second

J, joule
J/K, joule per kelvin

K, kayser
K, kelvin *(degree symbol improper)*
k, kilo *(prefix,* 1,000)
k, thousand (7k = 7,000)
kc, kilocycle; *see also* kHz (kilohertz), kilocycles per second
kcal, kilocalory
keV, kiloelectronvolt
kG, kilogauss
kg, kilogram
kgf, kilogram-force
kHz, kilohertz (kilocycles per second)
kL, kiloliter
klbf, kilopound-force
km, kilometer
km², square kilometer
km³, cubic kilometer
km/h, kilometer per hour
kn, knot *(speed)*
kΩ, kilohm
kt, kiloton; carat
kV, kilovolt
kVa, kilovoltampere
kvar, kilovar
kW, kilowatt
kWh, kilowatthour

L, lambert
L, liter *(also* l)
lb, pound
lb ap, apothecary pound
lb avdp, avoirdupois pound
lbf, pound-force
lbf/ft, pound-force foot
lbf/ft², pound-force per square foot
lbf/ft³, pound-force per cubic foot
lbf/in², pound-force per square inch
lb/ft, pound per foot
lb/ft², pound per square foot
lb/ft³, pound per cubic foot
lct, long calcined ton
ldt, long dry ton
LF, low frequency
lin ft, linear foot
l/m, lines per minute
lm, lumen
lm/ft², lumen per square foot
lm/m², lumen per square meter
lm·s, lumen second
lm/W, lumen per watt
l/s, lines per second
L/s, liter per second
lx, lux

Abbreviations

M, mega *(prefix,* 1 million)
M, million (3M = 3 million)
m, meter
m, milli *(prefix,* one-thousandth)
M_1, monetary aggregate
m^2, square meter
m^3, cubic meter
μ, micro *(prefix,* one-millionth)
μ, micron *(obsolete); use* μm, micrometer
mA, milliampere
μA, microampere
mbar, millibar
μbar, microbar
Mc, megacycle; *see also* MHz (megahertz), megacycles per second
mc, millicycle; *see also* mHz (millihertz), millicycles per second
mcg, microgram *(obsolete); use* μg
mD, millidarcy
meq, milliquivalent
MeV, megaelectronvolts
mF, millifarad
μF, microfarad
mG, milligauss
mg, milligram
μg, microgram
Mgal/d, million gallons per day
mH, millihenry
μH, microhenry
mho, mho *(obsolete); use* S, siemens
MHz, megahertz
mHz, millihertz
mi, mile *(statute)*
mi^2, square mile
mi/gal, mile(s) per gallon
mi/h, mile per hour
mil, mil
min, minute *(time)*
μin, microinch
mL, milliliter
mm, millimeter
mm^2, square millimeter
mm^3, cubic millimeter
mμ, *(obsolete); see* nm, nanometer
μm, micrometer
μm^2, square micrometer
μm^3, cubic micrometer
μμ, micromicron *(use of compound prefixes is obsolete); use* pm, picometer
μμf, micromicrofarad *(use of compound prefixes is obsolete); use* pF
mmHg, conventional millimeter of mercury
μmho, micromho *(obsolete); use* μS, microsiemens
MΩ, megohm
mo, month
mol, mole *(unit of substance)*
mol wt, molecular weight
mp, melting point
ms, millisecond
μs, microsecond
Mt, megaton
mV, millivolt
μV, microvolt
MW, megawatt
mW, milliwatt
μW, microwatt
MWd/t, megawatt-days per ton
Mx, maxwell

n, nano *(prefix,* one-billionth)
N, newton
nA, nanoampere
nF, nanofarad
nm, nanometer (millimicron, *obsolete)*
N·m, newton meter
N/m^2, newton per square meter
nmi, nautical mile
Np, neper
ns, nanosecond
$N\cdot s/m^2$, newton second per square meter
nt, nit

od, outside diameter
Oe, oersted *(use of* A/m, amperes per meter, *preferred)*
oz, ounce *(avoirdupois)*

p, pico *(prefix,* one-trillionth)
P, poise
Pa, pascal
pA, picoampere
pct, percent
pdl, poundal
pF, picofarad (micromicrofarad, *obsolete)*
pF, water-holding energy
pH, hydrogen-ion concentration
ph, phot; phase
pk, peck
p/m, parts per million
ps, picosecond
pt, pint
pW, picowatt

qt, quart
quad, quadrillion (10^{15})

°R, rankine
°R, roentgen
R, degree rankine
R, degree reaumur
rad, radian
rd, rad
rem, roentgen equivalent man
r/min, revolutions per minute
rms, root mean square
r/s, revolutions per second

s, second *(time)*
s, shilling
S, siemens
sb, stilb
scp, spherical candlepower
s·ft, second-foot
shp, shaft horsepower
slug, slug
sr, steradian
sSf, standard saybolt fural
sSu, standard saybolt universal
$stdft^3$, standard cubic foot (feet)
Sus, saybolt universal second(s)

T, tera *(prefix,* 1 trillion)
Tft^3, trillion cubic feet
T, tesla
t, tonne *(metric ton)*
tbsp, tablespoonful
thm, therm
ton, ton
tsp, teaspoonful
Twad, twaddell

u, (unified) atomic mass unit
UHF, ultrahigh frequency

V, volt
VA, voltampere
var, var
VHF, very high frequency
V/m, volt per meter

W, watt
Wb, weber
Wh, watthour
W/(m·K), watt per meter kelvin
W/sr, watt per steradian
$W/(sr\cdot m^2)$, watt per steradian square meter

x, unknown quantity

yd, yard
yd^2, square yard
yd^3, cubic yard
yr, year

Acronyms

Acronyms are abbreviations that are pronounced as words:

ALGOL (ALGOrithmic Language)

Amtrak (American Track)

ARAMCO (ARabian AMerican oil COmpany)

BASIC (Beginners' All-purpose Symbolic Instruction Code)

BIT *or* bit (BInary digiT)

CAD (Computer-Aided Design)

CAM (Computer-Aided Manufacturing)

COBOL (COmmon Business-Oriented Language)

FORTRAN (FORmula TRANslator)

laser (Light Amplification by Simulated Emission of Radiation)

loran (LOng-RAnge Navigation)

NATO (North Atlantic Treaty Organization)

NOW (National Organization for Women)

Pepco (Potomac Electric Power Company)

PERT (Program Evaluation and Review Technique)

radar (RAdio Detecting And Ranging)

SALT (Strategic Arms Limitation Treaty)

secant (SEparation Control of Aircraft by Nonsynchronous Techniques)

sonar (SOund NAvigation Ranging)

START (STrategic Arms Reduction Treaty)

UNICEF (United Nations International Children's Emergency Fund)

WAC (Womens Army Corps)

Waves (Women Accepted for Volunteer Emergency Service)

ZIP (Zone Improvement Plan)

Acronyms may be written in ALL CAPITALS if they form proper names. However, some acronyms are conventionally uppercase and lowercase:

Amtrak Pepco

The most common acronyms, those representing generic technical concepts rather than organizations or programs, are typically all lowercase:

laser radar sonar

Some acronyms appear either in capitals or in lowercase:

BIT *or* bit

See ABBREVIATIONS.

---

1. When you introduce new or unfamiliar acronyms, use the acronym and then, in parentheses, spell out the name or expression:

Our program fully complies with the provisions of STEP (the Supplemental Training and Employment Program). To implement STEP, however, we had to modify subcontracting agreements with four components suppliers.

NOTE: Some writers and editors prefer to introduce unfamiliar acronyms by first spelling out the component words and then placing the acronym in parentheses.

---

2. Avoid overusing acronyms, especially if your readers are unlikely to be very familiar with them.

Until readers learn to recognize and instantly comprehend an acronym (like *laser*), the acronym hinders reading. It creates a delay while the reader's mind recalls and absorbs the acronym's meaning. Therefore, you should be cautious about using acronyms, especially unfamiliar ones. Overloading a text with acronyms makes the text unreadable, even if you have previously introduced and explained the acronyms.

Acronyms are good shorthand devices, but use them judiciously.

Active/Passive

Active- and passive-voice sentences each convey actions. They differ in how they convey these actions by their different grammatical structures. Both types of sentences are good sentences, even though passive voice has received extensive bad press.

Active- and passive-voice sentences usually have three basic elements:

- The actor—the person or thing performing the action
- The action—the verb
- The receiver—the person or thing receiving the action

When the structure of the sentence has the actor in front of the action, the sentence is in the **active voice:**

> Australian companies manufacture millions of precision machine tools.

Companies is the actor; *manufacture* is the action; and *tools* receives the action. Because the actor comes before the action, the sentence is active. The subject of the sentence performs the action.

When the structure of the sentence has the receiver in front of the action, the sentence is in the **passive voice:**

> Millions of precision machine tools are manufactured by Australian companies.

In this sentence, the subject (*tools*) is not doing the manufacturing. The tools are being manufactured. They are being acted upon; they are receiving the action. Therefore, the subject—and the sentence—is passive.

1. Prefer active sentences.

Active sentences are usually shorter and more dynamic than passive sentences. They generally have more impact and seem more "natural" because readers expect (and are accustomed to) the actor-action-receiver pattern. Active writing is more forceful and more self-confident.

Passive writing, on the other hand, can seem weak-willed, indecisive, or evasive. In passive sentences, the reader encounters the action before learning who performed it. In some passive sentences, the reader never discovers who performed the action. So passive sentences seem static.

Passive sentences are useful—even preferable—in some circumstances, but you should prefer active sentences.

When to Use Passives

2. Use a passive sentence when you don't know or don't want to mention the actor:

> The failure occurred because metal shavings had been dropped into the worm-gear housing.
>
> Clearly, the site had been inspected, but we found no inspection report and could not identify the inspectors.

In the first example above, a passive sentence is acceptable because we don't know who dropped the metal shavings into the housing. In the second example, we might know who inspected the site but don't want to mention names because the situation could be sensitive or politically charged.

3. Use a passive sentence when the receiver is more important than the actor.

The strongest part of most sentences is the opening. Therefore, the sentence element appearing first will receive greater emphasis than those elements appearing later in the sentence. For this reason, a passive sentence is useful when you wish to emphasize the receiver of the action:

> Cross-sectional analysis techniques—the most important of our innovations—are currently being tested in our Latin American Laboratory.
>
> Minimum material size or thickness requirements will then be established to facilitate recuperator weight, size, and cost estimates.

In both examples, we wish to emphasize the receiver of the action. Note how emphasis changes if we restructure the first example:

> The most important of our innovations (cross-sectional analysis techniques) is currently being tested in our Latin American Laboratory.
>
> Our Latin American Laboratory is currently testing the most important of our innovations—cross-sectional analysis techniques.
>
> Our Latin American Laboratory is currently testing cross-sectional analysis techniques—the most important of our innovations.

The emphasis in each sentence differs, depending on sentence structure. The first revision emphasizes *innovations*, and it is

Active/Passive

still a passive sentence. The last two revisions are active, and both stress *our Latin American Laboratory*.

The ending of a sentence is also emphatic (although not as emphatic as the beginning), so the sentence ending with *techniques* does place secondary emphasis on *techniques*. However, the best way to emphasize *cross-sectional analysis techniques* is by opening the sentence with that phrase.

4. Use a passive sentence when you need to form a smooth transition from one sentence to the next.

Occasionally, writers must arrange sentence elements so that key words appearing in both sentences are near enough to each other for readers to immediately grasp the connection between the sentences. In the example below, for instance, the writer needs to form a smooth transition between sentences by repeating the key words *work packages*:

> We will develop a simplified matrix of tasks that will include all budgetary and operational work packages. These work packages will be scheduled and monitored by individual program managers.

The second sentence is passive. It is shorter and stronger as an active sentence:

> Individual program managers will schedule and monitor these work packages.

However, the active version does not connect as well with the previous sentence:

> We will develop a simplified matrix of tasks that will include all budgetary and operational work packages. Individual program managers will schedule and monitor these work packages.

For a brief moment, the second sentence seems to have changed the subject. Not until readers reach the end of the second sentence will they realize that both sentences concern work packages. Therefore, making the second sentence passive creates a smoother transition and actually improves the passage.

Passives and First Person

5. Do not use passive sentences to avoid using first person pronouns.

Some writers use passives to avoid using first person pronouns (*I, me, we,* or *us*). These writers mistakenly believe that first person pronouns are inappropriate in business or technical writing. In fact, the first person is preferable to awkward or ambiguous passive sentences like the examples below:

> It is recommended that a state-of-the-art survey be added to the initial redesign studies.

Who is recommending it? You? The customer? Someone else? And who is supposed to add the survey?

In the following sentences, things seem to be happening, but no one seems to be doing them:

> Cost data will be collected and maintained to provide a detailed history of the employee hours expended during the program. This tracking effort will be accomplished by the use of an established employee-hour accumulating system.

Writers who overuse the passive to avoid first person pronouns convey the impression that they don't want to accept the responsibility for their actions. This implication is why passive sentences can seem evasive even when the writer doesn't intend them to be.

Passives allow you to eliminate the actor. In some cases, eliminating the actor is appropriate and desirable. In other cases (as in the previous examples), eliminating the actor creates confusion and doubt. Active versions of these examples, using first person pronouns, are much better:

> We recommend that the initial redesign studies include a state-of-the-art survey.
>
> Using our employee-hour accumulating system, we will collect and maintain cost data to provide a detailed history of the employee hours expended during the program.

How to Convert Passives

Technical and scientific writers generally use too many passives. They use them unnecessarily, often more from habit than choice. Converting unneeded passives to actives will strengthen the style of the document, making it appear crisper and more confident. The following rules present three techniques for converting passives to actives.

6. Make sentences active by turning the clause or sentence around:

These methods are described in more detail in section 6.

Section 6 describes these methods in more detail.

A functional outline of the program is included in the Work Breakdown Structure (figure 1.1-2).

The Work Breakdown Structure (figure 1.1-2) includes a functional outline of the program.

Brakes on both drums are activated as required by the control system to regulate speed and accurately position the launcher.

The control system activates brakes on both drums as required to regulate speed and accurately position the launcher.

After these requirements are identified, we will develop a comprehensive list of applicable technologies.

After identifying these requirements, we will develop a comprehensive list of applicable technologies.

7. Make sentences active by changing the verb:

The solutions were achieved only after extensive development of fabrication techniques.

The solutions occurred only after extensive development of fabrication techniques.

The Gaussian elimination process can be thought of as a means of "decomposing" a matrix into three factors.

The Gaussian elimination process "decomposes" a matrix into three factors.

The Navy recuperator requirements are expected to bring added emphasis to structural integrity.

The Navy recuperator requirements will probably emphasize structural integrity.

Coalescence was always observed to start at the base of the column.

Coalescence always started at the base of the column.

8. Make sentences active by rethinking the sentence:

Special consideration must be given to structural mounting, heat exchanger shape, ducting losses, and ducting loads.

Structural mounting, heat exchanger shape, ducting losses, and ducting loads are especially important.

To ensure that a good alternate design approach is not overlooked, a comparison between plate-fin and tubular designs will be made during the proposed study program.

Comparing plate-fin and tubular designs during the proposed study program will ensure that we thoughtfully consider alternate design approaches.

This study will show what can be done to alleviate technology failure by selectively relaxing requirements.

This study will show how selectively relaxing requirements can alleviate technology failure.

It must be said, however, that while maximum results are gained by a design synthesis approach such as we propose, the area to be covered is so large that it will still be necessary to concentrate on the most important technologies and their regions of interest.

Our proposed design synthesis approach will yield maximum results. Nevertheless, the area of interest is very large. Concentrating on the most important technologies and their regions of interest will still be necessary.

Adjectives

Adjectives describe or modify nouns and other adjectives. They typically precede nouns or follow either verbs of sense *(feel, look, sound, taste, smell)* or linking verbs *(be, seem, appear, become):*

> The slow process . . . *(or* The process is slow.)
>
> Warm weather . . . *(or* The weather seems warm.)
>
> The cautious superintendent . . . *(or* The superintendent became cautious.)
>
> The news seemed bad. *(not* badly, *which is an adverb)*

Adjectives also tell which one, what kind, or how many people or things are being discussed.

Adjectives and Adverbs

Adjectives and adverbs are similar. They both describe or modify other words, and they both can compare two or more things. Sometimes they appear in similar positions in sentences:

> Harry felt **cautious**. *(adjective)*
>
> Harry felt **cautiously** along the bottom of the muddy stream. *(adverb)*

> The guard remained **calm**. *(adjective)*
>
> The guard remained **calmly** at his post. *(adverb)*

> The car came **close** to me. *(adverb)*
>
> The corporal watched the prisoner **closely**. *(adverb)*

NOTE: Not all adverbs end in *–ly* (for example, the adverbs *deep, fair, hard, wide).* Some adverbs have two forms: an *–ly* form and another form that is identical to the adjective *(deep/ deeply, fair/fairly, hard/hardly, wide/widely.)* You can determine whether words are adjectives by trying to put them in front of a noun. In the examples above, *cautious Harry* and *the calm guard* both make sense, so *cautious* and *calm* are adjectives. The *close car* does not mean what the original sentence meant, so *close* is an adverb in this context. See ADVERBS.

---

1. Use adjectives, not adverbs, following verbs of sense *(feel, look, sound, taste, smell)* and linking verbs *(be, seem, appear, become):*

> The engine sounded **rough**. *(not the adverb* roughly)
>
> The surface of the mirror felt **smooth**. *(not the adverb* smoothly)
>
> The accountant was **cautious** about her projections.
>
> *but*
>
> The accountant worked **cautiously** to develop her projections. *(adverb following the verb* worked)
>
> The auditor appeared **eager** to assist our division.
>
> *but*
>
> The auditor volunteered **eagerly** to assist our division. *(adverb following the verb* volunteered)

See ADVERBS.

EXCEPTION: *Harold felt badly because of flu.* This use of *badly* is currently acceptable, especially in spoken English. The older parallel form with *bad* is still correct and widely used. *Harold felt bad because of flu.* See Bad/ Badly in WORD PROBLEMS.

Comparatives and Superlatives

Adjectives have different forms for comparing two objects (the comparative form) and comparing more than two objects (the superlative form):

> Our word processor is slower than the new IBM Displaywriter. (Slower *is the comparative form.)*
>
> The Gemini software package was the slowest one we surveyed. (Slowest *is the superlative form.)*
>
> Stocks are a likelier investment than bonds if long-term growth is the goal. *(or* more likely)
>
> Nissan's likeliest competitor in the suburban wagon market is General Motors. *(or* most likely)
>
> The 1990 budget is more adequate than the I989 budget.
>
> The cooling provisions are the most adequate feature of the specifications.

NOTE: One-syllable words use *–er/–est* to form comparatives or superlatives. Two-syllable words use either *–er/–est* or *more/most.* Three-syllable words use *more/ most.* A few adjectives have irregular comparative forms: *good (well), better, best; bad, worse, worst; many, more, most.*

---

2. Use the comparative *(-er/ more)* forms when comparing two people or things and the superlative *(-est/most)* forms when comparing more than two:

Of the two designs, Boeing's seems more efficient.

The Shearson-American Express proposal is the most attractive. *(More than two options are implied, so the superlative is proper.)*

Weekly deductions are the best method for financing the new hospital insurance plan.

Weekly deductions are better than any other method for financing the new hospital insurance plan. *(The comparative* better *is used because the various options are being compared one by one, not as a group.)*

Nouns Used as Adjectives

Nouns often behave like adjectives, especially in complex technical phrases. Here is a typical phrase from an aircraft manual: *C–5A airframe weight calculation error percentage.* The first five words in this phrase are nouns used as adjectives: *C–5A, airframe, weight, calculation,* and *error.* These five nouns are called a noun string. Such nouns are extremely useful because, as in this case, English often does not have an adjective form with the same meaning as the noun.

Although useful and often necessary, nouns used as adjectives may be clear only to technically knowledgeable people:

aluminum honeycomb edge panels

What is aluminum? The honeycomb, the edges, or the panels? Only a knowledgeable reader can tell for sure. Sometimes, the order of the words suggests an interpretation:

aluminum edge honeycomb panels

From this phrase, we may expect the edges, and not the honeycomb, to be aluminum, but we still can't know for sure if *aluminum edge* and *honeycomb* equally modify *panels* or if *aluminum edge* and *honeycomb* combine to become a single modifier of *panels* or if *aluminum* modifies something called *edge honeycomb:*

(aluminum + edge) + honeycomb panels

or

(aluminum + edge + honeycomb) panels

or

aluminum + (edge + honeycomb) panels

In alphabetical lists of parts, the main noun being modified must be listed first. Therefore, the modifying words appear afterwards, usually separated by commas. The modifying words are typically listed in reverse order, with the most general modifiers closest to the main noun:

panels, honeycomb, aluminum edge

or

panels, edge, aluminum honeycomb

or

panels, aluminum edge honeycomb

A helpful technique for discovering or clarifying the structure of noun strings is to ask the question, *What kind?* Begin with the main noun being modified and proceed from there to build the string of modifying nouns:

panels

What kind of panels?

honeycomb

What kind of honeycomb?

aluminum edge

In this case, we have assumed that *aluminum edge* describes a particular type of honeycomb. Because *aluminum* and *edge* jointly modify *honeycomb,* they act as one word. We usually show that two or more words are acting together as joint or compound modifiers by hyphenating them:

aluminum-edge honeycomb panels

See HYPHENS.

---

3. Arrange nouns used as adjectives in technical expressions so that the more general nouns are closest to the word they are modifying:

semiautomatic slat worm gear

automatic slat worm gear

semiautomatic strut backoff gear

automatic strut backoff gear

NOTE 1: The structure of such phrases (as well as the logic behind this rule) is revealed in catalogued lists. You can display the structure by reversing the order of the noun string and using indentation to show levels of modification:

```
gear
   backoff
      automatic strut
      semiautomatic strut
worm
   automatic slat
   semiautomatic slat
```

Adjectives

Note 2: Some technical writers and editors rarely use internal punctuation (either hyphens or commas) to separate nouns in noun strings. In many scientific and technical fields, hyphens that would normally connect parts of a unit modifier are eliminated:

methyl bromide solution (*not* methyl-bromide solution)

black peach aphid (*not* black-peach aphid *or* black peach-aphid)

grey willow leaf beetle

swamp black currant seedlings

Hyphens in many technical words are, however, very hard to predict: *horse-nettle* vs. *horseradish* or *devilsclaw* vs. *devils-paintbrush.* In instances where the first word is capitalized, the compound is often hyphenated: *China-laurel, Queen Annes-lace, Australian-pea,* etc. See Hyphens.

Note 3: Commas are not used to separate nouns in noun strings. However, we use commas to separate true adjectives when the adjectives **equally** modify the same noun:

grey, burnished, elliptical sphere

sloppy, poorly written, inadequate proposal

See Nouns and Commas.

Adverbs

Adverbs are modifiers that give the how, where, when, and extent of the action within a sentence. Most adverbs end in *–ly*, but some common adverbs do not: *so, now, later, then, well,* etc. Adverbs often modify the main verbs in sentences:

The engineer **slowly** prepared the design plan. *(How?)*

The supply ship moved **close** to the drilling platform. *(Where?)*

They **later** surveyed all participants in the research project. *(When?)*

The crude oil flowed **rapidly** from the ruptured pipeline. *(Extent?)*

Adverbs can also modify adjectives or other adverbs:

Their proposal was **highly** entertaining.

Costs were **much** lower than expected.

The well was **so** deep that its costs became prohibitive.

The board of directors cut costs **more** severely and **more** rapidly than we anticipated.

1. Place adverbs such as *only, almost, nearly, merely,* and *also* as close as possible to the word they modify:

The bank examiners looked at only five accounts. (*not* The bank examiners only looked at five accounts.)

The engineer had almost finished the specifications. (*not* The engineer almost had finished the specifications.)

Adverbs and Adjectives

Adverbs and adjectives are quite similar. They each modify or describe other words, and they often appear in similar positions in sentences, but they have quite different meanings:

The lab technician **carefully** smelled the sample. *(Adverb)*

The cheese smelled **bad**. *(Adjective)*

The new motor worked **badly** the first day. *(Adverb)*

Not knowing the language, they stayed **close** to the interpreter. *(Adverb)*

We **closely** studied the blueprints. *(Adverb)*

The election was so **close** that no one was a clear winner. *(Adjective)*

2. Use adverbs following most main verbs:

Our accountants predicted **accurately** that cash flow would be a problem.

The manager asked **quickly** for the up-to-date estimates.

The test engineers calculated **roughly** the expected power.

Note 1: Adjectives, not adverbs, follow verbs of sense *(feel, look, sound, taste, smell)* and linking verbs *(be, seem, appear, become):*

The adhesive felt **cool** and **rubbery** when dry.

The surface of the wing appeared **uneven**.

See Bad/Badly in Word Problems.

Note 2: Some adverbs have two forms, one without the regular *–ly* and one with it: *close/closely, deep/deeply, late/lately, loud/loudly, quick/quickly, slow/slowly, wide/widely.* Sometimes the two adverbial forms have different meanings:

We submitted the invoice **late**.

We were involved **lately** in some takeover discussions.

The loose flywheel moved very **close** to its housing.

The flywheel is monitored **closely** during the trial run.

In other instances, the two forms mean almost the same thing, so the choice depends on personal preference or individual idiom (based on the surrounding words):

Go **slow**. *vs.* Go **slowly**. *(Either form is correct.)*

The evaluation team wanted to play **fair**. *(The phrase* play fairly *means the same but sounds a little stiff and overly formal.)*

The evaluation team wanted to respond **fairly**. (Fair *would sound awkward with the verb* respond.)

See Adjectives.

Comparative and Superlative Forms

Adverbs, like adjectives, have different forms to show comparison of two things (the comparative form) and comparison of more than two things (the superlative form). The comparative uses an *–er* form or *more*; the superlative uses an *–est* or *most:*

The counselor left sooner than expected. *(comparative)*

The fluid returned more slowly to its original level. *(comparative)*

They debated most successfully the wisdom of expanding into the West Coast market. *(superlative)*

The most rapidly moving car turned out to be the new Ford high performance model. *(superlative)*

Note 1: Some adverbs have irregular comparative and superlative forms: *well, better, best; badly, worse, worst; little, less, least; much, more, most.*

Note 2: See Adjectives for a discussion of whether to use *–er* or *more* for comparatives and *–est* or *most* for superlatives. The rules for adverbs are identical to those for adjectives.

Agreement

Agreement is a basic grammatical rule of English. According to this rule, subjects of sentences must agree in number with their verbs. Singular subjects (nouns or pronouns) require singular verbs and plural subjects (nouns or pronouns) require plural verbs:

The proposal was finished. *(not the plural* were finished)

She is the engineer who designed the valve. *(not the plural* are)

The boilers have become corroded. *(not the singular* has become)

They are our competitors on most major procurements. *(not the singular* is)

See Nouns, Pronouns, and Verbs.

The notion of agreement also refers to the singular/plural agreement between pronouns and their antecedents (the words the pronouns stand for) and between types of pronouns (first, second, or third person) when those pronouns have the same or similar types of antecedents:

Jane Swenson submitted her report. (The *pronoun* her *agrees with its antecedent* Jane Swenson.)

See Pronouns and Verbs.

1. The subject of a sentence (nouns or pronouns) should agree in number with the sentence verb:

The geologist is analyzing the well data. (*singular noun and singular verb)*

The employees are discussing the benefit package. (*plural noun and plural verb)*

I am going to attend the international conference in June.

We are designing a light-sensitive monitoring system.

The Elements of Geometry is the basic textbook.

Our textbooks are usually translated into Russian, French, and German.

Midwest states normally include Kentucky and Missouri.

A list of Midwest states normally includes Kentucky and Missouri.

Note: A noun ending with an *–s* or *–es* is usually plural. A verb ending with an *–s* or *–es* is usually singular. *Employees* is plural. The verbs *is* and *includes* are both singular. Some verbs do not change their form to reflect singular and plural: *will include, included, had included, will have included*, etc.

See Nouns and Verbs.

Agreement problems sometimes occur because the subject of the sentence is not clearly singular or plural:

None of the crew is going to take leave.

or

None of the crew are going to take leave.

Some writers become confused, too, when the subject is separated from the verb by words or phrases that do not agree in number with the subject:

Only one of the issues we discussed is on the agenda for tomorrow's meeting.

Few aspects of the problem we are now facing are as clear as they should be.

The availability of rice, as well as of medical supplies, determines the life expectancy of a typical adult in Hong Kong.

Normal wear and tear, along with planned obsolescence, is the reason most automobiles provide only an average of 6.5 years of service.

The number of the subject does not change if the subject follows the verb:

What are your arguments for tertiary recovery in reef-producing ranges?

There are five new pumps in the warehouse.

Discussed are the basic design flaws in the preliminary specifications and the lack of adequate detail in the drawings.

Finally, some noun subjects look plural because they end in *–s* or *–ics,* but they are still singular:

Politics has changed drastically with the advent of television.

The news from Algeria continues to be discouraging.

Measles rarely occurs in adults.

2. Subjects connected by *and* require a plural verb:

The ceiling panels and the fasteners have been fabricated.

The regional engineer and the field geologist agree that we should plug and abandon the well.

A personal computer and a photo copier are essential business tools today.

Exception: Sometimes words connected by *and* become so closely linked that they become singular in meaning, thus requiring a singular verb:

Bacon and eggs is my favorite breakfast.

My name and address is on the inside cover.

3. Singular subjects connected by *either . . . or, neither . . . nor,* and *not only . . . but also* require a singular verb:

Either the tail assembly or the wing design is causing excessive fuel consumption.

Neither the district engineer nor the superintendent has approved the plans.

Not only the cost but also the design is a problem.

NOTE: When one of a pair of subjects is plural, the verb agrees with the subject closest to it:

Either the tail assembly or the wing struts are causing excessive fuel consumption.

Either the wing struts or the tail assembly is causing excessive fuel consumption.

4. When used as a subject or as the modifier of the subject, *each, every, either, neither, one, another, much, anybody, anyone, everybody, everyone, somebody, someone, nobody,* and *no one* require singular verbs:

Every proposal has been evaluated.

Each engineer is responsible for the final proofing of engineering proposals.

Everyone has received the pension information.

Somebody was responsible for the drop in production.

No one but the design engineer knows the load factors used in the calculations.

NOTE: Although words ending with *–one* and *–body* require a singular verb, sentences with such words often become awkward when a pronoun refers to the words:

Everyone turns in his report on Monday.

Using the singular pronoun *his* maintains the agreement with the subject, but if the *everyone* mentioned includes women, the expression is sexist. Some writers and editors argue that male pronouns *(he, his, him, himself)* are generic, that they refer to both males and females. Others maintain that this convention discriminates against women. Writers and editors who share this view prefer to include both men and women in their sentences:

Everyone turns in his or her report on Monday.

Finally, some liberal editors argue that *everyone* implies a plurality, so the plural *their* becomes the acceptable pronoun:

Everyone turns in their reports on Monday.

The sexism problem is avoidable in most sentences simply by making the subject plural and eliminating such troublesome words as *everyone*:

All engineers turn in their reports on Monday.

See PRONOUNS and SEXIST LANGUAGE.

5. When used as a subject or as the modifier of a subject, *both, few, several, many,* and *others* require plural verbs:

Both proposals were unsatisfactory.

Several were available earlier this month.

Few pipes were still in service.

6. *All, any, more, most, none, some, one-half of, two-thirds of, a part of,* and *a percentage of* require either a singular or a plural verb, depending upon the noun they refer to:

All of the work has been assigned. *(singular)*

All of the trees have been removed. *(plural)*

Most sugar is now made from sugar beets.

Most errors were caused by carelessness.

Some of the report was written in an overly ornate style.

Some design features were mandatory.

One-half of the project has been completed.

One-half of the pages have been proofed.

A percentage of the room is for storage.

A percentage of the employees belong to the company credit union.

Agreement

7. Collective nouns and expressions with time, money, and quantities take a singular or a plural verb, depending upon their intended meaning:

The committee votes on pension policy when disputes occur. (Committee, *a collective noun, is considered singular.*)

The committee do not agree on the interpretation of the mandatory retirement clause. (Committee, *a collective noun, is considered plural.*)

The audience was noisy, especially during the final act.

The audience were in their seats by 7:30 p.m.

Two years is the usual waiting period. (Two years *is an expression of time considered as a single unit.*)

The 2 years were each divided into quarters for accounting purposes. (Two years *is an expression of time considered as a plural of* year.)

Six dollars is the fee.

Six dollars were spread out on the counter.

Five liters is all the tank can hold.

Five liters of wine were sold before noon.

NOTE: Sometimes sentences with collective nouns become awkward because they seem both singular and plural. In such cases, rephrasing often helps:

Audience members were in their seats by 7:30 p.m.

Apostrophes

Apostrophes signal omitted letters, possession, and the plural of letters and symbols. An apostrophe (') can appear with or without a following *–s*.

1. Apostrophes indicate omitted letters or words in a contraction:

It's not going to be easy. (It is not going to be easy.)

It won't be easy. (It will not be easy.)

We will coordinate with the manufacturer who's chosen to supply the semiconductors. (who is chosen)

NOTE: Use contractions in letters and memos to help establish an informal tone. Avoid contractions in more formal, edited documents. See TONE.

2. Apostrophes indicate possession:

Boeing's airframe manufacturing capabilities are world renowned.

The unit's most unique capability is its amplification of weak echoes.

- When the possessive word is plural and ends in *–s*, the apostrophe follows the *–s*:

The suppliers' requests are not unreasonable considering the amount of time required for fabrication.

We consider the states' environmental quality offices to be our partners in reclamation.

NOTE: Irregular plurals that do not end in *–s* require an *'s:*

The report on women's status in the executive community is due next Friday.

Materials for children's toys must conform to Federal safety standards.

- When the possessive word is singular, the apostrophe comes before the *–s*:

Rockwell International's process for budgeting is one of the most progressive in the industry.

The circuit's most unusual capability is its error detection and correction function.

- When the possessive word is singular and already ends with an *–s*, the apostrophe follows the *–s* and may itself be followed by another *–s* (although most writers prefer the apostrophe alone):

General Dynamics' (*or* Dynamics's) management proposal is very project specific.

Our project manager would be Martin Jones. Dr. Jones' (*or* Jones's) experience with laser refractors has made him a leader in the field.

NOTE: The possessive form of the pronoun *it* is *its*, not *it's (it's* is the contraction of *it is* or *it has*):

Possessive: Its products have over 10,000 hours of testing behind them.

Contraction: It's (It is) in the interests of economy and efficiency that we pursue atmospheric testing as well.

Similarly, the possessive form of *who* is *whose*, not *who's*. *Who's* is a contraction for *who is* or *who has*.

See POSSESSIVES and Who's/Whose in WORD PROBLEMS.

3. Apostrophes indicate the passage of time in certain stock phrases:

a month's pay

an hour's time

4 days' work

3 years' study

4. Apostrophes may precede the *–s* in the plural of letters, signs, symbols, figures, acronyms, and abbreviations, although the trend is to omit the apostrophe unless omitting it would be confusing:

The X's indicate insertable material. (*or* x's *or* Xs *but not* xs)

Our risk management process is designed to eliminate the if's and but's.

All of our senior staff have PhDs. (*or* Ph.D.'s *or* Ph.D.s)

The manufacturer indicates fragile material by placing #'s in any of the last three positions in the transportation code.

Packagers should code all categories, including the A's and I's. (*not* As *or* Is *nor* as *or* is)

General Dynamics began its task definition program in the early 1990s. (*or* 1990's)

The tracer tests will be run on all APOs in Europe. (*or* APO's)

The Bureau of Land Management has prepared three EAs (Environmental Assessments) for those grazing allotments. (*or* EA's)

Appendices/Attachments

Appendices (often informally referred to as attachments) are more and more common in documents, especially those intended for busy peers, supervisors, and managers who do not have time to wade through pages of data and analysis. Appendices and attachments are acceptable (often desirable) in letters and memos as well as reports.

The following types of information can and often do appear in appendices or attachments:

Background data
Case studies
Computations
Derivations
Detailed component descriptions
Detailed test results
Excerpts from related research
Histories
Lengthy analyses
Parts lists
Photographs
Raw data
Sources of additional information
Supporting letters and memos
Tables of data

The word *appendix* has two acceptable plurals: *appendices* and *appendixes*. *Appendices* is still widely used by educated speakers and writers, but *appendixes* is growing in popularity because it follows the regular method for making English words plural. The style used by the U.S. Government is:

- Appendix—appendices
- Index—indexes
- Matrix—matrices

1. Use appendices to streamline reports and memos that would otherwise be too lengthy.

In business and technical reports and memos, assess your readers' need to know the background and analysis behind the relevant conclusions and recommendations.

Relevant conclusions and recommendations should appear very early in most business and technical reports, often as part of an executive summary. Busy readers can therefore receive a streamlined report of 8 to 10 pages (instead of the traditional formal report of 30 to 50 pages) with appendices containing appropriate background information, detailed results, and lengthy analyses.

See SUMMARIES.

2. Avoid making appendices a dumping ground for unnecessary information.

Because the appendices are not part of the body of the report, some writers believe they have the license to include in the appendices every scrap of information they know about the subject. This practice leads to massive, often confusing appendices that discourage readers.

Would a knowledgeable reader need the information in the appendices to interpret the conclusions and recommendations? If so, then the appendices are justified. In writing your document, determine who the readers will be and ask yourself what additional information these readers will need to better understand your approach, analysis, results, conclusions, and recommendations.

One rule of thumb is that appendices should contain only information prepared for the project in question. Background information from files and tangential reports (general background information) should not appear in appendices. Often, readers know such background information anyway.

To summarize, if a reader needs certain information to understand a report, this information belongs in the body of a report. All other information belongs either in appendices or in backup files.

3. Number or letter appendices and attachments sequentially.

Sequential numbering or lettering is essential: appendix A, appendix B, etc.; or attachment 1, attachment 2, etc. Numbers and letters are both correct, so either is acceptable. In longer documents, your choice may depend upon whether you have numbered or lettered the sections or chapters. If your sections or chapters are numbered, then use letters to label appendices. Conversely, if your sections or chapters are lettered, use numbers for the appendices. The system

Appendices/Attachments

you use to label appendices should indicate a clear distinction between the appendices and the body of the document.

Typically, appendices are numbered in the order in which the references to them appear in the body of the report. So the first appendix mentioned in the report becomes appendix A (or appendix 1), the second one mentioned is appendix B (or appendix 2), and so on.

NOTE: Give each appendix or attachment a title. Referring to appendices or attachments only by number is not informative and can be confusing. In the text, refer to the appendix or attachment by both number and title.

---

4. Refer to all appendices and attachments in the body of the document.

Refer to all appendices or attachments in the body of the document so that readers know that the information within them is available.

Your references should be informative rather than cryptic. A cryptic reference (such as *See appendix C*) does not tell readers enough about the appended information. The following references are informative:

> Particulate counts from all collection points in the study area appear in appendix C, Particulate Data.

> Attachment 5, A Report on Reserve Faulting in the Boling Dome, provides further evidence of the complex faulting that may control production.

> See appendix A (Prescription Trends During the 1970s) for further analysis of valium use and abuse since its introduction.

Bibliographic Form

Bibliographic forms appear in standard bibliographies at the end of chapters, articles, and books. Whatever the exact form, complete bibliographic entries include the name of the author, the title, and the full publication history (including the edition, the publisher or press, the city of publication, the date of publication).

The forms of bibliographic entries vary greatly, depending on the professional background of the author, the profession's needs and traditions, the type of publication, and the publisher. The bibliographic form that we recommend represents a standard format useful for a variety of professions and publishers.

However, we advise you to find out the specific format requirements (including bibliographic form) of the publisher to whom you are submitting a document.

NOTE: In the following rules, the titles of publications in bibliographic entries are italicized. Underlining replaces italics when documents are typed or when italics is not available.

See UNDERLINING and ITALICS.

---

1. For a book, give the name of the author or authors, the date of publication, the full title, the volume number, the edition, the city of publication, and the publisher:

Book by one author

Dempster, Jacob B. 1982. *The Art of Fine Book Publishing.* New Haven: The Cottage Press, Inc.

Book by two authors

Gallo, George, and L. J. Lane. 1978. *Paper and Paper-Making.* Baltimore: The Freedom Press & Co.

Book by three authors

Green, H. J., Ellen Jacoby, and James Reed. 1976. *The Art of Graphic Illustration.* New Orleans: The Creole Community Press.

Book by more than three authors

Grundvik, K., et al. 1971. *The Evolution of the Printing Press.* Los Angeles: The Hispanic Press.

Book by one editor

Hough, R. William, ed. 1968. *Fine Lettering.* New York: Simon and Schuster.

Book by two editors

Millman, Howie J., and Fred Stein, eds. 1974. *Preparing Leather Book Covers.* Boston: J. L. Cabot and Sons Publishing.

Two volumes by an organization

Modern Language Association of America. 1974. *Scholarly Publishing in North America.* 2 vols. New Haven: The Classical Press.

Chapter of a book

Williams, Clive. 1979. "The Opacity of Ink." In *The Art of Printing,* edited by Jason Farnsworth. New York: Holt, Rinehart & Winston.

NOTE 1: In these entries, the date directly follows the name of the author or authors. This convention complements the author/date style of citations in the text. See CITATIONS. In this style, the text of a document contains parenthetical references:

A 1981 study revealed that fleas transmit the virus (Babcock 1981). This study relied on two earlier studies (Duerdun 1976 and Abbott 1973).

or

A 1981 study revealed that fleas transmit the virus (Babcock). This study relied on two earlier studies (Duerdun 1976 and Abbott 1973). *[Because the date of Babcock's study is already in the sentence, including the date in the citation is unnecessary.]*

NOTE 2: Publications in the humanities usually cite the publication date following the name of the publisher:

Smithson, Arthur J. *The History of Modern China.* New York: Simon and Schuster, 1976.

This bibliographic form complements the footnoting pattern of citations routinely used by most scholars in the humanities. For more information on this style, see *The Chicago Manual of Style,* 13th edition. See also FOOTNOTES.

NOTE 3: Bibliographic entries in the physical and biological sciences often capitalize only the first word of the title:

Smithson, Arthur J. 1976. *The history of modern China.* New York: Simon and Schuster. [China *is capitalized because it is a proper noun.*]

---

2. For a journal and for a magazine article, give the name of the author or authors, the year of publication, the full title of the article (in quotation marks), the name of the journal or magazine, the volume, the month or quarter of publication, and the pages:

Article by one author

Broward, Charles Evans. 1981. "Traveling the Southern California Desert." *UCLA Chronicle* 15 (Spring): 45-54.

Article by two authors

Calleston, Dwight R., and James Buchanan. 1976. "The Desert Tortoise: Its Vanishing Habitat." *The Californian* 7 (April): 23-28. *[Follow the book format above for articles with more than two authors.]*

Article appearing in more than one issue

Stevens, Harold, and Jason Drew. 1976. "The Family of Bighorn Sheep." *The Bighorn Sheep Newsletter* 8 (Fall and Winter): 34–35, 28–31.

Article from a popular magazine

Trump, Josiah. 1969. "The Desert Indians." *Time*, December 12, 45–49.

Review of a published book

Williams, Ellen. 1980. Review of *Prospecting in the Southern Desert* by Amy Van Pol and James Freeman. *The Californian* (July): 24–31.

See Quotation Marks.

Note 1: As with books, these entries cite the year of publication immediately after the name of the author or authors. In publications for the humanities, the date appears (with the month) after the volume of the journal or magazine:

Stillman, Wendy. "Photographing Desert Sunsets." *UCLA Chronicle* 15 (Spring 1981): 4-8.

Note 2: Some editors, especially in the biological and physical sciences, prefer to omit the quotation marks around the title of the article and to capitalize only the first word of the title:

Stillman, Wendy. 1981. Photographing desert sunsets. *UCLA Chronicle* 15 (Spring): 4–8.

3. For unpublished material, give the author or authors, the title (in quotation marks), and as much of its history as available:

Dissertation or thesis

Johnson, Dugdale. 1983. "The Habitat of the Desert Tortoise: Its Inter-Relationship with Man." D.Sc. diss., University of Southern California.

Professional paper

Rusk, Joan, and Elaine Yardley. 1980. "The Diseases of the Bighorn Sheep." Paper presented at the annual meeting of the Bighorn Sheep Society, Los Angeles, 24–26 May.

Personal communication

Turgott, Edward. 1983. Letter to the author, 31 May.

Note: The formats for other unpublished documents (television shows, radio shows, interviews, duplicated material, diaries, etc.) should supply as much bibliographic information as possible. The bibliographic form should allow readers to locate the document easily.

4. For public documents, give the country, state, county, or other government division, the full title, and complete publication information:

Iowa. State Assembly. Committee on Farm Commodities. 1974. *Report to the Farm Bureau on Corn Subsidies.* 45th Assembly, 2nd. sess.

U.S. Congress. House. Committee on Ways and Means. 1945. *Hearings on Import Duties on Shellfish.* 79th Cong., 1st sess.

U.S. Bureau of the Census. 1984. *Gross and Net Fishing Revenues, 1980.* Prepared by the Commerce Division in cooperation with the Commodity Division. Washington, DC: United States Government Printing Office.

Alphabetizing Bibliographic Entries

5. Alphabetize bibliographic entries by the author's last name:

Adam
Adams
Berg
Berger
Bergerson
Michael
Michaels
Michaelsen
Michaelson
Mickael
Zucker

If two or more authors have the same last name, alphabetize according to first names or initials. A set of initials always precedes a first name beginning with the same letter:

Brown, A. W.
Brown, Andrew
Brown, J. B.
Brown, Jane
Brown, John

If single- and multiple-author entries begin with the same last name, list the single authors first:

Davis, Jeanne
Davis, Jeanne, and Kristen Cooper
Davis, Jeanne, Kristen Cooper, and Ellen James

Treat all names beginning with *Mc* and *Mac* as though they begin with *Mac*. Alphabetize them letter by letter, as you would with other words:

Bibliographic Form

Mabrey
McDonald
MacDougal
McHenry
MacMillian

If you attribute the document or item to an institution or agency, the first word in the institution's or agency's name becomes the key word for alphabetizing:

Atomic Energy Commission

Boston Globe

MacMillian Institute

Manchester Chronicle

Merrimack Morning News

U.S. Department of Commerce (*not* Department of Commerce)

U.S. Geological Survey

Water Resources Division, U.S. Geological Survey

NOTE: In names beginning with articles (a, an, and the), alphabetize by the second word in the name, but list the article if the article is part of the legal name:

Albany State College
The American University
Antioch College
Brown University
The Johns Hopkins University
Syracuse University

Boldface

Boldface type features thicker and darker letters than normal type: **boldface** type compared to normal type.

Boldface type is emphatic because of the contrast between it and surrounding print. You can use boldface type effectively whenever you need a word, phrase, sentence, heading, or title to stand out.

Until recently, boldface type was available only in printed material. Typewriters could not provide boldface type unless they had changeable typewheels or type elements.

Today's printers, driven by word processing software on computers, can easily provide boldface, so more and more boldface is appearing in business letters, memos, and technical reports.

1. Use boldface to highlight headings or key words and phrases requiring emphasis.

The above guideline, for instance, appears in boldface and color, both because it is similar to a heading (despite being a complete sentence) and because it provides key information. Boldface type (even without color) is emphatic because it draws attention to itself on a page otherwise filled with normal type.

Boldface type is particularly effective in distinguishing between different levels of headings. First-level headings are frequently centered and appear in boldface type. Second-level headings might appear at the left margin, but they can also be centered. If a second-level heading is centered, it should appear in normal type—the contrast between boldface and normal type thus distinguishes between first- and second-level headings.

Be careful about overusing boldface type. If you use too much boldface type for emphasis, its effect will be lost. In fact, boldface type creates more strain on the eyes than normal type, so too much of it in a text is disturbing, not emphatic. Try especially to avoid long boldface passages.

See EMPHASIS, HEADINGS, WORD PROCESSING, and DESKTOP PUBLISHING.

2. Use boldface for index section titles and for the titles of tables or illustrations.

In a complicated index, boldface type could indicate major sections and normal type could indicate subsections. Similarly, boldface type can highlight the titles of tables and illustrations.

See INDEXES.

Brackets

Brackets are a pair of marks [ ] used to set off comments, corrections, or explanatory material. Although similar to parentheses, brackets do have different uses, as the following rules indicate.

See PARENTHESES.

1. Use brackets to insert comments or corrections in quoted material:

"Your quoted price [$3,750] is far more than our budget allows."

"Our engineers surveyed the cite [site] for its suitability as a waste disposal cite [site]."

See QUOTATIONS.

NOTE 1: In these examples, the brackets indicate that the material quoted did not have the information included within the brackets.

NOTE 2: A common use of brackets, especially in published articles, is to insert *sic* in brackets following an error:

"We studied the affect [sic] of the new design on production outputs."

Sic, borrowed from Latin, means "thus" or "so." It tells readers that the text quoted appears exactly as it did in the original, including the error. In the example above, the word preceding *[sic]* should have been *effect*.

2. Use brackets to enclose parenthetical or explanatory material that occurs within material that is already enclosed within parentheses:

We decided to reject the bid from Gulf Industries International. (Actually the bid [$58,000] was tempting because it was far below our estimate and because Gulf Industries usually does good work.)

See PARENTHESES.

NOTE: You can sometimes use dashes instead of the outer parentheses and then replace the brackets with parentheses:

this

The Board of Directors—or more accurately, a committee of the actual owners (Hyatt, Burke, and Drake)—are answerable to no one but themselves.

not this

The Board of Directors (or more accurately, a committee of the actual owners [Hyatt, Burke, and Drake]) are answerable to no one but themselves.

NOTE: Some writers and editors consider the version without brackets preferable because having both parentheses and brackets in the same sentence can look clumsy and can be confusing. See DASHES.

3. For mathematical expressions, place parentheses inside brackets inside braces inside parentheses:

({[( )]}).

See MATHEMATICAL NOTATION.

4. No other marks of punctuation need to come before or after brackets unless the bracketed material has its own mark of punctuation or the overall sentence needs punctuation:

this

The procedure was likely to be costly. (Actually, the cost [$38 per unit] included some of the research and development expenses.)

not this

The procedure was likely to be costly. (Actually, the cost, [$38 per unit], included some of the research and development expenses.)

Capitals

Capitalization follows two basic rules—the first two rules cited below. Unfortunately, these two rules cannot begin to account for the number of exceptions and options facing writers who have to decide whether a word should be capitalized.

Because of the number of exceptions and options, this section includes many minor rules that supplement the two basic rules. Together, the basic and supplementary rules provide guidance, but you should also check an up-to-date dictionary for additional guidance if the proper choice is still not clear. See REFERENCES.

Once you have decided whether to capitalize a word, record your decision in a list of editing reminders. Such a list will help you maintain consistent capitalization, especially if your document is long and complex. See EDITING and PROOFREADING.

1. Capitalize the first letter of proper names—that is, those specific, one-of-a-kind names for a person, place, university or school, organization, religion, race, month or holiday, historic event, trade name, or titles of a person or of a document:

John F. Kennedy
Gail Sawyer
David Lewis
Jeanne Kirkpatrick
Henry Ford
Nancy Kassebaum
Sally

the Far East
China
the Eastern Shore (Maryland)
Massachusetts
Grove County
Baltimore City (or Baltimore)
United States of America
Lake Michigan
the Missouri River

the University of Utah
Western High School
the Golden Daycare Center
Shell Oil Company
the Prudential Life Insurance Co.
the American Legion
the Elks
the United Mine Workers
the Republican Party

Baptists
Judaism
Japanese
Hindus

May
September
Fourth of July
New Year's Day

the Reformation
World War I
Battle of Bull Run
the Crucifixion

Cyclone (fence)
Xerox copier
Band-Aids
Kodak
Coca-Cola

Mrs. Louise Brantly
Mr. Wing Phillips
Dr. Georgia Burke
Professor Robert Borson
Lieutenant Jeb Stuart

Handbook of Chemical Terms
The New York Times
The American Heritage Dictionary
"Time-Sharing" in *Training* magazine

See TITLES.

NOTE 1: In everyday English usage, the terms *capitalization* and *to capitalize* mean that only the initial letter of a word appears with a capital letter. So, rule 1 above would usually be clear to English speakers if written as follows: "Capitalize proper names . . . ." The expanded versions of rule 1 and the other rules in this discussion of capitals are intended to remove any ambiguities as to which letters in a word should be capitalized.

NOTE 2: As the many instances of lowercase *the* above indicate, *the* is usually not capitalized unless it has become part of the full official name:

The Hague
The Johns Hopkins University

NOTE 3: With proper names several words long, conjunctions, short prepositions, and articles *(a, an,* and *the)* are not capitalized:

the Federal Republic of Germany
Johnson and Sons, Inc.
"Recovery of Oil in Plugged and Abandoned Wells"

See rule 6 in the following discussion.

NOTE 4: Capitalize the first letter of an individual's title only when it precedes the individual's proper name:

Professor George Stevens (*but* George Stevens, who is a professor . . .)

Captain Ellen Dobbs (*but* Ellen Dobbs, who is the captain of our company . . .)

President Henry Johnson (*but* Henry Johnson, president of Johnson Motors . . .)

See TITLES.

NOTE 5: Adjectives derived from proper names are capitalized only when the original sense is maintained:

a French word *(but* french fries)
Venetian art *(but* venetian blinds)
Siamese cuisine *(but* siamese twins)

Even in these cases, dictionaries often differ; for instance, the current *American Heritage Dictionary* recommends *Siamese twins* rather than the form preferred above. So you often have to use your judgment. However, be consistent throughout a document.

Capitals

2. Do not capitalize the first letter of common nouns—that is, those nouns that are general or generic:

a geologist
my accountant
the engineers
your secretary

a country
a planet
a river
north
the city

a trade school
college
high school
a holiday
the swing shift

a copier
the facial tissue

a foreman
my mentor
my supervisor
the doctor

spring
summer
fall
winter

twentieth century
the thirties (*however*, the Gay Nineties)

NOTE 1: One useful test to determine whether a noun is common is to ask if *a* or *an* does or can precede it in your context. If *a* or *an* makes sense before the noun, then the noun is common:

a pope (*but* the Pope)
an attorney
a U.S. senator

but

a President *(referring to any President of the United States)*

Because of special deference, the word *President* is always capitalized when it refers to any or all of the Presidents of the United States. This supersedes rule 2 above.

NOTE 2: Titles that follow a noun rather than precede it are not capitalized:

Theo Jones, who is our comptroller . . .
Betty Stevens, my secretary . . .
Rene Leon, who is a staff geophysicist . . .

NOTE 3: Common nouns separated from their proper nouns (or names) can occasionally be capitalized:

—Titles of high company officials, when the titles take the place of the officials' names:

We spoke to the President about the new labor policy.

The State Director has to sign before the plan goes into effect.

—Names of departments when they replace the whole name of the department:

We sent the letter to Accounting.

According to Maintenance, the pump had been replaced just last month.

—Names of countries, national divisions, governmental groups when the common noun replaces the full name (often in internal government correspondence):

From the beginning of the Republic, a balance of powers was necessary.

The State submitted a brief as a friend of the court.

The Department has a policy against overtime for employees at professional levels.

The House sent a bill to the Conference Committee.

—Names of close family members used in place of their proper names, especially in direct address:

Please understand, Mother, that I intend to pay my fair share.

Before leaving I spoke to Mother, Father, and Uncle George.

NOTE 4: Capitalize plural common nouns following two or more proper nouns unless the common nouns represent topographical features (such as lakes, rivers, mountains, oceans, and so on):

West and South High Schools
the Korean and Vietnam Wars
the State and Defense Departments

but

the Mississippi and Missouri rivers
the Wasatch and Uinta mountains
the Pacific and Indian oceans

3. Capitalize the first letter of the first word of sentences, quotations, and listed items (either phrases or sentences):

Researchers propose to complete eight projects this year.

The technical specifications stated: "All wing strut pins should have a 150 percent load factor."

The accountant discussed the following issues:

—Budget design
—Cost overruns
—Entry postings

NOTE: The first letter of a word following a colon or a dash within a sentence is often capitalized, although some editors prefer not to. A good rule of thumb is that full sentences and long quotations (usually sentences) begin with a capital letter after a colon or dash:

The Bible states: "The race is not to the swift."

We followed one principle: Short-term investments must be consistent with long-term goals.

or

We followed one principle—Short-term investments must be consistent with long-term goals.

4. Capitalize the first letter of the names of directions when they indicate specific geographical areas. Do not capitalize the first letter of the names when they merely indicate a direction or a general or unspecified portion of a larger geographical area:

the Deep South
the Midwest
the Near East
the North
the Northwest

blowing from the southeast
eastern Missouri
southern Italy
the northern Midwest
toward the south
traveling north

NOTE: Sometimes titles are not clearly a geographical area—for instance, *East Texas*. If local custom identifies *East Texas* as including a particular number of counties, then the capital *E* is correct. If, however, *east Texas* means merely the general eastern portion of the state, then the lowercase *e* is correct. Of course, *eastern Texas* (rather than *east Texas)* would be a clearer means of indicating direction rather than geographical area.

5. Capitalize the first letter of names for the Deity, names for the Bible and other sacred writings, names of religious bodies and their adherents, and names denoting the Devil:

Christ
God
He, Him
Messiah
Son of Man
the Almighty
Thee

God's Word
the Good Book
the Old Testament
the Word

a Lutheran
an Episcopalian
Episcopal Church
Lutheran Church

His Satanic Majesty
Satan
the Great Malevolence

6. Capitalize the first letter of the first word and all main words of headings and subheadings and of titles of books, articles, and other documents. Do not capitalize the first letter of the articles *(a, an,* and *the)*, the coordinate conjunctions *(and, but, or, nor, for, so, yet)*, or the short prepositions *(to, of,* etc.) unless they appear as the first word:

"An Examination of Church-State Relations"
Declaration of Independence
Oil and Gas Journal
The Geology of East Texas
"The Greening of Panama" in *Scientific American*

See HEADINGS.

7. Capitalize in titles and headings the first letters of the initial word and of all later words in a hyphenated compound except for articles, short prepositions, and short conjunctions.

See rule 6 above.

A Report on Tin-Lined Acid Converters
Up-to-Date Power-Driven Extraction Methodologies
State-of-the-Art Technology
Seventy-Five World Leaders as Voting Representatives

8. Capitalize the first letter of the geological names of eras, periods, systems, series, epochs, and ages:

Jurassic Period
Late Cretaceous
Little Willow
Paleozoic Era
Upper Triassic

NOTE 1: Unless they are part of a proper name, do **not** capitalize structural terms such as *arch, basin, formation, zone, field, pay, pool, dome, uplift, anticline, reservoir*, or *trend* when they combine with geological names:

Cincinnati arch
Delaware basin
East Texas field
Ozark uplift

NOTE 2: Experts disagree about the capitalization of *upper, middle, lower* and *late, middle, early.* The following list from the *United States Government Printing Office Style Manual* (1984) provides the best summary of the difficult capitalization conventions in this technical area. Note that both *upper Oligocene* and *Upper Devonian* are correct, although the capitalization of *upper* is inconsistent:

Alexandrian
Animikie
Atoka
Cambrian:
  Upper, Late
  Middle, Middle
  Lower, Early
Carboniferous Systems
Cayuga
Cenozoic
Cincinnatian
Chester
Coahuila
Comanche

Capitals

Cretaceous:
 Upper, Late
 Lower, Early
Des Moines
Devonian:
 Upper, Late
 Middle, Middle
 Lower, Early
Eocene:
 upper, late
 middle, middle
 lower, early
glacial:
 interglacial
 postglacial
 preglacial
Glenarm
Grand Canyon
Grenville
Guadalupe
Gulf
Gunnison River
Holocene
Jurassic:
 Upper, Late
 Middle, Middle
 Lower, Early
Keweenawan
Kinderhook
Leonard
Little Willow
Llano
Meramec
Mesozoic:
 pre-Mesozoic
 post-Mesozoic
Miocene:
 upper, late
 middle, middle
 lower, early
Mississippian:
 Upper, Late
 Lower, Early
Missouri
Mohawkian
Morrow
Niagara
Ochoa
Ocoee
Oligocene:
 upper, late
 middle, middle
 lower, early
Osage
Ordovician:
 Upper, Late
 Middle, Middle
 Lower, Early
Pahrump
Paleocene:
 upper, late
 middle, middle
 lower, early
Paleozoic
Pennsylvanian:
 Upper, Late
 Middle, Middle
 Lower, Early
Permian:
 Upper, Late
 Lower, Early
Pleistocene
Pliocene:
 upper, late
 middle, middle
 lower, early
Precambrian:
 upper
 middle
 lower
Quaternary
red beds
Shasta
Silurian:
 Upper, Late
 Middle, Middle
 Lower, Early
St. Croixan
Tertiary
Triassic:
 Upper, Late
 Middle, Middle
 Lower, Early
Virgil
Wolfcamp
Yavapai

NOTE 3: Topographical terms are usually capitalized, but the general terms *province* and *section* are not:

Hudson Valley
Interior Highlands
Middle Rocky Mountains
Ozark Plateaus
Uinta Basin

but

Navajo section
Pacific Border province

---

9. In text, do not capitalize the first letter of a common noun used with a date, number, or letter merely to denote time or sequence:

appendix A
collection 3
drawing 8
figure 5
page 45
paragraph 2
plate VI
section c
volume III

NOTE 1: The first letter of these common nouns should be capitalized if they appear in headings, titles, or captions: *Appendix A* or *Figure 5*.

NOTE 2: In these cases, *no., #,* or *No.* (for *Number*) is unnecessary:

Appendix A (*not* Appendix No. A)
page 45 (*not* page no. 45)
site 5 (*not* site #5)

NOTE 3: Some technical and scientific fields do capitalize a common noun used with a date, number, or letter. For example, The Society of Petroleum Engineers recommends in its *Style Guide* that writers observe the following style of capitalization:

Method 3
Sample 2
Table 4
Wells A22 and B7

---

10. Capitalize the first letter of proper nouns combined with common nouns, as in the names of plants, animals, diseases, and scientific laws or principles:

Boyle's law
Brittany spaniel
Cooper's hawk
Down's syndrome
Fremont silktassel
Gunn effect
Hodgkin's disease
Virginia clematis

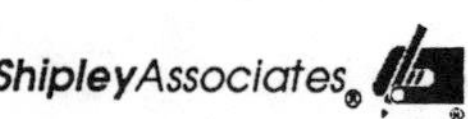

Captions

Captions for visuals include the title and any explanatory material immediately under (or sometimes over) a visual aid. Readers initially identify visual aids using conventional references: *Figure 14, Map 3, Chart 16,* etc. However, readers' eyes need to be guided beyond mere identification.

Good captions are what guide readers not only to see but also to understand. Good captions both label visuals with titles and explain to readers what they are seeing and how to interpret the information captured in the visual.

See VISUAL AIDS. See also CHARTS, GRAPHS, ILLUSTRATIONS, MAPS, PHOTOGRAPHS, and TABLES.

In the past, many technical and scientific documents used only short, simple titles (captions) for visuals. Such titles, which provided minimum information, were often so short and cryptic that they sounded telegraphic:

Figure 23. Glass containers

Table 2. Problem options

Table 14. Water and soil impacts

Telegraphic captions are only appropriate when the visual aids are self-explanatory, thus requiring no interpretation. But even then, the telegraphic style can be confusing. In the above examples, for instance, are the table 2 options really problems, or are the options solutions to a single problem? Similarly, does table 14 include water impacts as well as soil impacts, or is the subject some sort of data about water and a separate presentation about impacts on soil types? As these examples illustrate, avoid telegraphic captions.

1. Use action captions whenever possible.

Action captions provide both a title and interpretative information (usually expressed in a complete sentence) to help readers understand the central point(s) that you want the visual to convey:

> **Figure 4. Cabin-Temperature Control System.** *Constant cabin temperature control is maintained by the system's modulated cabin sensor.*
>
> **Figure 23. Check Valve.** *The risk of bad air entering the chamber is near zero because the check valve permits air flow in one direction only.*
>
> **Table 17. Air Intersect Data.** *Only stations 23 and 45 experienced significant increases in CO levels during the study period.*

The figure 4 action caption gives the title of the figure and then emphasizes that the cabin has a constant temperature—a benefit provided by the feature (modulated cabin sensor) described in the figure. The caption states clearly what the writer wants the reader to learn from the drawing.

The figure 23 action caption gives the title and then tells the reader the principal message—that the check valve provides near-zero risk. Further, it states **how** the check valve provides near-zero risk.

The table 17 action caption names the data in the table and then highlights significant data. By pointing out what is most important in the table, the caption helps the reader interpret the table, which might be very complex, and reinforces the major points that the writer will make in the text.

The following are additional examples of action captions for figures and tables:

> **Figure 1. Axial-Flow Design.** *The axial-flow design has the greatest performance potential.*
>
> **Figure 2. Life-Cycle Cost Projections.** *General Framitz's design-to-cost strategy will guarantee low life-cycle costs.*
>
> **Figure 3. Project Management System.** *Our project management system ensures maximum responsiveness to program requirements at all levels.*
>
> **Table 1. Population Impacts.** *If population redistribution trends continue, the Southwest will exceed baseline figures by 1996.*
>
> **Table 2. Cost of Mitigation Measures.** *The socioeconomic mitigation measures proposed are effective but very costly.*
>
> **Figure 4. Seasonal Streamflow Patterns.** *Keta River and White Creek peak in mid-October during Snow Geese migration and provide the only suitable feeding and resting habitat within a radius of 150 miles.*
>
> **Table 3. Projections of New Jobs During the Next 10 Years.** *Contrary to media opinion, the Thunder Basin Project will create–not destroy–jobs in the Sequaw Valley: at least 500 within the next 10 years.*
>
> **Figure 5. Test Results of Thermal Model 2.** *Flame-envelope thermal Model 2 results in lower ambient temperatures but produces diffuse radiation.*

Captions

> **Figure 6. Limits of Multiplexer Design.** The analog input multiplexer design limits components that are not included in self-testing to a few passive components.

NOTE: You can create action captions without using complete sentences or a separate title—if the captions tell readers how to read and interpret the visual aid:

> **Figure 14. Declining production through the 1970s**
>
> *or*
>
> **Figure 14.** *Declining production through the 1970s*

In these examples (both acceptable versions of a caption), the title for the figure is combined with a phrase telling readers about the production trend during the 1970s. As the two examples illustrate, you can use either boldface type or italics to highlight the caption.

A longer version of the figure 14 caption would include a separate title and then add a complete sentence interpreting the figure:

> **Figure 14. Production (1970-1979).** *Production declined steadily through the 1970s.*

Whether or not an action caption is a complete sentence, it should provide a point of view on the visual. It tells readers not only what the visual is about but also what the visual means.

---

2. Number figures and tables sequentially throughout the document, and place the number before the caption.

Figures and tables should be numbered sequentially as they appear in the document. If you present an important figure or table twice, treat it as two separate visuals and number each according to its position in the sequence. See VISUAL AIDS.

Figure and table numbers should be whole numbers: *Figure 1, Figure 2, Figure 3,* etc. If you are numbering visuals by chapter, then use a hyphen to separate chapter number from visual number: *Figure 14-2* (chapter 14, figure 2), *Table 2-8* (chapter 2, table 8). You can also use the decimal numbering system with hyphens to designate visual numbers within a section of a report if the report's sections have been numbered decimally: *Figure 23.2-1* (section 23.2, figure 1), *Table 7.4-13* (section 7.4, table 13). If the visual aid has several parts and you need to identify all parts, use parentheses and lowercase alphabetical characters to designate subparts: *Figure 34(a), Figure 34(b), Figure 34(c).*

NOTE 1: The style of punctuation for captions varies. Some editors prefer a colon or a period and a dash following the number. Some editors prefer no punctuation and leave three or four spaces between the number and the caption:

> Figure 14-2: Federal shipbuilding and repair budget
>
> Figure 14-2.–Federal shipbuilding and repair budget
>
> Figure 14-2   Federal shipbuilding and repair budget

NOTE 2: In captions, the words *figure* and *table* should be capitalized. However, when you are referring to visuals in the text, even if you refer to a specific visual, do not capitalize *figure* or *table* unless it begins a sentence:

> As shown in figure 33, . . .
>
> According to table 14.2-4, . . .
>
> *however*
>
> Figure 33 shows . . .
>
> Table 14.2-4 presents . . .

See CAPITALS.

---

3. Use periods following action captions but no punctuation following telegraphic captions.

Action captions are usually complete sentences and should therefore end with a period. Telegraphic captions, on the other hand, are like titles or headings and are normally not complete sentences, so they require no punctuation.

If you mix action and telegraphic captions, end all of them with periods. See LISTS and PERIODS.

---

4. Captions may appear below or above the visual, but be consistent throughout a document.

Some graphics specialists argue that captions should always appear above their visuals because the captions (which comes from the word *head*) are like titles. Others argue that captions should always appear below their visuals because the visuals are more important than the captions and placing captions below their visuals is more aesthetic. Still others argue that captions for tables should appear above tables but captions for figures should appear below figures.

Be consistent. Treat tables no differently than figures. If you're going to place captions above or below visuals, then do so throughout your document. Deciding whether to place captions above or below visuals requires judgment, but the mechanics of reading suggest the placement principles in the next two rules.

5. Place short or telegraphic captions above their visuals.

Short captions form a quick introduction to the visual and should be seen first as readers are reading from the top of the page down. Short captions are very much like titles and would function as titles.

6. Place long captions, especially action captions, below their visuals.

Placing a lengthy caption above a visual would make the visual look top heavy and therefore not aesthetically appealing. Furthermore, a lengthy caption above a visual would slow readers, and they would therefore be apt to skip the caption. If you are using action captions and some of them become lengthy (more than two lines), then place all of the captions below their visuals.

The key, again, is to be consistent throughout the document.

Charts

Charts are some of the most frequently used and valuable types of visual aids. Unfortunately, the term *chart* has different meanings for different people.

Webster's New Collegiate Dictionary defines *chart* as a map, table, graph, or diagram. That definition exemplifies the confusion many people have over the names of different types of visual aids.

Originally, *chart* meant a document, although most charts were maps. When maps were combined with tabular data (e.g., the mileage charts on modern road maps), *chart* came to mean a tabular or matrix display. When the tabular data were plotted on a coordinate graph, the word *chart* became synonymous with *graph*, especially if the data were displayed in bars or circles. Bar and circle (pie) graphs (or charts) thus became associated with geometric shapes and were also called diagrams.

For the purposes of this *Style Guide*, we define charts as those visual aids that fall into these loose categories: **bar charts, surface charts, pie charts, flow charts, organizational charts, Gantt charts,** and **combination charts** (hybrids). Note, however, that some writers and illustrators refer to bar and surface charts as graphs and to pie charts as circular diagrams.

Many charts do not fall into neat categories, especially those involving combinations of displays. Such combinations are frequently the most inventive, dramatic, and effective visual displays of information, so we urge you not to become overly concerned with nomenclature.

The best visuals are those that rapidly and effectively communicate their central ideas, regardless of what one might call them.

See VISUAL AIDS and GRAPHS.

General Rules for Constructing Charts

1. If appropriate, use scales to indicate the quantity, magnitude, and range of each axis.

If the horizontal (x) axis or the vertical (y) axis indicates quantities, magnitudes, and ranges, use scales that show the axis minimum and maximum, as well as the numeric intervals. (See the vertical scales on figures 1, 2, 3, and 7, and the horizontal scales on figures 4, 6, and 8.)

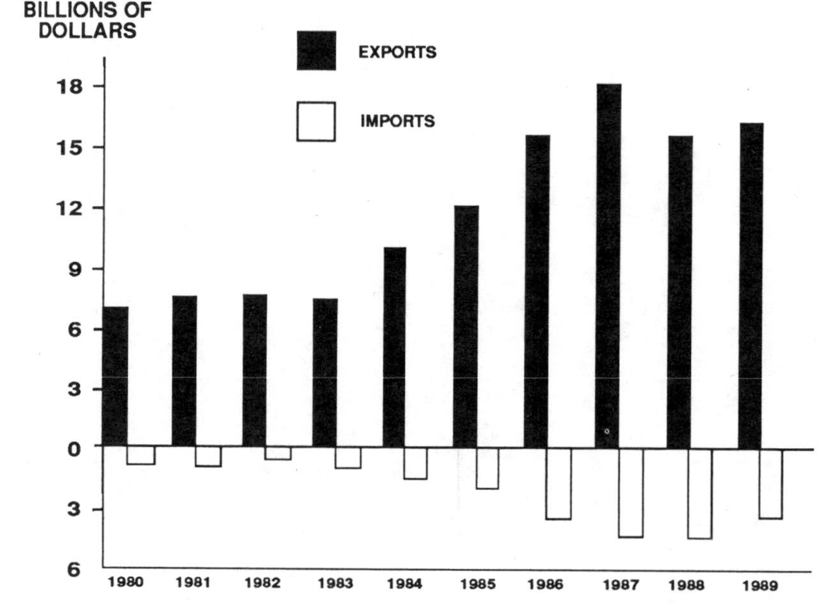

Figure 1. U.S. Aerospace Balance of Trade. *The U.S. aerospace industry has maintained a favorable balance of trade over the last decade and still dominates the U.S. market.*

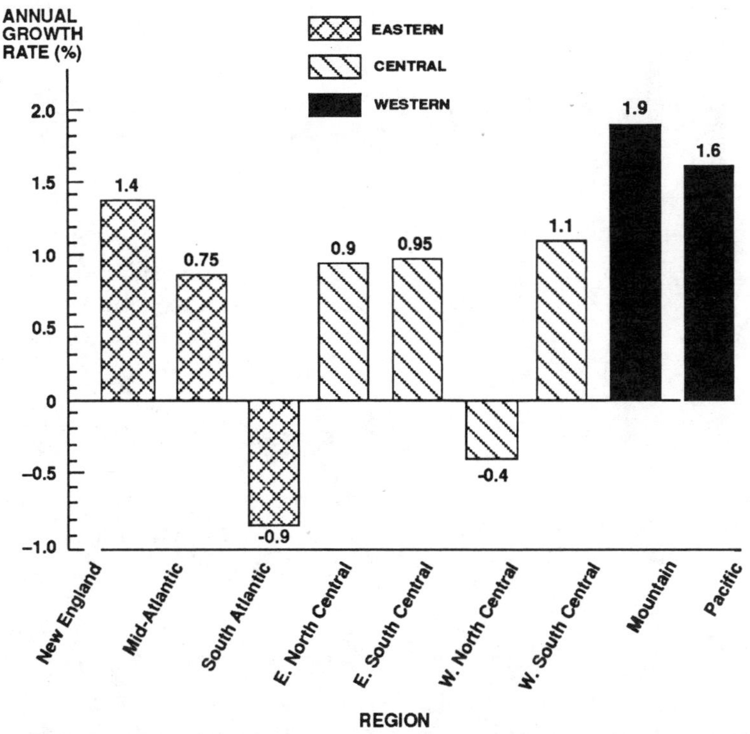

Figure 2. Employment Growth Rates in 1988. *Despite the employment growth in western states, national employment growth in 1988 reflects an uneven and sluggish national economy.*

Label the minimums and maximums. Also label a sequence of intervals along the scale. If the minimum is 0 and the maximum is 1,000, for instance, you might label the scale in steps of 100. These interval labels indicate the scale and allow readers to interpolate data. Do not use so many labels that the scale becomes crowded; however, do not use so few that readers cannot easily interpolate data. Generally, try to leave one or two spaces between interval labels. See GRAPHS.

2. If appropriate, use tick marks to help readers interpolate data.

Tick marks are short lines on and perpendicular to an axis that indicate the intervals along a scale. Use longer tick marks beside interval labels; use shorter tick marks between labels. Generally, try to use twice as many tick marks as labels (so that you have tick marks at the midpoints between labels).

Do not use too many tick marks. The more tick marks you use, the more crowded the scale becomes. Do not create finer distinctions than necessary for the data being shown. The tick marks on figure 1 are appropriate. The tick marks on figure 2 are far more detailed than necessary, especially because the data labels above or below each bar already show the size of the bar. Detailed interpretation of figure 2 is unnecessary, so the tick marks (spaced only 0.1 increments apart) are also unnecessary. See GRAPHS.

3. Orient horizontally all letters, numbers, words, and phrases in headings, legends, and labels.

All of the letters, numbers, and words on a chart should be readable from one reading perspective. Readers should not have to rotate the page to read different parts of a chart.

EXCEPTION: In some cases, the vertical axis label must be oriented vertically, usually because of space restrictions.

4. Place footnotes and source information below the chart.

Footnotes typically explain or clarify the information appearing in the entire chart or in one small part of it. Often, footnotes tell what the data apply to, where they came from, or how accurate they are:

> [1]All data are in 1990 dollars.
>
> [2]For major industrial groups only.
>
> [3]According to the National Stockmen's Council. The AABP estimates that production has declined only 3.55 percent since 1981.

The footnotes for each chart are numbered independently from footnotes in the text and from footnotes in other visuals. Begin with footnote 1 and proceed sequentially for that single visual; for the next visual, start the numbering again. Within the body of the chart, use superscripted footnote numbers. Place the footnote explanations (in numerical order) immediately below the chart and flush with the

Charts

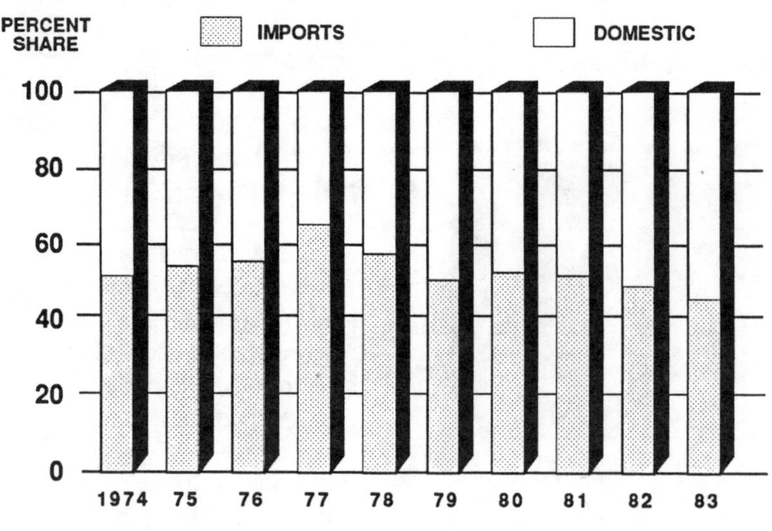

Figure 3. Subcompact Car Sales. *From 1977 to 1983, U.S. manufacturers lost about 20 percent of the subcompact car market. (Source: Ward's Automotive Reports, Bureau of Industrial Economics.)*

left margin. Repeat the superscripted footnote number and then provide the appropriate explanation, followed by a period.

If the chart covers more than one page, place the appropriate footnotes with each page. If caption, footnotes, and text appear below a chart, place the footnotes ahead of the text but below the caption.

If footnote numbers would be confusing in the body of the chart, use letters ([a], [b], [c], [d], etc.), asterisks (*, **, ***), or other symbols.

Source information may appear in footnotes if the referenced source provided only that data indicated by the footnote and not the data for the rest of the chart:

> [4]From *The Wall Street Journal*, May 14, 1984.
>
> [5]Source: U.S. Department of the Interior.

Source information may also appear within parentheses in the caption (regardless of where the caption appears) or within brackets under the caption if the caption appears ahead of the chart:

> Figure 1. U.S. Aerospace Balance of Trade: 1980-89 (U.S. Department of Commerce)
>
> Figure 1. U.S. Aerospace Balance of Trade: 1980-89
> [U.S. Department of Commerce]

See FOOTNOTES.

5. Ensure that the visual characteristics of the chart reflect the magnitude and importance of the data being represented.

The value of charts is their visual impact. Consequently, writers can mislead readers by producing visuals that give more or less prominence to an idea or piece of data the writer wishes to emphasize or deemphasize.

Distorting bar lengths or sizes or pie slice areas can mislead readers into thinking that something is larger or smaller than it really is. Similarly, using bright colors for insignificant data and dull colors for significant data can confuse readers and lead some to think that the insignificant is really significant. To ensure that you have presented a truthful and accurate picture of the situation being depicted, strive to make the visual impression created by the chart consistent with reality. See VISUAL AIDS.

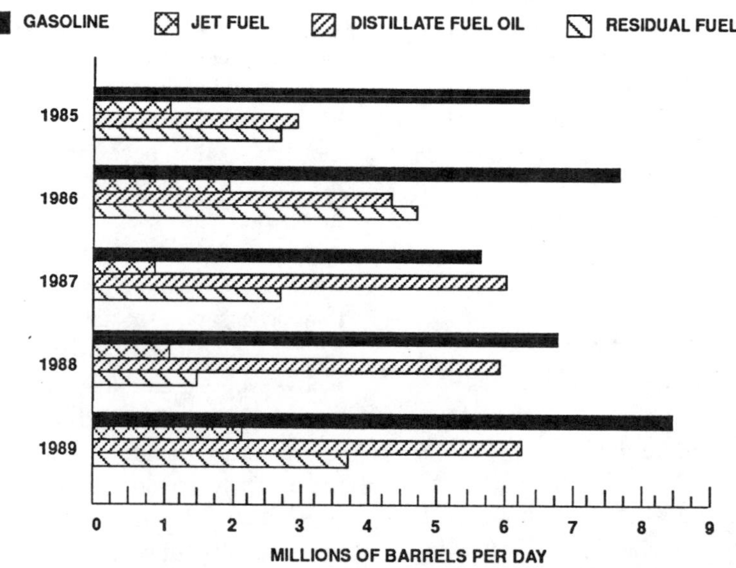

Figure 4. Petroleum Products Supplied (1985-1989). *Gasoline and distillate fuel oil probably will remain our principal products in the 1990s.*

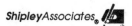

Bar Charts

Bar charts depict the relationship between two or more variables, one of which is usually time. These charts typically show how the other variables change over time. Consequently, bar charts are useful for depicting trends (see figure 1). Because bar charts can show multiple variables, they can also depict how several variables change relative to one another over time (see figure 6).

Bar charts are **not** useful if the quantities depicted do not differ significantly. And if you expand or distort the scales to dramatize slight differences, the bar chart will look suspicious to alert readers and might damage your credibility.

Bar charts may be horizontal or vertical. In vertical bar charts, time is usually plotted along the x (horizontal) axis (see figures 1 and 3). In horizontal bar charts, time is usually plotted along the y (vertical) axis (see figures 4 and 6).

Some writers and illustrators argue that vertical bar charts are better for showing trends (figure 1) and that horizontal bar charts are better for comparisons (figures 4 and 5) and for showing magnitude changes (figure 6). Certainly, readers are more used to seeing trends shown along a horizontal axis. However, comparisons and magnitude changes are usually clear in either orientation. Use your judgment.

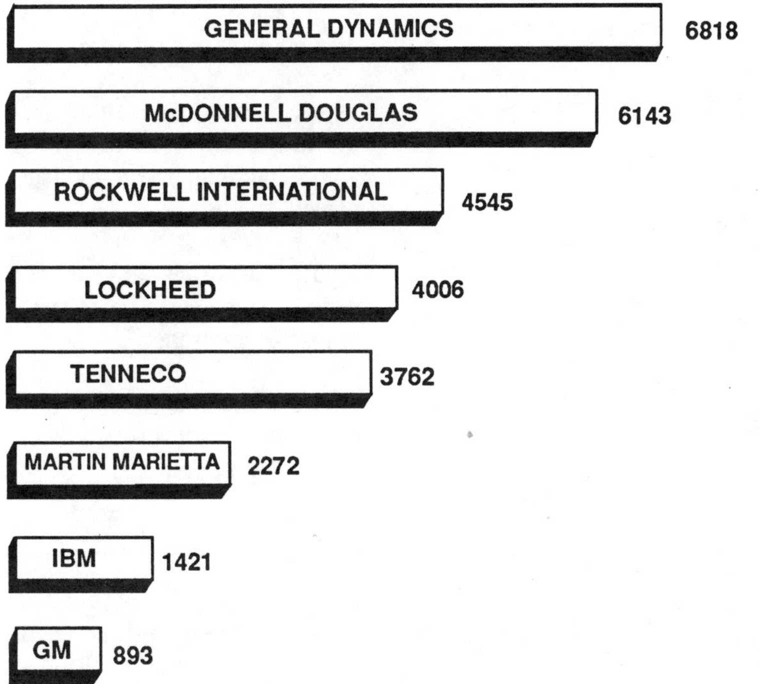

Figure 5. Contracts in 1983 for the Eight Largest DoD Contractors. Five of these eight contractors come from the aerospace sector, which continues to dominate DoD procurement.

Bar charts may be used with other visual forms, such as line or coordinate graphs (see GRAPHS), maps (see MAPS), or pie charts (see figure 11).

6. Clearly label each bar.

Ensure that readers understand what each bar represents. See figures 1 through 9 for examples.

7. Make the bars wider than the spaces between them.

See figures 1 through 9. A bar chart with the spaces wider than the bars would seem "airy." The dominant visual effect in a bar chart should be the bars.

8. Use different bar patterns to indicate differences in types of data.

Bar patterns allow you to distinguish areas, regions, groups, and parts. Patterns also allow you to focus readers' attention on areas of the chart you consider most important. Bar patterns include but are not limited to the following:

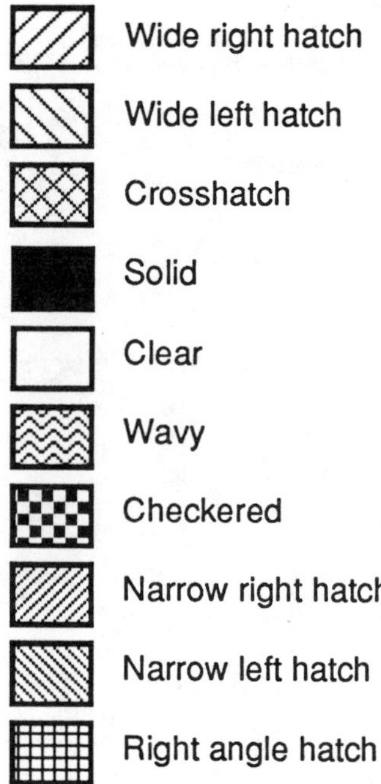

Figure 1 uses a simple black/white contrast to dramatize the difference between imports and exports. To further emphasize those differences, figure 1 also places exports above the zero dividing line and imports below the line. Note that the vertical axis reflects positive numbers on both sides of the zero dividing line.

Figure 2 uses a crosshatch pattern to indicate eastern regions, a wide left hatch pattern to indicate central states, and solid bars to indicate western states. The solid bars dominate the chart, causing readers to focus on the growth rates of the western regions, which are the highest in the country. The writer might have wished to emphasize the declining growth rates in the South Atlantic and West North Central regions, and could have done so by using empty bars for other regions and solid bars for the two declining regions.

Figure 3 uses combination dotted and empty bar patterns within the same bars to indicate percent shares.

Figure 4 uses four bar patterns to distinguish between four types of petroleum products.

Figure 6 uses two bar patterns to isolate the bars that reflect two very different scales.

9. If you use different bar patterns, provide an explanation that identifies the bars.

In figure 6, the bar patterns are clear without an explanation. In figures 1, 2, 3, 4, 7, 8, and 9, however, an explanation is necessary. They present the bar patterns in small boxes along with labels indicating what each pattern represents.

10. Use paired bars to depict sets of data having different scales.

Figure 6 shows a paired bar chart. That kind of chart is necessary when the data being depicted can be divided into two sets of data that operate on different numerical scales. In figure 6, GNP is measured in billions of dollars and industrial demand for molybdenum is measured in millions of pounds. Depicting these relationships would be difficult unless the chart allows for two distinct x-axis scales.

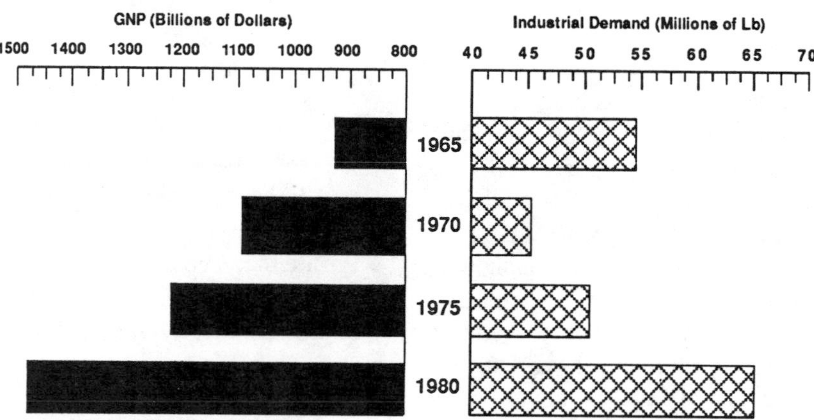

Figure 6. U.S. Molybdenum Demand. *We expect that molybdenum demand will increase at roughly the rate that the GNP increases.*

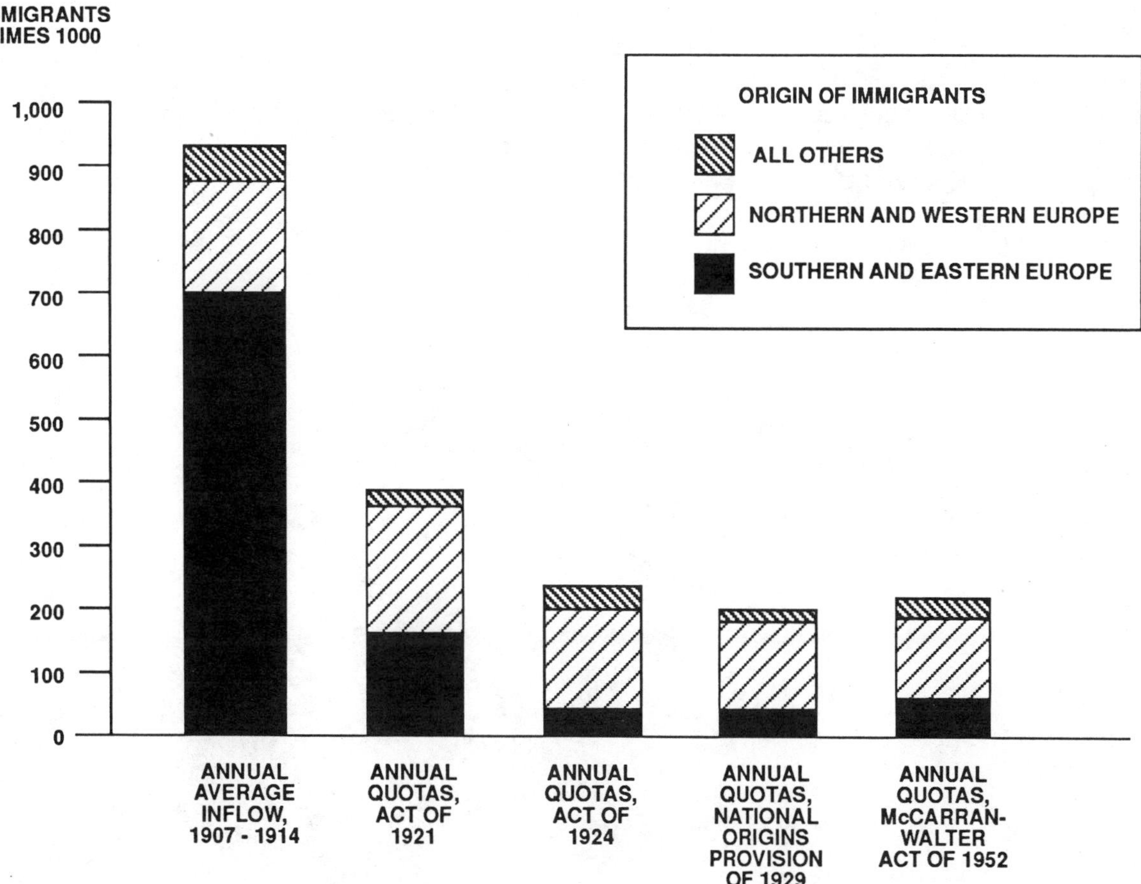

Figure 7. Immigration Under Major Federal Laws (1907-Present). *Federal immigration quotas became increasingly restrictive during the present century, even though still favoring immigrants from northern and western Europe.*

11. Use segmented bars to depict three or more variables.

Segmented bars (figures 7 through 9) allow you to show multiple variables. Figure 7, for example, depicts quota quantity, quota times, and origins of immigrants. Figure 8 shows species, estuaries, and numbers of sightings.

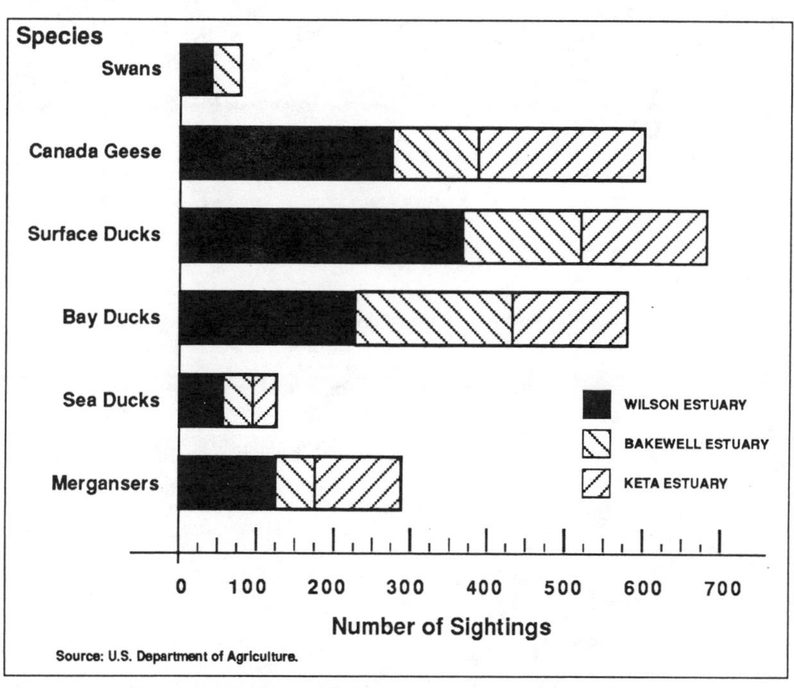

Figure 8. Waterfowl Sightings. *In 1982, waterfowl sightings were down 10 percent, probably because of the drought in the Canadian wetlands.*

Charts

Figure 9 is a three-dimensional bar chart. Its principal intent is to demonstrate South Korea's rapid expansion into the international marketplace by showing three variables: the (1) quantity; (2) timing; and (3) national origin of machine tools, electronics, and auto production. The segmentation of the bar adds a "fourth" dimension by showing each country's production of these three items.

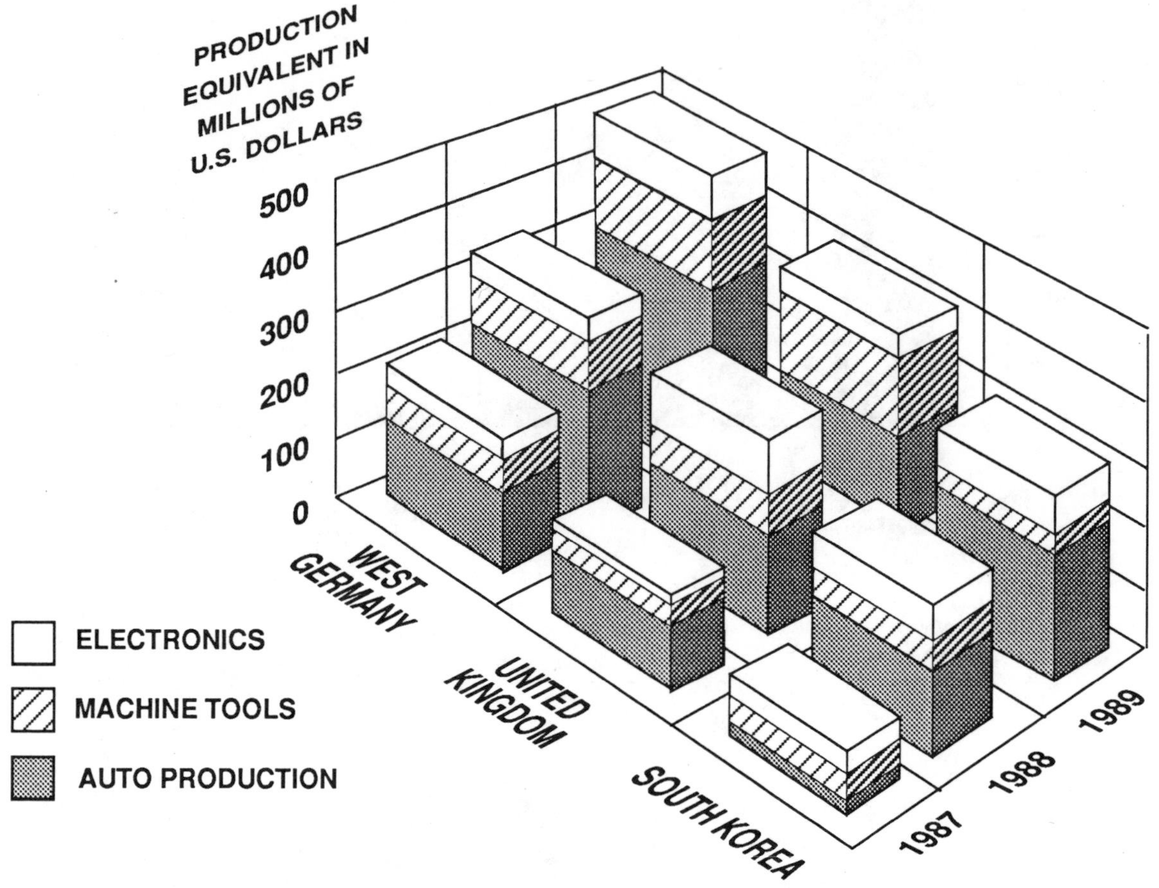

Figure 9. South Korea's Sudden Invasion of the International Market. *South Korea gained a large share of the international market in a relatively short period of time.*

Pie Charts

Pie charts are circles (pies) divided into sectors (slices) to show the relationship of parts to a whole. The sectors must add up to 100 percent.

Pie charts are useful for general comparisons of relative size. However, they are not useful if accuracy is important. Further, pie charts are not useful for showing a large number of items.

The eye can measure linear distances far more easily than radial distances or areas. Therefore, visual comparisons of bars on a bar chart are much easier than visual comparisons of sectors in a pie chart. Moreover, readers can usually make more accurate judgments about data relationships expressed in a linear fashion. So if you need accuracy, use a bar chart. If you need to show how parts relate to one another and to a whole—and if precise numbers are not important—use a pie chart.

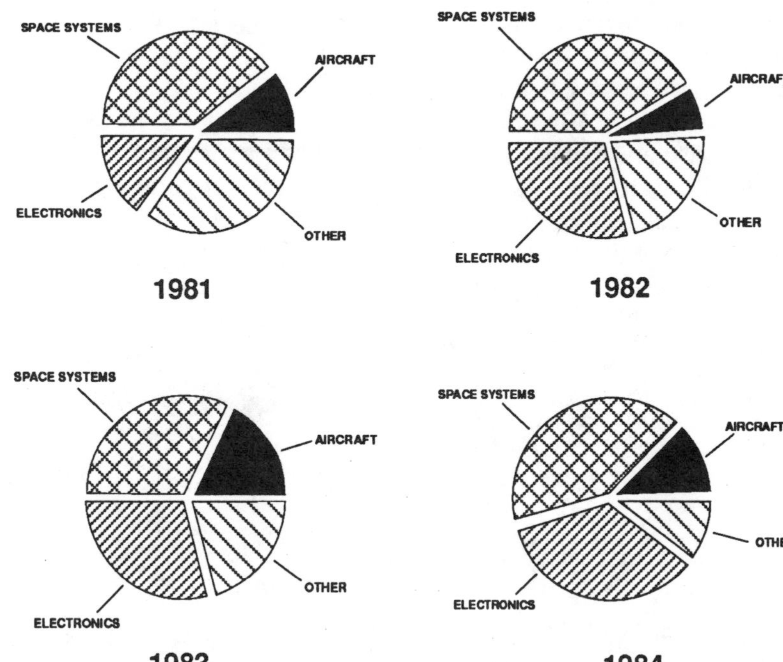

Figure 10. DoD Prime Contract Awards for RDT&E. *Space systems will continue to receive the greatest dollar awards from DoD.*

12. Identify each sector of the pie and, if appropriate, the percentage it represents.

Pie charts do not have axes and therefore cannot be very precise, so if percentages are important, identify them (see figure 12).

Always identify each sector of the pie. You can do this by using labels (figures 10 and 11) or fill patterns and an explanation block (figure 12). For further information on fill patterns, see the preceding discussion of bar charts.

13. Differentiate adjacent pie sectors by using alternating fill patterns or colors.

To help readers distinguish the sectors, use alternating fill patterns or colors (see figures 10 through 12). Reserve the solid (or black) fill pattern for the prominent sectors, the ones you wish to emphasize. Never use the same fill pattern for adjacent sectors.

14. Ensure that the size of each sector reflects the data it represents.

The size of the sector conveys a powerful visual message. Readers often "grasp" a pie chart simply by perceiving the relative size of the sectors, even when accompanying data labels clearly indicate what percentage each sector is supposed to reflect.

15. Group small percentage items under a general label, such as "Other."

Pie charts should have no more than 8 to 10 sectors, depending on the size of the pie. The larger the pie, the more sectors you can safely divide it into. However, beyond some reasonable number of sectors (10), a pie chart becomes too busy and therefore difficult to read.

If you have a number of small percentage items, you should group them and give them a common label, such as "Other Parts," "Other Exports," or simply "Other" if the context of

Charts

the chart and the names of the other labels indicate what "Other" refers to. If you have items of moderate size (say 10 to 20 percent) that are unimportant and would distract readers, you might group them under a common label too. (See figure 10, where the "other" category occupies over 25 percent of the pie labeled "1981.")

16. Use pie-bar combination charts to show the composition of an important sector of the pie.

Figure 11 shows a combination pie-bar chart. Here, the focus of the chart is on multi-engine exports, and the bar associated with that pie sector is a segmented bar indicating the types of multi-engine aircraft being exported and their percentage of the whole.

Each sector of a pie can potentially be expanded into a segmented bar. In this way, you are adding one more variable to the pie chart.

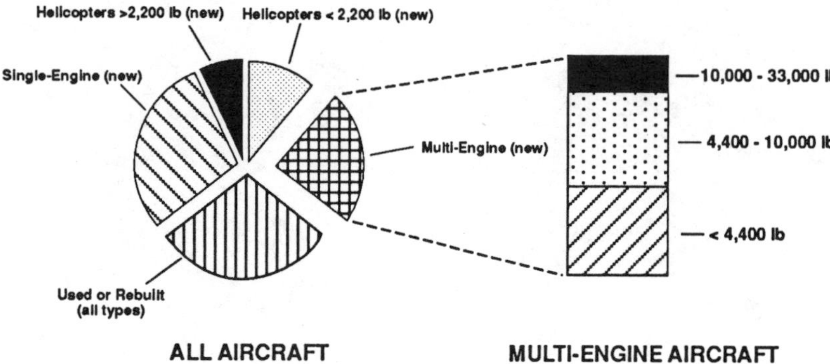

Figure 11. Multi-Engine Aircraft Sales in 1983. *Of the new multi-engine aircraft sold in 1983, nearly half weighed less than 4,400 lb and carried fewer than four passengers.*

17. Use a series of pie charts to add time as a variable.

Another way of adding a variable is to use a series of pie charts (see figures 10 and 12). The most common reason for using a series is to add time as a variable.

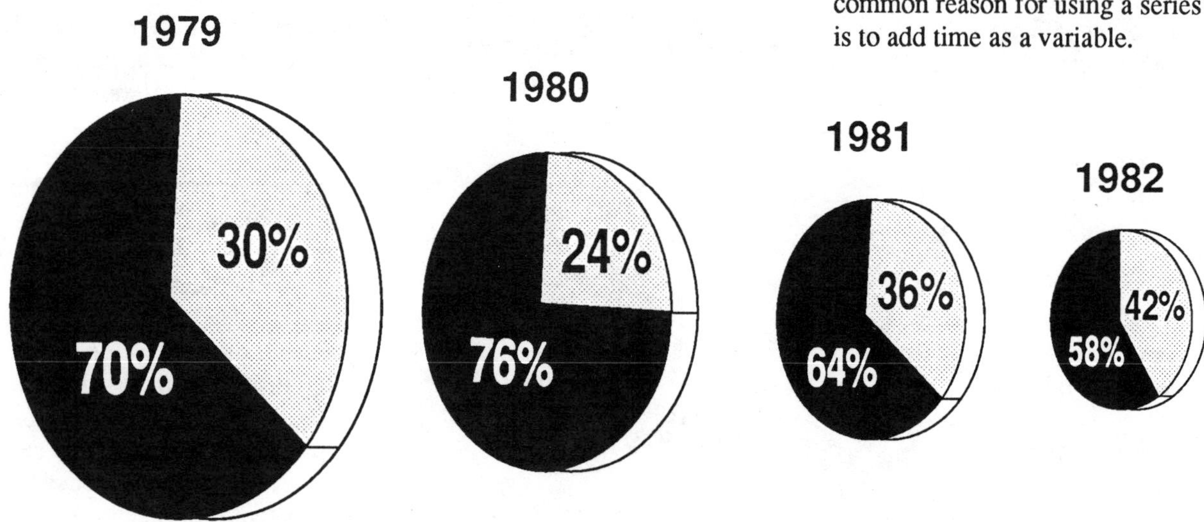

Figure 12. Airbus Industrie Market-Share Value. *Airbus has increased its market-share value from 30 to 42 percent because of its economic, widebody design.*

Organizational Charts

Organizational charts depict the structure of an organization. These charts typically show the divisions and subdivisions of the organization, the hierarchy and relationship of the groups to one another, lines of control (responsibility and authority), and lines of communication and coordination. Organizational charts help readers visualize the structure of an organization and the relationships within it.

18. Use squares or rectangles to indicate divisions and subdivisions within the organization.

The conventional means of indicating divisions, subdivisions, groups, project teams, functional areas, etc., is to enclose the name of the organizational unit within a square or rectangle.

You might distinguish between higher and lower units by changing the size of the rectangle or by changing its border (from boldface or thick lines representing upper-level units to thinner, normal lines representing lower-level units).

19. Structure an organizational chart from the top down.

This rule is important for two reasons: It reflects the way we read, and it reflects our perception and understanding of organizational structure.

Readers of English read from left to right and from top to bottom. Therefore, an organizational chart should be structured from left to right and top to bottom. The left to right progression might or might not be useful, depending on the type of organization you are depicting. However, the top to bottom progression is always useful, simply because almost all organizations are based on a hierarchy.

Accordingly, you should display the structure of the organization in descending order of authority—with the highest authority or level at the top of the chart and the lowest authorities or levels at the bottom of the chart. This structure reflects the metaphor of top-down management and thus reinforces the readers' expectations about organizational structure.

If the organization you are describing does not operate on a top-down basis, be inventive and create an organizational display that does reflect the organization's operational style and structure.

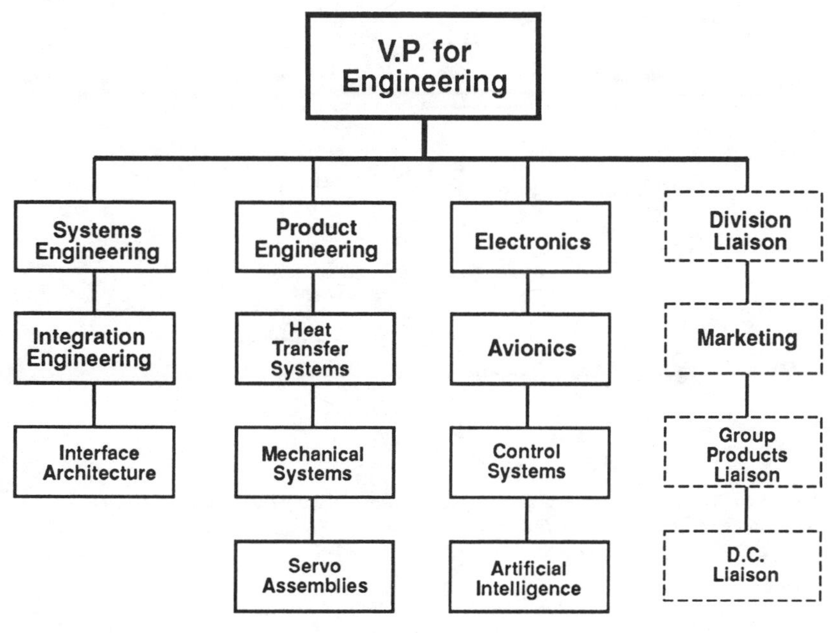

Figure 13. Engineering Department Organization. *The Vice President will coordinate with the Division Liaison office to ensure that all lobbying in Washington, D.C., will comply with the Procurement Integrity Law of July 18, 1989.*

20. Use solid lines to indicate direct relationships and dotted or dashed lines to indicate indirect relationships.

Solid lines usually show direct lines of control. Dashed or dotted lines usually indicate lines of communication or coordination.

In figure 13, the dashed lines forming the rectangles along the right side of the chart indicate that the Vice President for Engineering coordinates with the Division Liaison office and has lines of communication and coordination down through the Division Liaison organization, but the Vice President's direct authority extends through Systems Engineering, Product Engineering, and Electronics.

Charts

Flow Charts

Flow charts depict a process. They show readers the parts of a process and how those parts are related.

Flow charts use a symbol system to indicate the types of activities and control or transfer points being depicted.

Squares and rectangles typically indicate activities in the process. In figure 14, for instance, the upper left rectangle represents "Ore Crushing," the first activity taking place in this ore processing system. The arrow linking this rectangle to the rectangle directly to the right indicates that, after being crushed, the ore undergoes a chemical bath.

The arrows indicate the sequence of activity in the process and show a chronological (and sometimes cause-and-effect) relationship between linked activities or control points.

Circles typically indicate control or transfer points. Control points are those points in the process where the activities are monitored, started, stopped, or in some other way controlled. Transfer points are those points where the sequence of activity leaves one flow chart and continues on to another. In figure 14, the two right-most circles indicate that the ore has been processed and is ready for packaging. To continue following the process, the reader must go to the packaging flow chart (which is shown in figure 15).

The "Pack" circles in figure 14 represent all of figure 15. Consequently, figure 14 is the more general flow chart. If "Ore Crushing" involved a series of steps, the writer could have turned the "Ore Crushing" symbol in figure 14 into a circle and then constructed another subordinate flow chart (like figure 15) that represented all of the activities involved in crushing the ore.

Note that by putting all of the packaging activities into one subordinate flow chart, the writer has avoided significant repetition in figure 14.

Diamonds typically represent decision points. Often, as in figures 14 and 15, these decisions are represented by simple yes/no questions. Diamonds normally have three lines linking them to other symbols: one incoming line indicating what precedes the decision, one outgoing line indicating "yes," and the other outgoing line indicating "no."

Other symbols are possible, particularly in data processing and other specialized fields, such as architecture and electrical engineering. These symbols often have very specific meanings and have become traditional means of expression in particular scientific and technical applications. If you need to create flow charts for these specialized areas, consult appropriate trade journals and textbooks.

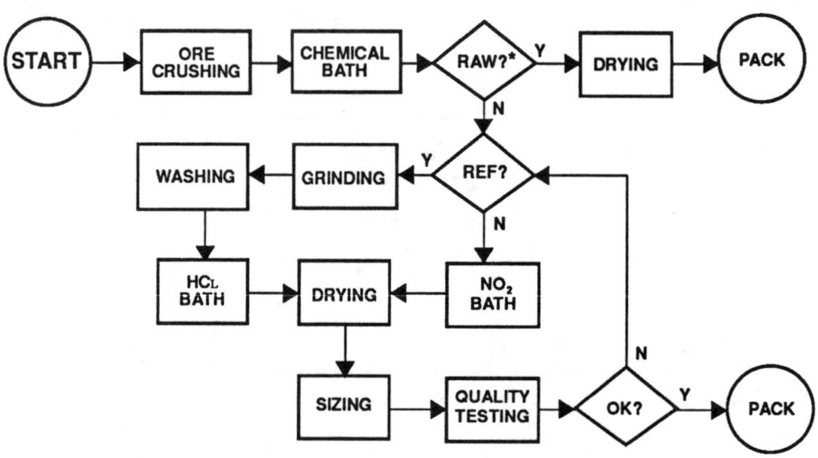

*Raw (semifinished) ore bypasses most of the final packaging procedures.

Figure 14. Ore Processing. *The quality and quantity of the ore that is packed is checked at three critical decision points, indicated by diamonds and Y (yes) and N (no) labels.*

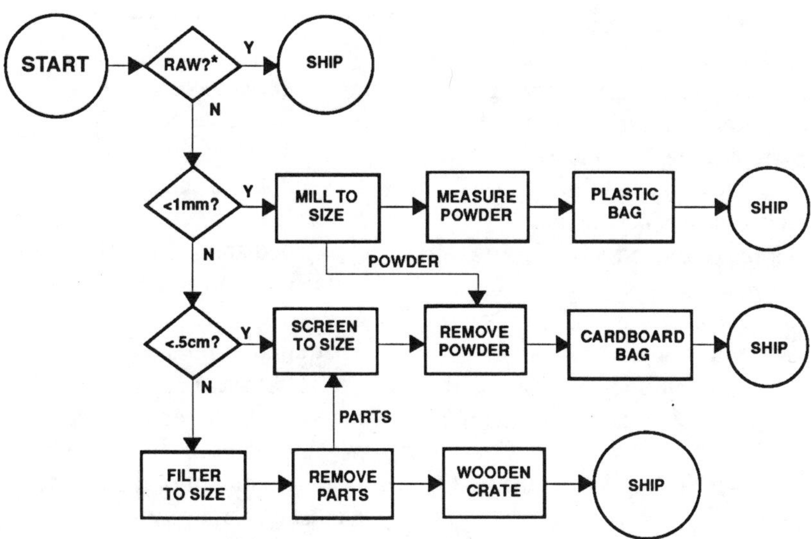

*Raw ore is shipped in bulk to customers who do not require sized or packaged ore.

Figure 15. Processed Ore Packaging. *For your convenience, we can ship ore to you in three ways: (1) in sealed plastic bags, (2) in cardboard bags, and (3) in wooden crates.*

24. Use footnotes to explain symbols, abbreviations, and connections with other flow charts.

As in figures 14 and 15, footnotes help explain abbreviations and activities or control points. Footnotes can also help readers understand the structure and sequence of related flow charts.

21. Place the starting activity in the upper left corner of the chart and proceed to the right and down. Place the ending activity in the lower right corner of the chart.

Readers will expect the flow chart to begin in the upper left corner. Don't disappoint them. If possible, try to end the flow chart in the lower right corner.

22. Break large or complicated flow charts into smaller, simpler flow charts.

Flow charts that become too large or too complicated are unreadable as well as intimidating. To avoid repetition and to keep flow charts from becoming too long, break them into general (overview) charts and subordinate (component) charts.

23. Use arrows to show the sequence or direction of flow within the flow chart.

Flow charts with activities or control points linked only by lines are often confusing. Place an arrow head on the end of the line to indicate the sequence or direction of flow (see figures 14 and 15).

Charts

Surface Charts

Surface charts (figure 16) show the effect of cumulative additions on a range of data. These charts resemble multiple line graphs (see GRAPHS), but their purpose is not to allow for precise interpretation but to display relative changes between parallel or different data; therefore, the surface chart is considered a chart and not a graph.

Surface charts are created by plotting data accumulations (usually two or more variables over a period of time) and then coloring or shading the area between successive lines to demonstrate both the effect of accumulation and the relationships between the variables plotted.

Surface charts are effective only when they depict gradual changes. Further, you cannot use them if any of the curves overlap.

See GRAPHS and VISUAL AIDS.

25. Use different patterns to shade areas beneath lines. If possible, use color as well.

The effect of a surface chart comes from the visual impact of the shaded areas, so use patterns to illustrate the area between successive lines. (For an illustration of possible patterns, see Bar Charts.) If possible, color the shaded areas. Use the brightest color for the area you wish to highlight or the area that is most important.

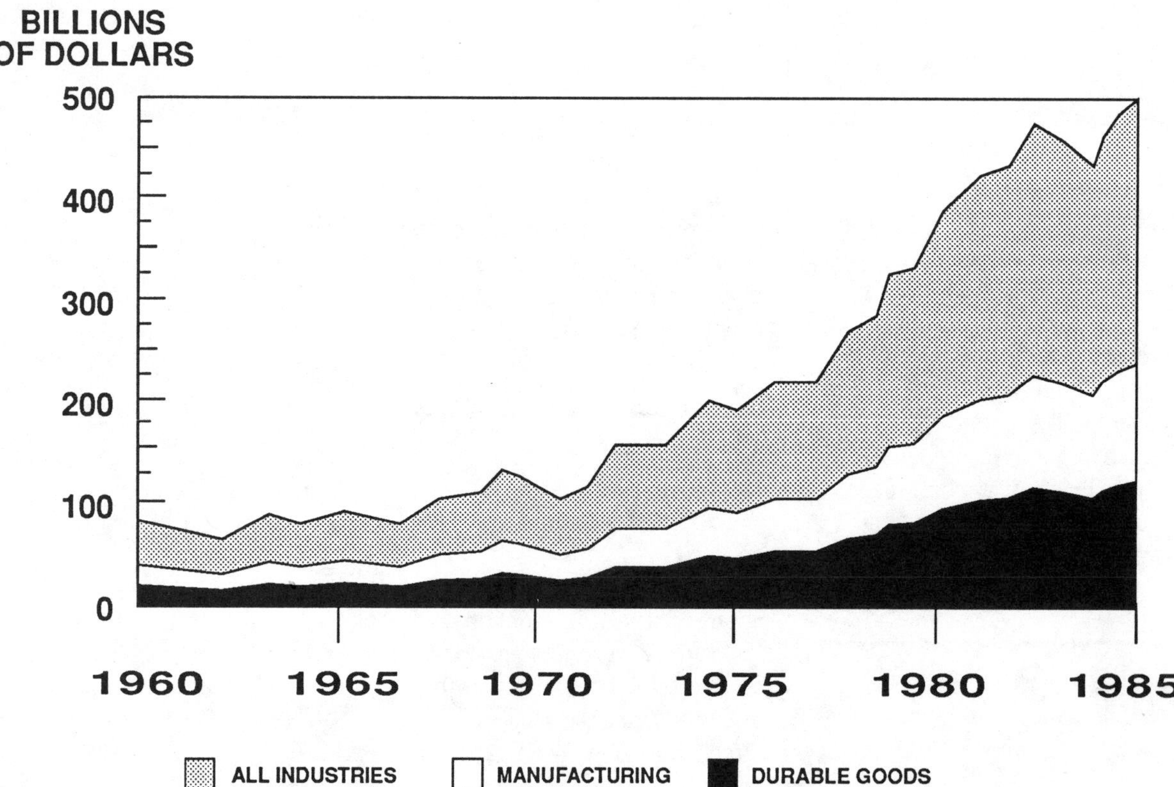

Figure 16. New Plant and Equipment Expenditures in the United States (1960-1985). *Despite the brief slowdown in the early 1980s, the long-term trend illustrates continued business expansion and associated optimism.*

Gantt Charts

Gantt charts are horizontal bar charts used to schedule tasks, projects, and programs. Gantt charts help readers visualize a sequence of activity occurring over a long period. They help readers see how sequential and concurrent activities are related to each other in time and how activities depend on one another for completion on schedule.

The horizontal (x) axis is always time. Time may be represented in decades, years, quarters, months, weeks, days, and hours. If necessary or helpful to readers, include more than one level of time on the x-axis (see figure 18). To make Gantt charts easier to read, use vertical dotted or dashed lines to mark major time periods (see figures 17 and 18).

26. List activities in chronological order beginning at the top of the page and moving down.

Gantt charts suggest strict chronology. Do not violate the reader's expectation that the events listed from top to bottom along the vertical (y) axis will appear in chronological order.

27. Clearly label or identify the bars.

Always identify what each bar represents, either with a bar label along the left margin or with an explanation block (as in figure 17). Traditionally, the bar labels appear on the left side of the chart.

Note, however, that in figure 17 the engine-interface control-system activities that follow certain engine-production activities are indicated only by the empty bars, as shown in the explanation block. If these

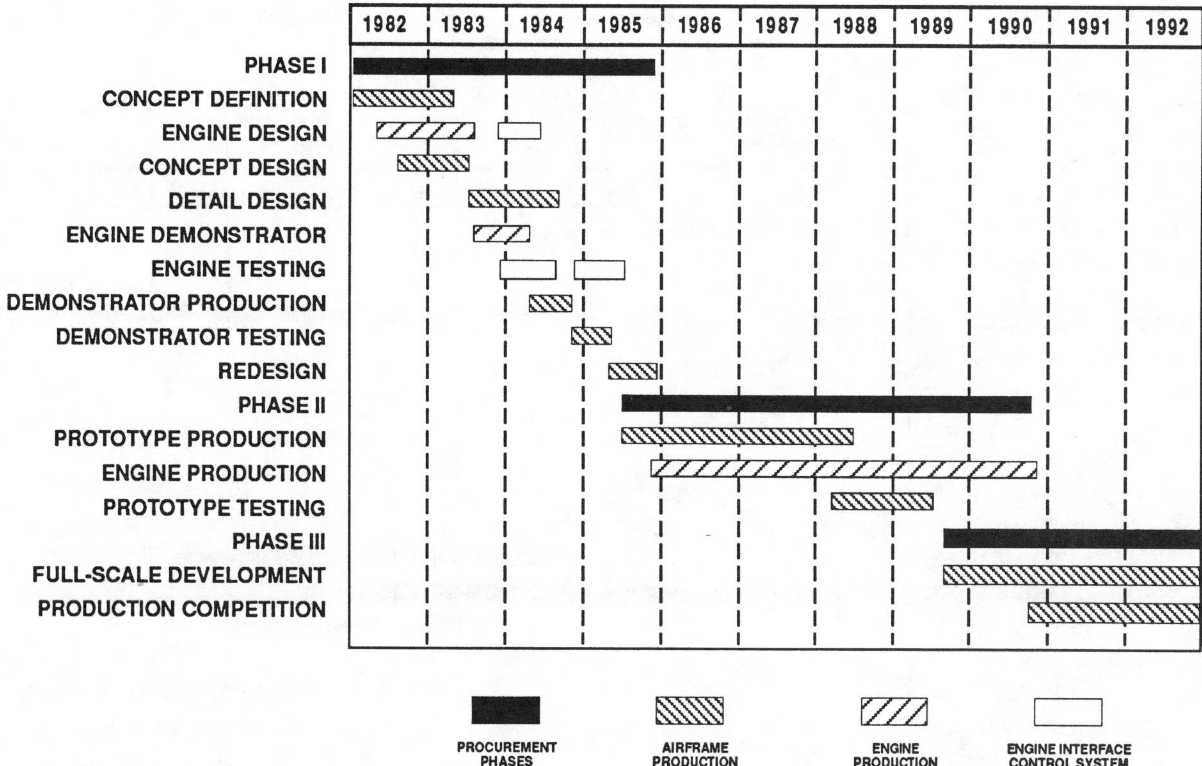

Figure 17. F25AF Production Schedule. *To lower production risk, we have scheduled the end of Phase I before the end of 1985; we can do this because of our self-funded R&D work on program and engine concept definition and design.*

interface activities were more important as stand-alone items, they would require their own rows.

28. If appropriate, indicate milestones on the chart.

Milestones may be indicated with small circles, dots, or triangles. If you have reporting, control, or performance events or deadlines that constitute milestones for tracking and monitoring progress, then indicate them on the chart.

29. Use bar patterns to identify groups of related activities. If you do so, also include an explanation block telling what the patterns represent.

Bar patterns (see Bar Charts) can be used to indicate similar or identical activities that occur at different times. In figure 17, for instance, all airframe-production activities are shown with narrow left hatch bars. The bars representing engine-production activities have a wide right hatch pattern. These patterns enable readers to see how related activities fit within the whole sequence.

If you use bar patterns, always include an explanation block to the right or at the bottom of the chart.

Combination Charts

Combination charts are not distinct categories of charts, but writers and graphic artists often combine chart types in such unique and creative ways that the result seems to constitute a new category.

Remember that a chart is only as good as the effect it creates. Charts should communicate quickly and simply. They should be integrated with the text and should convey information more forcefully or dramatically than is possible in text.

If you can combine chart types to convey a rich, unusual, interesting, or dramatic message, then do so. You do not gain extra points for adhering strictly to some predetermined form. Let your purpose, readers, medium, data, and ideas dictate the form of chart (or other visual aid) that would be most effective.

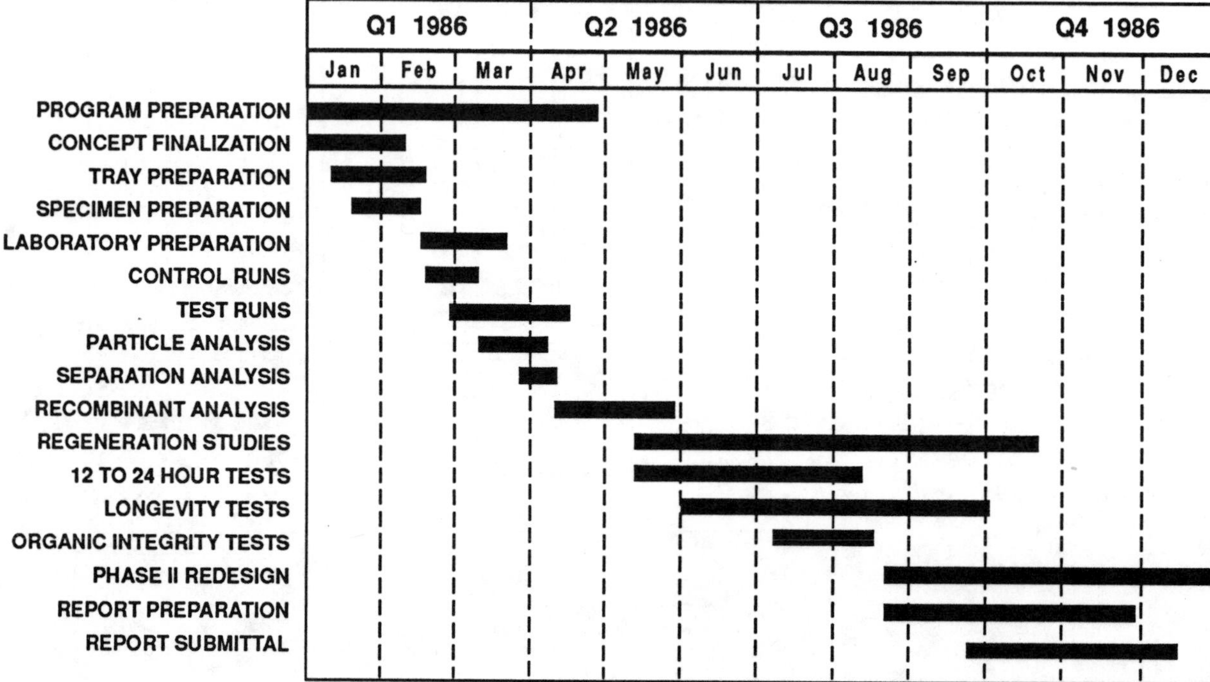

Figure 18. DeLorge Recombinant Test Schedule. *Notice that we will conduct control runs and tests runs concurrently, not sequentially, in our own, fully staffed laboratories and test facilities.*

Citations

Citations (bibliographic entries) enable writers to identify in the text itself the sources of their information. The methods of citation vary, depending on the technical field and its traditions, the type of publication, and the publisher. Many professional societies and journals also have their own method of citation.

The method of citation that we recommend represents the standard convention in the physical sciences and engineering disciplines. However, if you are writing for a particular professional society or technical journal, you should follow its method of citation.

1. Enclose the author's name and the date of the publication in parentheses following the material quoted or the ideas referred to. Attach at the end of the text an alphabetical list of the cited works:

> One critic called the whole dispute a "galaxy of confusion" (Jameson 1976). In reply, the spokesman for the conservative wing rebutted Jameson point by point (S. Clarke 1977).

See Bibliographic Form.

This system is the briefest, most efficient system for citing sources. The information in parentheses is so brief that it does not interrupt the text, and the author's name indicates the source.

Note 1: This system, or some variation of it, is favored by physical and biological scientists, as well as many social scientists. Scholars in the humanities still prefer to use footnotes. See Footnotes.

Note 2: An alternative method uses only numbers in the text, not the author's last name and date:

> One critic called the whole dispute a "galaxy of confusion" (1). In reply, the spokesman for the conservative wing rebutted Jameson point by point (2).
>
> *or*
>
> One critic called the whole dispute a "galaxy of confusion" [1]. In reply, the spokesman for the conservative wing rebutted Jameson point by point [2].

The numbers appearing within parentheses or brackets are keyed to a list of sources that appears at the end of the text. The list is not alphabetized because it follows the order in which the sources were cited in the text. If a single citation changes early in the document, then all later citations and numbers must be changed. Consequently, this alternative method of citation is less efficient.

2. Use a consistent format for citing the name of the author and the date of publication:

> (Jakobson 1981)
> (Bains and Eveslong 1984)
> (Federal Science Committee 1979)
> (Smithson, Haarke, and Bruppe 1982)
> (U.S. Department of Agriculture 1978)

Note: Some authors and journals prefer to place a comma between the author and the date:

> (Jakobson, 1981)

Another common variation is to include the page number or volume and page number following the date:

> (Jakobson 1981, 43-48)

The abbreviations *p.* and *pp.* (for *page* and *pages*) are unnecessary:

> (Bains and Eveslong 1984, 156)
> (Federal Science Committee 1979, 2:34-36)

In the last example, *2* is the volume number.

Whatever the format used, authors should be consistent in their method of citation within the same document.

3. Include a full alphabetized list of cited sources following the article or chapter:

Book with a single author

Bricke, Larry N. 1984. *Canadian Political Parties.* Toronto: New Country Press.

Book with two authors

Campbell, Josiah, and Wallace Daughterly. 1976. *Conflict in the Provinces.* Edmonton, Alberta: The Royal Penny Press.

Journal or magazine article

Mahoney, Edward G. 1978. "A Dissident's View of Canadian Politics." *The Political Review* 2:56-59.

Note 1: In these bibliographic entries, the date of publication comes immediately after the name of the author. In the more common bibliographic form, the date appears after the name of the publisher:

Bricke, Larry N. *Canadian Political Parties.* Toronto: New Country Press, 1984.

See Bibliographic Form.

Note 2: The titles may be underlined rather than italicized if italics is not available.

Cliches

Cliches are worn-out phrases that were originally effective, even vivid:

innocent bystander
irony of fate
too funny for words
cool as a cucumber
moot point
far and wide

Such phrases are so common that writers and speakers use them habitually, without thinking. Their familiarity makes cliches convenient. So, when writers are struggling to express an idea, using a cliche becomes a tempting alternative to serious thought. See WORDY PHRASES.

The Origin of Cliches

The word *cliche* comes from French and is often still written with the French accent: *cliché*. Writers of English typically omit the accent mark because the word has been anglicized. See SPELLING.

Many cliches were originally metaphors and were therefore vivid. Their wittiness and sparkle made them memorable, so they were repeated often. However, the vividness of the original metaphor is dulled by repetition and the expression becomes a cliche.

The first person in medieval Europe to associate the concept of avoidance with the Black Death must have created a vivid image in listeners' minds. But today's users of the expression *to avoid it like the plague* experience little if any of the original effect. Today, the cliche means little. We've heard it too often.

Other cliches developed and survived because they sounded good:

bag and baggage
rack and ruin
not wisely but too well
snug as a bug in a rug
willy-nilly

The alliteration (repetition of consonants) and repetition of *bag* in the expression *bag and baggage* likely ensured the phrase's survival. Similarly, *willy-nilly* has survived so long that its original meaning has been lost: "whether you are willing or unwilling." Now *willy-nilly* implies haphazard or weak actions. The logical choice in its original meaning has faded. Now the cliche has more sound than substance.

---

1. Use cliches sparingly, if at all.

Writers would find eliminating **all** cliches a hard row to hoe. Reasonable cliches are fine in certain contexts, but the one in the preceding sentence is clearly inappropriate. The context of this discussion makes a cliche based on farm work ridiculous.

However, some cliches—in the right context—are valuable:

Following the testimony, the judge had to sift through 1,000 pages of unreadable and often contradictory testimony.

Here, the cliche of *sifting through* many pages is not objectionable. It is, in fact, a fine metaphor given the circumstance to which it applies. In this case, the cliche does not clash with the context.

So one test of a cliche's acceptability is the degree to which it is relevant to the context in which it occurs and the extent to which it goes unnoticed. If the cliche does not call attention to itself, it is probably acceptable. The moment a writer (or reader) knows the expression is a cliche, it is unacceptable in most contexts.

NOTE: Sometimes a cliche can be used to advantage if its meaning or phrasing allows the writer to play against the cliche itself, as in the following quote from Oscar Wilde:

"Truth is never pure, and rarely simple."

By rephrasing the cliche, Wilde asks readers to reexamine the cliche about *pure and simple truth.*

Some Common Cliches

English contains hundreds of cliches. The following list includes some of the more common ones currently in use:

A bad scene
a can of worms
acid test
active consideration
add insult to injury
agree to disagree
all things considered
all too soon
along these lines
among those present
ample opportunity
an end run
armed to the teeth
a roundhouse punch
as a matter of fact
as the crow flies
at a loss for words
at one fell swoop
attached hereto
auspicious moment
avoid it like the plague
awaiting further orders

Cliches

Back at the ranch
back to the drawing board
bag and baggage
bated breath
beat a hasty retreat
be at loggerheads
beginning of the end
benefit of the doubt
best-laid plans
better late than never
better left unsaid
beyond the shadow of a doubt
bite the bullet
bitter end
blissful ignorance
block out
bloody but unbowed
bolt from the blue
bone of contention
bottom line
bright and shining faces
broad daylight
brook no delay
brute force
budding genius
built-in safeguards
burning question
burning the midnight oil
busy as a bee
by leaps and bounds
by the same token

Calm before the storm
capacity crowd
cast a pall
casual encounter
chain reaction
charged with emotion
checkered career/past
cherished belief
chief cook and bottle washer
circumstances beyond my control
city fathers
civic wrath
clear as crystal/day
colorful display
come full circle
common/garden variety
confirming our conversation
conservative estimate
considered opinion
consigned to oblivion
conspicuous by its absence
contents noted
controlling factor
cool as a cucumber
crying need
curiously enough
cut a long story short
cut down in his prime

Dark horse
date with destiny
days are numbered
dazed condition
dead as a doornail
deadly earnest
deafening crash
deficits mount
deliberate falsehood
depths of despair
diamond in the rough
dig in your heels
discreet silence
do not hesitate to
doom is sealed
doomed to disappointment
dotted on the landscape
dramatic new move
drastic action
due consideration
dynamic personality

Each and every
easier said than done
eat, drink, and be merry
eloquent silence
eminently successful
enclosed herewith
engage in conversation
enjoyable occasion
entertaining high hopes of
epic struggle
equal to the occasion
errand of mercy
even tenor
exception that proves the rule
existing conditions
express one's appreciation
eyeball to eyeball

Failed to dampen spirits
fair sex
fall on bad times
fall on deaf ears
far and wide
far be it from me
far cry
fateful day
fate worse than death
feedback loop
feel free to
feel vulnerable
festive occasion
few and far between
few well-chosen words
fickle finger of fate
final analysis
fine-tune one's plans
finishing touches
fit as a fiddle
floral tribute
food for thought
fools rush in
foregone conclusion
foul play
from the sublime to the ridiculous

Gala occasion
generation gap
generous to a fault
gild the lily
give the green light to
glowing cheeks
go down the drain
goes without saying
goodly number
good team player
grateful acknowledgement
grave concern
green with envy
grim reaper
grind to a halt

Hale and hearty
hands across the sea
happy pair
hastily summoned
have the privilege
heartfelt thanks/appreciation
heart of the matter
heart's desire
heated argument
heave a sigh of relief
height of absurdity
herculean efforts
hook, line, and sinker
hook or crook
hope for the future
hope springs eternal
hot pursuit
how does that grab you?
hunker down
hurriedly retraced his steps

Ignominious retreat
ignorance is bliss
ill-fated
immaculately attired
immeasurably superior
impenetrable mystery
in close proximity
inextricably linked
infinite capacity
inflationary spiral
innocent bystander
in no uncertain terms
in our midst
in reference/regard to
in short supply
internecine strife
in the limelight
in the nick of time
in the same boat with
in the twinkling of an eye
in this day and age
into full swing
iron out the difficulty
irony of fate
irreducible minimum
irreparable/irreplaceable loss
it dawned on me

Cliches

Just deserts
just for openers

Keep options open

Labor of love
lashed out at
last analysis
last but not least
last-ditch effort
leaps and bounds
leave no stone unturned
leaves much to be desired
leave up in the air
lend a helping hand
let well enough alone
like a bolt from the blue
limped into port
line of least resistance
little woman
lit up like a Christmas tree
lock, stock, and barrel
logic of events
long arm of the law
long-felt need

Make good one's escape
man the barricades
marked contrast
masterpiece of understatement
matter of life and death
mecca for travelers
method to/in his madness
milk of human kindness
miraculous escape
moment of truth
momentous decision/occasion
monumental traffic jam
moot point
more in sorrow than in anger
more sinned against than sinning
more than meets the eye
more the merrier
motley crew

Narrow escape
nearest and dearest
needs no introduction
never a dull moment
never before in the history of
nipped in the bud
none the worse for wear
no sooner said than done
not wisely but too well

One and the same
ongoing dialogue
on more than one occasion
on unimpeachable authority
open secret
order out of chaos
other things being equal
outer directed
overwhelming odds
own worst enemy

Pales into insignificance
paralyzed with fright
paramount importance
part and parcel
patience of Job
pay the piper
peer group
pet peeve
pick and choose
pie in the sky
pinpoint the cause
pipe dream
place in the sun
play hardball
play it by ear
point with pride
poor but honest
powder keg
powers that be
pretty kettle of fish
pros and cons
proud heritage
proud possessor
pull one's weight

Rack and ruin
ravishing beauty
red-letter day
regrettable incident
reigns supreme
reliable source
remedy the situation
right on
riot-torn area
ripe old age
round of applause
rude habitation

Sadder but wiser
saw the light of day
scathing sarcasm
sea of faces
seat of learning
second to none
seething mass of humanity
select few
selling like hotcakes
shattering effect
shift into high gear
shot in the arm
sigh of relief
silence broken only by
silhouetted against the sky
simple life
skeleton in the closet
snug as a bug in a rug
social amenities
something hitting the fan
spectacular event
spirited debate
steaming jungle
stick out like a sore thumb
stick to one's guns
straight and narrow path
structure one's day
such is life
sum and substance
superhuman effort
supreme sacrifice
sweat of his brow
sweeping changes
sweet sixteen

Take the bull by the horns
take up the cudgels
telling effect
tender mercies
terror stricken
thanking you in advance
there's the rub
this day and age
those present
throw a monkey wrench
throw a party
throw caution to the winds
thrust of your report
thunderous applause
tie that binds
time immemorial
time of one's life
tongue in cheek
too funny for words
too numerous to mention
tough it out/through
tower of strength
trials and tribulations
trust implicitly
tumultuous applause

Uncharted seas
unprecedented situation
untimely end
untiring efforts
up tight

Vale of tears
vanish into thin air
viable alternative

Watery grave
wax eloquent/poetic
weaker sex
wear and tear
wend one's way
whirlwind tour
wide open spaces
words fail to express
word to the wise
work one's wiles
worse for wear
wrought havoc

Colons

Colons signal readers to keep reading because related thoughts or a list will follow. In this role, colons differ from periods, semicolons, and even commas, all of which signal a pause or even a full stop.

1. Colons link related thoughts, one of which must be capable of standing alone as a sentence.

Colons emphasize the second thought (unlike semicolons, which emphasize both thoughts equally, and dashes, which emphasize the break in the sentence and can emphasize the first thought).

Colons shift emphasis forward: They tend to make the second thought the most important part of the sentence. When such is the case, the colon indicates that explanation or elaboration follows:

> The Franklin Shipyard needed one thing to remain solvent: to win the Navy's supercarrier contract.
>
> The Franklin shipyard needed one thing to remain solvent: It had to win the Navy's supercarrier contract.

See CAPITALS.

NOTE: The two complete thoughts in the second example could also appear as two sentences:

> The Franklin Shipyard needed one thing to remain solvent. It had to win the Navy's supercarrier contract.

However, linking these thoughts with a colon emphasizes their close connection. Writing them as two sentences is less emphatic if the writer wishes to stress that the **one thing** Franklin needs is to win the contract.

2. Colons introduce lists or examples:

> Our management development study revealed the need for greater monitoring during these crucial phases:
>
> 1. Initial organization
> 2. Design and development
> 3. Fabrication and quality control

> The Mars Division's audit of field service personnel centers found the following general deficiencies:
>
> 1. Service personnel do not fully understand the new rebate policy.
> 2. Parts inventories are inadequate.
> 3. The centralized customer records are not operational, although the computer terminals have all been installed.

NOTE: The items listed do not require periods unless they are complete sentences. See LISTS.

3. Colons separate hours from minutes, volumes from pages, and the first part of a ratio from the second:

> The deadline is 3:30 p.m. on Friday.
>
> See *Government Architecture* 15:233.
>
> The ratio of direct to indirect costs is 1:1.45.

4. Colons follow the salutation in a formal letter:

> Dear Ms. Labordean:
>
> Ladies and Gentlemen:

See LETTERS.

5. Colons separate titles from subtitles:

> *Government Architecture: Managing Interface Specifications*

Commas

Commas keep English sentences readable, especially long, involved sentences. Without commas, readers wouldn't know when to pause. But as the following rules show, correct placement of commas reflects the grammar and syntax of the language, not merely places to pause.

See PUNCTUATION for information on mandatory and optional uses of commas.

1. Commas separate complete thoughts joined by these simple conjunctions: *and, but, or, for, nor, so, yet:*

He was a Russian linguist in communications intelligence, and he has logged over 5,000 hours as a C–130 navigator in the Air Force.

We are known for our land-based missile delivery systems, but we also design and manufacture shielded fiber optics cables.

EXCEPTION: You may omit this comma if both complete thoughts are short:

The chairman resigned and the company failed.

The simple conjunctions cited above are called coordinate conjunctions. When they link two complete thoughts, the resulting sentence is called a compound sentence. See CONJUNCTIONS and SENTENCES.

NOTE: If you use any other transitional or connecting word (*however, furthermore, consequently,* and so on) to join two complete thoughts, use a semicolon. See SEMICOLONS and TRANSITIONS.

2. Commas separate items in a series consisting of three or more words, phrases, or even whole clauses:

Control Data's Integrated Support Software System provides compatibility between tools and workers, consistent tool interfaces, ease of learning, user friendliness, and expandability.

The user may also return to control program to perform such other functions as database editing, special report generation, and statistical analyses.

The Carthage-Hines agreement contained provisions for testing the Pennsylvania sands, developing local permeability pinchouts, and exploring for undeveloped oil reserves in subthrust traps.

NOTE 1: A comma separates the last two items in a series although these items are linked by a conjunction (*and* in the above examples, but the rule applies for any conjunction). This comma was once considered optional, but the trend is to make it mandatory, especially in technical and business English. Leaving it out can cause confusion and misinterpretation. See PUNCTUATION.

NOTE 2: If all of the items in the series are linked by a simple conjunction, do not use commas:

The user may also return to control program to perform such other functions as database editing and special report generation and statistical analyses.

NOTE 3: In sentences containing a series of phrases or clauses that already have commas, use semicolons to separate each phrase or clause:

Our legal staff prepared analyses of the Drury-Engels agreement, which we hoped to discontinue; the Hopkinson contract; and the joint leasing proposal from Shell, Mobil, and Amoco.

See CONJUNCTIONS and SEMICOLONS.

3. Commas separate long introductory phrases and clauses from the main body of a sentence:

Although we are new to particle scan technology, our work with split-beam lasers gives us a solid experiential base from which to undertake this study.

For the purposes of this investigation, the weapon will be synthesized by a computer program called RATS (Rapid Approach to Transfer Systems).

Oil production was down during the first quarter, but when we analyzed the figures, we discovered that the production decline was due to only two of our eight wells.

NOTE: In the last example, the *when we analyzed* clause does not open the sentence, but it must still be separated from the main clause following it. It introduces the main thought of the last half of the sentence.

EXCEPTION: If the introductory thought is short and no confusion will result, you can omit this comma:

In either case the Carmichael procedure will be used to estimate the current requirements of the preliminary designs.

4. Commas enclose parenthetical expressions.

Parenthetical expressions are words or groups of words that are inserted into a sentence and are not part of the main thought of the sentence. These expressions describe, explain, or comment on something in the sentence, typically the word or phrase preceding the parenthetical expression:

> The transport will, according to our calculations, require only 10,000 feet of runway.
>
> The survey results, though not what we had predicted, confirm that the rate of manufacturer acceptance will exceed 60 percent.

Parentheses and dashes may also enclose parenthetical expressions. Use commas most of the time, but when you want to make the expression stand out, enclose it with parentheses (which are more emphatic than commas) or dashes—which are more emphatic than parentheses. See PARENTHESES and DASHES.

5. Commas separate nonessential modifying and descriptive phrases and clauses from a sentence, especially those clauses beginning with *who, which,* or *that*:

> These biocybernetic approaches, which merit further investigation, will improve performance of the man/machine interface.

In this sentence, *which merit further investigation* is not essential because the reader will already know which biocybernetic approaches the sentence refers to. The clause beginning with *which* is nonessential and could be left out:

> These biocybernetic approaches will improve performance of the man/machine interface.

If several biocybernetic approaches were listed, however, and if the writer needed to identify only those meriting further investigation, the clause would be essential, could not be left out, and would **not** take commas:

> Improving the performance of the man/machine interface meant identifying those biocybernetic approaches that merit further investigation.

The *that* in the preceding example commonly introduces essential clauses although *which* sometimes appears.

Modifying or descriptive clauses should always follow the words they modify. If they cannot be removed from the sentence without changing the meaning, they are essential and must not be separated by commas from the word they modify. If they can be removed, they are nonessential and must be separated by commas from the main thought in the sentence:

> *Essential:* She is the Dr. Gruber who developed analytical engine compressor stability models for NASA.

She is the Dr. Gruber does not make sense as an independent statement. The descriptive clause beginning with *who* is essential and therefore cannot be separated by a comma from *Gruber.*

> *Nonessential:* Our Design Team Leader will be Dr. Janet Gruber, who developed analytical engine compressor stability models for NASA.

Our Design Team Leader will be Dr. Janet Gruber does stand alone as a complete and independent thought. In this case, the descriptive clause beginning with *who* is nonessential. Separating it from *Gruber* with a comma shows that it is additional and nonessential information. Note that a comma would follow *NASA* if the sentence continued.

See PRONOUNS for a discussion of relative pronouns.

6. Commas separate two or more adjectives that equally modify the same noun:

> This configuration features an advanced, multimission payload capacity.

NOTE: If two or more adjectives precede a noun, however, and one adjective modifies another adjective—and **together** they modify the noun—you must use a hyphen:

> They had designed a no-flow heat exchange.

A good test for determining whether two or more adjectives equally modify a noun is to insert *and* between them. If the resulting phrase makes sense, then the adjectives are equal, and you should use commas to replace the *ands:*

> old and rusty pipe (*therefore* old, rusty pipe)

Commas

however

old and rusty and steam pipe *(The* and *between* rusty *and* steam *makes no sense. Therefore, the phrase should be* old, rusty steam pipe.)

See Hyphens and Adjectives.

7. Commas separate items in dates and addresses:

The proposal was signed on March 15, 1990.

Contact Benson Aerodynamics, Lindsay, Indiana, for further information.

Note: A comma follows the year when the month **and day** precede the year. However, when the date consists only of month and year, a comma is not necessary:

The final report will be due January 15, 1990, just a month before the board meeting.

but

The final report will be due in January 1990.

See Punctuation.

When the date appears in the day-month-year sequence, no commas are necessary:

The report is due 15 January 1990.

8. Commas separate titles and degrees from names:

The chief liaison will be Roger Hillyard, Project Review Board Chairman.

Mary Sarkalion, PhD, will coordinate modeling and simulation studies.

Modeling and simulation studies will be the responsibility of Mary Sarkalion, PhD.

Note: When the degree or title appears in the middle of a sentence, commas must appear before and after it.

9. Commas follow the salutation in informal letters and the complimentary closing in all letters:

Dear Joan,

Sincerely,

See Colons and Letters.

10. Commas enclose the names of people addressed:

So, Bob, if you'll check your records, we'll be able to adjust the purchase order to your satisfaction.

11. Commas set off (enclose) the following transitional words and expressions when they introduce sentences or when they link two complete thoughts: *accordingly, consequently, for example, for instance, further, furthermore, however, indeed, nevertheless, nonetheless, on the contrary, on the other hand, then, thus:*

Consequently, the primary difference between CDSP and other synthesis programs is development philosophy.

Synthesis programs are now common in industry; however, CDSP has several features that make it especially suitable for this type of study.

or

Synthesis programs are now common in industry; CDSP has, however, several features that make it especially suitable for this type of study.

See Semicolons.

Note: A few of these transitional words *(however, thus, then, indeed)* are occasionally part of the main thought of the sentence and do not form an actual transition. When such is the case, omit the punctuation before and after the words:

However unreliable cross-section analysis may be, it is still the most efficient means of scaling mathematical models.

Thus translated, the decoded message can be used to diagram nonlinear relationships.

12. Commas, like periods, always go inside of closing quotation marks. Commas go outside of parentheses or brackets:

The specifications contained many instances of the phrase "or equal," which is an attempt to avoid actually specifying significant features of a required product.

Thanks to the USGS (United States Geological Survey), we have an up-to-date water resources survey for Dade County.

Note: British usage places commas and periods inside or outside of the quotation marks, depending on whether they are or are not part of the quotation.

See Spacing.

Compound Words

Compound words are words formed when two or more words act together. The compound may be written as a single word (with no space between the joined words), with a hyphen between the joined words, or with spaces between the joined words:

footnote
ourselves
right-of-way
3-minute break
delayed-reaction switch
land bank loan
parcel post delivery

The form of the compound varies with custom and usage as well as with the length of time the compound has existed.

Compound words usually begin as two or more separate, often unrelated words. When writers and speakers begin using the words together as nouns, verbs, adjectives, or adverbs, the compound generally has a hyphen or a space between words, depending on custom and usage. As the new compound becomes more common, the hyphen and space might drop, and the compound might be written as one word:

on-site *has become* onsite
co-operate *has become* cooperate
rail road *has become* railroad
auto body *has become* autobody

However, because of custom or usage, some compounds retain the hyphen or space between words:

all-inclusive
deep-rooted
living room
middle-sized
re-cover *(to cover again)*
re-create *(to create again)*
rough-coat *(used as a verb)*
sand-cast *(used as a verb)*
satin-lined
steam-driven

sugar water
summer school
terra firma
throw line
under secretary

Because new compound words are continually appearing in the language and because even familiar compounds might appear in different forms, depending on how they are used in a sentence, writers might have difficulty deciding which form of a compound to use. Recent dictionaries can often help by indicating how a word or compound has appeared previously.

However, for new compounds and for compounds not covered in dictionaries, use the principles of clarity and consistency, as well as the following guidelines, to select the form of the compound.

---

1. Write compounds as two words when the compounds appear with the words in their customary order and when the meaning is clear:

test case	report card
sick leave	barn door
flood control	social security
real estate	civil rights

NOTE 1: Many such combinations are so common that we rarely think of them as compounds (especially because they do not have hyphens and are written with spaces between words). In many cases, writing them as a single word would be ridiculous: *floodcontrol, realestate.*

NOTE 2: We continue to pronounce such compounds with fairly equal stress on the joined words, especially when one or more of the words has two or more syllables (as in *social security).*

---

2. Write compounds as single words (no spaces between joined words) when the first word of the compound receives the major stress in pronunciation:

airplane
cupboard
doorstop
dragonfly
footnote
nightclerk
seaward
warehouse

NOTE 1: The stress often shifts to the first word when that word has only one syllable, as in the preceding examples.

NOTE 2: Words beginning with the following prefixes are not true compounds. Such words are usually written without a space or a hyphen:

*after*birth
*Anglo*mania
*ante*date
*bi*weekly
*by*law
*circum*navigation
*co*operate
*contra*position
*counter*case
*de*energize
*demi*tasse
*ex*communicate
*extra*curricular
*fore*tell
*hyper*sensitive
*hypo*acid
*in*bound
*infra*red
*inter*view
*intra*spinal
*intro*vert

Compound Words

*iso*metric
*macro*analysis
*meso*thorax
*meta*genesis
*micro*phone
*mis*spelling
*mono*gram
*multi*color
*neo*phyte
*non*neutral
*off*set
*out*back
*over*active
*over*flow
*pan*cosmic
*para*centric
*parti*coated
*peri*patetic
*plano*convex
*poly*nodal
*post*script
*pre*exist
*pro*consul
*psuedo*scientific
*re*enact
*retro*spect
*semi*official
*step*father
*sub*secretary
*super*market
*thermo*couple
*tran*sonic
*trans*ship
*tri*color
*ultra*violet
*un*necessary
*under*flow

Note 3: Words ending with the following suffixes are not true compounds. Such words are usually written without a space or hyphen:

port*able*
cover*age*
oper*ate*
plebis*cite*
twenty*fold*
spoon*ful*
kilo*gram*
geo*graphy*
man*hood*
self*ish*
meat*less*
out*let*
wave*like*
procure*ment*
partner*ship*
lone*some*
home*stead*
north*ward*
clock*wise*

3. Hyphenate compounds that modify or describe other words:

rear-engine bracket
tool-and-die shop
two-phase engine-replacement program
down-to-cost model

See Hyphens and Adjectives.

Note 1: Such compounds are hyphenated only when they come before the word they modify. If the words forming the compound appear after the word they are describing, leave out the hyphens:

bracket for the rear engine (*but* rear-engine bracket)
a shop making tools and dies (*but* tool-and-die shop)
a program with two phases (*but* two-phase program)

Note 2: When the meaning is clear, such compound modifiers may not need hyphens:

land management plan
life insurance company
per capita cost
production credit clause
speech improvement class

Note 3: Do not hyphenate if the first word of the compound modifier ends with *-ly:*

barely known problem
eminently qualified researcher
highly developed tests
gently sloping range

however

well-developed tests
well-known problem
well-qualified researcher

4. Treat compounds used as verbs as separate words:

to break down
to check out
to follow up
to get together
to go ahead
to know how
to run through
to shut down
to shut off
to stand by
to start up
to take off
to trade in

The parallel compound nouns are usually either written as one word or hyphenated:

breakdown
checkout
follow-up
get-together
go-ahead
know-how
run-through
shutdown
shutoff
standby
start-up
takeoff
trade-in

However, some verb phrases are identical to the compound noun form:

cross-reference *(both a noun and a verb)*

When in doubt, check your dictionary.

Conjunctions

Conjunctions connect words, phrases, or clauses and at the same time indicate the relationship between them. Conjunctions include the simple coordinate conjunctions (*and, but, or, for, nor, so, yet*), the subordinate conjunctions (*because, since, although, when, if, so that*, etc.), the correlative conjunctions (*either . . . or, neither . . . nor, both . . . and*), and the conjunctive adverbs (*however, thus, furthermore*, etc.).

Coordinate Conjunctions

The simple coordinate conjunctions are *and, but, or, for, nor, so*, and *yet*. They often connect two independent clauses (complete thoughts):

> The geologist analyzed the drill cores, and the engineer planned the future drilling operations.
>
> Our proposal was a day late, but we were not eliminated from competition.
>
> The pump will have to be replaced, or we will continue to suffer daily breakdowns.
>
> We rejected his budget, yet he continued to argue that all contested items were justified.

See SENTENCES.

These simple connectors establish the relationship between the thoughts being coordinated:

—*And* shows addition

—*Or* shows alternative

—*Nor* shows negative alternative

—*But* and *yet* show contrast

—*For* and *so* show causality

NOTE 1: When you use a coordinate conjunction to connect two independent clauses or complete thoughts, place a comma before the conjunction, as in the sentences above. See COMMAS. However, you may omit the comma when the two clauses are short and closely related. Also, a semicolon can replace both the comma and the conjunction. See SEMICOLONS.

NOTE 2: The conjunctions *and* and *or* (preceded by a comma) also connect the last two items in a series:

> The engineer designed an emergency exit door, a narrow outside stairway, and a concrete support pad.
>
> She requested full written disclosure, an apology, or financial compensation.

See COMMAS.

---

1. Ensure that in choosing *and* and *or* you select the conjunction that conveys exactly what you mean.

At first glance, *and* and *or* merely join two or more items, but they can and often do imply much more:

And

In the following sentences *and* does more than merely connect the ideas. What *and* implies is stated in parentheses following each example:

> He saw the accident, and he called the police. *(therefore)*
>
> My boss is competent, and David is not. *(contrast)*
>
> He changed the tire, and he replaced the hub cap. *(then)*
>
> Explain the cost savings, and I'll approve your proposal. *(condition)*

Or

The conjunction *or* usually means one of two possibilities *(I want either a Ford or an Oldsmobile)*. However, *or* sometimes has other, occasionally confusing, implications:

> The faulty part or the worm gear seemed to be causing our problem. *(Are the faulty part and the worm gear the same? Only knowledgeable readers would know for sure.)*
>
> Add to the bid, or I'll reject your offer. *(negative condition)*
>
> He began doing the schematics, or at least he appeared to be doing them. *(correction)*

See WORD PROBLEMS.

---

2. Occasionally, sentences can begin with a coordinate conjunction.

This advice contradicts the rule that many of us learned in school: "Never begin a sentence with *and.*" Some writers and editors still offer this advice, but most have now recognized that this so-called rule has no basis. Even Shakespeare began some of his sentences with coordinate conjunctions.

A coordinate conjunction at the beginning of a sentence links the sentence to the preceding sentence or paragraph. Sometimes, the linking is unnecessary:

> We objected to the proposal because of its length. And others felt that it had errors in fact.

Conjunctions

The *and* at the beginning of the second sentence is simply unnecessary. It adds nothing to the thought and may easily be omitted:

> We objected to the proposal because of its length. Others felt that it had errors in fact.

Using a conjunction to begin a sentence is not grammatically incorrect. Sometimes, it is good stylistic variation. But it tends to look and sound informal, so avoid this practice in formal documents.

---

3. Do not use *and* or *but* before *which* (or *that, who, whose, whom, where*) unless you use a preceding parallel *which* (or *that, who, whose, whom, where*):

> We explored the DeMarcus itinerary, which you explained in your letter but which you failed to mention in Saturday's meeting.

> The meetings should take place where we met last year or where we can arrange for equally good facilities.

The following sentence violates this principle. Consequently, it is awkward and nonparallel:

> The plans called for a number of innovative features, especially regarding extra insulation, and which should save us much in fuel costs. (*Deleting the* and *would solve the lack of parallelism in this sentence.)*

See PARALLELISM.

Subordinate Conjunctions

In contrast to the limited set of coordinate conjunctions, subordinate conjunctions are a varied and diverse group:

> after, although, as, because, before, if, once, since, that, though, until, when, where, while

> in that, so that, such that, except that, in order that, now (that), provided (that), supposing (that), considering (that), as far as, as long as, so long as, sooner than, rather than, as if, as though, in case

> if . . . (then)
> although . . . yet/nevertheless
> as . . . so
> more/–er/less . . . than
> as . . . as
> so . . . (that)
> such . . . as
> such . . . (that)
> no sooner . . . than
> whether . . . or (not)
> the . . . the

Subordinate conjunctions introduce subordinate clauses and phrases (dependent clauses and phrases that do not convey complete thoughts and are therefore not independent):

> After the engineer gave her talk
> Because of the voltage loss
> When the test results come in
> While still producing fluids
> In that you had already made the request
> Except that the procedure was costly
> Provided that you calculate the results
> As though it hadn't rained enough
> If we fail
> As aware as he is, so
> So expensive that it was prohibitive
> Whether or not you submit the report

These subordinate clauses and phrases must be attached to independent clauses (complete thoughts) to form sentences:

> After the engineer gave her talk, several colleagues had questions.

> In that you had already made the request, we decided to omit the formal interview.

> If we fail, the project stops. (*or* If we fail, then the project stops.)

> As aware as he is, he must be sensitive to the personnel problems.

See SENTENCES.

NOTE 1: A subordinate clause or phrase that opens a sentence should be followed by a comma. See COMMAS. The preceding sentences illustrate this rule.

NOTE 2: When the subordinate clause or phrase follows the independent clause or main thought of the sentence, no commas are necessary:

> The experiment failed because of the voltage loss.

> We would have denied the request except that the procedure was so costly.

> We wondered whether you would turn in your report.

NOTE 3: Occasionally, the subordinate clause or phrase interrupts the main clause and must have commas on both sides of it to indicate where the clause or phrase appears:

> The President and the Joint Chiefs of Staff, after receiving the latest aerial reconnaissance photos of the area, decided on a naval blockade of all ports.

> Our budgetary problems, regardless of the Madiera Project expense, would have taken care of themselves if the prime rate hadn't gone up three points.

---

4. Subordinate conjunctions can begin sentences:

> When the test results come in, we'll have to analyze them carefully.

> Because the project manager was unfamiliar with the budget codes, we failed to expense the costs of fabrication.

NOTE: The old school rule "Never begin a sentence with *because*" was and remains a bad

rule. You may begin a sentence with *because* as long as the dependent clause it introduces is followed by an independent clause or complete thought.

5. Distinguish between some subordinate conjunctions that have overlapping or multiple meanings (especially *because/since/as* and *while/although/as*).

Avoid using *since* and *as* to mean "because":

> Because the Leiper Project failed, several engineers were reassigned to electro-optics. (*not* Since the project failed . . .)
>
> Because we had ample supplies, no new batteries were ordered. (*not* As we had ample supplies . . .)

Avoid using *while* and *as* to mean "although":

> Although many employees begin work at 8 a.m., others begin at 7 a.m. (*not* While many employees begin work at 8 a.m. . . .)
>
> Although the value of the test results declined, we still felt we could meet the deadline. (*not* As the value of the test results declined . . .)

Correlative Conjunctions

Correlative conjunctions are pairs of coordinate conjunctions:

> both . . . and
> either . . . or
> neither . . . nor
> not only . . . but also

6. Make the constructions following each coordinate conjunction parallel:

> The committee was interested in both real estate holdings and stock investments. (*not* . . . both in real estate holdings and the stock investments.)
>
> The investigation revealed that either the budget was inaccurate or our records had gaps. (*not* The investigation revealed either that the budget was inaccurate or our records had gaps.)

NOTE: Faulty parallelism problems occur when the same phrase structure or word patterns do not occur after each coordinate conjunction:

> He was aware that not only was the pipe too small but also that the pipe supports were made of aluminum instead of stainless steel.

This sentence is confused because the two *that*'s are not parallel. The first *that* comes before *not only*, and the second *that* comes after *but also*. A parallel version of the sentence is much smoother:

> He was aware not only that the pipe was too small but also that the pipe supports were made of aluminum instead of stainless steel.

See PARALLELISM.

Conjunctive Adverbs

Conjunctive adverbs are adverbs that function as conjunctions, typically by connecting independent clauses or complete thoughts. The most common conjunctive adverbs are *accordingly, also, besides, consequently, further, furthermore, hence, however, moreover, nevertheless, otherwise, then, therefore, thus,* and *too*.

See TRANSITIONS.

7. Conjunctive adverbs used to join two complete thoughts must be preceded by a semicolon and followed by a comma:

> Aircraft assembly is a lengthy production process; however, the individual assembly steps must still be tightly controlled.
>
> Increasing pressure in the T-valves is potentially dangerous; nevertheless, we will not be able to monitor effluent discharge without doing so.

See SEMICOLONS and COMMAS.

NOTE: You can omit the comma following the conjunctive adverb if the sentence is short:

> I think; therefore I am.

8. Conjunctive adverbs at the beginning of a sentence are usually followed by a comma:

> Therefore, I am recommending that Osage abandon plans to build another coal-fired generator.
>
> However, sulfur compounds might not be the answer either.

NOTE 1: You may omit this comma if the sentence is short:

> Thus the plan failed.

NOTE 2: If the adverb appears at the beginning of the sentence but does not behave as a conjunction, it is part of the sentence and cannot be followed by a comma:

> Then the seam split at the forward discharge valve, and the boiler lost pressure rapidly.
>
> Regardless of how we examined the problem, we could not resolve the fundamental dispute between offshore drilling companies and the leaseholders' association.

Dashes

Dashes are excellent devices for emphasizing key material and for setting off explanatory information in a sentence. They can also be used to indicate where each item in a list begins and to separate paragraph headings from succeeding text. See HEADINGS, LISTS, and PUNCTUATION.

You can create dashes on a typewriter by typing two unspaced hyphens. Most word processing software has a special code for dashes so that dashes appear as a solid line, not two separate hyphens. Using this code makes your text appear to be typeset, not typed on a typewriter.

When you use a dash between two words, leave no space on either side of the dash. See SPACING.

---

1. Dashes link introductory or concluding thoughts to the rest of the sentence.

Dashes linking thoughts emphasize the break in the sentence. Dashes often make the first thought the most important part of the sentence:

> Winning the Navy's supercarrier contract—that's what the Franklin Shipyard needed to remain solvent.

Dashes can act like colons, however, and throw emphasis to the last part of the sentence:

> We subjected the design to rigorous testing—but to no avail because stress, we discovered, was not the problem.

Often, the information following the dash clarifies, explains, or reinforces what came before the dash:

> We consider our plan bold and unusual—bold because no one has tried to approach the problem from this angle, unusual because it's not how one might expect to use laser technology.

Dashes can also link otherwise complete sentences:

> The technical problem was **not** the design of the filter—the problem was poor quality assurance.

---

2. Dashes interrupt a sentence for insertion of thoughts related to, but not part of, the main idea of the sentence:

> The F-18 had been in the design phase—airfoil studies were being done by Barnett Industries—for 6 years before the Air Force canceled its contract.

In this case parentheses could replace the dashes; with parentheses, the sentence becomes slightly less emphatic. See PARENTHESES.

---

3. Dashes emphasize explanatory information enclosed in a sentence:

> Two of Barnett's primary field divisions—Industrial Manufacturing and Product Field Testing—will supervise the construction and implementation of the prototype.

In this case, commas or parentheses could replace the dashes. The commas would not be as emphatic as dashes; the parentheses would be more emphatic than commas, but less emphatic than dashes. See PARENTHESES and COMMAS.

---

4. Dashes link particulars to a following summary statement:

> Reliability and trust—this is what Bendix has to offer.

> Developing products that become the industry standard, minimizing the risk of failure, and controlling costs through aggressive management—these have become the hallmarks of our reputation.

Decimals

Decimal numbers are a linear way to represent fractions based on multiples of 10. The decimal *0.45* represents the following fraction:

$^{45}/_{100}$

See FRACTIONS.

The decimal point (period) is the mark dividing the whole number on the left from the decimal fraction on the right:

504.678

In some countries, writers use a comma for the decimal point:

504,678

1. Use figures for all decimals and do not write the equivalent fractions:

4.5 (*not* 4 $^{5}/_{10}$)
0.356 (*not* $^{356}/_{1000}$)
0.5 (*not* $^{5}/_{10}$)
0.4690 (*not* $^{4690}/_{10000}$)

2. If the decimal does not have a whole number, insert a zero before the decimal point:

0.578 (*not* .578)
0.2 (*not* .2)

NOTE: This rule has a few exceptions, including:

Colt .45
A batting average of .345
A probability of *p* =.07

3. Retain the zero after the decimal point or at the end of the decimal number only if the zero represents exact measurement (or a significant digit):

0.45 *or* 0.450
28.303 *or* 28.3030

NOTE: Also retain the final zero in a decimal if the zero results from the rounding off of the decimal:

23.180 *for* 23.1789 *(if the decimal number is supposed to be rounded to three digits in the decimal fraction)*

4. Use spaces but not commas to separate groups of three digits in the decimal fraction.

In the metric system, the decimals may be broken into groups of three digits by inserting spaces:

56.321 677 90
707.004 766 321

but 567.4572 (*not* 567.457 2)

You can use commas to separate groups of three digits that appear in the whole number part of the decimal:

56,894.65
500,067.453 467

However, do not use commas to separate groups of three digits in the decimal fraction:

4.67234 (*not* 4.672,34)

2344.000 567 (*not* 2344.000,567)

See METRIC SYSTEM.

5. In columns, line up the decimal points:

```
 56
  0.004
115.9
 56.24445
  0.6
```

NOTE: Whole numbers without decimals (e.g., *56* above) do not require a decimal point.

6. Do not begin a sentence with a decimal number:

this

The timer interrupts the processor 14.73 times a second.

not this

14.73 times a second the timer interrupts the processor.

See NUMBERS.

Desktop Publishing

Desktop publishing permits businesses and individuals to produce documents that look professionally designed and printed.

Before desktop publishing, the production of printed documents required time-consuming and expensive graphics design (layout), paste-up of the artwork, and typesetting. Now, with the personal computer, the laser printer, and word processing and graphics software programs, almost any business can afford its own in-house system for producing high-quality documents electronically.

Businesses equipped for desktop publishing can now design and prepare a printing master (often called a camera-ready copy) for proposals, brochures, advertising literature, user manuals, newsletters, letterhead stationery, flyers, annual reports, or other important documents. After preparing a printing master, most businesses still use an outside printer if they want high-quality, multicolored documents. When simple black and white copies are sufficient, companies can make copies from the printing master using their own photocopy machines.

Desktop publishing systems range from the most rudimentary (a personal computer and laser printer) to the very sophisticated—including electronic typesetters, networked computers, and powerful desktop publishing software.

When to Use Desktop Publishing

Desktop publishing can be an expensive and time-consuming tool if you use it unnecessarily. Actually, the initial investment in desktop publishing isn't significantly greater than for a good word processing system. Remember, however, that your costs also include the learning curve for employees to become comfortable with a new system, especially new software. Also, the more sophisticated your system, the more you will be initially dependent on only one or two skillful operators.

For each document, set clear production priorities.

For high-priority, client-focused documents, use desktop publishing. For less critical documents, stay with simpler formats and less sophisticated desktop features. The more complicated your basic format, the more time needed to correct and to change things. So if you are working with a tight deadline, keep your documents simple.

Invest money and time in a desktop system if the volume and quality of your printed materials warrant it.

Consider, also, that once you invest money and time preparing documents with one desktop system, you can't readily transfer important documents over into another desktop system (unless the two happen to be compatible).

How to Use Desktop Publishing Effectively

If you decide that a document requires desktop publishing, use the following guidelines to help you design and produce high-quality, professional documents.

Remember that one of the best ways to learn how to design documents is to imitate the professionals. For example, if you are going to be producing a newsletter, collect as many published newsletters as you can so that you will have a file of ideas and models.

1. Experiment with different layouts and different desktop tools.

Many of the best graphic designs grow from insights and successively improved drafts, not compliance with abstract rules.

One way to start is to develop two, three, or even four initial concepts (sample pages) for your document. Be creative and don't reject options too quickly.

Next, take your samples to colleagues and to your supervisor for their reactions. Find out which sample they like and why. Then, return to your computer and tinker some more. Work with the preferred version, but clean it up even more.

Finally, take your mature version to your supervisor or manager for final review and approval.

2. Test your designs by asking if they are appropriate for the document's intended purpose and audience.

Is your message light and informal? Then work toward a design that is open and informal. Heavy columns; dense paragraphs; and complex, technical graphics would be out of place.

Is your message serious and formal? Then focus more on the content and avoid graphic embellishments (like arrows, shaded boxes, dramatically different type styles, etc.). Remember that a serious and formal document still need not be dense and forbidding; it can still rely on open space and a clear design (see rule 3 below).

Keep asking yourself (and others) if readers will get the message, if they will like how the document looks, if the format is effective without being cute or distracting.

3. As you explore design options, be sure to work with <u>all</u> the computer tools available in your desktop system: margins, columns, borders (divider lines, headers, and footers), type (style and size), headings, visuals, etc.

Remember that the learning curve for mastery of a desktop publishing system can be 3 months, 6 months, or a year or more. Actually, new versions of desktop publishing software require you to be learning new techniques and tools all the time.

Margins

Each page and each part of a page has margins—that is, the white space separating pieces of text from each other or from the sides of the paper. Your computer may have default (standard) margins, but these will often not be suitable. Try different margins to see how they can help you highlight text and emphasize main ideas.

Remember that blank (white) space on a page is a powerful tool for making your document effective and readable. See EMPHASIS.

Columns

No single desktop tool is as effective as using more than a single column on a page. For years, professionally designed and printed documents have used columns, so using columns will make your text seem more professional.

Columns also make text more readable. The eye can read a narrow column about 50 characters wide (six or seven words) faster than lines as wide as a full page.

Two or three columns are basic to most desktop publishing situations, but four or even five columns can be useful on occasion. Normal text would rarely require four or five columns (on regular 8½- x 11–inch pages), but a lengthy list of plant names or cities would go very nicely in four or even five columns.

As the Sample Style Sheet (pp. 66-67) illustrates, you can also present your basic text in one column, with all or part of another column left blank.

An electronic master page (actually an electronic style sheet) is a valuable desktop tool. A well-designed master page becomes the starting point when you begin to move word-processed text into your desktop system. A master page is also useful when several people are working on the same document because each of them can use the same master page as a starting point.

Borders

Borders help frame your text. They can be as simple as a basic rule or line around the entire text on a page. They can also be complex and involved—for example, a line of asterisks or a line of stars.

Divider lines are simply that—lines used to divide or set off a column or a section of text. They can be very fine (hairline) or quite heavy (perhaps 12 pt.). Too many divider lines make a page look cluttered, but a fine divider line between sections can emphasize logical divisions within the text.

Borders often include headers or footers, which remind readers who is publishing the document and which section a page is in. Common footers are the company or agency name and logo: Sky Aviation (plus the logo). Common headers are the number and title of a chapter: Chapter III—Affected Environment.

Desktop Publishing

Type (Style and Size)

All desktop publishing systems allow for different typefaces (styles) and for letters with different point sizes.

Typeface Style. The preferred typeface styles available for desktop publishing are those with proportional spacing (usually called laser fonts):

Avant Garde typeface

Bookman typeface

Times typeface

Helvetica typeface

New Century Schoolbook typeface

Palatino typeface

N Helvetica Narrow typeface

Proportional spacing is important because separate letters (characters) take up different widths on the page. To make the different letters flow together in a pleasing manner, a desktop publishing program uses proportional spacing so that, to the eye, the letters seem to be equally spaced even though the actual spacing is variable depending on which letters are next to each other.

Nonproportional (non-laser) typefaces are monospaced—that is, they use the same space between letters:

Courier typeface

Geneva typeface

New York typeface

Chicago typeface

Monospaced typefaces look chunky or stiffer than proportional typefaces. A typeface like Courier, for example, looks very much like old-fashioned typewriter printing because, as with a typewriter, Courier is monospaced.

Avoid monospaced (non-laser) typefaces if you want a desktop-published document to look its best, its most professional.

Typefaces also fall into two broad groups: serif and sans serif. Serif typefaces have a fine line or hook that finishes characters. In the above lists the serif typefaces are: Bookman, Courier, Times, New Century Schoolbook, Palatino, and New York. The sans serif ones (those without the fine lines) are Avant Garde, Chicago, Geneva, Helvetica, and North Helvetica Narrow.

A frequent practice is to use serif type for the text and sans serif for headings; this is the pattern suggested in the accompanying Sample Style Sheet.

For each typeface, different styles of letters are also available:

Palatino (bold)

Palatino (shadow)

PALATINO (SMALL CAPS)

Palatino (italic)

As you choose between these different letter styles, remember that text in all caps is more difficult to read than text using lowercase letters. As with any desktop feature, use different letter style sparingly or you will risk having your text look cluttered.

Typeface Size. A single typeface can have letters of different sizes, with the larger point numbers indicating larger letters:

36-point

24-point text

18-point text

14-point text

12-point text

10-point text

9-point text

Variations in the size of type are especially valuable when titles or headings have to be set off from the rest of a document.

A Caution About Type Style and Size. Avoid using too many different styles and sizes. Readers can't keep straight which heading is the second level and which is the third or fourth level when the type sizes are confusingly similar. Also, documents with three or four typeface styles on a single page begin to look cluttered.

Headings

Many writers, especially in business letters and memos, fail to consider how helpful a consistent, well-developed set of headings can be to readers. As the Sample Style Sheet indicates, establish a consistent system of headings and stick with it throughout your document. See HEADINGS and EMPHASIS.

Visuals

Artists (graphics specialists) used to be the sole source for visuals. Next came clip art (master copies) of common visuals that could be photocopied and pasted into a document. Now generic electronic art is available for transfer into a document, and optical scanners permit you to scan a piece of existing artwork and then transfer an electronic copy of this artwork into your desktop version.

Graphics packages now allow anyone to design bar charts, draw figures, produce shaded boxes, reduce or enlarge logos, etc. Once the graphic work is done (often in a separate graphics program), the final figure is moved over and inserted (pasted) into the desktop version of the document. See VISUAL AIDS.

---

4. As soon as you have arrived at a basic design, prepare a style sheet for all writers.

Style sheets are essential whether one writer or many writers will be working on the document. Such style sheets tell writers how to break up their text using headings, how long (roughly) their paragraphs should be, what sorts and sizes of graphics will work best—in short, a good style sheet helps ensure that what the writer produces will fit the chosen format.

Too often writers write text without considering the final format. The result is that they (or an editor many weeks later) have to go through the text shortening a discussion, changing an introduction, and adjusting all the graphics. Time and money are wasted because much of the text must be rewritten to match the format.

As the Sample Style Sheet (pp. 66-67) indicates, a good style sheet shows and tells writers what the format will be. The whole page is laid out as it will appear. All headings indicate exactly what size and design of typeface will be used.

All writers on a project should receive a style sheet before they begin writing the text. Even a writer working alone can profit from a style sheet so that everything written in a long document will be consistent with a single style. See WORD PROCESSING.

A style sheet is different from an electronic master page. An electronic master page allows a computer operator to preset certain format codes so that pages of text can be translated with minimal effort into that desired format. Both a master page and style sheets can help you produce a consistent, highly professional final document.

---

5. Don't forget the basics just because you have a fancy design.

As always, final proofreading and checking are essential.

With desktop publishing (as with word processing), the ease of changing something is an invitation to problems. For instance, if you change a subheading in the middle of a chapter, you will need to change it in many other places: the introduction to the chapter, the table of contents for the document, the index, the summary of key points in the chapter, etc. See WORD PROCESSING.

A Final Caution

Just because computers now allow everybody to design and produce documents, not all do-it-yourself efforts are successful. Some documents are cluttered and disorganized. Others are well designed but poorly written.

A high-quality, professional document still takes many hours and a lot of money. Recognizing these difficulties, some companies and agencies choose to use outside professionals (graphics specialists and writers) when a document is crucial.

Desktop Publishing

Sample Style Sheet

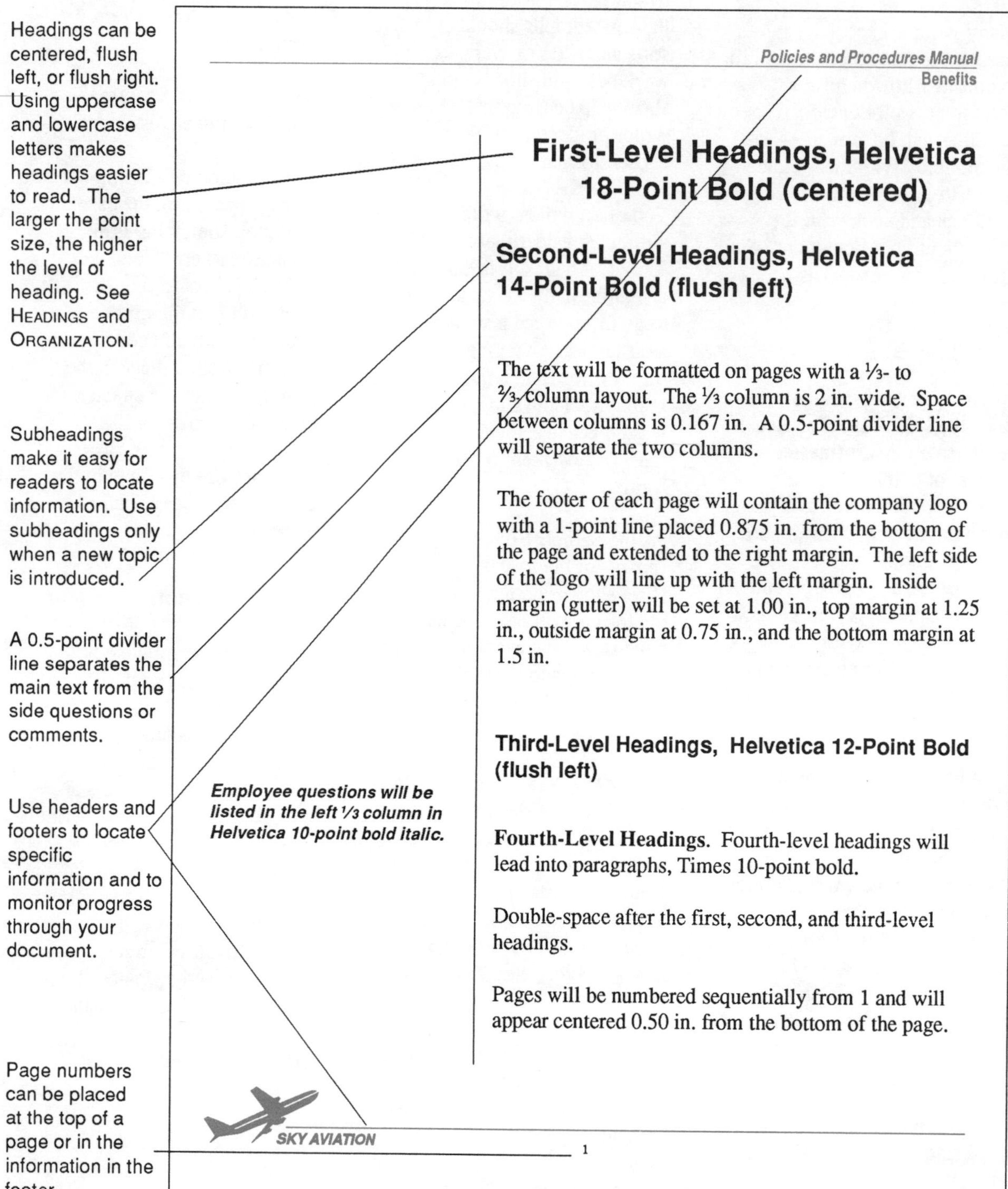

Headings can be centered, flush left, or flush right. Using uppercase and lowercase letters makes headings easier to read. The larger the point size, the higher the level of heading. See HEADINGS and ORGANIZATION.
Subheadings make it easy for readers to locate information. Use subheadings only when a new topic is introduced.
A 0.5-point divider line separates the main text from the side questions or comments.
Use headers and footers to locate specific information and to monitor progress through your document.
Page numbers can be placed at the top of a page or in the information in the footer.
Policies and Procedures Manual
Benefits
First-Level Headings, Helvetica 18-Point Bold (centered)
Second-Level Headings, Helvetica 14-Point Bold (flush left)
The text will be formatted on pages with a ⅓- to ⅔-column layout. The ⅓ column is 2 in. wide. Space between columns is 0.167 in. A 0.5-point divider line will separate the two columns.
The footer of each page will contain the company logo with a 1-point line placed 0.875 in. from the bottom of the page and extended to the right margin. The left side of the logo will line up with the left margin. Inside margin (gutter) will be set at 1.00 in., top margin at 1.25 in., outside margin at 0.75 in., and the bottom margin at 1.5 in.
Third-Level Headings, Helvetica 12-Point Bold (flush left)
Employee questions will be listed in the left ⅓ column in Helvetica 10-point bold italic.
Fourth-Level Headings. Fourth-level headings will lead into paragraphs, Times 10-point bold.
Double-space after the first, second, and third-level headings.
Pages will be numbered sequentially from 1 and will appear centered 0.50 in. from the bottom of the page.
SKY AVIATION
1

A good style sheet provides very clear and specific instruction to contributors so that all contributors' material is consistent.

Sample Style Sheet (continued)

Displayed lists emphasize a series of important items. See LISTS.

Boxes and screens highlight and emphasize text and visuals. See EMPHASIS and VISUAL AIDS.

Next to headings, captions are the most-read part of your document. Use action captions whenever possible. Keep them short and to the point. See CAPTIONS.

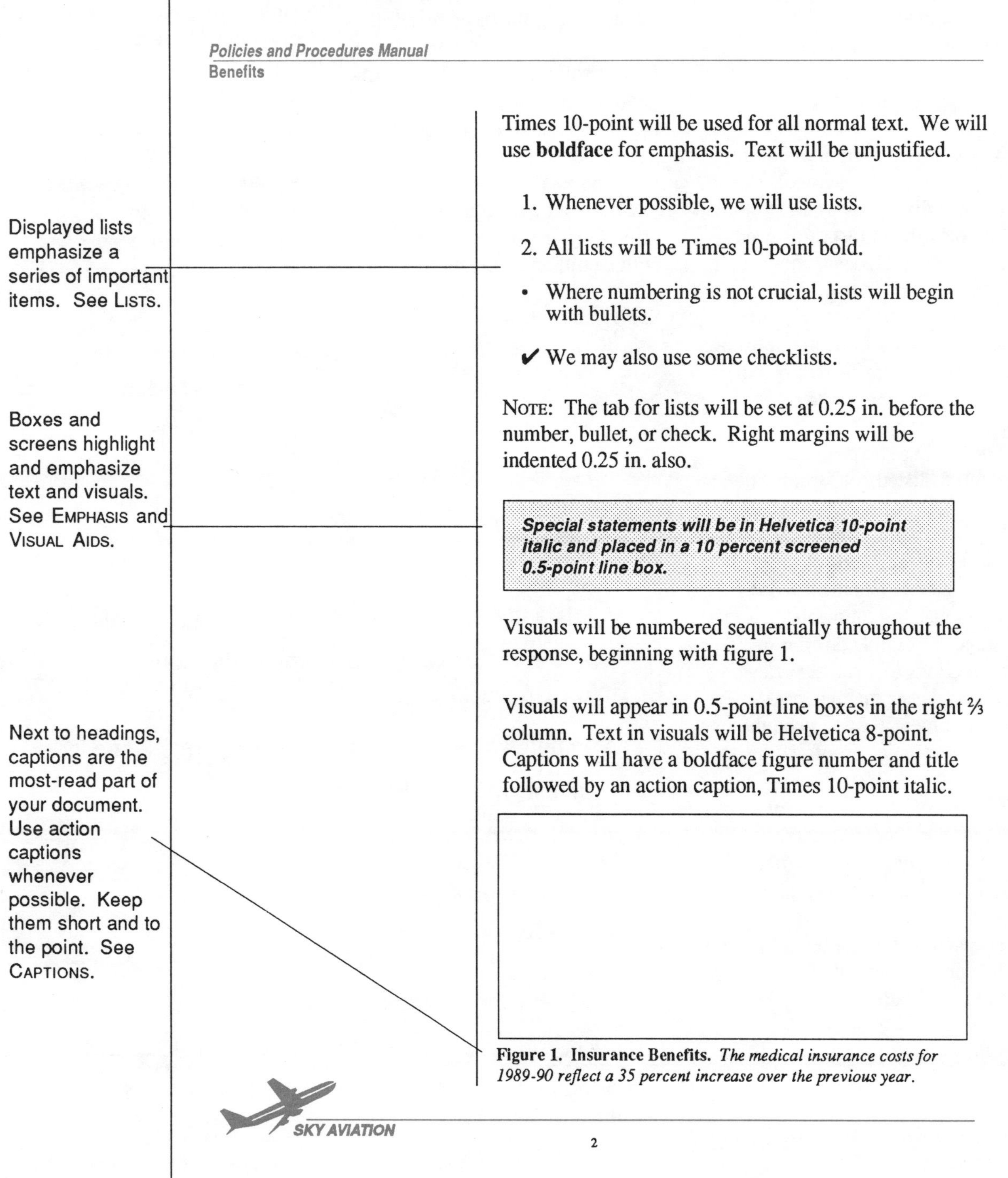

Policies and Procedures Manual
Benefits

Times 10-point will be used for all normal text. We will use **boldface** for emphasis. Text will be unjustified.

1. Whenever possible, we will use lists.
2. All lists will be Times 10-point bold.

- Where numbering is not crucial, lists will begin with bullets.

✔ We may also use some checklists.

NOTE: The tab for lists will be set at 0.25 in. before the number, bullet, or check. Right margins will be indented 0.25 in. also.

Special statements will be in Helvetica 10-point italic and placed in a 10 percent screened 0.5-point line box.

Visuals will be numbered sequentially throughout the response, beginning with figure 1.

Visuals will appear in 0.5-point line boxes in the right ⅔ column. Text in visuals will be Helvetica 8-point. Captions will have a boldface figure number and title followed by an action caption, Times 10-point italic.

Figure 1. Insurance Benefits. *The medical insurance costs for 1989-90 reflect a 35 percent increase over the previous year.*

SKY AVIATION

2

Editing and Proofreading Symbols

Editors, writers, secretaries, reviewers, proofreaders, typesetters, printers—those people who work with documents must have a system for indicating changes to a text.

The standard system of editing and proofreading symbols (listed in most dictionaries) is far more complex than most of us need because it includes symbols that were developed to allow copyeditors, typesetters, printers, and others involved in publishing to make minute corrections to a text about to be printed.

The editing and proofreading symbols listed below constitute a simplified set of the standard symbols. This simplified set addresses the needs of most business and technical writers who must communicate suggestions and editorial corrections to writers, reviewers, or secretaries in a business environment. If you need the complete set of proofreading symbols, see *The Chicago Manual of Style,* 13th edition, p. 94, or the *United States Government Printing Office Style Manual* (March 1984), p. 5.

The example in the box illustrates the simplified method of editing and proofreading a printed piece of text. This example also follows the rules cited below.

Editing on a Computer

Editing and proofreading on a computer is easier than using hard copy and symbols. Remember, however, that if you make silent (unmarked) corrections to someone else's text, you may be changing the intent or even the basic meaning.

If your software has a TEXT NOTE (sometimes DOC COMMENT or DO NOT PRINT) feature, you can use it to question the writer about the intent or meaning. With this feature, your questions will not print. Be sure your questions are both tactful and constructive.

See WORD PROCESSING.

1. Use consistent proofreading symbols to indicate changes or corrections to text:

Symbol	Meaning
℘	Delete or take out.
∧	Insert a phrase, word, or punctuation mark.
∿	Transpose letters, words, or phrases.
⊐	Move to the right.
⊏	Move to the left.
≡	Use capital letter(s).
/	Use lowercase letter(s).
⁀‿	Close up a space.
#	Add a space.
¶	Make a new paragraph.

Original

¶ Writers and Secrtaries of word pro cessing spec ailists have to agree on what to use when editingand proofreading drat materials. without; such an agreement and a consistent convetion, erros kreep in and quality writing is impossible.

Corrected

Writers and secretaries or word processing specialists have to agree on what symbols to use when editing and proofreading draft materials.

Without such an agreement, errors creep in and quality writing is impossible.

Editing and Proofreading Symbols

NOTE 1: Professional proofreaders sometimes use a different symbol in the margin than they use in the text. For instance, the # sign in the margin indicates that a space should be added. In text a slash mark indicates where the space should be added:

\# The incorrect/proposal

NOTE 2: In addition to the proofreading symbols shown above, some reviewers also use the symbol *sp* to indicate a spelling error. Most editors would correct a spelling error by inserting, deleting, or transposing letters, but if the reviewer wants the author to make the corrections, then indicating spelling errors with *sp* is helpful.

2. Use marginal marks to indicate corrections made within lines.

Changes to a text are sometimes difficult to see, particularly those changes made in pencil or black ink, which readers may have trouble distinguishing from surrounding print. To highlight changes or corrections, you should use a red or green pencil for changes. Even the change in color is sometimes difficult to see, however, particularly for color-blind reviewers.

So indicate changes by marking the change within the line but also using marginal marks to show that a change appears on the line beside the mark. Professional proofreaders use marginal proofreading symbols to highlight changes, but even a simple checkmark or an *X* can be effective in catching the reader's eye.

Be consistent, whether you use standard marginal proofreading symbols or simply a checkmark to indicate that a change has occurred in the line beside the checkmark.

An Example of Multiple Proofreadings

The Grayson plant operated by Mogo, re-covers almost all of the propane, butane and
gaoline, but no ethane and the rsidue gas is sold to TransState Pipeline Co.. TPS
processes the the residue stream and re-covers most the ethane and remaining
NGL'S. TPS purchases thegas at the Grayson plant outlet and then transmits it some
6 miles to its procesing plant near Abilene, Tex. Once there, the residue steam is
processed within some thirty-six hours and the resulting products are sold both to
other companies although TPS does shipe some of the products to its chemical nearby
subsidary. The TPS operation clearly compliments the Mogo operation at Grayson, so
we shoould consider bidding on the TPS facilities (if, of course, the price is reasonable.
Actually, we've heared rumors that TPS is interested in selling.)

Editing and Proofreading Symbols

3. Use different colors of ink for different proofreadings (either by the same person or several people).

A text going through multiple revisions can become difficult to decipher if the different revisions are not somehow indicated. A very good system is to change the color of the reviewer's or proofreader's pencil (as in the example below).

The first reviewer might indicate changes with a red pencil, the second reviewer with a green pencil, the third with a blue pencil, and so on. The color of the suggestion thus indicates when and by whom the suggestion was made. This system is particularly effective during peer or group review.

4. Keep a list of editorial or proofreading decisions so that you can be consistent and so that you can summarize for the writer the changes you routinely make.

The list of editorial or proofreading decisions is sometimes called an editorial style sheet. Writers themselves sometimes develop it, or they wait for an editor or proofreader to develop one. The earlier it can be developed, the better.

Items on this list would include all decisions about punctuation, capitalization, spelling, or word usage. To illustrate, a proofreader working with the example on the prior page could make these sorts of decisions:

Grayson plant (*not* Grayson Plant)

MOGO (*not* Mogo)

Comma in a series precedes and: propane, butane, and gasoline

TransState Pipeline Co. (*not* Company)

TPS (TransState Pipeline Co.) *rather than* TransState Pipeline Co. (TPS)

NOTE: As the above examples suggest, some language decisions about a document are not clearly right or wrong. Instead, an editor or proofreader has to pick the preferred form and then stay with that choice throughout the document.

See STYLE and PUNCTUATION.

Electronic Mail

Electronic mail is the exchange of messages using computers linked on a network. One person writes a message and then sends it to one or more readers. Often, hard (printed) copies of the message won't even exist because both the sender of the message and the readers will delete the message from the system without printing a hard copy.

(**Voice Mail** is similar to electronic mail and is also becoming popular. See the end of this entry for a discussion of voice mail.)

Millions of workers now use electronic mail. The number of individual messages is staggering even today, and estimates suggest that by the year 2000 electronic messages will annually total some 60 billion worldwide.

Today, most electronic communication is done over closed computer networks called LANs (local area networks). LANs can be small and local or large and nationwide.

More and more commonly, a network connects field offices all over the country with the home or central office. International networks now exist and are growing rapidly. Despite their size, such networks are usually closed to anyone outside the company or agency.

Some public networks now exist to serve subscribers with a special interest—for example, medical practitioners who want access to a medical database or financial analysts who want financial information. New standards within the industry promise to make public networks more accessible and far more widely used during the 1990s.

Many managers see electronic mail reducing phone calls and eliminating unnecessary paperwork. They foresee a totally electronic office, one without files and files of hard copies. They also see more efficient and more rapid decisionmaking.

Other managers see the problems associated with electronic mail. The main one is the problem of poor or incomplete documentation. Unless companies or agencies keep an accurate record of internal decisionmaking, they will be unable to explain and defend their decisions.

As they rely more and more on electronic mail, companies and agencies will need comprehensive guidelines about what needs to be retained in company files (electronic or hard copies) and what can be deleted or destroyed.

A second problem is that electronic mail will not prevent misunderstandings and erroneous messages. A written message is neither better nor less ambiguous just because it is in electronic form. For instance, electronic mail may be less efficient than discussions on the phone because electronic mail does not permit the instantaneous feedback possible in a phone call.

Despite some problems with its use, electronic mail is part of today's high-tech business world. It is now a valuable tool, and it will become even more valuable as employees learn how best to use its strengths and avoid its weaknesses.

Using Electronic Mail Efficiently

1. Choose electronic mail when you want to communicate information rapidly and when the information is better conveyed by computer than by phone or hard (printed) copy.

Electronic mail is especially efficient when the persons you want to contact are unavailable. Electronic mail allows you to send the message so that it will be available when the recipients return to their computers.

Electronic mail is also valuable when the data or information would be inconvenient to deliver over the phone. For instance, several names, addresses, and phone numbers are time consuming to dictate over the phone. Hard copy is, of course, an option, but hard copy might take several days to arrive if it has to go by outside mail or even through an internal mail system. A fax is another option, but it often requires the sender and receiver to go to fax stations somewhere else in their buildings.

Use the phone when you want to get feedback or a response to your message. For instance, if you have a request or if your message requires extra tact and

Electronic Mail

the personal touch, use the phone. The computer screen can seem cold and unfeeling, for example, when the writer has to send unpleasant or negative messages.

Use hard (printed) copies when you want to keep a record of your message. For example, you might want to summarize a meeting where important departmental decisions were made. A second example would be personnel decisions, which potentially become part of an employee's personnel file. In either case, of course, you could write the document using electronic mail and then print a hard copy for your files.

---

2. Write an eye-catching entry (subject) line.

Make sure your entry line will stand out from a long list of entry lines that appear on the reader's screen. As electronic mail becomes more popular, more and more entries will confront a reader who calls up a list of electronic mail files. If your entry line doesn't catch a reader's attention, your file might not even be opened!

Write entry lines that get your message across in a few words:

this

—Scoping Meeting Nov. 9 at 10 p.m.
—Cost Overruns of 20% on A-345 Prototype
—Please Sign Divisional Budget by July 5

not this

—Scoping Meeting
—Cost Overruns
—Divisional Budget

See HEADINGS.

---

3. Preview key content up front and limit your document to one screen (page) if possible.

Electronic mail readers do not like being forced to scroll through several screens. Present your main points quickly, and preview the remaining content so that readers will know what is coming.

If possible, limit your document to one screen (page).

Work toward the principle of "no surprises." A reader opening an electronic mail file and looking at the first page (screen) should know both the main point of the message and the content to follow. Whenever possible, design this one screen using emphasis techniques, such as lists, headings, and single-sentence paragraphs. See EMPHASIS.

this

We propose increasing the division's supplemental budget for July by $5,000 to account for cost overruns on the XYZ project. Here is why we are making this proposal.

1. Actual labor rates required from January through June and their projection into July
2. Several additional fact-finding trips projected during July
3. Increased managerial interest in XYZ

not this

As you know during the recent managerial coordination meeting (June 15), the subject of XYZ came up. Concerns expressed included the timing of the project, especially work during July. Also, the engineering representatives indicated that several extra trips might be necessary during July . . . .

See ORGANIZATION and EMPHASIS.

For longer documents, consider writing a separate executive summary for the first page (screen) and then including other data as necessary. In many cases, the executive summary might be sufficient by itself, with the background or supporting data merely referenced or transmitted in hard copy to follow up the electronic version. See SUMMARIES.

Be careful not to waste space on your first screen with, for example, a long distribution list or excessive spaces between date, headings, and text.

You could delay a long distribution list until the end of your document. In other instances, you might give key readers on the first page (for political purposes), with a full courtesy copy (cc) list on the final page.

---

4. Review and revise (as necessary) your file before sending it to readers.

The immediacy of electronic mail is both its strength and its weakness. Although readers can get the message almost as fast as if it were given by phone (or fax), the message itself might profit from review, both for errors and undesirable content. See WORD PROCESSING.

Depending on your potential readers, take time to clean up your document. A few errors will detract from the message; many errors will destroy your credibility and the impact of your message.

With hard (printed) copies—especially those written with heat and anger—a cooling period has always been desirable. Consider allowing a cooling period before you send certain electronic files to recipients. Give yourself at least 1 day to reconsider your message. Often you will change the message, and sometimes you may even decide not to send it.

5. Signal clearly the end of your message.

Readers resent being left hanging or scrolling to an empty screen, wondering if they have missed something.

End most documents in two clear ways. First, conclude with a brief summary or review of the content. You might restate a request or a deadline, or you might even list again the reasons for your request. Second, give your documents a quick complimentary close—*Sincerely, Thanks, See you Thursday,* etc., plus your name (or initials). See LETTERS and MEMOS.

Voice Mail

Voice mail (voice messaging) is becoming a popular alternative to electronic mail. The main benefits of voice mail are to avoid "telephone tag" and to get your message across quickly and efficiently.

A voice mail system connects your telephone to a computer that digitizes and stores telephone messages on a magnetic disk. Such a system does much more than standard telephone-answering machines: It assigns a date and time to each message, distributes the message to many receivers, pages receivers, and redirects messages when receivers are not available at a particular location. It will also tell you if your message has been picked up or not.

Even though many companies have their own voice mail system, the service is also available by subscription. A voice mail service will issue you a telephone number, which then lets you send messages to any number of users with a single call.

Using Voice Mail Efficiently

6. Be sure to identify yourself and give your listener the date, time, and your phone number.

Don't assume that your listener will recognize your voice; also, not every system will automatically record the date, time, and your phone number.

7. Think before you speak.

Take a minute before dialing to review mentally your main points and your intent in making the call—perhaps even jot a list of points to cover. Unless you do one or both of these things, you are likely to ramble and to confuse your listener. Rambling is a problem if you are limited in the time you have to record your message.

8. Speak clearly and repeat important information.

Misunderstandings are inevitable, so work to reduce them in your recorded messages. Speak clearly and slightly slower than you would normally. As necessary, spell out difficult words—for example, people's names or the names of places because names often have unusual spellings. Technical terms and associated numbers are also easy for a listener to confuse.

Repetition of meeting times, deadlines, and other important details is a courtesy. You might, for example, conclude by repeating your key request or recommendation, including any associated date or meeting time. See REPETITION.

Ellipses

Ellipses, which consist of three spaced periods (. . .), indicate omissions, primarily in quoted material. Some word processing systems have a function that produces an ellipsis with unspaced periods (...); this option is still rare in printed texts, possibly because it makes the text looked jammed together.

Ellipses are the opposite of brackets, which indicate insertions in quoted material. See BRACKETS.

---

1. Use an ellipsis within quoted material to indicate omissions of words, sentences, or paragraphs:

"Labor costs . . . caused an operating loss for January of nearly $10,000."

Original: Labor costs, which our executive committee has been studying, caused an operating loss for January of nearly $10,000.

"No tax increases for 1989 . . . will occur."

Original: No tax increases for 1986 in personal withholding will occur.

NOTE 1: If omitted material comes at the beginning of a sentence, the quoted material opens with an ellipsis, especially if the material appears to be a complete sentence:

" . . . the printed budget will remain unchanged."

Original: Despite a few inconsistencies, the printed budget will remain unchanged.

NOTE 2: If the omitted material comes at the end of a sentence, the quoted material ends with an ellipsis plus the ending punctuation of the sentence:

"The Department of Energy denied our request for an energy subsidy . . . . "

Original: The Department of Energy denied our request for an energy subsidy even though we felt our request would be cost effective.

NOTE 3: If one or more words are omitted at the end of a quoted sentence, use three spaced periods followed by the end punctuation mark for the sentence: "*energy subsidy* . . . ." See SPACING.

Note 4: Instead of spaced periods (. . .), the *United States Government Printing Office Style Manual* recommends asterisks (* * *). However, this practice rarely occurs outside of printed federal government materials. Even there, use of asterisks is not consistent.

---

2. Do not use an ellipsis to omit words if such omissions change the meaning or intent of the original quotation:

"Chairman James Aubrey indicated that financing the debt load would . . . seriously undermine efforts to recover delinquent loans."

Original: Chairman James Aubrey indicated that financing the debt load would not detract from or seriously undermine efforts to recover delinquent loans.

---

3. Do not use an ellipsis to open or close a quotation if the quotation is clearly only part of an original sentence:

this

We discussed the "three legal loopholes" mentioned in the last Supreme Court decision on school busing.

not this

We discussed the " . . . three legal loopholes . . . " mentioned in the last Supreme Court decision on school busing.

---

4. Use a line of spaced periods to indicate that one or more entire lines of text are omitted:

Friends, Romans, countrymen,
lend me your ears;

I come to bury Caesar, not to
praise him.

. . . .

He was my friend, faithful and just
to me:

NOTE 1: The line of periods does not tell a reader how much was omitted. The writer is responsible for retaining the intent and meaning of the original material.

NOTE 2: Poems and other long quotations do not require quotation marks. Instead, indentation and extra lines above and below the quoted material indicate that it is a quotation. See QUOTATION MARKS.

---

5. Use an ellipsis to indicate omitted material in mathematical expressions:

$a_1, a_2, \ldots, a_n$

$1 + 2 + \ldots + n$

See MATHEMATICAL NOTATION.

---

6. Use an ellipsis to indicate faltering speech:

I protest . . . or maybe I should only suggest that you have made a mistake.

I wonder . . . perhaps . . . if . . . that is a wise choice.

Emphasis

Emphasis, properly used, is one of your most powerful writing tools. Proper emphasis ensures that your most important ideas are noticed first and that they never go unnoticed. Effective writers control their readers' eyes and minds with emphatic devices. Effective writers do not write documents—they **design** them for maximum visual impact.

Emphasis applies to all levels of writing—from the layout and structure of an entire document to individual sentences and words. On any level, you emphasize words and ideas by manipulating **position** and **appearance.**

Position refers to the placement of words within a sentence, paragraph, or section.

Appearance refers to the layout of ideas on a page and to the physical character of the words or ideas: spacing, indentation, boldface type, underlining, type size, type style, color, etc.

See Boldface, Spacing, and Desktop Publishing.

1. Open and close with your important ideas.

The beginning and the ending of documents, sections, paragraphs, and sentences are more prominent than the middle.

The first and last words in a sentence receive the greatest emphasis. The opening and closing sentences in a paragraph are more prominent, as are the opening and closing paragraphs in a section or subsection.

Therefore, emphasize your important ideas by placing them in these stronger positions. Because readers encounter the opening first, always try to begin with the **most important** ideas.

Your details—the data, explanation, support, elaboration—belong in the middle.

In longer paragraphs, sections, and documents, end with important ideas, even if you repeat something stated earlier.

See Organization.

2. Subordinate minor ideas.

Your major ideas deserve more attention. Therefore, you should subordinate minor information by using less space to discuss it or by placing the minor information in an appendix.

The minor information can include raw data; lengthy but relatively unimportant discussions of systems, techniques, or processes; and routine explanations of matters related to but less important than your central ideas.

Do not spend inappropriate amounts of time discussing unimportant matters. If you do, you throw the document out of focus.

See Appendices/Attachments.

3. Repeat important ideas.

Repetition is emphatic because it reinforces the idea in the reader's mind. However, repetition might be either ineffective or effective.

Ineffective repetition occurs when writers repeat something too quickly—without sufficient intervening discussion—and when they use the same combination of words to express an idea.

Effective repetition occurs when an important idea appears in several different forms—typically at the beginning and ending of the section or paragraph concerning the idea. The first occurrence of the idea is introductory; the next occurrence is summary. Between them is explanation or elaboration, example, description, definition, or proof.

See Repetition and Key Words.

4. Use space to isolate important ideas.

Leaving more space around important ideas makes the page look less cluttered and also draws attention to the ideas. Instead of double spacing between paragraphs, leave three spaces. Or center an important idea in the middle of a page and leave extra spaces on both sides of it.

See Desktop Publishing.

Emphasis

5. Use headings to highlight information.

Headings stand out and are therefore always emphatic. Use standard headings or headlines—longer headings that summarize and announce conclusions, directions, accomplishments, and startling or unusual facts. Theme headings, which announce the major thrust of a section, are especially emphatic.

Headings always draw attention to the information that follows them. They allow readers to be selective in reading, and they allow them to set the document aside and return later to a specific section.

See HEADINGS.

6. Use lists to highlight serial information.

Lists are visually more emphatic than paragraphs. Typically, lists are indented, have space between each item, and use numbers, letters, bullets, or dashes to indicate where each item begins. Readers pay more attention to displayed (vertical) lists than they do to standard text.

See LISTS.

7. Use visual aids to emphasize important ideas.

Visual aids are naturally emphatic. They draw the reader's eye simply because they are different from text. One of the best ways to emphasize information is to make it visual. Create charts, graphs, drawings, schematic diagrams, flow charts, tree diagrams, illustrations, etc.

See VISUAL AIDS, CHARTS, GRAPHS, ILLUSTRATIONS, MAPS, PHOTOGRAPHS, and TABLES.

8. Use single-sentence paragraphs to emphasize ideas.

Single-sentence paragraphs are more emphatic because they are shorter. They demand less effort to read, so readers tend to pay more attention to them. Use them judiciously, however. Too many single-sentence paragraphs make a document look choppy and as if it has no paragraphs.

See PARAGRAPHS.

9. Use typographical features to emphasize words or sentences.

CAPITAL LETTERS, underlining, **boldface type**, *italics*, and other typographical features are more emphatic than normal text. Be careful not to overuse them. Too much typographical variation makes the text look chaotic.

See UNDERLINING, BOLDFACE, and ITALICS.

10. Use color to emphasize.

Use color to highlight, to emphasize, to contrast, to compare, to warn, and to pacify. Color makes reading easier and faster and the material more memorable.

Color creates feelings and moods. How it does this is unknown, but we do know that red and yellow stimulate and blue soothes—warning signs in red, kitchens in yellow, and hospital quiet rooms in blue.

- Choose appropriate colors.

Choose colors that reinforce your message. Remember, the message is the medium and the medium is the message. Use red for warnings and critical items. The statement "We are in the red" sends a clear, color-coded message.

Generally, use light blue to denote a sense of clarity, sincerity, and freshness. Use dark blue to denote power, authority, and formality. Red and yellow are attention grabbers, but yellow is hard to see in print. Green is a good background color, just as it often is in nature. Purple is the color of royalty, but it, like yellow, is hard to see in print. Metallic colors (gold, silver, bronze) are associated with richness, but they are expensive to print.

Remember that some colors in combination evoke special memories and emotions—red and green for Christmas; orange and black for Halloween; and red, white, and blue for patriotism.

These traditional combinations of colors should be avoided except when used in their conventional ways.

Use black for the outline and the text on your illustrations. Use color to highlight special parts of your illustrations. Remember that colored text will appear smaller than the same type or line in black, so you will have to increase the type size and line weight to get the effect that you want.

- Be consistent.

Use color consistently in your illustrations. Include a color key or code if necessary. Do not distract your readers by switching colors—stay with the same colors for the same message. This will help your readers focus on your message rather than your medium.

- Keep the colors few and simple.

Use, at most, two or three colors, and highlight only the most significant items. Remember, also, that the more colors you use, the more expensive will be your printing. As in this *Style Guide*, a single color can be a cost-effective way to emphasize key points.

- Use two or more colors carefully.

Select colors that will contrast, which means selecting colors from opposite points on the color wheel. One color much lighter or darker than another part of an illustration will give the impression of vibrating.

Avoid reds and greens together. About 10 percent of people cannot distinguish clearly red from green.

Backgrounds should be a pale, subtle color, making them less dominant than the foreground. The foreground should be strong and bright to get your readers' attention. Bright colors work best in short headings and parts of illustrations. Use bright colors sparingly.

- Use white space as a color.

Effective use of white space on your illustrations will enhance the use of color in other areas. Remember, white is a color—all colors. Use it.

False Subjects

False subjects are pronouns like *it* and *there* that have no concrete antecedents; that is, the pronouns do not refer to anything real. They are abstractions.

False subjects often occur at the beginning of a sentence and displace the true subject:

> It is this phase that is important.

In this sentence, *it* seems to stand for *phase*, but replacing the pronoun with its apparent antecedent creates nonsense:

> This phase is this phase that is important.

The true subject of the sentence is *phase*. Beginning with the true subject creates a shorter, much crisper sentence:

> This phase is important.

False subjects can also appear within sentences:

> We decided that it was important for the costs to be explained.

The false subject *it* weakens the middle of the sentence and adds unnecessary additional words. The sentence is far stronger without the false subject:

> We decided that explaining the costs was important.
>
> *or*
>
> We decided to explain the costs.

---

1. Eliminate false subjects.

Whenever possible, eliminate pronouns that lack concrete antecedents. Getting rid of these false subjects makes your writing more concise and often clearer.

Sometimes, however, the false subject is necessary, as in the expression *it is raining*. The word *it* is an abstraction, but what could you say in its place? Ask yourself, what is raining? No other word or words will be as functional or as expedient as the false subject. In such limited circumstances as *it is raining* or *it is noon,* false subjects are acceptable. Otherwise, try to eliminate them.

Below are additional before and after examples of false subjects. Note how much simpler, more direct, and shorter the sentences are when we eliminate the false subjects along with any accompanying words:

> In designing a thermal protection system, it is possible to meet the 1,100-degree fire requirement yet not be reliable. (*20 words*)
>
> Thermal protection system designs can meet the 1,100-degree fire requirement without being reliable. (*14 words*)

> Within the family of hydrates, there are several solid metal oxides that both chemically combine with water (hydration) and mechanically retain water (capillary condensation). (*24 words*)
>
> Within the family of hydrates, several solid metal oxides both chemically combine with water (hydration) and mechanically retain water (capillary condensation). (*21 words*)

> It will also be possible, as the study proceeds, to identify and extract important performance degradations resulting from failure to improve a given technology. (*24 words*)
>
> As the study proceeds, identifying and extracting important performance degradations resulting from failure to improve a given technology will also be possible. (*22 words*)
>
> *or*
>
> As the study proceeds, we can also identify and extract important performance degradations resulting from failure to improve a given technology. (*21 words*)

> From table 5.3, it appears that the use of relatively compact heat-transfer surfaces in the 10- to 20-fins/in. range will provide the compactness necessary to achieve the Navy goal of reduced size and weight. (*34 words*)
>
> As table 5.3 suggests, using relatively compact heat-transfer surfaces in the 10- to 20-fins/in. range will apparently provide the compactness necessary to achieve the Navy goal of reduced size and weight. (*31 words*)

> There are five factors that influenced our decision to repartition the system. (*12 words*)
>
> Five factors influenced our decision to repartition the system. (*9 words*)

> It will be the responsibility of the team manager to ensure that the total required time-phased quantity and skill mix can be supplied from the onsite pool. (*27 words*)
>
> The team manager will ensure that the required time-phased quantity and skill mix can be supplied from the onsite pool. (*20 words*)

Footnotes

Footnotes are the most common method of citing sources, especially in the humanities. As their name implies, footnotes originally appeared at the bottom of a page, but now they usually appear at the end of a chapter or article, making typing and page layout easier.

Some word processing software programs allow writers to insert footnotes on each page. Consider using this software feature, assuming you wish to use footnotes, because readers find footnotes at the bottom of the page easier to read.

Instead of using footnotes, writers in the physical and biological sciences usually cite the author and the date of publication by enclosing them within parentheses in the text. These citations are developed fully in bibliographies that appear at the end of the text. See CITATIONS and BIBLIOGRAPHIC FORM.

Titles of books, journals, and newspapers may be underlined rather than italicized if italics is not available.

See TITLES.

---

1. Use raised Arabic numerals immediately following a quotation or paraphrase to indicate that the quotation or paraphrase has a footnote:

> Within your text you may have a quotation from a published book or article: "Writers should always use quotation marks for exact quotations."[1] Sometimes you may be paraphrasing someone's ideas.[2] In these cases, your footnote number should come as close to the idea as possible,[3] even if the particular sentence goes on to discuss a second source.[4] Naturally, in a normal document, you should avoid having footnotes after every sentence or phrase.

NOTE: The footnote number comes after all punctuation, except for a dash. Footnotes are numbered sequentially within a chapter of a book and within an article.

See QUOTATIONS and QUOTATION MARKS.

---

2. In the first footnote to a source, include the author or authors, the full title, complete publishing information, and the pages being referred to:

Book by one author

1. David G. Peters, *The Energetic West* (Los Angeles: The Peter Pauper Press, 1982), 90.

Book by two authors

2. Frank S. Sloan and Jane Seymour, *The Road West in the 1850's* (Salt Lake City: The Popular Press, 1976), 34-35.

Book by more than three authors; information from several pages

3. Ralph Davidson, et al., *The Western Fault System* (Omaha: University of Nebraska Press, 1968), 126-127, 175, and 189.

Journal article

4. Janice Wesley, "Metal Matrix Alignment in Fiber Production," *Massachusetts Institute of Technology Journal*, 16 (October 1981): 45-46.

Public document

5. U.S. Congress, Senate, Foreign Affairs Committee, *Report on Two Chinas in the Coming Decade*, 91st Cong., 2d sess., 1981 (Washington, DC: United States Government Printing Office, 1983), 187-188.

Dissertation or thesis

6. O. X. Jones, "The Influence of Congressional Resolutions on Trade with China: A Study of Inconsistencies" (Ph.D. dissertation, University of Maryland, 1982), 87-88.

Personal letter

7. Senator Frank Church of Idaho to O. X. Jones, 23 November 1975. Personal files of O. X. Jones, Portland, Oregon.

Interview

8. Sidney Sung, interview during the annual meeting of the American Political Association, Seattle, Washington, November 1983.

NOTE 1: Footnotes are similar in form to paragraphs. The first line is indented, and all items are punctuated as if the information were the first sentence in the paragraph. The items are usually separated by commas.

NOTE 2: Writers can add a comment or additional facts to a typical footnote:

> 8. Sidney Sung, interview during the annual meeting of the American Political Association, Seattle, Washington, November 1983. Mr. Sung, the cultural attache in San Francisco for the People's Republic of China, granted this interview with the understanding that all of his comments would be off the record until after the 1984 U.S. Presidential election.

Footnotes

NOTE 3: Superscripts are a common way to number footnotes presented either at the bottom of the page or at the end of the chapter or article:

[9]Jason K. Bacon, *The Two-China Policy* (New York: Columbia University Press, 1976), 85.

3. In second and subsequent references, make footnotes brief. Generally, include only the author's last name and the page number of the material referred to:

Second or subsequent footnote for one author

10. Bacon, 56-57.

Second or subsequent footnote for two authors

11. Sloan and Seymour,18-21.

Second or subsequent footnote in which two or more authors by the same last name have been mentioned in first footnotes

12. Bacon, Two-China Policy, 76.

NOTE: This convention for second and subsequent footnotes eliminates the need for such Latin abbreviations as *ibid., op. cit.,* and *loc. cit.* These abbreviations make footnotes difficult to read.

Fractions

Fractions are mathematical expressions for the quotient (division) of two quantities: ½. In this fraction, the slash mark means *1* divided by *2*. Strictly speaking, decimals are also fractions. See DECIMALS.

1. Spell out and hyphenate fractions appearing by themselves in ordinary text, especially if they are followed by *of a* or *of an:*

two-thirds of an inch (*not* ⅔ of an inch)

. . . decreased by one-third

one-half foot

one-fourth inch

one-tenth

one-hundreth of a mile

two one-thousandths

eighty-four one-thousandths *(better 0.084)*

NOTE 1: The longer a fractional expression becomes, especially if whole numbers are involved, the more desirable it is to express the fraction in figures (or a decimal):

56/64

98/100 *(or* 0.98)

2½ times

6¾ *(or* 6.75)

29⅓

NOTE 2: Measurements, especially in scientific and technical documents, require figures:

⅓-foot step

½-inch pipe

⅔-inch-diameter pipe

7½ meters

8½- by 11-inch paper

See NUMBERS and HYPHENS.

NOTE 3: Express fractions in figures when they are combined with abbreviations or symbols:

5¼ V

34⅓ km

8½ hr

5½" x 6 ⅔"

Such fractions and abbreviations are most common in figures or in field reports.

See NUMBERS.

Gobbledygook

Gobbledygook is not a recent problem. Some 200 years ago, opponents of Benjamin Franklin argued that to vote a man had to own property. Franklin's supporters disagreed and stated their case as follows:

> It cannot be adhered to with any reasonable degree of intellectual or moral certainty that the inalienable right man possesses to exercise his political preferences by employing his vote in referendums is rooted in anything other than man's own nature, and is, therefore, properly called a natural right. To hold, for instance, that this natural right can be limited externally by making its exercise dependent on a prior condition of ownership of property, is to wrongly suppose that man's natural right to vote is somehow more inherent in and more dependent on the property of man than it is on the nature of man. It is obvious that such belief is unreasonable, for it reverses the order of rights intended by nature.

Franklin agreed with this argument but knew that people wouldn't be moved by such pompous oratory. So he explained his position as follows:

> To require property of voters leads us to this dilemma: I own a jackass; I can vote. The jackass dies; I cannot vote. Therefore the vote represents not me but the jackass.

Gobbledygook is language that is so pompous, long-winded, and abstract that it is unintelligible. Some dictionaries trace the term to the verb *gobble*, describing the sounds made by turkeys, and it is tempting to believe that writers of gobbledygook resemble this Thanksgiving favorite. Actually, such writers are usually well intentioned. They might even take pride in writing what they consider to be sophisticated and complex language.

Perhaps the best way to appreciate gobbledygook is to read a couple of recent samples:

> This office's activities during the year were primarily continuing their primary functions of education of the people to acquaint them with their needs, problems, and alternate problem solutions, in order that they can make wise decisions in planning and implementing a total program that will best meet the needs of the people, now and in the future.
>
> Because the heavy mistletoe infestation in the Cattle Creek drainage area has rendered the residual timber resources useless for timber production, the ultimate goal is to establish a healthy, viable new stand of Douglas fir.

The average reader has to read these passages several times before beginning to decipher such nonsense. Why are the passages so difficult?

—**Words and phrases are abstract.** What does *alternate problem solutions* mean? Similarly, are *residual timber resources* the same thing as *trees?* If so, the writer should say *trees*. See Wordy Phrases and Redundant Words.

—**Words and phrases are pompous sounding.** Are the *office's activities* primarily their primary functions? Is a *healthy timber stand* different from a *viable timber stand?* If not, then the writer should stick with the simpler word: *healthy*.

—**Sentences are long and clumsy.** By themselves, the 57 words in the first paragraph would make reading difficult, but the clumsy phrasing makes the reading impossible. The 35 words in the second paragraph are closer to a reasonable number, but the writer delays the major thought in the sentence with a massive introductory clause (beginning with *because)*. As written, the sentence demands that readers remember a long opening condition while they try to absorb the main thought. The sentence would be clearer if the main and introductory clauses were reversed.

See Sentences, Strong Verbs, Active/Passive, and Parallelism.

How to Avoid Gobbledygook

1. Use concrete and specific words and phrases whenever possible:

this

> The environmental effects are often so slight and so hard to distinguish from other effects that we fail to appreciate their impact on the climate. We may even fail to appreciate the importance of properly assessing their environmental impact.

not this

> The environmental effects, although extremely important, are often so subtle and so confounded with and perhaps complicated by other environmental effects, which are no less important, that we neither gain a recognition of nor fully learn to appreciate the climatic effects that in fact exist and the resulting advantages of properly recognizing the environmental conditions that are the result of the aforementioned environmental effects.

this

To complete the recreational plan, we will need pictures of all tables, fireplaces, and other existing camping facilities in the state park.

not this

In order to bring the proposed recreational plan to completion; to evaluate existing recreation site appurtenances and facilities; and to include applicable facilities such as tables, fireplaces, etc., in the proposed new recreational plan, it will be necessary to receive photographs of all current appurtenances and facilities located within the state park area.

See Wordy Phrases and Redundant Words.

---

2. Avoid pompous words and phrases.

The word *appurtenance* in the preceding example is an excellent example of a pompous word. Most readers will not understand *appurtenance*, and forcing them to look up the word in a dictionary might not clarify the passage. Two recent desk dictionaries define *appurtenance* quite differently: "something added to another, more important thing; accessory" *(The American Heritage Dictionary)* and "an incidental right (as a right-of-way) attached to a principal property right and passing in possession with it" *(Webster's New Collegiate Dictionary)*. Which meaning should readers choose? More to the point, why make them choose?

If a word is not in common usage, avoid it or use it in such a way that the context provides a definition. In the example above, *appurtenance* surely fails the test. Here are some other pompous words and phrases with possible substitutes in parentheses:

Accordingly (so)
acquaint (inform or tell)
activate (start)
additional (more)
adhere (stick)
ameliorate (improve)
apprise (tell or inform)

Cognizant (aware)
commence (begin)
compensation (pay)
component (part)
concur (agree)
configuration (shape, design)
conflagration (fire)
curtail (slow, shorten)

Demonstrate (show)
descend (fall, climb down)
donate (give)

Encounter (meet)
evacuate (leave, empty, clear)
exhibit (show)

Fabricate (make)
factor (fact)
feasible (likely, possible)
fracture (break)
function (work, act)

Implicate (involve)
impotent (weak)
incinerate (burn)
increment (amount, bit)
indubitably (doubtless, undoubtedly)
inform (tell)
in isolation (alone, by itself)
initiate (begin)

Locality (place)
locate (find)

Major (chief, main)
manifest (show)
manipulate (operate)
manufacture (make)
modification (change)
moreover (besides)

Necessitate (compel)
necessity (need)

Paramount (main, chief)
perspective (view)
phenomenal (unusual)
philosophy (belief, idea)
potent (strong)
practically (nearly, most, all but)
proceed (go)
purchase (buy)

Ramification (result)
render (make)
request (ask)
reside (live)
residence (home)

Sophisticated (complex)
spotlight (stress)
state (say)
stimulate (excite)
succor (help)
sufficient (enough)

Thoroughfare (aisle, street)
terminate (end, fire)
transmit (send)

Utilization (use)
utilize (use)

Vacillate (waver)
veracious (true)
visualize (imagine, picture)

---

3. Make sentences direct and clear.

Sentence length is only one sign of complexity. A 10-word sentence can be unclear because it is poorly structured or contains abstract and pompous words. A 50-word sentence, on the other hand, may be clear and easily understandable. Generally, however, the longer a sentence becomes, the more complex its structure is likely to be and the more difficult it will be to read:

this

If you support a relative who is unable to work because of old age or poor health, you can claim a deduction of $XXXX. You can claim this deduction if you support your widowed mother or your spouse's widowed mother, whether or not she is able to work. If you support a

Gobbledygook

daughter who lives with you because you or your spouse is old or in poor health, you can claim a deduction of $XXXX.

not this

A tax deduction can be claimed in respect to any person whom the individual maintains at his own expense and who is (1) a relative of his, or of his wife, and is incapacitated by old age or infirmity from maintaining himself or herself, or (2) his or his wife's widowed mother, whether incapacitated or not, or (3) his daughter who is resident with him and upon whose services he is compelled to depend by reason of old age or infirmity.

See SENTENCES, STRONG VERBS, ACTIVE/PASSIVE, and PARALLELISM.

Gobbledygook and Jargon

Gobbledygook and jargon can both make reading difficult, but they are not the same.

Jargon chiefly includes terms known and used by a specific technical or professional group. Carpenters, for instance, have a number of jargon terms: *stud, joist, sill plate, header, cap plate, trip-L-grip,* etc. All such fields use a specialized vocabulary. See JARGON.

Gobbledygook can include terms that constitute technical jargon, but gobbledygook generally also includes nontechnical words that are simply unfamiliar, unnecessary, or too large. Using jargon is inappropriate only if readers will not comprehend it. Gobbledygook offends everyone. Good writing can include some jargon, particularly if the words are defined or understandable within the context, but good writing never includes gobbledygook.

Graphs

Graphs depict numerical data and are useful for showing trends, cycles, cumulative changes, relationships between variables, and distributions. They are not as effective as tables in providing precise data, but readers should be able to extract relatively accurate numerical data from the lines plotted. Graphs are better than tables if you want to help your readers understand the meaning of your data.

Graphs are normally plotted on grid lines, with a horizontal axis (x-axis/abscissa) and a vertical axis (y-axis/ordinate). The axes may also be diagonal or radial (as in figure 1). Grid lines are usually equally spaced in horizontal and vertical directions and reflect the numerical scales along each axis. However, grids may be irregular, reflecting probability distribution curves or logarithmic scales (see figure 7).

Including grid lines on graphs was the status quo for many years. Recently, however, graphs have begun to appear without grid lines, principally because many graphs are now produced by computer (see figures 2 through 7). Omitting grid lines is now acceptable. However, if readers are expected to extract precise data from graphs, you should not omit grid lines unless you combine the graph with a table (see figure 5).

In this *Style Guide*, graphs are distinguished from charts, including bar, pie, and surface charts. For information on those visual forms, see CHARTS. For general information on visual aids, see VISUAL AIDS. See also ILLUSTRATIONS, MAPS, PHOTOGRAPHS, and TABLES.

The most common graphs are line or coordinate graphs and logarithmic graphs. Other types of graphs exist, however, such as graphs using polar coordinates (see figure 1); these other types of graphs are beyond the scope of the following discussion, which is limited to line or coordinate graphs. Some of the basic principles are, however, similar—for example, the use of informative captions. See CAPTIONS.

1. Make graphs simple and easy to read.

Ensure that each graph has a single important point to make or a single relationship to show. Tell your readers what the relationship is. Be careful not to confuse readers by assuming that they understand the relationship between variables; for instance, do not use *versus* without an explanation of the relationship between the variables.

Don't try to do too much with each graph. Complicated graphs are often confusing, even to technically competent readers.

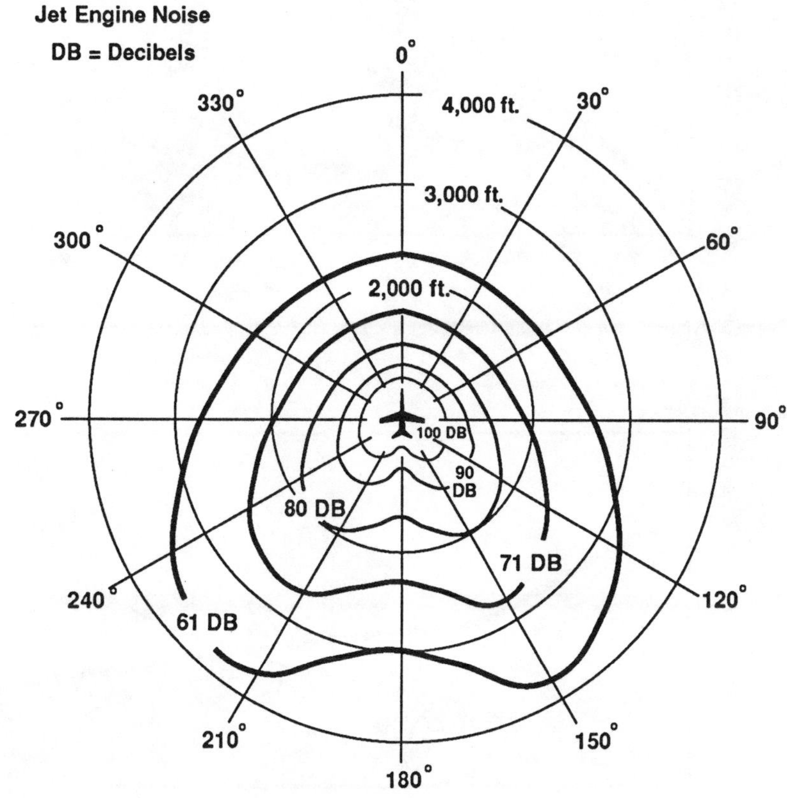

Figure 1. Jet Engine Noise. *The decibel level does not depend on where a listener is standing in relation to the plane, if the listener is within 2,000 feet of the plane. Beyond 2,000 feet, the listener's position is significant.*

Graphs

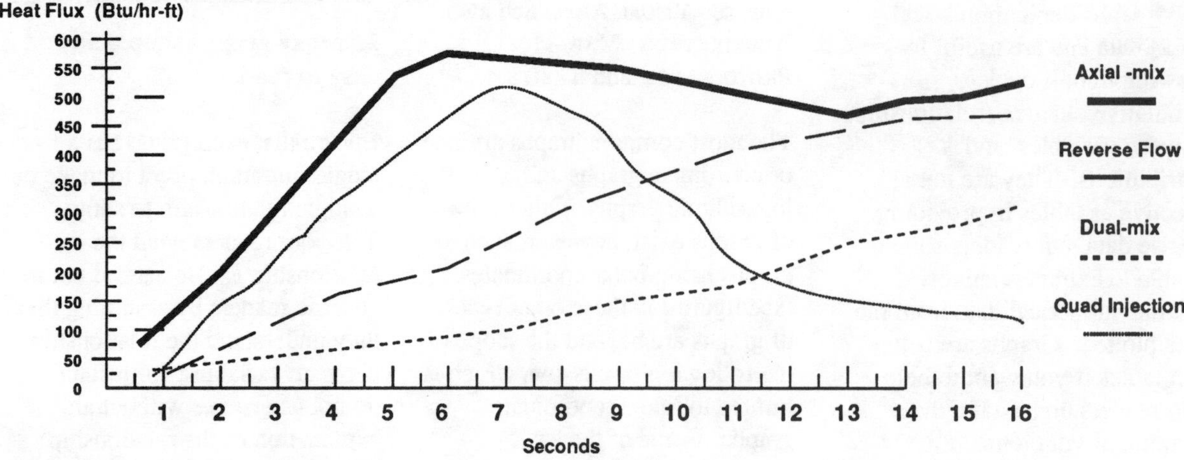

Figure 2. Comparison of Combustor Designs. *The axial-transverse mix is the most efficient of the four designs considered.*

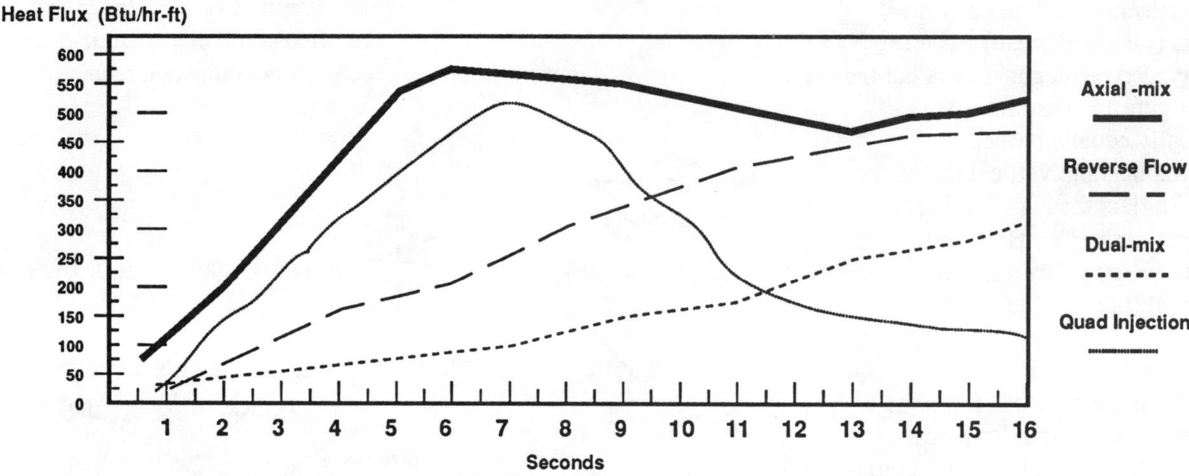

Figure 3. Comparison of Combustor Designs. *Of the four designs considered, the axial-transverse mix is the most efficient.*

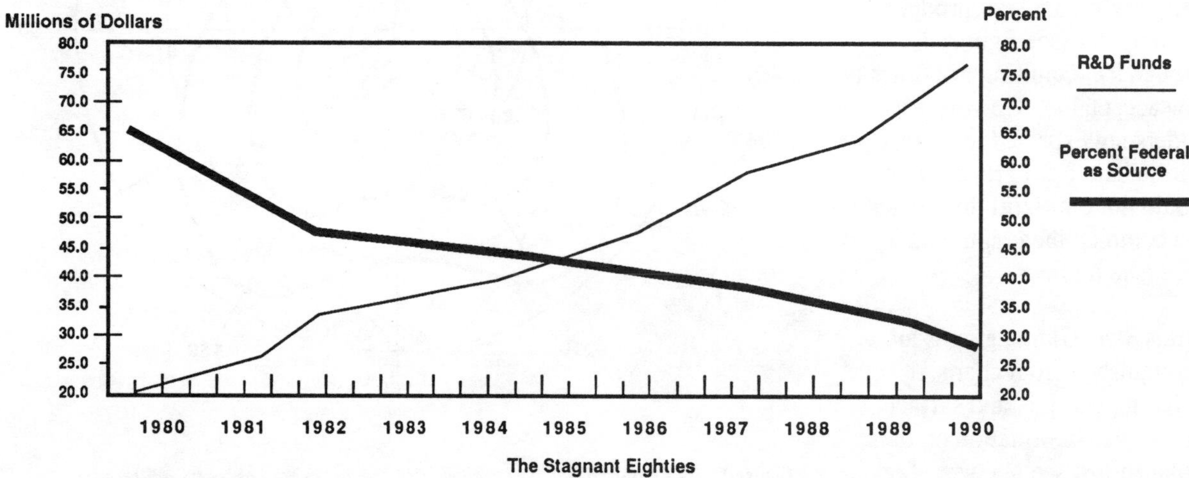

Figure 4. Federal Support of R&D Programs. *Federal support of research and development programs has steadily declined since 1980.*

Simplify graphs by eliminating everything that does not contribute to the central message of the graph. Do not use more labels, numbers, tick marks, or grid lines than necessary to do the job. Too much clutter makes graphs difficult to read.

2. Use informative captions to identify the purpose of each graph.

Give each graph a figure number and a title, and use informative captions to tell readers the meaning of the data (see figures 1 through 7). See CAPTIONS.

3. Label each axis and provide the appropriate scale for the data being plotted.

Use axis labels to identify each axis. Indicate the units of measurement in the axis label or place the units of measurement within parentheses after or below the axis label:

Wheat Shipments, in Metric Tons
Wheat Shipments (Metric Tons)
Wheat Shipments
(Metric Tons)

If time is one variable, plot it on the abscissa. See figures 2 through 4.

Scales must increase from bottom to top along the ordinate axis and left to right along the abscissa. Scale maximums and minimums must appear on the farthest grid lines along each axis. Scale labels must appear at appropriate intervals to facilitate data interpretation. See the next rule.

Generally, scales are indicated along the left and bottom axes; however, if you enclose the graph in a box (see figures 3 and 4) and the graph is unusually wide, you may label the ordinate scales on both left and right axes.

Occasionally, you might want to plot two or more lines that have different scales. If so, show the different scales on the left and right ordinate axes (see figure 4). Use explanation blocks, axis labels, and different line patterns to show readers which line pertains to which scale. Avoid putting the different scales on the same left or right axis. Try to put different ordinate scales on opposite ordinate axes so that you emphasize their difference.

4. Ensure that scales accurately reflect the data being presented.

Do not use scales that exaggerate or distort the numerical relationships that actually exist. You can make small and insignificant differences look important by using a minute scale, and you can hide critical differences by using an overly large scale.

Your graphs should reflect the reality of the data being plotted. Therefore, your choice of scale is critically important.

5. Use tick marks to aid data interpretation.

Tick marks are short lines on and perpendicular to an axis that indicate the numerical interval along the axis. Tick marks reflect the axis scale.

Generally, you should have twice as many tick marks as scale labels (the numbers indicating the scale interval). However, tick marks may be more numerous (four per scale label is acceptable; eight per label is less so). Avoid using more tick marks than necessary.

The scales and tick marks must be sufficiently detailed to allow readers to extract data values by determining where any data point on the plotted line falls on each axis. Most readers interpret data by placing a straight edge on the plotted line parallel to one axis and then reading the scale labels and tick marks along the perpendicular axis to determine the *x* or *y* value of points on the line.

The tick marks corresponding to scale labels must be twice as long as the tick marks that do not correspond to scale labels.

6. Make your key data lines heavier than axis and grid lines and less important data lines.

Axis and grid lines are less important than data lines and must therefore be thinner and lighter. The visual emphasis in the graph must be on the plotted (data) lines, not on the grid lines or axes. Equally, your important data lines must be more emphatic than less important data lines.

Note that in figures 2 and 3, the data line for the axial-mix configuration is much heavier

Graphs

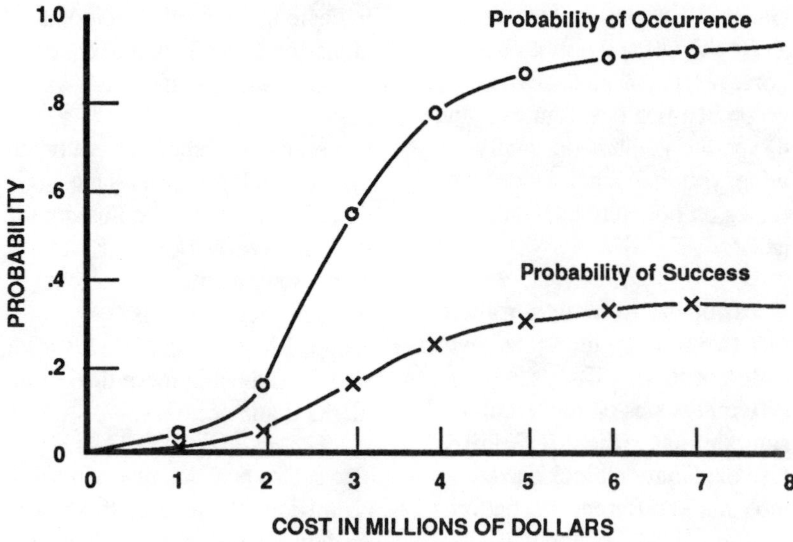

Cost (KS)	Probability Occurrence	Cumulative Probability	Probability Success	Cumulative Probability
0	0.000	0.000	0.000	0.000
724	0.004	0.004	0.001	0.001
1,445	0.022	0.026	0.014	0.015
2,172	0.094	0.120	0.045	0.060
2,896	0.202	0.322	0.086	0.146
3,620	0.243	0.565	0.097	0.243
4,344	0.200	0.765	0.076	0.319
5,068	0.128	0.893	0.046	0.365
5,792	0.066	0.959	0.019	0.384
6,516	0.027	0.986	0.007	0.391
7,239	0.010	0.996	0.002	0.393
7,963	0.003	0.999	0.000	0.393
8,687	0.000	0.999	0.000	0.393

Figure 5. Cost Impact Distribution. *Increasing the cost beyond about $5 million fails to increase the probability of success.*

than any of the other lines on the graph. Because the axial-mix configuration is the focus of the graph, its line thickness is greater. Similarly, in figure 4, the line representing declining federal support of R&D is shown in boldface, and the line representing total R&D funds is of a standard width.

7. Use multiple lines, if necessary, to show the relationships between three or more variables, and use different line patterns to depict different variables.

Lines of different patterns are useful for plotting more than two variables. Line patterns include solid, thin solid, wide solid, thin dashes, wide dashes, small dots, large dots, hollow (two thin lines together), and mixed dots and dashes of varying sizes. If you use different line patterns, include an explanation to the right of or below the graph that identifies the lines. The explanation must include an example of each line (see figures 2, 3, and 4).

Whether or not you use an explanation block, always clearly identify each line (as well as each axis and scale). See figures 1 through 4.

8. Do not smooth out data lines.

Make graphs as realistic as possible, even if the data lines are "jerky" and erratic. The small but unsightly dips that make lines look ragged also make them look real. Data lines that are too smooth and polished look unreal.

9. Label important values on a data line.

If you wish to highlight or discuss certain important values on data lines, label them within the grid system. Readers will pay more attention to labeled data values and will not be forced to interpret data values (see figure 1).

To help readers interpret the data, use markers on the plotted line to indicate plotted points (see figure 5). The types of markers include circles, dots, x's, dashes, and asterisks. You can also help readers interpret data by combining the graph with a table, as in figure 5.

10. If labels or numbers appear within the grid, blank out the grid area beneath the labels or numbers.

Grid lines can "mask" letters and numbers. So if your labels or numbers appear within the grid, blank out the grid lines beneath the labels or numbers by creating a white rectangular area (see figure 1). Make these blank areas no larger than necessary and try to minimize your use of them within the same graph. Too many blank areas make the graph look choppy and erratic.

11. Orient all labels, numbers, and letters so that they are parallel with the horizontal axis.

Placing all lettering horizontally on the page makes graphs easier to read. The labels in figures 1 through 4 are preferable to the vertical ordinate label in figure 5. However, some federal agencies require that the labeling of the ordinate axis be vertical.

Overly long vertical labels are an exception to this rule. If your ordinate axis label is too long to write horizontally, then write it vertically with the base of the letters parallel and adjacent to the ordinate axis. Readers should be able to read long vertical labels by turning the page clockwise. See CHARTS.

12. Place source and explanatory information below the graph and flush left.

If you have taken the information for the graph from another source, indicate that you have by providing a source line.

Source and explanatory information belongs below the grid area. If necessary, use superscripted numbers, letters, or symbols (such as *) to key data points, labels, or numbers to a footnote. Repeat the number or symbol in the footnote area (below and left of the graph) before providing sources or explanation. See CHARTS, TABLES, and BIBLIOGRAPHIC FORM.

13. Choose or design graphs that accurately and concisely convey your message.

Sometimes you can present the same data with different graphs (compare figure 6 and figure 7). General trends in certain types of data can sometimes be more clearly seen by plotting data on semilog coordinate paper (see figure 7). Such paper is produced with uniformly divided vertical lines and logarithmically divided horizontal lines.

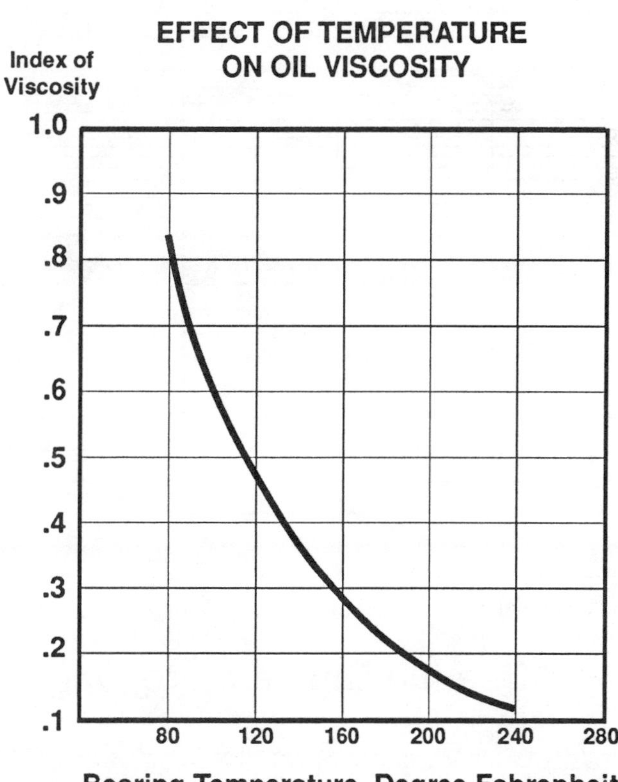

Figure 6. Effect of Temperature on Oil Viscosity. *Oil viscosity decreased in almost linear fashion as bearing temperature increased.*

Graphs

When a rectangular coordinate graph (see figure 6) gives a false impression of a curve's trend, a semilog chart can reveal whether the rate of change is increasing, decreasing, or constant. In addition, a semilog chart can aid in deriving empirical equations. Semilog graphs are not adapted to showing extreme or irregular trends in data or for showing change in absolute amounts.

Semilog charts never have a zero value on the logarithmic scale because as a positive variable approaches zero, its logarithm becomes negatively infinite.

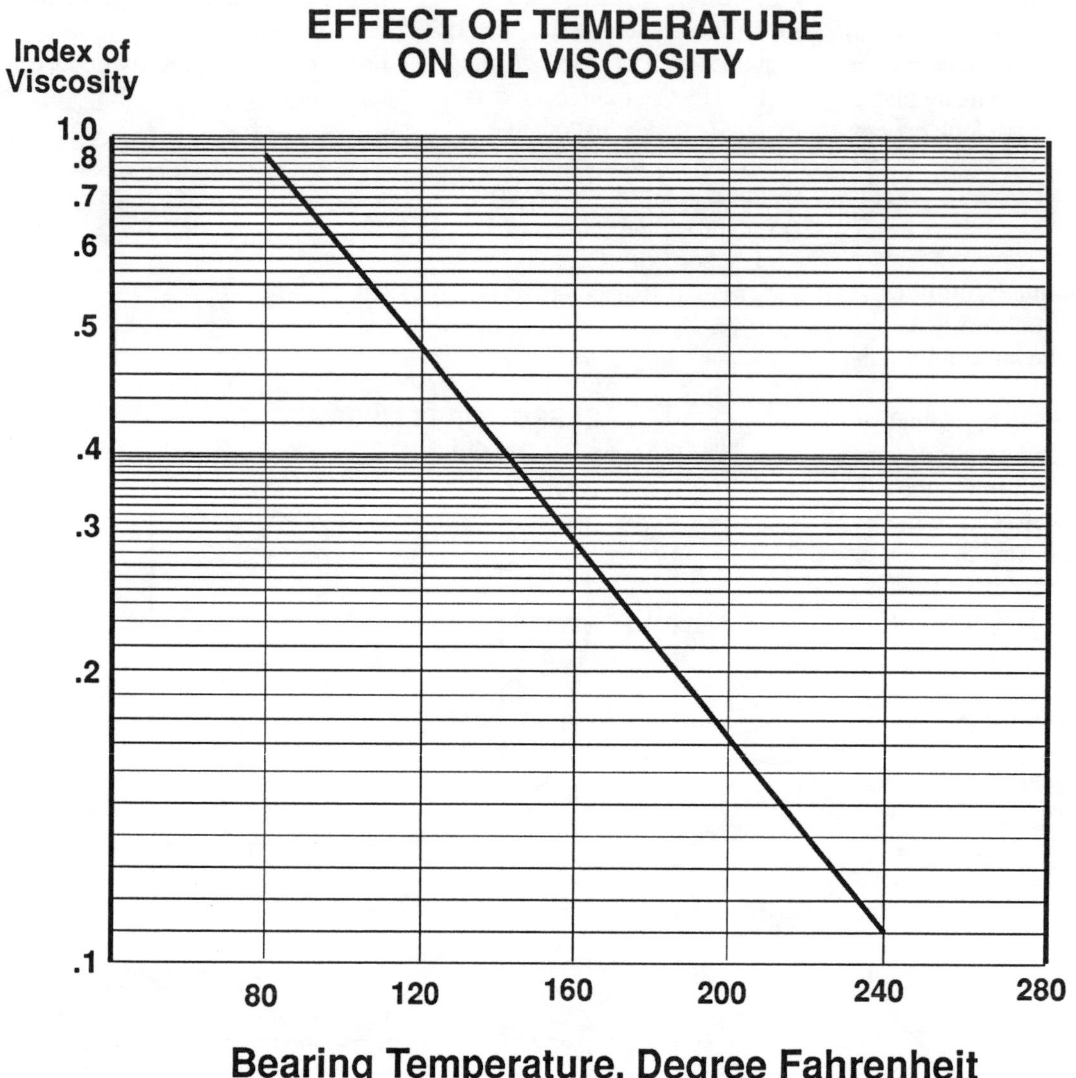

Figure 7. Effect of Temperature on Oil Viscosity. *The straight line shows that the rate of viscosity change is constant.*

Headings

Headings label the text under them and show logical divisions in the text.

Headings allow readers to skim.

Headings are like titles. They signal what is to come. They orient readers and thus make reading easier.

Headings reveal a document's organization, so readers can glance at the headings to determine where they need to read more closely and where they can skim. Headings are therefore especially useful for non-specialist readers who need to gain an overall sense of the text, but who do not have the time, interest, or knowledge to read the entire text.

---

1. Use headings whenever the text is longer than one single-spaced page or whenever the text conveys two or more major ideas.

Headings are among the most useful devices in writing. You should use them often enough (without overdoing them) to make the text as easy to read as possible.

---

2. Choose different levels of headings to indicate logical divisions and groupings in the text.

A chapter title, for instance, may be a major (or first-level) heading. Section titles in the chapter may be minor (or second-level) headings. Subsection titles could then be subheadings (third-level headings), and so on.

The level of the heading indicates its logical relation to other headings as well as to the whole. The levels are most apparent in an outline:

3.4 Component Descriptions

3.4.1 Gearbox Assembly
3.4.2 Brakes
3.4.3 Hydraulic Motors
3.4.4 AIU Interfaces

3.4.4.1 Controller
3.4.4.2 Encoder
3.4.4.3 Tachometer

3.4.5 Servo Valves

In both text and outlines (such as a table of contents), the levels may be indicated by a numbering system (like the one above) or by the placement, size, or appearance of the heading.

See OUTLINES and TABLES OF CONTENTS.

---

3. To show the level of the heading, use the three types of typographical variation: the <u>placement</u> of the heading on the page, the <u>size</u> of the type, and the <u>appearance</u> of the type.

Placement variations include centering, placing the heading flush left, indenting, and using a run-in heading (placing the heading on the same line as the text following it):

A CENTERED HEADING

A FLUSH-LEFT HEADING

An Indented Heading

A Run-in Heading. The text begins following the period (or dash) and two spaces.

Sometimes, a run-in heading has only three spaces between it and the succeeding text:

A Run-in Heading   When you do not use punctuation (as in this case), you should make the heading visually distinct from the text in the rest of the paragraph. You might use boldface type or a larger typeface.

Size variations are possible when you can vary the point size of the lettering in the heading. The larger the point size, the greater the level of the heading. A 24–point heading is on a higher level than a 12–point heading, etc.:

A 24-point He

An 18-point Headi

A 14-point Heading

A 12-point Heading

Appearance variations include ALL CAPITAL LETTERS, <u>underlining</u>, **boldface type,** different type faces, and *italics*. See EMPHASIS.

Heading Levels

Use the following placement and appearance lists to create different levels of headings. The variables are listed in decreasing order of importance:

<u>Placement</u>

1. Centered
2. Flush left
3. Indented
4. Run-in (on the same line as text)

Headings

As the preceding list shows, a centered heading is on a higher level than a flush-left heading. A flush-left heading, on the other hand, is on a higher level than an indented heading.

Appearance

1. ALL CAPITALS
2. Underlining
3. **Boldface**
4. *Italics*

The appearance variations may be added singly or in combination. Thus, a heading may be in all capital letters, or it may be underlined, or both. Appearance variations used in combination create higher level headings than headings with a single appearance feature. So an underlined, all-capital-letter heading is on a higher level than a heading featuring only all capital letters.

Appearance, size, and placement variations used together allow writers many heading types—and consequently many heading levels.

See WORD PROCESSING and DESKTOP PUBLISHING.

The Number of Levels

How many levels should you use? Dozens are possible, but readers could not comprehend that many levels of subordination. Practically speaking, you should use no more than four or five levels, depending on your readers. The less technical or less educated your readers, the fewer levels you should use. Experienced and well-educated scientific readers are more used to reading text with multiple levels of subordination. If you suspect that your readers will have trouble remembering the heading levels, use fewer levels.

Numbers with Headings

4. Use a numbering system with your headings if you have more than four levels of headings or if your document is lengthy and you or your readers will need to refer to sections of it by number.

Report writers normally construct their tables of contents by listing the headings and subheadings in their reports. If you use a numbering system with your headings, include the numbers in the table of contents.

See NUMBERING SYSTEMS, TABLES OF CONTENTS, and OUTLINES.

Effective Headings

5. Make your headings informative, specific, and inclusive.

Informative, specific headings allow readers to determine immediately the contents of a section. Unfortunately, many standard headings are neither specific nor informative: *Introduction, Discussion, Results,* and so on. Better versions of these would be as follows: *Purpose of the Drilling Proposal, Implications of Three Proposed Tests, Valid Data from the Third Test.*

Inclusive headings signal that only material mentioned in the heading will actually be covered in the section. If the heading is *Valid Data from the Third Test,* then no data from the second or first test should appear following the heading.

6. Make headings parallel in structure.

Parallel structure means that all headings at the same level have the same basic grammatical structure. So if one heading opens with an *–ing* word, the other headings will also:

this

Developing the Appropriate Tests
Sending Out for Bids
Selecting the Winner
Agreeing on Preliminary Contract Talks

not this

Developing Appropriate Tests
Sending Out for Bids
Selection of the Winner
Preliminary Contract Talks

See PARALLELISM.

Question Headings

Most headings are declarative. They state or announce a topic:

Facilities in the Local Impact Area
Summerhill Treatment Plant
Complex Traps in Gulf Coast Fields
The Geomorphology of Exploration

An alternative heading form is the question heading:

How Great Is the Avalanche Danger?
Will Surface Water Quality Be Degraded?
What Are the Alternatives?
Should Exxon Proceed with the Project?
Will the Public Accept Our Position?
How Likely Is a Major Bank Default?

As long as you don't overdo them, question headings offer interesting possibilities and can be very effective. Question headings not only announce the topic but also stimulate interest because they pose questions that curious readers will want to see answered.

Question headings are generally more engaging than declarative headings because they seem to speak directly to the reader. However, be careful not to pose obvious or condescending questions:

Doesn't Everyone Know about Anticlines?

7. Use the same type of heading at each heading level.

Be consistent. If you decide to use question headings, use them for all headings at that heading level. Mixing question and declarative headings at the same level is confusing. However, you can use question headings at a major level and then use declarative headings at subordinate levels, or vice versa.

Hyphens

Hyphenation is one of the trickier aspects of English. There are many rules of hyphenation—including some that apply only in limited circumstances—and all of the rules have exceptions. Below are the most common conventions of hyphen usage. For further discussions of hyphenation, refer to *The Chicago Manual of Style, The Gregg Reference Manual,* or the *United States Government Printing Office Style Manual.* See REFERENCES.

Hyphens Connect

Fundamentally, hyphens show a connection. Typically, the connection is between two words or between a prefix and a word. The connected words (known as compounds) can function as nouns, verbs, or adjectives:

Connected words as nouns

brother-in-law
ex-mayor
follow-up
foot-pound
know-how
run-through
self-consciousness
two-thirds

Connected words as verbs

to blue-pencil
to double-space
to spot-check
to tape-record

Connected words as adjectives

all-around person
black-and-white print
coarse-grained wood
decision-making authority
high-grade ore
high-pressure lines
interest-bearing notes
little-known program
long-range plans
low-lying plains
matter-of-fact approach
off-the-record comment
old-fashioned system
part-time employees
30-fold increase
three-fourths majority
twenty-odd inspections
up-to-date methods
well-known researcher

Unfortunately, not all connected (or compounded) nouns, verbs, and adjectives require hyphens. Here are a few of the exceptions:

Connected but unhyphenated nouns

ball of fire
breakdown
fellow employee
goodwill
problem solving
quasi contract
takeoff
trademark
trade name

Connected but unhyphenated verbs

to downgrade
to handpick
to highlight
to proofread
to waterproof

Connected but unhyphenated adjectives

barely known researcher
bright red building
crossbred plants
halfhearted attempts
highly complex task
10 percent increase
twofold increase
unselfconscious person
very well known researcher
worldwide problem

As the above examples illustrate, connected words have three possible forms. They can appear as two separate words *(highly motivated),* as one word formed by connecting the two original words with a hyphen *(high-pressure),* and as one word formed by joining the original two words *(highbrow).* See COMPOUND WORDS.

Convention and tradition often dictate which form the connected words will take. If you are not sure which form is correct, refer to a current dictionary. See REFERENCES.

Rules of Hyphenation

1. Hyphenate two or more words that act together to create a new meaning:

a counterflow plate-fin
the V-space between units
the Grumman F-14A airplane
one-half of the annular ring
to double-check the tests

Hyphens

This rule indicates a potential use of the hyphen, not a mandatory one. In some instances the two words become a single word, without a hyphen: *highlight, bumblebee, barrelhead.* In other instances, the two words remain separate: *base line, any one* (one item from a group), *amino acid.* The words sometimes remain separate because combining them would produce strange-looking forms: *aminoacid, beautyshop, breakfastroom.* Because the presence or absence of a hyphen is often a matter of convention, check a current dictionary if you are not sure how the compound word should be written.

See CAPITALS for the proper capitalization of hyphenated words in titles.

2. Hyphenate two or more words that act together to modify another word:

brazed-and-welded construction
cross-counterflow unit
engine-to-recuperator mountings
full-scale testing
no-flow heat exchanger
pressure-drop decrease
3-year, multimillion-dollar program
12-foot-wide embayment
up-to-scale modeling
U-tube arrangement
well-documented success

This rule applies only when the connected or compound modifier occurs **before** the word it modifies. See rule 4 below.

3. Hyphenate compound numbers from twenty-one to ninety-nine and compound adjectives with a numerical first part:

thirty-four
eighty-one
five-volume proposal
13-phase plan
24-inch tape
500-amp circuit

but

22 percent fee

See NUMBERS.

4. Do not hyphenate connected words that function as adjectives if they occur after the word they modify:

The boiler was brazed and welded.
The compartment is 32 feet wide.
The program is well documented.

but

The brazed-and-welded boiler
The 32-foot-wide compartment
The well-documented program

5. Do not hyphenate connected words that act as adjectives if the first word ends in *-ly:*

highly motivated engineer
poorly conceived design
vastly different approach
completely revised program

NOTE: The words ending in *-ly* are actually adverbs. The *-ly* form indicates the structure of the modifying phrase, so a hyphen is unnecessary.

6. Prefixes generally do not require hyphens:

counterblow
midpoint
nonperson
progovernment
supercar
undersea

NOTE 1: Hyphens do appear when the prefix precedes a capitalized word:

un-American
mid-August
non-Soviet

NOTE 2: Hyphens do connect some prefixes to words (especially those ending in a vowel such as *anti-, de-, co-, re-, pre-,* and *pro-): anti-inflationary, re-create.* If you are not sure whether a prefix requires a hyphen, refer to a current dictionary or to the 1984 edition of the *United States Government Printing Office Style Manual.*

See COMPOUND WORDS and REFERENCES.

7. Hyphenate words that must be divided at the end of a line.

Words are always divided between syllables, and hyphens should appear at the end of the line where the word division has occurred. Try not to end more than two consecutive lines with hyphens. Try not to divide at the end of the first line or at the end of the last full line in a paragaraph. Do not divide the last word on a page.

Hyphens

Hyphens and Technical Terminology

The use of hyphens in technical expressions varies considerably. Some writers try to adhere strictly to the rules outlined above. But many, because of tradition, convention, or local preference, violate the rules of hyphenation when they believe that the technical expression will be clear:

> We will need a high pressure hose.

In this sentence, *high* obviously modifies *pressure.* The sentence refers to a hose that is capable of withstanding high pressures. It is not a pressure hose that happens to be high (off the ground). Yet if we followed the rules of hyphenation strictly, the sentence should be:

> We will need a high-pressure hose.

Hyphens are often omitted in technical expressions because the expressions without the hyphens are clear to technical readers. The context clarifies the expression. In many cases, however, missing hyphens can cause confusion or a complete lack of comprehension, as in this sentence from an aircraft maintenance manual:

> Before removing the retaining pin, refer to the wing gear truck positioning actuator assembly schematic.

Nontechnical (or technical but unknowledgeable) readers can only guess which words are associated with which other words. Does *truck* link with *wing gear,* or does *truck* modify *positioning?* Hyphens would help clarify the modifier relationships:

> wing-gear truck-positioning actuator assembly

If convention or tradition allows you to eliminate hyphens where they would normally appear in compound words, do so unless eliminating them will mystify some readers. If you are going to err, err on the side of caution. Proper use of hyphens will not baffle knowledgeable technical readers, and it will help those readers who are not familiar with a technical expression.

See ADJECTIVES.

Illustrations

Illustrations, diagrams, and drawings include a wide range of visuals whose purpose is to depict parts, functions, relationships, activities, and processes that would be difficult or impossible to describe in text.

Producing good illustrations almost always requires a professional graphic artist. The following discussion does not address the art or mechanics of creating effective illustrations, diagrams, and drawings. Instead, it focuses on how writers should conceive of and use illustrations and what writers can do to assist graphic artists.

The visual possibilities of illustrations are enormous. The examples shown in this section represent a very small part of what is possible. In designing illustrations, diagrams, and drawings, use your imagination and seek advice early in the writing process from a graphic artist. Consider the alternatives before settling on final designs.

For further information on illustrations and visual aids, see Visual Aids. See also Charts, Graphs, Maps, Photographs, and Tables.

For information on captions, see Captions.

1. Use illustrations, diagrams, and drawings to visualize a system, process, or piece of equipment that would be difficult to describe in text.

Illustrations are very effective at showing views of objects or systems that do not exist (a drawing of a proposed tool), that are abstractions (organizational or functional systems), or that would be impossible to show otherwise (exploded views or cutaways).

Illustrations allow readers to see inside something that is sealed; to see opposite and hidden sides of an object simultaneously; and to see, in close-up, the details of a small assembly that would otherwise not be visible while looking at the larger object that contains the small assembly (see figure 1).

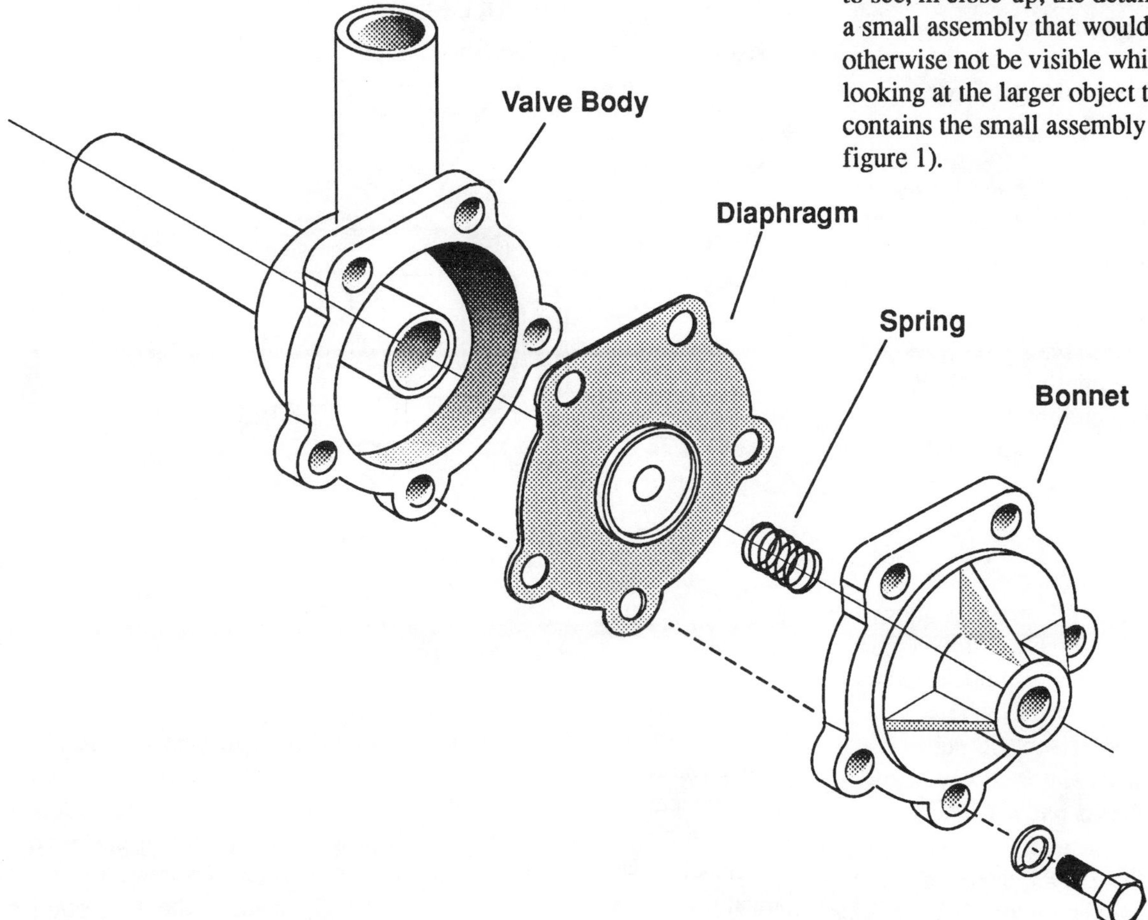

Figure 1. Spring-Actuated Diaphragm. *Remove the bonnet slowly to prevent losing small parts that are under spring compression.*

Illustrations

Exploded views allow you to exaggerate (magnify) certain parts of an object to show the details of the exaggerated part while keeping the rest of the object in its correct perspective (see figure 2). Typically, exploded views accomplish two objectives simultaneously: They show how and where the magnified part fits in with the larger object, and they show how the magnified part is constructed.

Cutaways are like an orange sliced in half: They show the internal structure (assembly) of an object that is normally sealed (see figure 3).

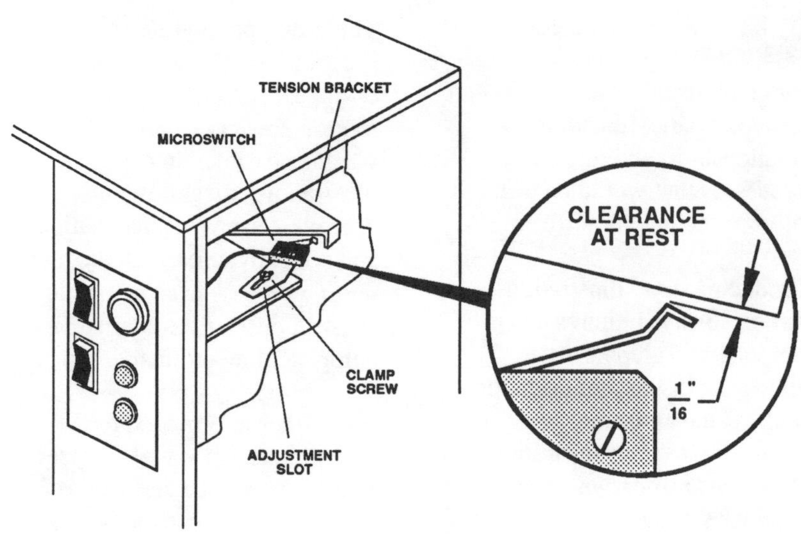

Figure 2. Switch Adjustment. *The 1/16-inch switch adjustment can be made in less than 60 seconds with only the use of a simple screwdriver and a feeler gauge.*

2. Keep illustrations simple, and give each one a perspective that enables readers to understand it.

Illustrations and drawings should be focused. That is, they should present a single concept. Therefore, they should be clean and uncluttered. Everything not pertaining to the single concept should be eliminated. No detail should be present that does not contribute to the presentation of that single concept.

As well as being simple, a good illustration has a clear perspective. Illustrations allow you to distort reality, so you must ensure that readers understand the perspective from which the illustration presents its subject. Illustrations almost always show their subjects out of context. Therefore, you might need to establish what the reader is viewing and how that thing relates to other things in its real environment.

FULL-FLOATING AXLE

1 HUB
2 SPINDLE
3 GREASE SEAL
4 INNER BEARING
5 RETAINING RING
6 OUTER BEARING
7 LOCK NUTS

Figure 3. Full-Floating Axle. *Radial and axial thrust loads are carried by the spindle, leaving the driving axle free of all but torque loads.*

Size scales might be necessary if the size and relationship of the object depicted to other things in its environment are not clear. You can also use labels to indicate size, direction, orientation, and nomenclature (see figures 1 through 6). If you do not indicate size and distance relationships, readers might not be able to determine the correct proportions of the object shown or its correct orientation in the world outside of the illustration or drawing.

3. Label each illustration clearly and, if necessary, label the parts of the object shown.

Figure 1 shows a typical nomenclature illustration. The valve body is shown as one unit because it is not the focus of the illustration. The bonnet, spring, and diaphragm are the reason this illustration exists, so each is labeled separately. Center lines drawn through the axis of each part show how the parts fit together.

Labeling of the significant parts of a drawing is crucial for reader comprehension. You may use word labels, lines, and arrows, (figures 1, 2, and 4), or you may use numbers, letters, or symbols in the drawing itself (figure 3) with an explanation block.

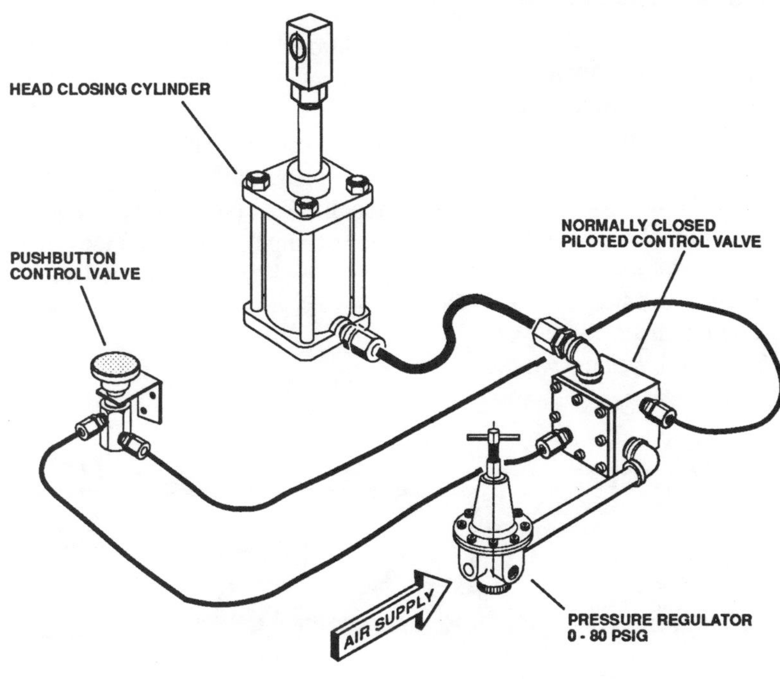

Figure 4. Pneumatic Operating and Control System. *By eliminating electrical controls, potential spark hazards are avoided, allowing operation in hazardous environments.*

4. Ensure that all letters, numbers, and labels are horizontally oriented on the drawing or illustration.

The language appearing on any part of a drawing or illustration should never be vertically oriented unless the bases of the individual letters or numbers are horizontal, as in this example:

E
X
A
M
P
L
E

The lettering and numbering on an illustration should be oriented so that readers can read it without reorienting the illustration. If you run out of space, use arrows and move the labels away from the busy area of the illustration. If necessary, omit the labels and use letters, numbers, or symbols and an explanation block (see rule 3 above).

5. In a series of illustrations, make the viewing angle consistent.

If you are showing the same object in a series of illustrations, and the point of the series is to show assembly/disassembly steps or operational phases, ensure that readers see the object from the same perspective in each illustration. Changing the perspective is very confusing.

6. If necessary for clarity, remove surrounding detail from illustrations.

Figure 4 shows a schematic drawing or illustration in which surrounding but irrelevant detail has been removed. You often see this sort of illustration in subsystem pictorials. Removing the surrounding detail allows readers to focus on the system being shown. The drawing isolates its subject and therefore provides an excellent focus.

7. Use line patterns in an illustration to show how different subsystems interact within a system.

If you are showing how different subsystems fit together and function, you might need to use different line patterns, as in figure 5. The line patterns allow readers to isolate subsystems while viewing the whole system. For additional examples of line patterns, see GRAPHS.

If you use line patterns, provide an explanation explaining what the different patterns represent. For example, in figure 5 the diesel fuel line and the coolant lines use different line patterns.

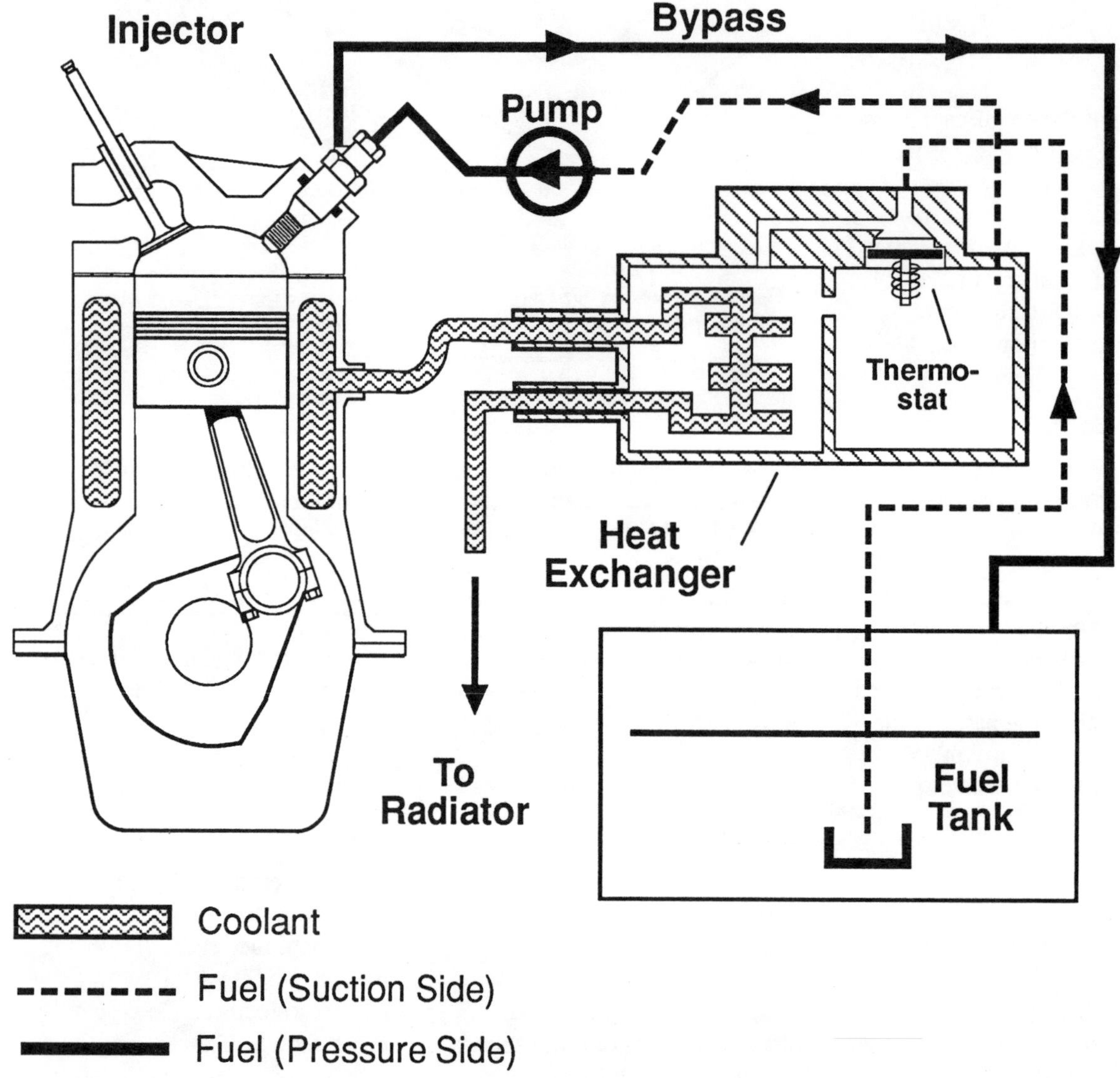

Figure 5. Diesel-Fuel Preheating System. *The burning of the fuel is approximately 10 percent more effective with the fuel preheating system.*

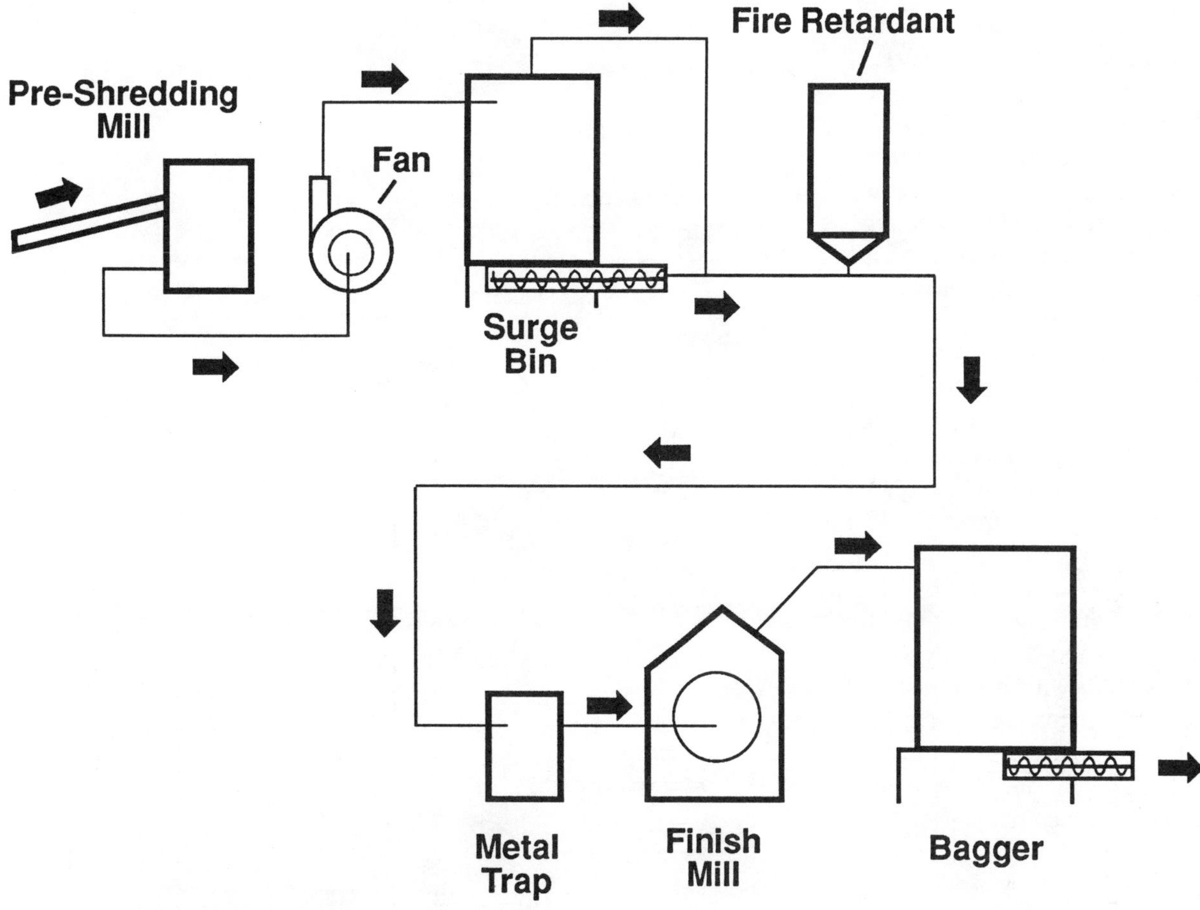

Figure 6. Two-Mill System with Surge Bin. *The two-mill system produces a more uniform product, and the surge bin allows continuous bagging during interruptions in raw material input.*

8. If your drawing shows a process, structure the process from top to bottom and left to right.

Figure 6 is a schematic flow sheet. It shows a process and the equipment used in that process. This type of drawing should be oriented from top to bottom and left to right so that readers "read" it as they would read text. In all process drawings, readers will expect the process to start at the left and end at the right. Don't disappoint them. See CHARTS.

9. Use color in your illustrations.

Use color in your illustrations if economically and technically possible. Color helps you explain your data and sell your ideas. The power of color as a writing tool is often underexploited. Years ago when asked for cars of a color other than black, Henry Ford said, "Give them any color they want so long as it's black." Today Ford automobiles and documents come in multitudes of colors. However, most of us think of our documents only in black and white. Use color if you can.

See EMPHASIS.

10. Use special purpose illustrations when necessary.

Work closely with graphics personnel when you need special illustrations. For example, you might need a realistic rendering of a proposed product for use in promotional literature or in a proposal.

Figure 7 is an example of a realistic illustration produced on a computer. The initial step was to do the line drawing; although the line drawing in figure 7 was done on a computer, it could have been done using traditional projection and hand drawing. Next, realistic details are added, either with computer or with an airbrush. Computer hardware and the software programs to add such realistic details are available but are not yet in common use.

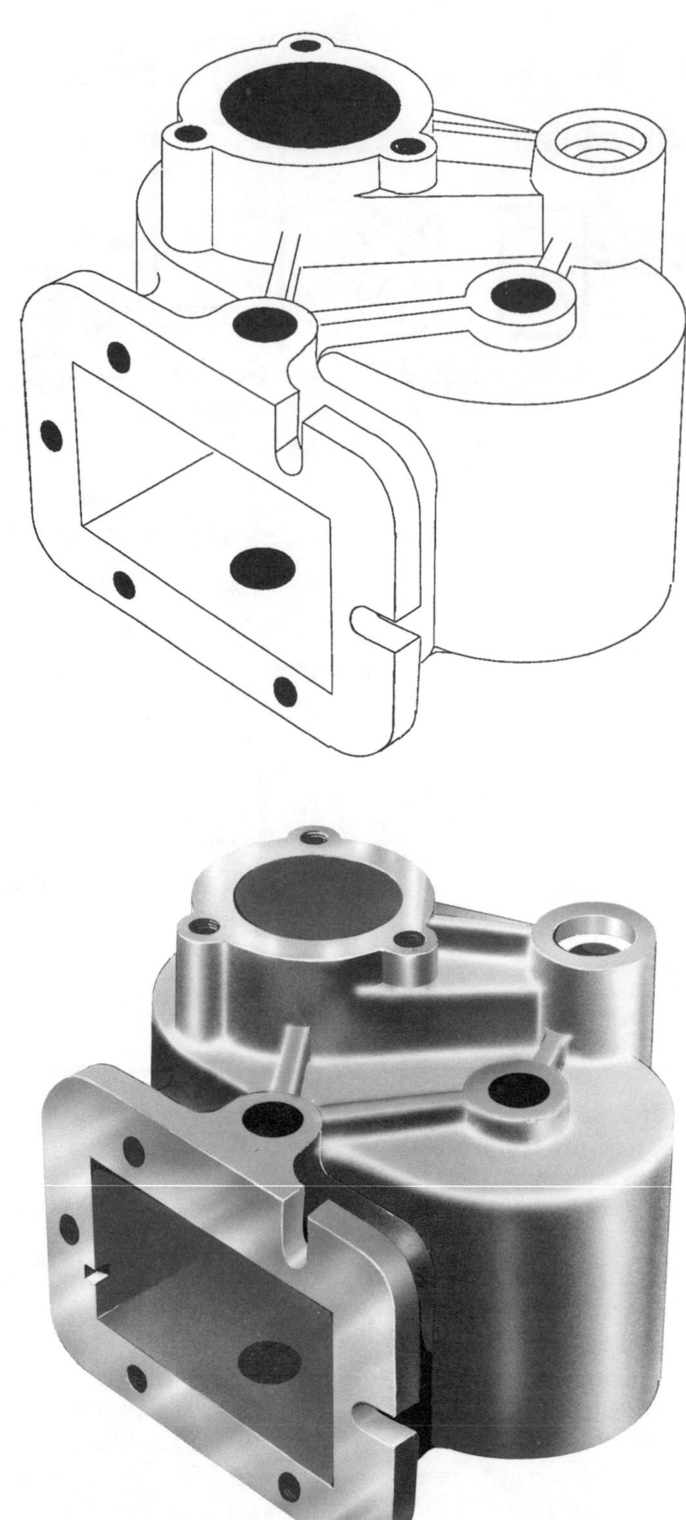

Figure 7. Power Take-Off Housing. *Made of ductile iron using standard sand casting and cores, this housing is completely machined on a single N.C. Mill.*

Indexes

Indexes (or indices) are alphabetical lists of the subjects within a document. For each subject, the index gives a page number (or sometimes a section number) so that readers can easily find where a specific subject is discussed.

Published documents usually have indexes unless the document is so short that an index is unnecessary—as, for example, in a brochure or in a marketing summary.

The longer a document, whether published or not, the more helpful an index becomes.

The following rules present the basics of indexing, but the subject is complex enough that if you want to prepare a detailed index, consult chapter 18 in *The Chicago Manual of Style,* 13th edition. See REFERENCES.

---

1. Provide an index for any document longer than 50 pages and for any document that will have many and frequent readers.

The 50-page threshold is a judgmental suggestion. Whether you decide to provide an index also depends on how many readers will be using your document. For example, if you are preparing an internal policy manual that will have only 30 or 40 pages, even a manual this short can be confusing when many employees want to look up specific answers to their questions. In such a manual, both a good table of contents and a simple index would be helpful. See TABLES OF CONTENTS.

For documents with few readers, no index is necessary even if the document exceeds 50 pages. For example, an internal report or a legal brief that is going to have maybe only three or four one-time readers before going into the files certainly doesn't require an index.

---

2. Adjust the scope of your index to the needs of your readers.

Indexes can be fairly simple or very detailed, and they can cover special areas of interest.

A simple index primarily includes key words from the document. Such words are usually those that appear in the title, chapter headings, and subheadings. Such an index might list only two or three topics from each page of a document.

A detailed, professional index can be quite exhaustive, often listing 10, 15, or more topics from each page in a text. Because such indexes are very time consuming and expensive, they are unnecessary for most unpublished documents. Even published documents sometimes might not need such a detailed index.

See the index for this *Style Guide* for an example of a detailed index.

Detailed indexes can also be prepared for special areas of interest. For example, a separate index might list all the people's names in a historical discussion. Separate indexes sometimes exist for geographical names or for works of art (as in a list of musical titles). Such special indexes usually supplement, not replace, the traditional subject index.

---

3. Begin to prepare an index by identifying key words and concepts that readers would likely be interested in locating, given the purpose of the document.

Indexing is not a mechanical task. Anyone preparing an index has to have a good grasp of the content and of the purpose of the document. For this reason, the author of a document is often the best person to prepare the index. The author knows what themes, questions, and relationships are likely to occur to readers. The author can then begin to choose the topics that would help readers to use the document.

Not every fact nor every reference automatically appears in an index. For example, if a text mentions the *Mississippi River,* should the index list this reference under *River* or under *Mississippi?* Should the index even list either reference at all?

Answers depend on the purpose of the document. A document discussing all sorts of geographical features might have major index entries on national parks, lakes, rivers, bayous, etc. If the Mississippi itself was merely mentioned in passing as one of a list of well-known U.S. rivers, then it might not appear in the index, and it would surely not be a major (separate) entry in the index.

Indexes

A document discussing major U.S. rivers, their length, their flow, their flood stages, their pollution, etc., would likely list the Mississippi, the Ohio, and every other river discussed in the document. These individual names would be major entries in the index. Then under each river would appear subheadings:

> Mississippi River, 8, 12, 15-18; flood control for, 28; pollution on and near, 65, 68-70; source of, 14; tourism on, 48-49

4. Use either a computer program or traditional hand-sorted cards to prepare the actual index.

Most word processing programs have an indexing feature. With this feature, writers can identify key words and phrases either while they are writing the draft or after they have finished the draft. Usually, they code these words and phrases with a computer code that will not appear in the printed copy. The word processing program can, however, identify the code and will alphabetize the identified words and phrases into major entries and will attach the proper page numbers to them.

Such mechanical indexes can be helpful, but they do not replace the many judgments necessary when a full, detailed index is needed. Only a human indexer (or the author of the document) can make such judgments.

A CAUTION: A word processing index might not contain the correct page numbers if the final copy is to be inserted into a desktop publishing system. See DESKTOP PUBLISHING.

The traditional indexing system uses individual cards (preferably with typed citations) as the basis for the index. The indexer goes through the entire text (in its final desktop or typeset form) preparing separate cards for each potential entry and for subheadings within entries. Next, the cards are alphabetized and subheadings properly arranged. Finally, the total index is input.

5. In a detailed index, use subheadings and cross-references.

Subheadings and cross-references are essential aids when readers don't know how to find key information. All detailed indexes should include both subheadings and cross-references. Even short indexes should include common cross-references as a convenience for readers.

Subheadings are important because they reveal how various topics relate to each other. In most cases, subheadings have a grammatical or syntactic relation to the main heading and are presented alphabetically:

> Automobiles, 18-20; design of, 43, 48-49; maintenance costs of, 123, 126; maintenance guidelines for, 115-118; optional equipment for, 84-85; resale values of, for retailers, 79; resale values of, for wholesalers, 78

In other instances, the subheadings are merely a list of items:

> Fortune 500 companies: Amoco, 45; Exxon, 53; Ford, 17-19; General Dynamics, 115-119; General Motors, 10-11; Texaco, 58, 62-64

As in the preceding examples, the main heading is usually flush with the margin while the succeeding lines are indented. Traditionally, commas separate headings or subheadings from page numbers, and semicolons separate the different subheadings. Subheadings are alphabetized. No final punctuation follows the entry, including all its subheadings.

Inclusion of *See* and *Also see* references is important when readers are likely to look up a variety of topics.

See references are useful when the indexer has had to choose between several different main headings:

> Businesses. *See* Fortune 500 companies
>
> Corporations. *See* Fortune 500 companies

Also see references are usually restricted to added information:

> Texaco, 58, 62-64. *Also see* Fortune 500 companies

6. Don't forget basic proofreading and cross-checking.

Nothing destroys reader faith and your credibility more than errors in the index. Users rightly expect to find what you tell them is on a specific page.

Plan, therefore, to build in time for a careful proofreading and even cross-checking of items. If possible, go through the entire index verifying that the cited information is indeed on the pages noted. For published indexes, the publisher is usually responsible for this final cross-check of an index for accuracy.

Introductions

Introductions introduce—as the name suggests. An introduction conducts the reader into a document, usually by establishing the reason for the document's existence; its relation to other documents or projects; and any special circumstances, facts, conditions, or decisions that help the reader understand the body of the document.

The body of the document is more project or product oriented—it focuses on the situation or thing being described or analyzed. The introduction (as well as the conclusion) is more reader oriented—it orients the reader by providing a context for the reading. In short, the introduction prepares the reader for what will follow.

When to Write an Introduction

Although introductions usually come first in a document, you should write them last. The introduction is often the hardest part of the document to write because it sets up information that appears throughout the rest of the document. So skip the introduction until you have written most, if not all, of the body of the document.

The Different Types of Introductions

Introductions differ, depending on the type of document in which they appear.

Introductions to formal reports are often fairly long, especially if they summarize technical or scientific literature. These introductions often provide lengthy background or historical information that allows uninformed readers to develop a perspective on the text that follows. These introductions also sometimes define special terms or establish the assumptions on which the succeeding analysis was based.

Introductions to informal reports and to letters and short memos often are quite short. These introductions are usually not called introductions, nor are they separated from the rest of the text by headings. These introductions usually set up the major points that follow, and they can refer to previous documents, meetings, or conversations.

Finally, introductions can function as executive summaries in both technical and nontechnical reports. See SUMMARIES.

Introductions to Formal Reports

Formal reports are likely to have the most developed and structured introductions. No two introductions are alike, but most include some of the following information:

—The **problem** or **opportunity** prompting the project or investigation

—The **goals** or **purposes** of the project or investigation

—The likely **audience** for the project or investigation

—The **scope** of the project or investigation

—The **sources** of relevant information

—The **methods** used in the project or investigation

—This project's or investigation's **relation** to previous or concurrent projects or investigations

—Any useful working **definitions**

The **problem or opportunity** that the document addresses arises from the historical background. What work was done that stimulated this project? What other work has been done in this or related fields? Often, this section will survey relevant literature. See CITATIONS.

If this project is part of a larger or related project, state the relationship briefly. Brevity is important because readers rarely want or need to learn the point-by-point history of a project or related projects.

The **purpose** of the project explains why the project was undertaken and what it is expected to achieve. The key objectives might read as follows:

> 1. To evaluate the ground-water resources of the alluvial aquifer of the Carmel Valley, California, ground-water basin
>
> 2. To develop a two-dimensional, digital, ground-water flow model of the aquifer that will aid in the understanding of the geohydrology of the aquifer
>
> 3. To identify data inadequacies that might be needed for future studies of this aquifer

Introductions

NOTE: Several objectives can combine to form the overall purpose of the project.

The **scope** refers to the limits of the project and the document itself. Provide the scope by stating what the document will cover and what it will not cover.

The **methods** explain how a project was conducted: how the investigator developed the experimental design, constructed or designed the apparatus, collected the data, analyzed the results, and developed the conclusions. If the methods were routine, provide no more than a brief summary. If the methods were unusual or original, explain them thoroughly in the introduction or consider discussing methods in a separate section or subsection of the document. See REPORTS.

Introductions to Informal Reports

Introductions to informal reports often function as executive summaries, which include conclusions and recommendations along with the necessary background information.

Readers of informal reports are often busy managers or supervisors. They are usually aware of the general details of an investigation or project but trust subordinates to evaluate the problem properly and to solve it efficiently. Such readers will become impatient with lengthy digressions and unnecessary explanation, support, and justification. Consequently, they typically want a succinct executive summary. Only if questions arise will they go beyond the summary and read the background information and analysis.

The key feature of a combined introduction and executive summary is a statement of major conclusions and recommendations. A full list of conclusions and recommendations often appears later in the report, but you should never force managers or supervisors to search for them.

See REPORTS and SUMMARIES.

Introductions to Letters and Memorandums

Introductions to letters and memos establish the writer's tone and approach as well as set the stage for the ideas and supporting details that follow. See LETTERS and MEMOS.

Establishing a Tone

Letters and memorandums are intended to be more personal and less formal than reports. To convey this more human dimension, some writers choose to use personal pronouns: *I*, *you*, and *we*. Others open with personal remarks or social greetings, much as we often do in personal conversations. Even writers whose purpose is avowedly serious might "break the ice" by calling the reader by name:

> Please let us know, Jim, if our proposal for the replacement pumps begins to answer your needs.

See TONE.

Setting the Stage

Setting the stage might mean no more than a brief phrase: *As we discussed yesterday* . . . or *According to our records* . . .

In other instances, writers might decide to provide the background for the document before stating the point. This background or set-up is quite common in letters conveying bad news, such as enforcement of a financial penalty or a personnel reprimand.

However, be cautious about spending too much time setting the stage. Almost always, the best strategy is to get to the point quickly.

See ORGANIZATION.

Italics

Italics (slanted typeface) is available only in printed material or on word processing systems capable of printing italics. In handwritten or typed material, underlining replaces italics. See UNDERLINING.

Because italics is unavailable to many writers, some conventions concern only printers. For example, in printed mathematical expressions, letters are italicized and numerals are set in normal type. This distinction is not normally made in handwritten or typed material. The following standard rules apply in most technical and business documents.

---

1. Use italics for words used as words:

> In all offshore contracts, *consolidation* does not mean what it normally means.
>
> The Anaguae reservoir study was confusing because the author kept referring to the anomolous formations as *anonymous* formations.

NOTE 1: Use italics to emphasize words, phrases, and even letters when discussing them as examples of language. This use of italics (or underlining) sets the words or phrases apart from the other words in the sentence:

> Traditionally, the symbol *M* has been used to mean million. In some disciplines, *M* means thousand, so one indicates million with the symbol *MM*.
>
> One should avoid opening letters with the phrase *In reference to*. Similarly, according to our corporate guidelines, one should never end a letter by saying *Very truly yours*. Both phrases are too wordy.

NOTE 2: Quotation marks sometimes replace italics (underlining) as a way of highlighting words and phrases, especially in handwritten texts, where even underlining is less easy for a reader to see:

> After some discussion, we decided to order "A Dictionary of Mining, Minerals, and Related Terms" and the "Society of Petroleum Engineers Publication Style Guide." The two volumes should help us prepare articles for the "Journal of Petroleum Technology" and "Petroleum Transactions."

---

2. Use italics for foreign words and phrases that have not yet been absorbed into English:

> The initial concept of the United Nations captured a certain *Weltanschauung*.
>
> The *couturier* insisted on keeping the new dress designs secret.
>
> The staple crop in South Africa is *kaffir*, which is a form of sorghum raised for cattle fodder.

NOTE: Some foreign words and phrases have become so common in English that they are not italicized:

> ad hoc
> habeas corpus
> per annum,
> rendezvous
> vice versa

Some recent dictionaries indicate if words are still considered foreign, but others do not. If your dictionary does not, use your judgment to determine if a word is sufficiently foreign to be italicized. Foreign words usually retain their foreign spellings, pronunciations, and meanings.

---

3. Use italics for titles of books, magazines, newspapers, movies, plays, and other works individually produced or published:

> To remain current on advances in space technology, we subscribed to *Aviation Week*.
>
> The documentary *Before Their Time* showed what is possible when companies wisely invest IR&D funds.

See TITLES.

NOTE 1: Sections of these published works are not italicized. So chapters, magazine articles, acts within a play, and editorials in a newspaper require quotation marks, not italics:

> Last week's *Time* had an article entitled "The Roots of International Terrorism."
>
> The final chapter of the annual report is entitled "Prospects for Growth in the 1990s."

See QUOTATION MARKS.

Italics

NOTE 2: In some typed documents, especially in the publishing business, the titles of books, magazines, and newspapers are in all capital letters and are not underlined:

DELTAIC OSCILLATION
FORBES
GEOTIMES
THE WALL STREET JOURNAL

4. Use italics for the names of aircraft, vessels, and spacecraft:

Discovery
Friendship 6
H.M.S. *Intrepid*
NS *Savannah*
U.S.S. *Iowa*
U.S.S. *Nautilus*

NOTE: In these examples only the names are italicized, not the abbreviations or numerals associated with the names.

5. Use italics for names of genera, subgenera, species, and subspecies. Names of higher groups (phyla, classes, orders, families, tribes) are not italicized:

the genera *Quercus* and *Liriodendron*

the family Leguminosae

See the *Council of Biology Editors Style Manual* for additional information and examples. See REFERENCES.

Jargon

Jargon has two meanings. First, it means using familiar words in unfamiliar ways (using *hot* to mean *crucial* or *exciting*) or using excessive "shorthand" to describe something that would normally require more words (a police officer saying, "That guy was really a ninety-nine," which is police jargon for code 99, the radio code indicating an unbalanced person).

Second, *jargon* means technical or specialized language unfamiliar to a particular reader or listener. Thus, one person's technical or specialized vocabulary becomes another person's jargon. The following discussion focuses on this second, more common meaning of the word *jargon.*

Every technical discipline needs and has its own vocabulary.

Medical doctors have innumerable special terms, often derived from Latin: *amebic dysentery, uvula, gastric hernia.*

Lawyers also use a number of common terms that have developed special meanings: *property, liability, consideration, conveyance. Consideration,* for instance, means a payment of some kind as a sign of agreement on a contract. This special legal meaning is not obvious to the uninitiated, who might not even know the word has a special meaning. In some contexts, readers might not know whether the ordinary meaning or the technical legal meaning is intended.

The cooks and waitresses in restaurants might develop special slang terms and abbreviations, so when a patron picks up a check, the items written on it are not immediately clear. This is a form of jargon, one very local and limited, yet still very useful.

Carpenters and architects also have their own language: *joist, rafter, gambrel roof, header, sole plate, cross bridging.* These jargon words have special meanings and are useful terms, but someone not familiar with carpentry is not likely to understand them.

See Style, Scientific/Technical Style, and Tone.

---

1. Do not use jargon unless your readers will understand it. If they will not understand—and you must use a term—then define it.

The doctor who gives a diagnosis only in medical terminology has failed to communicate with most patients. Similarly, the engineer who speaks only through coordinate graphs and equations will baffle, and perhaps alienate, the general reader who wants an overall sense of the proposed engineering project.

Here are two technical examples, both of which may use jargon unfamiliar to nontechnical readers:

> Wastewater treatment that employs fixed-film biological BOD removals has been shown to be more efficient than was predicted in our pilot studies. This result may be due to product mix, concentration, primary treatment, media type, wall effects, etc.

> Dry rubble stones shall consist of trap rock; granite; gneiss; or other approved hard, durable, tough rock. They should be sound, free from weathered or decomposed pieces, shattered ends, and structural defects, and shall be approved by the Contracting Officer.

In both of these examples, a general or nontechnical reader would encounter unfamiliar terms and abbreviations: *BOD, primary treatment, media type, trap rock, gneiss, shattered ends, structural defects,* etc. To the right reader, these terms have perfectly legitimate meanings, but to the uninitiated reader, the words might be confusing or nonsensical.

Jargon and the Social Sciences

Writers in the social sciences—especially in psychology and sociology—have often been accused of using excessive jargon. Writers in both fields use many common English words with special, often stipulated meanings: *response, learning, training, feeling, concept, idea, group, class, family,* etc.

A psychologist discussing a *tertiary mediated response* is referring to a response coming through an intermediate person and delivered thirdhand. The concept and its expression are valuable in a limited context and to a limited audience. Otherwise, they are meaningless.

Jargon

Similarly, a sociologist in talking about families might need to define where the family ends—perhaps at second cousins twice removed. So the sociologist begins to use the term *extended family* for all relatives, including second cousins twice removed. To an uninitiated reader, the term will likely be confusing or awkward.

Here is an example of how difficult a jargon-filled passage from the social sciences can become:

> Another very common psychological use of the analysis of variance is seen in test development techniques and procedures where the measurement or test specialist has designed a new test instrument and administered it to a large normative sample of subjects, including students.

Rewritten, this passage can be shorter and clearer:

> An analysis of variance allows specialists to analyze the questions on a newly developed test by comparing a large number of student responses.

Jargon-filled writing is always difficult to uninitiated readers, but making the writing clear and concise does aid comprehension. Often, the context in which jargon appears helps readers understand what the writer intended.

Jargon and Gobbledygook

Jargon and gobbledygook are not quite the same. Gobbledygook is the use of abstract or pompous words and long, convoluted sentences. It is clearly bad writing. Jargon, by contrast, is a specialized vocabulary for a particular technical field and is often useful shorthand. See GOBBLEDYGOOK.

Key Words

Key words are like flags—they rise above the rest of the text and signify what is most important. In a paragraph, subsection, or section, the key words are those that give the text meaning. Key words impart the central message.

You can deliberately repeat key words and phrases to reinforce your message. Key words ensure that readers who are not reading carefully will still get the point of what you are saying and remember the most important ideas.

The example below is from a short section on condenser operation. Note how the writer drives home the message by using repeated key words as variations on an important theme:

> This highly effective water-separation process is possible because the condenser design positively prevents two potential **icing** problems: (1) blockage of the low-pressure side by **snow-laden cold** air and (2) **freezing** of condensate on the **cold** metal surfaces. The entering **cold-side** air is below the **freezing** point of water and, although the condenser **heats** it, the outlet **temperature** is still **below 32 degrees F.** Consequently, much of the entrained **snow** is not evaporated and must pass completely through the condenser without blocking the flow passages. Because **cold-side** air **temperatures** are consistently below the **freezing** point, the condenser must be carefully designed so that the metal surface **temperatures** remain above the **freezing** point.

The key words concerning temperature represent one important line of thought in this paragraph. An equally important line of thought concerns the design, mechanics, and operation of the condenser:

> This highly effective water-separation process is possible because the **condenser design** positively prevents two potential icing problems: (1) **blockage** of the low-pressure side by snow-laden cold air and (2) freezing of **condensate** on the cold **metal surfaces**. The **entering** cold-side air is below the freezing point of water and, although the **condenser** heats it, the **outlet** temperature is still below 32 degrees F. Consequently, much of the entrained snow is **not evaporated** and must **pass** completely through the **condenser** without **blocking** the **flow passages**. Because cold-side air temperatures are consistently below the freezing point, the **condenser** must be carefully **designed** so that the **metal surface** temperatures remain above the freezing point.

Note how the two sets of key words work together to create the overall effect and to establish both a primary problem (icing) and a primary need (a condenser design that will prevent it).

See PARAGRAPHS and TRANSITIONS.

The key words in the next paragraph provide both a solution and a sharp contrast:

> Figure 2-1 shows how the **condenser design prevents** these **icing** problems. A special **hot** section on the **cold-side** face **prevents ice blockage**. A small **flow** of **hot** air from the compressor outlet **passes** through the **hot** section tubes, **raising** the metal **temperatures above freezing** and allowing the **snow or ice** to be **evaporated** in the main core. The **hot** air then reenters the high-pressure **air-flow** at the turbine inlet.

Headings and Captions

Headings and captions should contain the most important of the text's key words. For example, a heading for the previous paragraphs on condenser design would contain key words:

> Condenser Design Prevents Icing

See HEADINGS, CAPTIONS, and EMPHASIS.

Letters

Letters are one of the principal forms of business communication. Good letters do more than convey information, actions, and decisions. They establish the personal style of the sender and the image of the sender's organization, and they act as surrogate conversations between parties.

Well-written letters are clear and concise. The important points appear early in the letter, usually in the opening sentence. The writer emphasizes crucial data and ideas, wastes no words, and includes nothing that is not relevant to the central themes of the letter. Readers understand clearly why the letter was written and what they should do after reading it.

Letter writing styles have changed over the years. Decades ago, lengthy, rambling letters were acceptable. Today, writers and readers prefer a simplified, concise letter, probably in response to the enormous increase in written communication that has occurred in the last 20 years. Today, busy readers do not have time to spend on lengthy digressions and explanations. They want the writer to get to the point quickly.

Letters and memos are similar in many respects. The principal distinction is that letters are written to persons outside the sender's organization and memos are written to persons inside the sender's organization. See MEMOS.

This section begins with a discussion of the principles of good letter writing. Then it describes the format styles of business letters, including the block, modified block, semi-block, and simplified styles, and the two most common styles of punctuation, open and standard. See PUNCTUATION.

Effective Letter Writing

---

1. Begin most letters with the most important point.

If you can, try to open the letter with the most important idea in the letter:

> Dear Mr. Smith:
>
> On March 1, we will meet with Bilko's attorneys to discuss the Bellocq acquisition, and we would like you to be present.
>
> *or*
>
> Please meet with us and Bilko's attorneys on March 1 to discuss the Bellocq acquisition.

> Dear Ms. Atkins:
>
> MOGO recommends plugging and abandoning the C.C. Baker 12. Production continues to decline and is now below economically feasible levels.
>
> *or*
>
> Because production on the C.C. Baker 12 continues to decline and is now below economically feasible levels, MOGO recommends plugging and abandoning this well.

> Dear Dr. Jones:
>
> The test results from the Hampstead facility indicate that exposure levels do not currently exceed EPA safety levels.

> Dear Mr. Johnson:
>
> For the reasons cited below, we have decided not to adopt your suggestion to delay platform renovations until the 4th Quarter. However, we will modify the containment area according to the revised specifications that you submitted.

The opening is the strongest part of a letter. Putting your important ideas somewhere other than the opening is unfair to busy readers. Furthermore, if you begin the letter with information that your readers know is relatively unimportant, they may begin to skim, and in skimming, they might miss important points.

Beginning with your important points establishes your purpose right away and gives readers a perspective for understanding the rest of what you have to say. See ORGANIZATION.

Sometimes, you cannot open with your most important idea because readers either will not understand it or will not accept it. If that is the case, then set up the major ideas with a brief explanation:

> Dear Ms. Atkins:
>
> Our 8-month effort to stimulate the C.C. Baker 12 has not succeeded, and production continues to decline. If we keep operating this well at current and projected production levels, production costs will outweigh revenues. Therefore, MOGO recommends plugging and abandoning this well.

Set-ups, like the one shown above, should always lead directly to your major point.

Never open a letter with these common techniques:

—Obvious references:

> This is in reference to your letter of February 15. *(See rule 2.)*

—Unnecessary social statements:

> Here's hoping that the weather in Tampa is fine and that your family is doing well in the new year.

—Mechanical enclosure indications:

> Enclosed is . . .
> Attached is . . .
> Enclosed herewith . . .
> Attached hereto . . .
> Enclosed please find . . .

—Statements that suggest your topic but do not indicate your position:

> Delaying platform renovation until the 4th Quarter is an idea worthy of consideration.

—Information that supports, explains, or illustrates your major points (unless that information legitimately sets up your major points):

> Delaying platform renovation until the 4th Quarter would mean rebudgeting funds that have already been allocated during 2nd Quarter. *(This is justification for your decision, but you should state the decision first, then justify it.)*

---

2. Subordinate references to previous documents, conversations, and meetings.

As noted above, you should never open a letter with references. References are never the major point of a letter. Therefore, they belong after the major point or before the text (in a subject or reference block). Here are some ways to work in references:

this

Dear Mr. Smith:

Thank you for agreeing to be present on March 1 during our meeting with Bilko's attorneys to discuss the Bellocq acquisition. As Mary Evans indicated when she phoned you yesterday with the invitation, we are especially concerned about the Forbish property.

not this

Dear Mr. Smith:

This confirms Mary Evans' telephone conversation with you on February 15 in regard to our March 1 meeting with Bilko's attorneys to discuss the Bellocq acquisition.

---

this

Dear Dr. Jones:

The test results from the Hampstead facility indicate that exposures do not currently exceed EPA safety levels. Your letter of July 23 expressed concern over the large amounts of radiation present.

not this

Dear Dr. Jones:

This is in reference to your letter of July 23 in which you expressed concern over the large amount of radiation present.

Subordinate references by placing them after the major point or by putting them in reference or subject blocks ahead of the text:

> RE: Your Letter of July 23 Concerning Radiation Levels at Hampstead

> SUBJECT: OUR NOVEMBER 9 TELEPHONE CONVERSATION ON PRODUCTION QUOTAS

> RE: Yesterday's Meeting on Supervisory Policy

> SUBJECT: Recommendation to P&A the C.C. Baker #12 (Re: your letter of April 5)

Avoid the following types of reference statements, especially as letter openings:

> This is in reference to your letter of . . .

> In reference to our telephone conversation concerning . . .

> This confirms our telephone conversation of . . .

> Reference is made to our recent meeting in which we . . .

> This is in response to your inquiry regarding . . .

NOTE: As indicated under rule 1, also avoid the following cliched references to enclosures:

> Enclosed herewith . . .

> Attached hereto . . .

You should indicate that you have *enclosed* or attached something, but do so later in the letter. Don't open your letter with *enclosed* or *attached,* and never add *herewith* or *hereto,* which sound legalistic (their first offense) and are also redundant (the *coup de grace*). Perhaps the worst reference to enclosures is the following:

> Enclosed please find . . .

If you enclose it, they will find it. Don't ever use this ridiculous statement.

Enclosures typically apply to letters because whatever accompanies the letter is enclosed within the envelope. Attachments typically apply to memos because memos generally do not come in envelopes. Whatever accompanies the memo must be attached (via rubber band, staple, or paper clip).

Always subordinate references to enclosures or attachments:

Dear Dr. Jones:

The test results from the Hampstead facility indicate that exposures do not currently exceed EPA safety

Letters

> levels. In your letter of July 23 (enclosure 1), you expressed concern over the large amounts of radiation present.
>
> On June 17, EPA representatives inspected the Hampstead facility (see enclosure 2). They did find traces of arsenic in the vent system but could not . . .

---

3. Ensure that your letters are clearly and logically organized.

Logical organization is crucial to effective letters. Readers should understand from the early paragraphs what the letter is about and how the writer has organized his or her thoughts.

Letter organization does not differ significantly from the logical organization of memos, manuals, specifications, proposals, and reports. However, the audience for a business letter is usually different from the audience for other types of documents, and letter readers typically read with a different purpose.

So you must organize your thoughts carefully, keeping your readers in mind. Unless you have a compelling reason to do otherwise, follow the organizational principles discussed under ORGANIZATION.

---

4. Throughout letters, emphasize key data and ideas.

Use headings, lists, numbering systems, visual aids, white space, single-sentence paragraphs, repetition, and other emphatic devices to highlight major points.

Letter writers sometimes mistakenly assume that the emphatic devices listed in the previous paragraph are inappropriate in letters. In fact, these devices help break up large blocks of text and make letters more readable. Do not fail to use them if the opportunity arises.

See EMPHASIS and WORD PROCESSING.

---

5. Avoid cliched letter closings.

Letter closings should be as simple and direct as letter openings. The closing might reiterate an important point stated earlier in the letter, or it might provide useful information, such as a due date, a response deadline, or the name and telephone number of a person to contact for assistance.

Avoid these kinds of statements (which have become cliches):

> Thanking you in advance . . .
>
> Should you have any further questions or be in need of further assistance . . .
>
> Do not hesitate to contact me . . .
>
> Feel free to contact me . . .

Instead, make an offer of assistance sound natural and direct:

> If you have further questions, please call me at 123-4567.

Also, avoid complimentary closings that sound overwrought or exaggerated:

> Very truly yours,
>
> Truly yours,
>
> Deepest regards,
>
> In sincerest appreciation,
>
> Thanking you for everything,

The best complimentary closings are simple and brief:

> Sincerely,
>
> Respectfully,
>
> Thank you,

See CLICHES.

Letter Format and Punctuation Styles

Format Styles

On the following pages are four style models: **block, modified block, semiblock,** and **simplified.** These models illustrate the use, placement, and punctuation of the following elements of letters:

Letterhead/return address
Date line
Reference line or block
Special notations
Inside address
Attention line
Salutation
Subject line or block
Text or body
Headings for continuation pages
Complimentary closing
Signature block
Reference initials
Enclosure initials
Courtesy copy and blind courtesy copy notations
Postscript

The elements in boldface type are standard; the others are optional. (NOTE: In the simplified style, the salutation and complimentary closing are omitted.)

In the **block** style, all of these elements appear flush with the left margin, and the paragraphs are not indented.

Block Style, Open Punctuation

OSAGE
GAS AND ELECTRIC
COMPANY, INC.
511 Franklin Road
Suite 8
Lincoln, Nebraska 68506
(402) 355-7070

May 31, 1990

In reply to Invoice 5068

American Gas Company
Engineering Department
3498 Anyplace Drive
Alameda, OH 87543

Attention Mrs. Joyce Johnson

Ladies and Gentlemen

Subject: The Form of the Block Letter, with Open Punctuation

The block format means that every line is flush with the left margin, even the date and the complimentary closing.

Open punctuation means that no punctuation follows the salutation and complimentary closing. Block letters may also follow the standard punctuation style (see the model of the modified block letter).

The date appears two to six lines below the letterhead, depending upon the length of the letter. Following the date is the reference line, which may include an invoice number, letter date, telephone date, file number, account number, or other pertinent information. The reference line is optional.

The inside address follows the spelling, format, and abbreviation style used in the letterhead of the organization receiving the letter. If you are writing to a specific person within the addressed organization, then begin the inside address with that person's name. Use an attention line only if the inside address does not contain a person's name (as in this example) but you want to route the letter to a specific person. Using an attention line indicates that the letter concerns a business matter and may be handled by anyone in the department receiving the letter. The attention line may contain the name of a department or group.

In the **modified block** style, the date, reference line, complimentary closing, and signature block appear right of center; everything else is flush left. The paragraphs are not indented.

The **semiblock** style is similar to the modified style except that the paragraphs are indented (usually five spaces).

The **simplified style** is similar to the block style except that the salutation and complimentary closing are omitted. Paragraphs are not indented.

For many years, the semiblock style was standard. Today's letter writers favor the block or simplified style for several reasons. First, leaving every element flush left is easier on word processors. Second, indenting paragraphs is no longer necessary because writers routinely leave one blank line between paragraphs. When paragraphs were not separated by a blank line, indentation was essential for showing where new paragraphs began.

Note, however, that the semi-block style has a more casual feel to it. Even the modified block, with some information moved right of center, seems less formal than the full block style.

Your organization might dictate a stylistic preference. If not, you should choose a style that is consistent with the image you wish to project. If you wish to appear formal and businesslike, use the block or simplified style. If you want to be more casual, then select the modified or semi-block style.

The chief distinction of the simplified style is the absence of salutation and complimentary closing. These omissions solve a problem unique to today's letter writers: how to write to women without offending them by using traditional but sexist language.

Salutations and complimentary closings are traditional but non-essential elements of letters. They are forms of social address that were mandatory when letter writing had a different social purpose than it does today. In a purely business climate, the traditional greeting *Dear* and the traditional closings, such as *Yours truly*, are not necessary. Therefore, if you wish, you may omit them and follow the simplified style.

Letters

Punctuation Styles

In the **open style**, the writer omits all nonessential punctuation, including a colon or comma after the salutation and a comma after the complimentary closing. See PUNCTUATION.

In the **standard** style, the writer uses minimal punctuation in the letter but does include a colon (or a comma) after the salutation and a comma after the complimentary closing. The standard style is almost always used in letters with indented paragraphs (the semi-block style).

The **closed (or close)** style has all but vanished from business letters written in the United States, although some European firms still use it. In the closed style, writers retain all of the punctuation marks used in standard punctuation and add others:

—A period after the date

—Commas after each line of the address, with a period after the final line:

Mr. Edwin Jones,
Wellhead Oil Company,
1359 Fifth Avenue,
Bellevue, MI 65431.

—Commas after each line in the signature block, with a period after the last line.

The **block** and **simplified** style models illustrate the open punctuation style. The **modified** and **semiblock** style models show standard punctuation.

Block Style, Open Punctuation

American Gas Company
Engineering Department
May 31, 1990
Invoice 5068
Page 2

The preferred salutation in a business letter not addressed to an individual is "Ladies and Gentlemen." "Gentlemen" shows sexual bias and may be offensive (see SEXIST LANGUAGE), and "To Whom It May Concern" is obnoxiously formal. You may avoid this problem by beginning the inside address with "Mrs. Joyce Johnson," and then writing "Dear Mrs. Johnson" as the salutation.

The optional subject line is underlined for emphasis, but some writers and editors prefer all capital letters. The subject line should be as specific and informative as possible, even if it requires more words. The subject line should tell readers specifically what this letter is about.

The text has block paragaraphs (no first-line indentation) that have one line between them. If the text extends beyond the first page, ensure that you have at least four lines of text on the second page. On the second page, the heading begins approximately six lines down from the top of the page (depending upon the length of the material on the second page). The text begins at least two spaces below the heading.

The complimentary closing is "Sincerely," which is a good choice for both informal and formal business letters. To leave space for the signature, the author's name and title appear four lines beneath the complimentary closing.

The author's and the typist's initials appear two lines below the author's title and are flush left. Immediately beneath the initials comes the enclosure line, with the number of enclosures indicated (in parentheses). The letter ends with the list of courtesy copies (cc) and, if appropriate, blind courtesy copies (bcc).

Sincerely

Marian R. Garvey

Marian R. Garvey
Chief Engineer

MRG:st
Enclosures (3)

cc Mrs. Florence Lynch
Edward Jenkinson
bcc Joseph Franks

Margins and Spacing

The left and right margins of letters should be roughly equal, but the exact spacing will vary depending on the length of the letter. In long letters, the margins are usually at least an inch and a quarter wide. In short letters, the margins can be wider; in extremely short letters, wide margins can be combined with double or triple spacing. Your goal should be to center the letter on the page, so you might have to reset the margins for letters of unusual size.

See WORD PROCESSING.

Letterhead/Return Address

All business letters should have either a printed letterhead or a return address with the same information as in a letterhead. Letterheads should contain the following:

Modified Block Style, Standard Punctuation

October 31, 1990

File SD 87/6
Your letter September 5, 1990

Mr. George Freed, Jr.
Assistant Manager
Stevenson Retail Mart
349 Highland Boulevard
Miami Beach, FL 96502

Dear Mr. Freed:

In modified block style, the date, reference block (optional), and complimentary closing are right of center (sometimes flush right); everything else is flush left. Paragraphs are not indented. In standard punctuation, a comma follows the complimentary close and a colon (formal) or comma (informal) follows the salutation.

The reference block, which is optional, can contain this letter's file number, as well as references to previous documents, meetings, or conversations. Often, reference blocks include the file number, subject, and date of relevant documents preceding this letter or to which this letter is responding.

The inside address includes the full name and title of the person addressed along with the company name and address (written as they appear in that company's letterhead). The inside address is conventionally three or four lines below the date, but you can leave additional blank lines if your letter is short.

The salutation follows those conventions described in the block and semiblock style models.

Do not indent paragraphs. To indicate where paragraphs begin and end, leave a blank line between paragraphs.

The second page continuation includes the name of the addressee, the date of the letter, and the file number. If the letter has a subject line, then the continuation heading should include the subject as well (file references are also optional). Place continuation headings six lines from the top of the page. Start the text four lines (or more if the continued text is short) below the heading.

303 Blossom Avenue   Des Moines, Iowa 50321   (525) 521-4911

—Logo (optional)

—Full legal name of the organization

—Full legal address—including post office box number, suite number, city, state, and the full ZIP code

—Area code and telephone number(s)

—Fax or cable instructions (optional)

In addition, departments, branch offices, and company officers may have their own letterhead, which may include titles, building numbers, and other specific identifiers:

E. G. Walters, Jr.
Office Manager
Viewmont Branch Office
High Fidelity Savings & Loan
1234 S. Main Street
Logan, IN 44444-4444
(123) 456-7890

If you are not using stationery with a printed letterhead, then you must include a return address that contains the same information that a letterhead would contain. The semiblock style illustrates the format for a typed return address; in block and simplified styles, such an address would appear flush with the left margin.

Date Line

Placement of the date line varies depending on the length of the letter and the style of the letterhead.

The date line should never extend into the right or left margins, but any other placement is possible, depending on the letterhead.

The date line usually appears two or three lines below the letterhead, but you can leave as many as six or seven lines if the letter is short. If your stationery does not have letterhead, then place the date on the line below the return address (as in semi-block style).

(See the four model letters for further information on placement of the date.)

The standard date line in the United States is month, day, and year: *March 15, 1990.* Do not use abbreviations.

Writers in the U.S. Government, including the military, and in many foreign countries prefer to list day, month, and year: *15 March 1990.*

Reference Line or Block

Reference lines appear beneath the date line, usually two lines down, but some companies prefer only a single line. Reference lines are typically aligned with the date or are flush with the left or right margin, depending on the format style of the letter:

this

March 15, 1990

Invoice SD-4576A

or this

15 March 1990

Invoice 45890

Reference lines are optional, but you should seriously consider using them, especially if the letter refers to several invoices, files, letters, or telephone conversations. References are easy to see under the date line, and they eliminate the need for writers to include such references in the crucial opening paragraph of the letter. Reference lines under the date line rarely need a lead-in, but one is optional if it can clarify the reference:

March 15, 1990
In reply to: Your telephone call of March 7, 1990

Sometimes, writers include the reference line or block below the inside address, either flush left or right of center. These reference blocks can begin with *RE:* and may run several lines. In the style adopted by the Department of Defense, writers list all references by number or letter in a reference block:

References:

A. DoD Directive 5202.43-1

B. SECNAVINST 452.1

C. COMCINCPAC Ltr 85-00064-5, dtd 23 April 1990

D. DoD Manual 34.2

Then when writers have to refer to those references in the body of the letter, they refer to them by number or letter:

Reference E suggests that formulation of a new European policy is imminent. However, reference F cites an EEC memorandum stating that economic goals set last year would not be changed until 1990.

This practice seems sensible if you are going to be discussing a number of references and don't want to repeat the name, subject, and date of the reference every time you refer to it.

When letters are longer than one page, reference lines sometimes appear under the date in the heading on all continued pages of the letter. (See the modified block style model for an example.)

Modified Block Style, Standard Punctuation

Mr. George Freed, Jr.
October 31, 1990
File SD 87/6
Your letter September 5, 1990
Page 2

The complimentary closing can be (1) directly aligned with the date in the heading, (2) flush right, or (3) five spaces right of center. The author's name and title should appear at least four lines below and flush with the left side of the complimentary closing.

The reference initials should appear flush left, two lines below the author's title. If you include the author's initials, they appear first and in all capitals. The typist's initials appear in lowercase letters following the author's initials. If someone other than the author will sign the letter and you want to include that person's initials, place them in all capitals to the left of the author's initials. Separate all initials with a colon.

Sincerely,

Frank Jefferson

Frank Jefferson
Sales Manager

FJ:CC:vb

Avoid postscripts if at all possible. If you must use one, place it at the end of the last page. Postscripts follow the paragraph style established in the text. They need not begin with the word *postscript* or with the abbreviation *PS* (but if they do, they must be followed by a colon). Following the postscript, you do not need another signature but may add one.

Semiblock Style, Standard Punctuation

434 Fish Lake Road
Salmon, ID 43287
June 8, 1990

In reply to: Invoice 45/765
May 6, 1990

Mrs. Joanne G. Kelsey
Executive Vice President
Year-Long Heating Company, Inc.
4376 Grand View Avenue
Anchorage, AK 98754

Dear Mrs. Kelsey:

Semiblock Style, Standard Punctuation

In semiblock style, the return address, date, and complimentary closing appear right of center. The inside address, salutation, and headings are flush left. All paragraphs are indented (usually five spaces). In standard punctuation, a colon (formal) or a comma (informal) follows the salutation and a comma follows the complimentary closing.

If the paper has no letterhead, then use a return address as shown above. If the paper has a letterhead, the date and optional reference block appear three or four lines below the letterhead.

The inside address opens with the name of the individual receiving the letter, followed by the person's title, the exact name of the company (spelled and punctuated as on that company's letterhead), and the address.

Salutations commonly begin with *Dear.* Formal salutations use the receiver's title and last name: *Dear Mrs. Kelsey.* Less formal salutations can use only a first name: *Dear Joanne.* Use a colon after the name in formal salutations, and a comma after the name in informal salutations. Abbreviate *Doctor* (Dr.) and all gender titles: *Messrs., Mr., Mrs.,* and *Ms.* Do not abbreviate other titles: *Senator, Mayor, General, Professor,* etc.

Special Notations

Special notations appear between the date (or reference line) and the inside address. Such notations include the following: SPECIAL DELIVERY, REGISTERED MAIL, CERTIFIED MAIL, CONFIDENTIAL, PERSONAL. These notations usually appear two lines above the inside address and are usually typed in all capital letters (for visibility). (See the simplified style model for an example.)

If two or more of these notations apply to a letter, the second and additional notations appear directly beneath the first one. Leave no blank lines between them. These notices also appear on the envelope, usually above the address, but placement varies according to the size of the envelope and the appearance of the address. Make sure that such notations are clearly visible.

Inside Address

The spacing of the inside address below the date (and reference line) will vary depending on the length of the letter.

The inside address usually includes (1) the addressee's courtesy title—*Mr., Mrs., Ms., Miss,* or *Dr.*; (2) the addressee's name; (3) the addressee's business title; (4) the name of the organization; (5) the street address and, if appropriate, the post office box, suite number, mail drop, or other mailing information; (6) the city and state; and (7) the full ZIP code:

Ms. Louise H. Hansen
Director of Manual Preparation
The Locklear Company, Inc.
Suite 3546, First National Building
456 Second Street
Houston, TX 82398

Dr. Edwin B. Roberts
Chief, Psychiatric Services
Saint Benedict's Hospital
P.O. Box 67
North Medford, OR 76598

NOTE 1: Proper titles are a complex issue, so if you are writing to national political figures, royalty, or foreign officials, check with a standard reference such as Lois Hutchinson's *Standard Handbook for Secretaries* (1969) or *Webster's Secretarial Handbook* (1983); these and other resources are listed in REFERENCES.

NOTE 2: If you are writing to a woman, try to determine her title preference: *Miss, Mrs.,* or *Ms.* If you cannot determine a preference, then omit the title entirely. *Ms.* used to be the preference in such cases, but a recent survey indicated that many married and single women did not wish to be addressed as *Ms.* under any circumstance (see SEXIST LANGUAGE). If you omit the title, do so in both the inside address and the salutation:

Carolyn D. Faust
Personnel Manager
Osage Power and Light
1212 Circuit Street
Omaha, NE 55532

Carolyn D. Faust: (*salutation*)

or

Dear Carolyn D. Faust:

NOTE 3: The spelling, format, and punctuation of the receiving organization's name and address should be consistent with the spelling, format, and punctuation shown on that organization's letterhead or typed return address.

NOTE 4: If you don't know who will read your letter or if you are writing to an organization rather than to an individual within the organization, then address either a position title or the name of the organization (or a department within it):

District Engineer
Andrews District Office
MOGO Oil Company
901 West Street
Andrews, OK 55555

Department of Geophysical
Research
New Orleans Regional Office
MOGO Oil Company, Inc.
657 Basin Street
New Orleans, LA 22222

NOTE 5: Do not use abbreviations in the inside address except for the standard U.S. Postal Service abbreviations for states. Use the following two-character state abbreviations both in the inside address and on envelopes:

Semiblock Style, Standard Punctuation

Mrs. Joanne G. Kelsey -2- June 8, 1990

<u>Headings</u>

Headings are excellent ways to highlight the organization of the letter and to emphasize key points or sections, especially if the letter is more than one page long. Set off the heading by leaving a blank line above and below it and by underlining the heading or typing it in boldface.

The continuation heading for the second and additional pages should appear as shown above. Continued pages should have at least three lines of text.

<u>Displayed Items</u>

Displayed lists are effective in business letters, especially those running more than one page and having a number of paragraphs. Optional formats for lists include:

- Bulleted lists. They are perhaps the most emphatic lists because bullets are so dark. On word processors and typewriters that do not have bullets, use a lowercase *o* followed by two spaces and fill in the center of the *o* with a pen. Indent the listed items on both the right and the left, as illustrated here.

—Lists introduced by a dash (an em dash or two hyphens). They are a little less emphatic than bulleted lists. The dash usually appears without a space between it and the text. Indent the listed items on both the right and the left.

1. Numbered or alphabetical lists. They help readers cross-reference items and are valuable if the items are listed in descending order of importance. Leave two spaces after the period. Indent the listed items on both the right and the left.

The complimentary closing should be *Respectfully* (formal) or *Sincerely* (less formal). The writer's name and title appear four lines below the closing.

The typist's initials appear flush left, followed by notations for enclosures and courtesy copies. (See the other letter models for examples of these items.)

Sincerely,

Ellen G. Sanderson

Ellen G. Sanderson

rgt

Alabama	AL	Maine	ME
Alaska	AK	Maryland	MD
Arizona	AZ	Massachusetts	MA
Arkansas	AR	Michigan	MI
California	CA	Minnesota	MN
Canal Zone	CZ	Mississippi	MS
Colorado	CO	Missouri	MO
Connecticut	CT	Montana	MT
Delaware	DE	Nebraska	NE
District of Columbia	DC	Nevada	NV
Florida	FL	New Hampshire	NH
Georgia	GA	New Jersey	NJ
Guam	GU	New Mexico	NM
Hawaii	HI	New York	NY
Idaho	ID	North Carolina	NC
Illinois	IL	North Dakota	ND
Indiana	IN	Ohio	OH
Iowa	IA	Oklahoma	OK
Kansas	KS	Oregon	OR
Kentucky	KY	Pennsylvania	PA
Louisiana	LA	Puerto Rico	PR

Simplified Style, Open Punctuation

SKY AVIATION
822 Ocean View Drive
Long Beach, California 90802
(714) 332-3978

March 15, 1990

CONFIDENTIAL

Ms. Susan Willey
Finance Officer
G. L. Findley and Company
345 Anchor Street
Portland, OR 76209

THE SIMPLIFIED STYLE LETTER

A simplified style letter, Ms. Willey, follows the format developed by the Administrative Management Society. Its chief features are a full-block format (everything flush left), open punctuation, and the omission of both the salutation and the complimentary closing.

As illustrated above, both the date and inside address appear as they would in a block letter (see the model of the block style letter). Notations such as CONFIDENTIAL and PERSONAL are optional.

A subject line (all capitalized) replaces the salutation, and the text begins three lines below it.

The reader's name usually appears somewhere early in the first paragraph. Such a reference is a nice personal touch. The paragaraphs are not indented.

Lists

Lists, especially numbered lists, are usually flush left with double spacing between items to set them off.

1. Listed item 1.

2. Listed item 2; and if the item has more than one line, subsequent lines are flush left. The idea is for typists to type as few extra spaces and punctuation marks as possible.

3. Listed item 3.

Rhode Island	RI
South Carolina	SC
South Dakota	SD
Tennessee	TN
Texas	TX
Utah	UT
Vermont	VT
Virgin Islands	VI
Virginia	VA
Washington	WA
West Virginia	WV
Wisconsin	WI
Wyoming	WY

NOTE 6: Address formats for Canadian and other foreign addresses vary slightly from American address formats. The biggest difference is that the name of the country appears on a separate line and is usually typed in all capital letters:

134 Western Province Boulevard
Edmonton, Alberta
CANADA
T5J 2H7

Unter den Eichen 56
Heidelberg 3886
FEDERAL REPUBLIC OF
GERMANY (W)

Attention Line

An attention line is necessary when the inside address does not contain either the name of an individual or the name of a department. In these cases, an attention line appears two lines below the inside address and is flush with the left margin:

H. Allen and Sons Insurance
Company
Suite 3409, Valley Bank Building
408 Pico Boulevard
Long Beach, CA 88888

Attention Miss Georgia Banks

or

Denver Regional Office
Midland Oil and Gas Company
4509 Western Avenue
Denver, CO 77777

ATTENTION EXPLORATION
DEPARTMENT

As these examples illustrate, you do not need a colon following *Attention.* Note that *attention* may be typed with an initial capital letter or with all capital letters. If you use all capitals, then type the name following *ATTENTION* in all capitals too.

Salutation

The salutation usually begins with the conventional greeting *Dear* and is followed by the title and name of the addressee. In the open punctuation style, nothing follows the salutation. In standard punctuation, use a colon (for formal letters) or a comma (for informal letters) after the salutation.

Here are some sample salutations when the writer knows the addressee's name and title:

Letters

Dear Mr. Neal:
Dear Frank: (*or* Dear Frank,)
Dear Mrs. Skoal:
Dear Miss Anderson:
Dear Ms. Branch:
Dear Cheryl: (*or* Dear Cheryl,)
Dear Dr. Burns:
Dear Professor Bettridge:
Dear President Maloney:
Dear Miss Dearden and Mr. Wu:
Dear Mrs. Anderson and Ms. Blaine:

When you don't know the addressee's name, you have several options:

Ladies and Gentlemen:
Gentlemen and Ladies:
Dear Sir or Madam:
Dear Madam or Sir:
Ladies: *(all women)*
Gentlemen: *(all men)*

or

Dear Colleagues:
Dear Friends:
Dear Members of the Council:
Dear Landowners:

Traditional salutations include such forms as *Gentlemen, Dear Sirs,* and *Dear Mr. ____.* Avoiding these sexist greetings is sometimes problematic. Many people consider *Ladies and Gentlemen* and *Dear Sir or Madam* to be overly formal and old-fashioned. If you know the gender of the person you are addressing, then *Dear Mr.* or *Dear Ms.* is acceptable. However, if you don't know that person's gender, then using a greeting that identifies gender could be a problem: *Dear Mr. Smith* (what if Smith is a woman?) or *Dear Ms. A. B. Cooper* (what if A. B. Cooper is a man?). Sometimes, a person's name suggests gender: John Smith, Mary Jones, George Hayes, Linda Meyers. However, you cannot always be certain: Actors Michael Learned and Glenn Close are women. See SEXIST LANGUAGE.

Simplified Style, Open Punctuation

Ms. Susan Willey
Page 2
March 15, 1990

Other types of lists using either bullets or dashes are usually indented at least five spaces:

- On word processors and typewriters that do not have bullets, type a lowercase *o* and fill in the center with a pen. The text in such a list is indented from both the right and left margins, as in this example.

— A dash, actually two unspaced hyphens on a typewriter or an em dash on a computer, is less emphatic than a bullet. Dashes usually appear with no space between them and the text following them. The text is aligned in a block.

The heading of continued pages is printed block fashion, as illustrated above. At least three lines of text should appear on continued page.

No complimentary close appears in a simplified style letter. However, the closing line of the letter can be a courteous closing: "We welcome the opportunity to work with you," or "Please call us at 123-456-7890 if we can assist you further." The writer's name and title (both in all capitals) appear five lines below the final paragraph; the name and title can be separated by a dash or comma.

Reference initials and notations about enclosures and courtesy copies follow the name and title of the writer, as shown below.

Kirk Youngblood, Jr.

KIRK YOUNGBLOOD, JR.—CHIEF ACCOUNTANT

KY:lgh
Enclosures (4)

cc Alvin G. Harris

Many people today suggest that gender should not be an identifier in the business and technical world. Some companies insist that their employees be addressed by first and middle initials and last name: *C. H. Hardy, B. W. Richmond,* etc. Many other companies insist that letter writers not use traditional but sexist salutations, such as *Gentlemen* and *Dear Sirs*. The dilemma occurs when you don't want to use a sexist salutation but don't like any of the alternatives. One solution is the simplified style, which omits the salutation altogether. Another solution is simply to omit the gender title: *Dear A. B. Cooper.*

NOTE 1: As noted above, when you don't know a woman's title, your best option may be to use the woman's name without a title:

Dear Helen Brown:

NOTE 2: Some writers prefer a more formal letter style, especially in the salutation:

> My dear Mr. Devon:
>
> My dear Susan:

These salutations sound too stiff to be acceptable today. Many people would also find them condescending. You should also avoid the following previously acceptable salutations:

> Dear Messrs. Franks and Harris *(for two men)*
>
> Dear Mesdames Long and Minor *(for two women)*

Even very educated readers in the U.S. would have difficulty pronouncing these French forms and would likely consider the writer odd.

Subject Line

Use a subject line to establish the letter's subject. Subject lines allow readers to file letters by subject and retrieve them fairly easily. If you use a subject line, make it as specific as possible so that readers know instantly what the letter is about. See HEADINGS.

Insert subject lines two lines below the salutation and two lines above the first line of the text. (See the block and semiblock style models for examples. See the simplified style model for slightly different spacing.)

Highlight the subject line by choosing underlining, all capital letters, or boldface type.

Text or Body

The text or body begins two lines below the salutation (or optional subject line). In simplified style, the text begins three lines below the subject line.

The text of most letters is single spaced, although double spacing is acceptable if the letter is very short. Leave a blank line between paragraphs regardless of line spacing and no matter which style you follow.

In block and simplified styles, do not indent paragraphs. In modified and semiblock styles, indent paragraphs (usually 3 or 5 spaces). Some organizations indent paragraphs up to 10 spaces.

Reversed indentation (sometimes called "hanging indentation") is a format option, especially in advertising letters. In these letters, the overall format can follow one of the four models of common business letters, but the paragraphs look like this:

> A hanging-indented paragraph begins flush with the left margin, but subsequent lines in the paragraph are indented, usually 3 or 5 spaces.

Long quotations within the text of a letter are indented 5 to 10 spaces on both the left and right margins. Double space before and after such quotations so that the quotations are framed by white space.

Use similar right and left indentation for lists. (See the semiblock and simplified style models for examples of how to set up lists; also, see LISTS.)

If the text continues beyond the first page, then ensure that at least three lines of text appear on the second page. If necessary, adjust margins and line spacing so that the first page is not too crowded and the second page and additional pages have enough text to justify a continuation page.

Headings for Continuation Pages

Continuation pages should begin with a heading containing the full name of the person receiving the letter, the page number, and the date. Two patterns are common. See the models of the block and simplified styles for a block pattern. See the models of the semiblock and the modified block for an alternative pattern.

The continuation heading can also repeat information mentioned on the first page in the reference line: invoice number, file number, date of a previous letter or memo, etc.

Complimentary Closing

The complimentary closing appears two lines below the closing line of the text. The block, modified block, and semi-block styles require complimentary closings. The simplified style omits the complimentary closing.

Alignment of the complimentary closing varies according to the format style of the letter. As the models indicate, the complimentary closing in block style appears flush with the left

Letters

margin. In modified and semi-block styles, the complimentary closing appears right of center and is sometimes flush with the right margin.

Your choice of a closing is one of the clearest ways you convey the level of formality and the degree of personal feeling you have toward the reader.

In most business letters—ones that are relatively formal without being stiff or distant—choose one of the following closings:

Sincerely,
Sincerely yours,
Thank you,

NOTE: In ordinary business letters, avoid these often-preferred but excessively formal closings:

Yours truly,
Very truly yours,
Yours very truly,

Truly has become a cliche in letter closings, so avoid it.

In informal, friendly letters, you might use these closings:

Best wishes,
Regards,
Best regards,
Kindest regards,
Cordially,

In highly formal letters, such as those addressed to dignitaries, high government or ecclesiastical officials, you might use one of the following closings:

Yours sincerely,
Respectfully yours,
Respectfully,

These formal closings usually match similarly formal salutations. If your letters demand more formality, check Lois Hutchinson's *Standard Handbook for Secretaries* (1977), *Webster's Secretarial Handbook* (1976), or one of the other resources listed in REFERENCES.

Signature Block

The signature block follows the complimentary closing. In simplified style, the signature block appears four or five lines below the last line of the text.

Alignment of the signature block varies with letter format styles. In block and simplified styles, the signature block is flush with the left margin. In modified and semiblock styles, the signature block is usually right of center (see those models).

The signature block consists of the following:

Company name *(optional)*
Handwritten signature of the writer
Full typed name of the writer
Title of the writer

The following three signature blocks (along with the complimentary closings) are typical. The first illustrates a company name:

Yours,

D. & L. DRILLING EQUIPMENT

Dwight G. Edwards

Dwight G. Edwards
Sales Manager

Sincerely,

Ivan G. Nostromo, Jr.

Ivan G. Nostromo, Jr.
Chief Engineer

Best wishes,

Howard

Howard G. Balock, PhD
Personnel Manager
Engineering Division

NOTE 1: The company name is necessary only when the letter represents a company policy, position, or decision, especially in legal matters. Note that the signature of the company official plus the typed name and title of the official also appear in the signature block.

NOTE 2: Sign formal and official letters with your full legal name. In informal and friendly letters, you need to sign only your first (as in the third example above). Do not include courtesy titles such as *Mr., Miss, Mrs., Ms.,* or *Dr.* in your written signature.

NOTE 3: Women's signatures generally include the woman's given and family names, with no courtesy title, such as *Ms., Miss,* or *Mrs.* These titles, if appropriate, would appear either with or without parentheses in the typed version of the name following the signature:

Sincerely,

Elaine Raddison

(Mrs.) Elaine Raddison
Treasurer

or

Mrs. Elaine Raddison

If a woman prefers to use her husband's full name, then the husband's name is typed below the signature:

Sincerely yours,

Elaine Raddison

Mrs. Thomas Raddison
Treasurer

NOTE 4: Academic titles and professional titles are not part of the signature. If you use them, they appear following the typed name. If used, these academic titles and professional titles replace *Dr.* or other courtesy titles preceding the name:

this

Grace Babbitt, M.D.

not this

Dr. Grace Babbitt, M.D.

NOTE 5: Secretaries who sign letters for the author should sign the author's name and then add their own initials either in the middle or on the right side under the signature:

Sincerely,

Diane F. Worth *jw*

Diane F. Worth
Benefits Specialist

If secretaries or others sign their own names, rather than the author's name, then they should sign *for* the author:

Sincerely,

James Westwood

For Frank Procter, P.E.
District Engineer

Reference Initials

The reference initials appear two lines below the last line of the signature block and are always flush with the left margin.

These initials consist of the secretary's or typist's initials and often the writer's initials.

If only the typist's initials appear, they are usually lowercase:

goj

If you include the writer's initials, type them in all capitals, followed by a slash mark or a colon, followed by the typist's initials in lowercase:

LHF/goj
LHF:goj

In some instances, the writer is different from the person signing the letter. In these cases, the signer's initials come first, the writer's initials come next, and the typist's come last:

TK/LHF/goj
TK:LHF:goj

Enclosure Notation

Enclosure notations remind readers that one or more items were enclosed with the original letter. Such notations usually come directly under the reference initials. (See the model letters for examples of their placement.)

Enclosure notations differ greatly in their forms. Here are some of the commonly accepted and correct forms:

Enclosure
Enclosure (4)
4 Enclosures
Enclosures 4
Enc.

Sometimes the types of enclosures are indicated:

Enclosures
1. Invoice 5487/87
2. File 54A-R333
3. Map 28g

NOTE: If the items "enclosed" were sent separately, indicate that as follows:

Enclosures
1. Invoice 5487/87

Sent separately
2. Map 28g
3. FFFF Price list

Courtesy Copy Notation

Courtesy copy (and blind courtesy copy) notations show the distribution of the letter. This notation comes immediately below enclosure notations and is flush with the left margin.

NOTE: The term *cc* used to refer to *carbon copy.*

Courtesy copy notations may appear as follows:

cc
cc:
Copy to
Copies to

The usual practice is to list all people receiving the letter besides the person addressed in the inside address or attention line:

cc G. L. Lane
H. D. Fisk
N. O. Pope

Letters

If some copies circulate to people without the addressee's knowledge, then these people's initials appear only on the internal copy following the abbreviation *bcc* (for blind courtesy copies):

bcc V. N. Hoopes
W. X. Salvatore

Postscript

Postscripts are additions to the letter after it has been typed or for items needing emphasis.

Postscripts appear two lines below the last line of the courtesy copy initials (or reference initials).

Postscripts may or may not start with *PS* or *PPS*. See the postscript in the modified block style model for an example without these abbreviations.

Envelopes

All business envelopes, regardless of size, must have the following on the front:

—The addressee's full name and address. These should be centered vertically on the envelope and should be centered horizontally between the return address and the right edge of the envelope.

—The sender's full name and full address. This return address is usually printed or typed in the upper left corner, two or three lines below the top edge and five spaces from the left edge of the envelope.

Besides the address and return address, envelopes may have the following:

—Special mailing notations *(Special Delivery, Certified Mail, Registered Mail)* come beneath the stamp in the upper right corner.

—Other miscellaneous notations *(Personal, Confidential, Please Forward, and Hold for Arrival)* appear above the receiver's address.

Note 1: The names and addresses should be consistent with those in the letterhead, the inside address, and the signature block of the letter.

Note 2: The address should contain no abbreviations except those in the legal name of an organization and in the Postal Service's two-character abbreviations for states. The name and address should be typed in block style:

Mr. Hank Stephenson
Financial Officer
G. H. Vogel and Company, Inc.
Mail Drop 567-3
650 First Avenue
Los Angeles, CA 90012

Note 3: Abbreviations are permissible in mass mailouts requiring addresses from computers. The U.S. Postal Service has provided standard sets of abbreviations for long names of cities and towns, as well as more general terms like *road* and *university.*

Note 4: Carefully fold letters before inserting them into envelopes. The two common methods of folding letters are as follows:

Folds for Long Business Envelopes (No. 10)

—Fold the bottom third of the letter up and crease. Next fold the top third of the letter down and crease. (Caution: The top fold should not come far enough down to bend or crease the third of the paper folded up from the bottom.)

Folds for Regular Business Letters (No. 6 ¾)

—Fold horizontally almost in half, with about one-half inch of the top of the paper visible above the folded position.

—Then fold the paper in the vertical direction. This time, fold the paper into thirds: the right third over the middle third, and then the left third over the other thirds. (If folded properly, the upper left corner of the letter is on the top of all of the folds.)

Lists

Lists include a series of items embedded within a paragraph (called **paragraph lists**) and a series displayed vertically (called **displayed lists**):

1. Listed item a
2. Listed item b
3. Listed item c
4. Listed item d

Paragraph Lists

1. Use a list within a paragraph whenever the list is short (fewer than six items) and you do not wish to emphasize the list:

Five collective protection countermeasures were identified: (1) simple activated-carbon absorption filters, (2) regenerative filters, (3) closed-loop or recirculation environmental control systems, (4) pyrolytic destruction of agents, and (5) corona discharge and other molecular disruption techniques.

2. Use numbers or letters to identify each item in a paragraph series. Enclose the number or letter within parentheses:

The HCF memory is in three sections: (1) program, (2) non-volatile RAM, and (3) scratch-pad RAM.

or

The HCF memory is in three sections: (a) program, (b) non-volatile RAM, and (c) scratch-pad RAM.

3. Capitalize the first word of each item in a paragraph list only if each item is a complete sentence or if an item begins with a proper noun:

We propose that the qualification program include (1) documentation of tests conducted on similar equipment, (2) service history of similar equipment, and (3) Bell Laboratories' testing of the equipment.

4. In paragraph lists, do not precede the list with a colon if the list follows a preposition or a verb:

The 1553 interface will be programmed to respond to (a) synchronize (without data word), (b) synchronize (with data word), (c) transmit status word, and (d) reset terminal.

NOTE 1: If this list becomes a displayed list, however, use the colon even though the list follows a verb:

The 1553 interface commands are:

a. Synchronize (without data word).
b. Synchronize (with data word).
c. Transmit status word.
d. Reset terminal.

NOTE 2: This example (where a colon follows a verb introducing a list) is more and more widely accepted. However, some editors would still revise the lead-in sentence to read as follows:

The 1553 interface has these commands:

Displayed Lists

5. Use a displayed list for a long series of items and for any series you wish to emphasize:

Five collective protection countermeasures were identified:

1. Simple activated-carbon absorption filters
2. Regenerative filters
3. Closed-loop or recirculation environmental control systems
4. Pyrolytic destruction of agents
5. Corona discharge and other molecular disruption techniques

6. Use numbers, letters, bullets, or dashes to identify each item in a displayed list.

Use numbers or letters whenever the list is lengthy, whenever the text must refer to items in the list, or whenever the items are listed in decreasing order of importance. The numbers or letters should not be enclosed by parentheses, but they should be followed by a period:

a. Definition of systems and subsystems
b. Progressive apportionment of figure-of-merit requirements to subsystems
c. Progressive definition of functional requirements for subsystems to meet mission requirements
d. Definition of subsystem design and interface constraints as dictated by the chosen deployment strategy

See NUMBERING SYSTEMS.

7. Use bullets or dashes to identify each item in a displayed list when the list contains items of equal importance and those items will not have to be referred to by number or letter:

We selected these means of accomplishing the scope of work for the following reasons:

Lists

- They respond to the program needs as defined in the RFP.
- They reflect the approach to project definition steps that experience indicates is effective in other isotope separation projects.
- They reflect our experience in assisting R&D personnel in transferring the requisite technology to documentation rapidly enough to support tight project schedules.

On word processors and typewriters that do not have bullets, create bullets by typing a lowercase *o* and using a black ink pen to fill in the center.

8. Capitalize the first word of each item in a displayed list:

- Item a
- Item b
- Item c

NOTE: The exception to this rule occurs whenever the listed items complete the thought begun in the introductory sentence (see rule 11, note 2.)

9. Use a colon to introduce a list when the sentence preceding the list contains such anticipatory words or phrases as *the following, as follows, thus,* and *these:*

The 1553 interface will be programmed to respond to the following mode commands:

a. Synchronize (without data word).

b. Synchronize (with data word).

c. Transmit status word.

d. Reset terminal.

10. Do not end the introductory sentence with a colon if the sentence is lengthy and the anticipatory word or phrase occurs very early in the sentence or if another sentence comes between the introductory sentence and the list:

The following steps are required to process the message received by the bit processor. Note that the sequence parallels both subsystem interface architectures.

1. Recognize a valid RT enable flag.
2. Read the 16-bit word from the bit processor.
3. Check the T/R bit.
4. Decode the subaddress field where incoming data will be stored.

11. End items in a displayed list with periods if one or more of the items is a complete sentence:

Western Aeronautics has a wide range of related experience:

- We built and tested crash-proof recorders for the T41 and T7G engine data analyzers.
- We designed, developed, tested, and manufactured the Central Air Flight Data Computer (CAFDC) systems for the Air Force.
- We produced the full range of flight data computers with 18 different designs flown on 35 different aircraft.

NOTE 1: The above listed items are clearly sentences, so periods are necessary. Sometimes, however, items may not be clearly sentences:

—Convene.

—Caucus.

—Vote.

—Adjourn.

Strictly speaking, each of these words is an imperative sentence and should require a period (see SENTENCES), but their shortness has led some editors to prefer no periods. Items without periods also reflect a trend in advertising and in media documents to use lists without punctuation.

NOTE 2: Sometimes a displayed list completes the sentence begun with the introductory statement. In this instance even though the listed items are not sentences, the final one will require a period. Also, note that such lists do not follow a colon and that they use commas or semicolons after all but the last item:

The life of a counterflow plate-fin recuperator may be prolonged by

1. increasing the fin thickness,
2. providing airflow passages inside the manifold hoops, and
3. providing for gas flow through the hollow side bars.

Lists with continued punctuation (as in this example) are now rare, probably because writers, influenced by advertising, are using capitals and spacing to make lists more visually emphatic.

Lists Within Lists

12. Whenever one list occurs inside another list, use numbers for the outer list and letters for the inner list:

1. The physical characteristics of the regenerator include (a) ferritic stainless steel construction, compatible with a moist, coastal salt-air environment; (b) an internally insulated turbine exhaust duct; (c) a horizontal configuration; and (d) high performance rectangular fins.
2. The performance data includes (a) 88 percent thermal effectiveness, (b) over 4,600 hours of operating time, and (c) no evidence of corrosion or fouling.

NOTE: For a third level of nested lists, use lowercase Roman numerals (*i, ii, iii,* etc.). Also use caution. Lists within lists within lists become confusing and irritating.

Lists and Parallelism

13. Ensure that items in lists are parallel in structure. Begin each item with the same type of word (noun, verb, adjective, etc.):

This programming language interface allows the simulation model programs to access the database in the following ways:

1. Retrieve records with specific key values.
2. Retrieve records in database sequences.
3. Insert records into the database.
4. Delete records from the database.
5. Modify and replace records in the database.

Each item begins not only with a verb, but also with the same kind of verb. The list would **not** be parallel if the verb or sentence forms were changed:

This programming language interface will allow the simulation model programs to access the database in the following ways:

1. Retrieve records with specific key values.
2. Records in data base sequences can also be retrieved.
3. Insertion of records into the database.
4. Deleting records from the database.
5. Modification and replacement of records in the database.

Lists, whether in paragraph or display form, must always be parallel. The items listed must be consistent in form and structure. See PARALLELISM.

Manuscript Form

Manuscript originally referred to handwritten copy. It now means the typed or word-processed (printed) copy from which a final copy is prepared. The final copy can be typeset and printed, or it can be photocopied from the manuscript and then circulated within an organization.

If you are writing for a particular publication, consult the editors for specific guidelines on the form your manuscript should take. In some cases, for example, you should submit an electronic copy (with a specified format) rather than hard copy. The following rules apply to most manuscripts, whether formally printed or not. See WORD PROCESSING.

---

1. Print (type) manuscripts on quality paper, usually 8½- by 11-inch bond.

Do not use erasable paper, onion-skin paper, or odd-sized paper. Odd-sized paper can create difficulties in photocopying. Corrections made on erasable and onion-skin paper are difficult to read.

---

2. Print (type) manuscripts using a standard type size and style.

Standard type sizes for documents are 10- or 12-point. Some typewriters and most computer printers allow for larger or smaller type sizes. Use larger type sizes for headings only. Avoid smaller type sizes except in such printed matter as forms and contracts and in tables, charts, maps, and other visual aids where space is limited.

Various computer type fonts, as well as interchangeable typing elements and print wheels, give writers a choice of typefaces and sizes. Nevertheless, in manuscripts you should avoid typefaces that present too radical an image for sustained reading. Do not use typefaces that are too fat or too thin, and avoid italics, script, and gothic typefaces for the bulk of your text. However, you can use exotic typefaces for effect if you use them sparingly. See EMPHASIS, WORD PROCESSING, and DESKTOP PUBLISHING.

---

3. Double- or triple-space manuscripts and leave generous margins at the top, bottom, and sides of each page.

Double- or triple-spacing and generous margins allow for editorial insertions and corrections. Usually the top and the left margins should be at least 1½ inches, and the bottom and the right margins should be at least 1 inch. Journals and presses often have their own requirements. Some provide paper with a ruled box to ensure that writers and typists leave proper margins.

Footnotes, bibliographies, and inserted material (such as extensive quotations) should also be double-spaced, especially if such items are being prepared for a final printed copy. Footnotes should be listed separately, chapter by chapter, rather than inserted at the bottom of each page. See FOOTNOTES and BIBLIOGRAPHIC FORM.

If your final copy will be prepared directly from manuscript and if your final copy will be single-spaced, resist having the manuscript single-spaced too early. Double-spaced manuscripts are much easier to revise and edit. On word processors, turning a draft double-spaced manuscript into a single-spaced final copy is especially easy.

---

4. Number manuscript pages consecutively, beginning at the first page of text or, if your text has chapters, at the chapter divider for the first chapter.

Page numbers should appear at the top of each page, centered or flush right.

Consecutive numbering throughout the manuscript is advisable, but in longer texts, especially technical publications, numbering by chapter is advisable: 4-65 for chapter 4, p. 65.

Chapter dividers and the first pages of chapters should have odd page numbers, although those page numbers are usually not printed in the text. These pages should appear on the right or facing pages of double-sided manuscripts. If you use a chapter divider, the divider page is p. 1, its reverse side is an unnumbered p. 2, and the first page of text is p. 3.

Front material (the table of contents, title page, preface, and list of illustrations) are usually numbered with small Roman numerals: *v, vi, vii.*

Avoid inserted pages. If you cannot, number them as follows: *36a, 36b, 36c,* etc. The inserted pages in this example would follow page 36.

Numbers for figures, tables, sections, and chapters should be Arabic. The numbers of figures and tables often reflect the chapter numbers as well: figure 6-8 for chapter 6, figure 8.

End material (appendices, glossaries, footnotes, and bibliographies) should follow the sequential numbering begun in the text. If the text is numbered chapter by chapter *(4-18, 4-19,* etc.), then end material should receive its own section numbers: *A-15* for p. 15 of appendix A.

---

5. Print corrections above the text, preferably in ink, and make them as legible as possible.

If corrections will not fit above the line in question, cut the text apart and insert a newly printed or typed version into the space left in the original copy. Avoid making elaborate insertions in the margins, and never use the reverse side of a page for corrections or comments. If inserted material is lengthy, use inserted pages and clearly number. See rule 4. Formal proofreading symbols are necessary only when you are dealing with professional typesetters and printers. See EDITING AND PROOFREADING SYMBOLS. If you use your own system for noting changes, ensure that typists understand the correction symbols.

Always keep both a complete hard copy and an electronic copy of your manuscript, including all corrections. This precaution is especially important if you are submitting your manuscript to a publisher. Also, be sure that your electronic copy has all of your final corrections and edits.

See WORD PROCESSING.

---

6. Develop and maintain consistent headings within a manuscript.

Word processors (computers) allow headings to be more varied than they could be with typewriters. If you have access to word processing, explore the options. If your manuscript will be printed, you have an even greater range of possibilities. Typeset and printed headings can be set in larger type sizes or different type styles, and they can be printed in boldface or color. See HEADINGS, WORD PROCESSING, and DESKTOP PUBLISHING.

---

7. Plan your tables, figures, and other visual aids as early as possible.

Plan your visual aids before writing much of the text, especially in technical documents. Many publications have strict guidelines for the size, style, and quality of visual aids. You should be aware of the visual aid opportunities and limitations before devoting too much effort to the text, and you should ensure that the visuals you produce will be consistent with a publisher's guidelines. Also, visual aids often take longer to produce than text. See VISUAL AIDS.

---

8. Avoid extensive cross-references throughout a manuscript, especially references to page numbers.

Page references might change every time a text has to be repaginated. If cross-references are necessary, use sections or chapter headings. Also, remember that extensive cross-references demand extra proofreading and checking for internal consistency.

Publishing a Book or Journal Article

If you wish to publish a book or journal article, ask the editors for a copy of any necessary editorial guidelines. In addition, you may wish to refer to *The Chicago Manual of Style,* 13th edition, and *The Chicago Guide to Preparing Electronic Manuscripts for Authors and Publishers.* See REFERENCES.

Maps

Maps show the geographic features of an area and indicate spatial relationships, locations, and distances. Maps can also show geologic features, mineral occurrences, watersheds, geographic distributions of people, housing, manufacturing sites, wells, crops, and how to get to grandmother's house.

For general information on using maps as visual aids, see VISUAL AIDS. See also CHARTS, GRAPHS, ILLUSTRATIONS, PHOTOGRAPHS, and TABLES. For information on captions for maps, see CAPTIONS.

1. Label and number all maps.

Because maps are a type of figure, label and number your maps *Figure 1, Figure 2,* etc., following the order that they and other figures are referenced in your text. If you use many maps in your document, consider labeling and numbering them *Map 1, Map 2*, etc., and inserting a separate list of maps along with the table of contents and the list of figures.

2. Name each map, explain its features, and include an action caption.

Name the map, indicating the principal feature(s) of the map (see figure 1). This name should be as brief as possible, but an accurate name is more important than brevity. Do not include the words *Map of* on a map as part of the name. But in the table of contents, add the phrase *Map of* or include *Map* in parentheses so that the readers can tell which figures are maps.

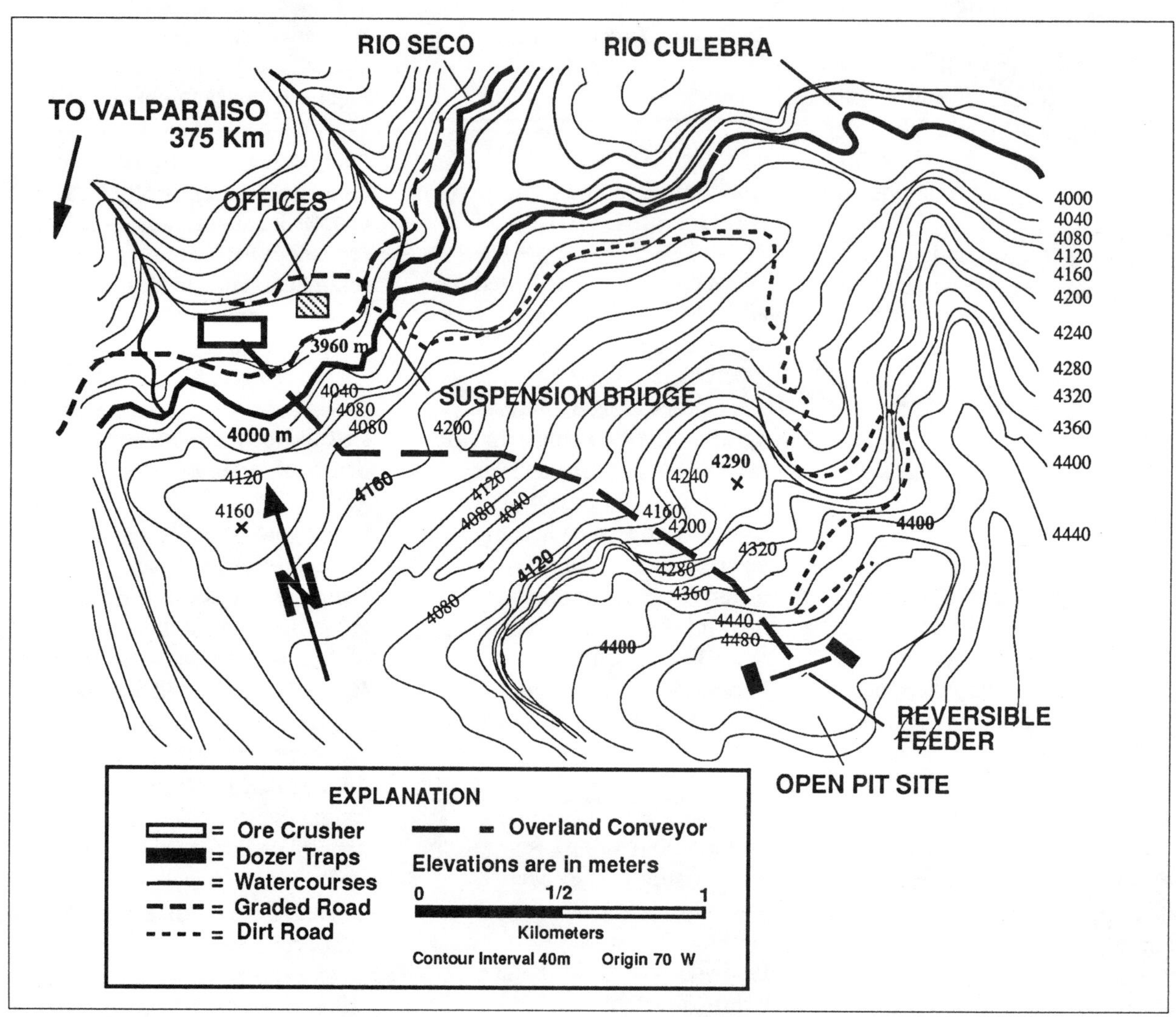

Figure 1. Proposed Route of Overland Conveyor. *The overland conveyor would transport raw ore from the open pit site to stamp mill site.*

Maps

Use an explanation block (legend, key) to ensure that readers understand all of the symbols, numbers, letters, patterns, and colors on your maps (see figure 1). Orient all of the letters, numbers, and labels horizontally on the page. Place the explanation where it does not interfere with items on the map. Keep the explanation block small enough that it does not overpower the map itself.

As part of the explanation block, include the scale. For documents circulated within the United States or England, label the scale with yards and miles rather than meters and kilometers. Considering, however, the possibility of international readers, include a conversion table or a parallel metric scale. For documents with a clear international readership, label the scale using the metric system. See Units of Measurement and Metrics.

Include an action caption (following the name of the map) that states the key message that you want the reader to learn from studying the map (see the action captions on figures 1 and 2). See Captions.

3. Ensure that maps are scaled correctly to show proper spatial relationships.

All maps must have a scale (see figures 1 and 2). The scale must be appropriate to depict the features you wish to emphasize—enough detail for readers to grasp

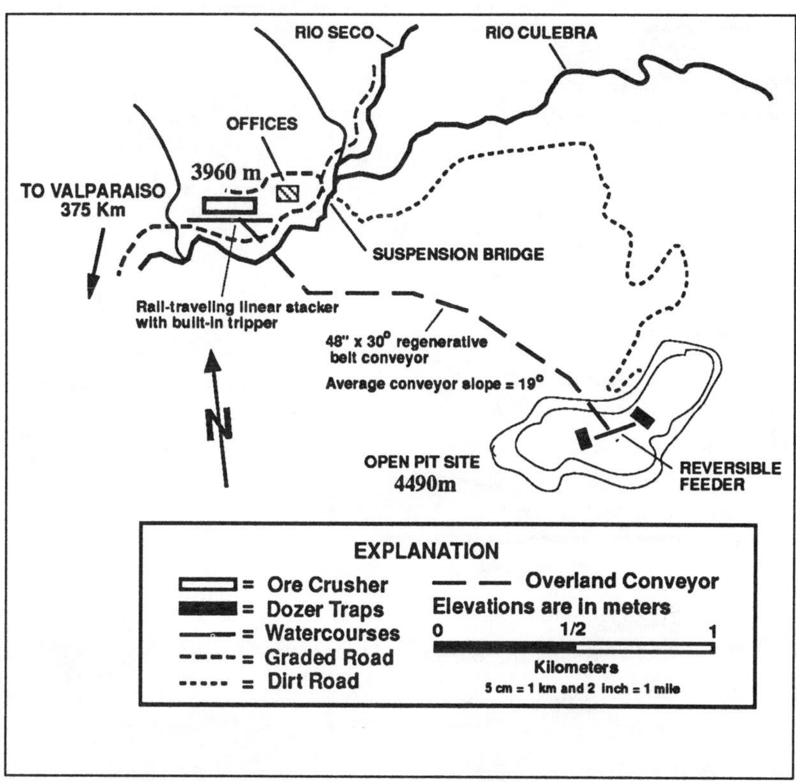

Figure 2. Proposed Route of Overland Conveyor. *Significant environmental damage of ore transportation would be eliminated because the ore would be transported by an overland conveyor, not by truck, which would require extensive road maintenance.*

the geographic relationships but not so detailed that important features are obscured. Too small a scale may distort the geographic perspective because your map becomes too large. If you use too large a scale, map features might become too small and the surrounding areas too large—the map overwhelms its purpose.

A general, planimetric map at 1:250,000 scale might be suitable for showing the principal physiographic features of a large area, but a more detailed map with contour lines at 1:24,000 scale might be needed to show nitrate-contamination of ground water in a municipal area or how steep the road is to grandmother's house.

Design your map for readability at the scale you select, remembering that changing the scale by reducing or enlarging often makes the map less readable. For example, the letter "o" usually becomes a dot when the map is reduced by a factor of 2 or more. Remember, also, that maps photocopied several times lose much of their contrast and clarity.

Choosing the proper scale is difficult if your range of scales is limited by your publication medium, which is usually controlled by your budget and by the size of the printing press at your local printer. If you can afford to create and print a large, fold-out, color map, you can do

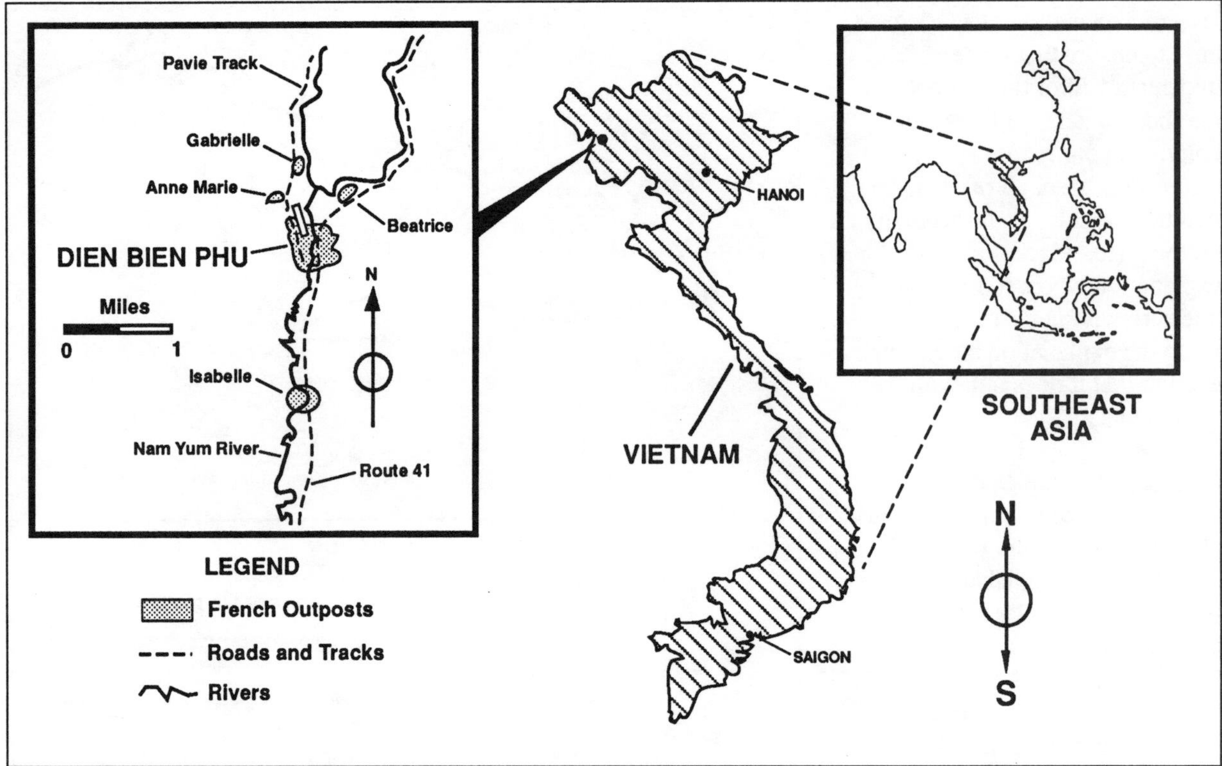

Figure 3. Disposition of Forces at Dien Bien Phu. *The satellite outposts around Dien Bien Phu were intended to cover the central position and to break up mass attacks against it. They were isolated and eliminated one by one in early spring, 1954.*

many things that you cannot do if your budget allows only a black-and-white, page-sized map.

Determine the type, scale, and size of your maps in the initial phases of project and document planning, not when you are preparing the final draft of your report. The earlier you plan your maps, the better their quality.

4. Simplify maps by eliminating unnecessary detail.

Maps must have a single purpose. Anything on the map that is extraneous to that central purpose—such as contour lines, unrelated roads, creeks, and trails—is clutter. Delete the clutter. Do not make readers waste time worrying over features that have nothing to do with the central purpose.

Figure 2 is the same map as figure 1, but without the contour lines. If your purpose for the map were to inform the public of the route of a proposed conveyor, the contour lines probably would be unnecessary. If the purpose of the map were for a mechanical engineer to design the conveyor, a more detailed map with more precise contour lines would be necessary.

Use inset maps either to establish the geographical location and perspective or to provide greater detail for some site or feature.

Inset maps used to establish the geographical location and perspective are essential when users of the map might not know where a country, state, or other geographical feature is located. In figure 3, for example, Vietnam's general location in Southeast Asia is indicated by the inset map to the right of the figure. Another example is a small-scale map to show **specifically** where a project is located in an area already known by the readers.

Figure 3 also illustrates the second type of inset map: a map giving greater detail on one feature or site. In figure 3 the inset map to the left of the figure blows up the Dien Bien Phu area to show the distribution of French-held outposts.

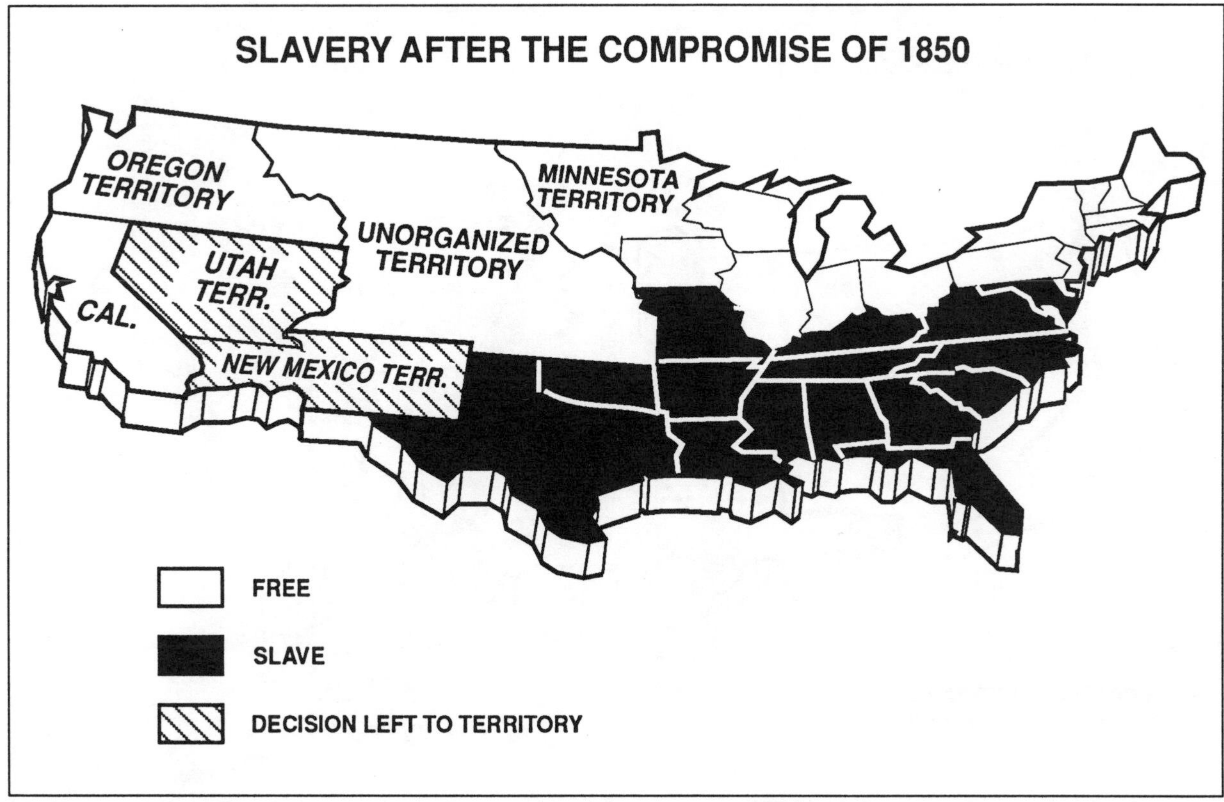

Figure 4. Slave Territory after the Compromise of 1850. *By 1850, rivalry between the slave states and free states was intense, and both free- and slave-state supporters were aggressively trying to add the undecided territories to their camps.*

Either kind of inset map should be as uncluttered and simple as possible, but consider retaining the names of major cities, interstates, or other key landmarks. Also, as figure 3 illustrates, include an explanation along with the inset if appropriate.

5. Use shading, color, and fill patterns to emphasize the features you want readers to focus on.

Shading, color, and fill patterns help distinguish features while calling attention to them (see figure 4). As long as you don't overdo them, these devices help readers see what you want them to see. For an example of different fill patterns, see CHARTS. You can also use overlays to identify and distinguish particular features, but be sure that the overlays are designed to copy well in the event that the document is photocopied.

6. Include a north arrow or include latitude/longitude reference, and always orient north toward the top of the page.

Unless you are using a map of Antarctica, you should orient the map so that north is toward the top of the page and south is toward the bottom (see figure 3). In any case, always include a north arrow. Maps of Antarctica (yes, we were serious) should be oriented with the South Pole toward the top of the page. Everything in Antarctica is upside down.

On a very large-scale map, a latitude/longitude reference is better than a north arrow because the north arrow will be accurate for only a small portion of the map.

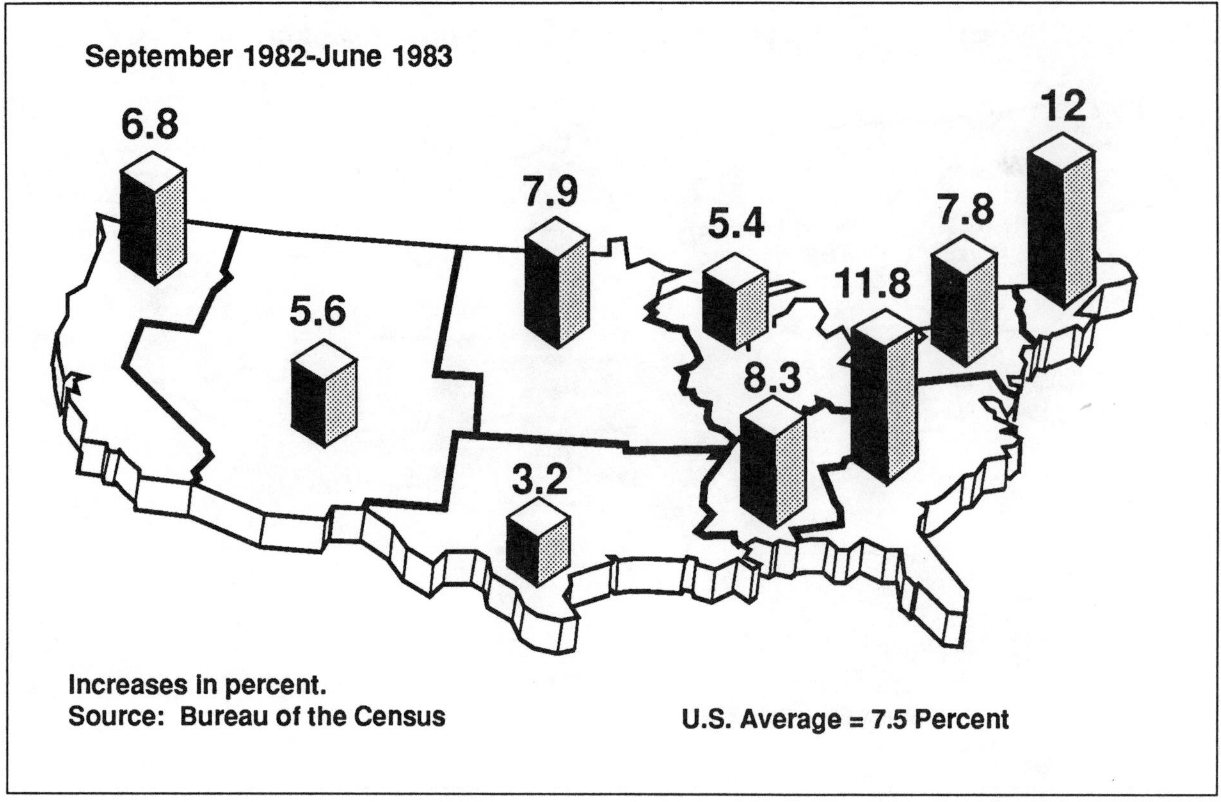

Figure 5. Percentage Increases for Retail Sales by Region. *Despite sluggish growth in Texas and the Rocky Mountain states, retail sales nationwide averaged a 7.5 pcercent increase during late 1982 and early 1983.*

7. Use larger lettering, differing line weights, or shading to label and to highlight principal points of interest on maps.

On figure 4, the principal point of interest is the area controlled by slave states, as shown by the solid shading. On figure 5 the blocks emphasize the geographical trends in retail sales during 1982 and 1983.

8. Combine maps with other visual aid types to create displays showing geographical distribution or geographical implications.

Figure 5 is a combination visual. The map of the United States provides a geographical perspective, and the block features indicate distribution by regions. Combination visuals give you many opportunities for visualizing complex relationships. Most of the time, you are limited only by your imagination.

Figure 6 combines the general features of a map (boundaries, major landmarks, etc.) with information from a GIS (geographical information system). More and more, computers are combining cartographic functions with database activities. As figure 6 shows, the project area is outlined, and the boxes convey information about the timber types in the project area.

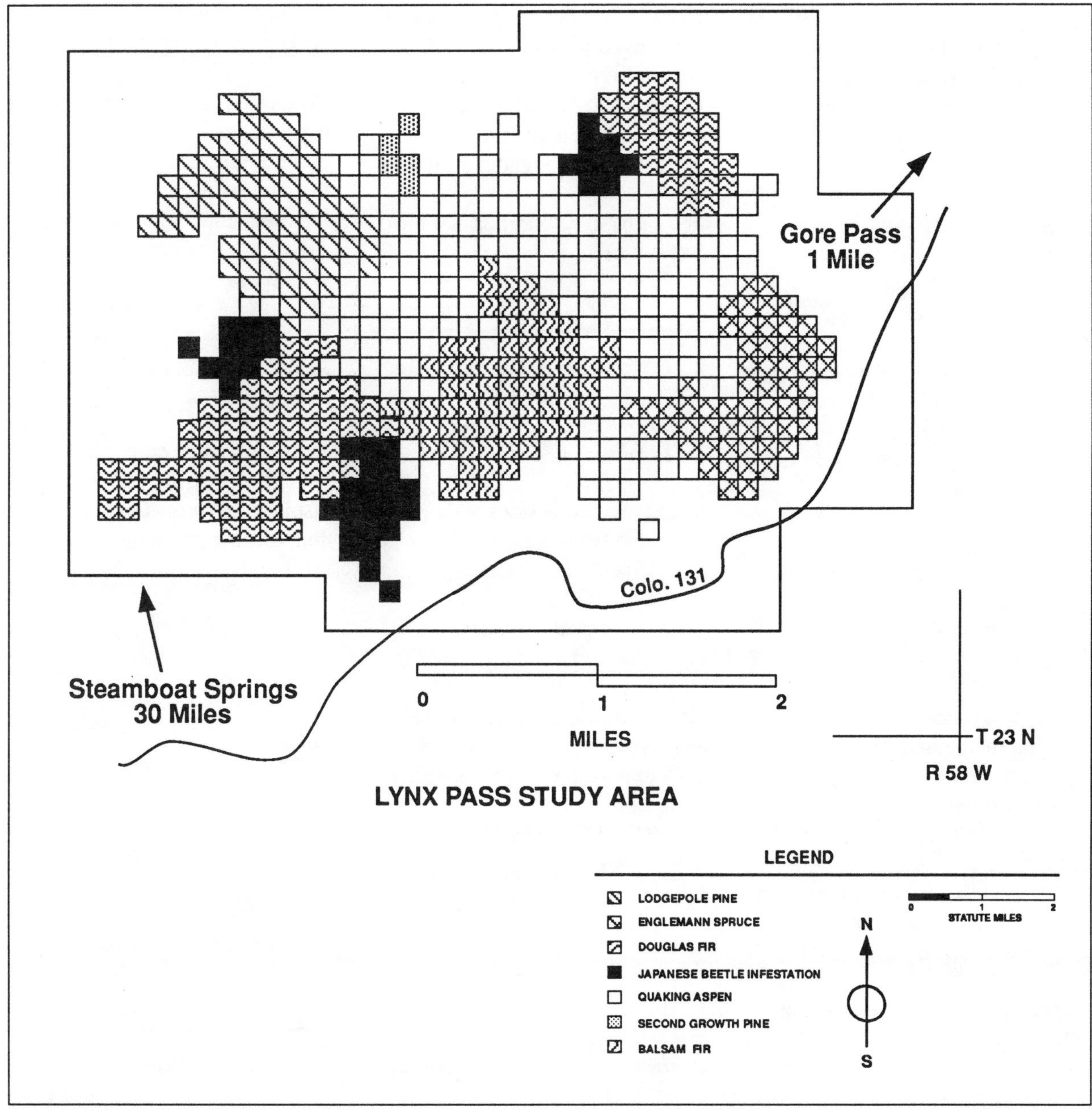

Figure 6. Timber Types in the Project Area. *The Japanese beetle infestation occurs only in the Douglas fir, but we fear that it might expand into other timber types.*

GIS displays, such as in figure 6, influence how writers and readers visualize and conceptualize information. With detailed data available, writers can explore options or alternatives merely by changing codes or adjusting boundaries. Of course, the accuracy of such GIS displays and related alternatives varies depending on the accuracy of the data initially inserted into the system.

Mathematical Notation

Mathematical notation varies from one journal to another and from one publisher to another. So before preparing manuscripts for professional submission, determine which style the editor or publisher prefers. Adhering to the preferred style is especially important if the manuscript will be typeset because setting mathematical symbols is often the most costly phase of typesetting.

The following principles of mathematical notation apply to most publications.

---

1. Be consistent in writing mathematical signs, symbols, and units.

Because the conventions for writing mathematical signs, symbols, and units vary, you must establish a consistent methodology and adhere to it. If you are writing the Greek letters sigma and theta, for instance, you can use either σ or ς for lowercase sigma and θ or ϑ for lowercase theta. Either form is acceptable, but be consistent in the one you choose.

A related principle is to be consistent in your choice of units from one equation to the next. If in one equation a figure is expressed in meters, then related equations should express equivalent figures in meters, not yards.

See SIGNS AND SYMBOLS.

NOTE: Consider keeping a list of the conventions you prefer for writing signs, symbols, and units. Referring to the list as necessary will help you maintain consistency throughout your text.

See EDITING AND PROOFREADING SYMBOLS.

---

2. Use displayed (separate-line) expressions for lengthy equations or for special equations.

Displayed expressions are separated from the text and are usually centered on the page with two or more spaces above and below the equation. Major equations and those equations too lengthy or too complicated to place within the text should be displayed. You can also display equations you wish to emphasize:

The initial form of the equation was

$$\int_a^b f(x)\,dx = \frac{b-a}{6}\left[f(a) + 4f\left(\frac{a+b}{2}\right) + f(b)\right]$$

---

3. Use expressions within the text when the equations are minor or routine, when they are short, and when they are not important enough to highlight.

Expressions within text are more difficult for readers to see. However, in many circumstances, the writer does not need to highlight an equation by displaying it. Expressions written within text must be simple enough for readers to comprehend easily:

The expression $1/(x+y)$ becomes increasingly smaller as the values of x and y increase.

When you convert displayed expressions into textual expressions, add parentheses or brackets as necessary to clarify the mathematical relationships:

$$\frac{3}{x-y}ab \quad \textit{becomes} \quad [3/(x-y)]\,ab$$

$$6+\frac{x+y}{3}+18 \quad \textit{becomes} \quad 6+(x+y)/3+18$$

Similarly, when converting a textual expression into a displayed expression, remove unnecessary parentheses and brackets:

$$1/(x/y) \quad \textit{becomes} \quad \frac{1}{x/y}$$

$$(a+3)/(b+6) \quad \textit{becomes} \quad \frac{a+3}{b+6}$$

---

4. Do not punctuate displayed expressions that continue a sentence in the text:

The revised equation is

$$y = A + B(x-x_1) + C(x-x_1)^2$$

---

5. Divide displayed expressions that extend more than one line before the equals sign or the sign of operation:

$$\int_a^b f(x)dx = \frac{1}{3}\Big[y_0 + y_n + 4(y_1 + y_2 + \ldots + y_{n-1})$$

$$+2(y_2 + y_4 + \ldots + y_{n-2})\Big]\Delta x$$

Mathematical Notation

NOTE 1: The opposite is true for expressions within text:

After conversion, the alternate version has $\pi(y_{i-1}+y_i)(\Delta x_i^2+\Delta y_i^2)= \pi(y_{i-1}+y_i)\left[1+(\Delta y_i/\Delta x_i)^2\right]^{1/2}\Delta x_i$

NOTE 2: Do not divide short expressions. If possible, avoid dividing any expressions.

6. For reference, number displayed expressions in parentheses to the right of the expression:

$$V^5 2\pi\int_a^b xf(x)dx \qquad (15)$$

NOTE: Unless you refer to the expressions elsewhere in the text, numbering of displayed expressions is unnecessary.

7. For grouped expressions, place parentheses inside brackets inside braces inside parentheses:

$$x=a\left(b\left\{c+\left[d+2(e+7)\right]\right\}\right)$$

NOTE: Sometimes these symbols appear by themselves or the sequence does not apply:

Sets

$\{a,b,c\}$

Expressions with Functions

$f(g(x))$

Expressions with Upper and Lower Limits

$[\tan\theta]_0^\pi$

See BRACKETS.

Memos

Memos is a shortened version of *memoranda* or *memorandums*. The longer, formal versions are correct, but the more convenient *memos* is widely used and acceptable.

Memos are essentially letters written to persons within the writer's organization. Hence, memos are often referred to as "interoffice correspondence." Memos also function as informal technical reports. Some oil companies, for instance, publish internal documents called geologic memorandums. In form, these documents are memos; in content, they are technical reports. So, no clear distinction exists between letters, memos, and reports. Nevertheless, memos are almost always intended for an internal audience, and they tend to be less formal than letters and reports.

Memo length varies, depending on the organization and the purpose of the memo. Some organizations insist that memos be no longer than one page. They argue that memos are for transmitting and storing day-to-day internal messages (memos are a more permanent record than telephone calls) and that messages requiring more than one page have enough content to justify a report.

Other organizations allow memos to be as long as necessary, and they are often as much as 20 pages long. In longer memos, the writer must use summaries, headings, lists, and other emphatic devices to break up the content and make the memo readable. See EMPHASIS.

Memo content also varies considerably—from brief notices of meetings to full-fledged analyses of alternatives and recommendations for action. The fact is that memos are useful devices for transmitting any type of information to other persons within your organization.

Effective Memo Writing

Because memos are essentially letters that stay within an organization, the principles of good letter writing apply equally to memos:

—Begin memos with the most important ideas.

—Subordinate references to previous documents, conversations, and meetings.

—Ensure that your memos are clearly and logically organized.

—Throughout memos, emphasize key data and ideas.

—Avoid cliched openings and closings.

For a thorough discussion of these principles, see LETTERS. See also ORGANIZATION, EMPHASIS, REPETITION, KEY WORDS, PARAGARAPHS, and VISUAL AIDS.

Memo Format

Memo format varies considerably from organization to organization. However, memos often have these components: **heading, body, signature line, reference initials, attachment notation,** and **courtesy copy notation.** See the model memo in this section for an illustration of these components.

The Heading

Memo headings, whether printed or typed, usually contain these elements:

To:
From:
Subject:
Date:

The order of these elements, their spacing and punctuation, and their placement on the page vary considerably. In printed memo forms, the heading elements often do not have colons. Typed headings usually have colons.

Some memos open with *To* and then give the subject line. Others place the date after the *To* line. Still others arrange the items in two parallel lists:

To	From
Department	Department
Subject	Date

Some memos omit the *From* line, opting instead for a typed name and signature at the end of the memo.

Two optional elements of the heading are a distribution list and a reference line or block.

The distribution list can appear in a box that follows or includes *To.* If used in the heading, the distribution list replaces the cc (courtesy copy) list at the end of the memo.

Memo (Printed Form)

To:	M. L. Abrams	Date: March 15, 1989
From:	Joan Abercrombie	
Subject:	Memorandum Format on Printed Forms	Invoice 45897 / A

On memorandum forms with To, From, and Subject printed, the names and subject title should be aligned with the left margin of the body of the memo (as shown here). If the printed items are flush left (as above), then the names (corresponding to To and From) should be aligned with the subject title. If the printed items are aligned flush right, then the names and subject title appear two spaces after the items (or colons).

The addressee's name appears without a gender title (Mr., Mrs., Ms., or Miss). If the memo is addressed to two or more people, list other primary readers after or beneath the first addressee. If the form does not have enough space to list all addresses, then write "Distribution" in the To line and list all addressees in a distribution list at the end of the memo. List all secondary readers in a cc line at the end of the memo.

The date is usually written with the month spelled out: March 15, 1989 (not 3/15/1989).

Brief reference lines can appear two lines beneath the date. (See the discussion of reference lines in LETTERS.) Extensive references to previous documents, meetings, or conversations must follow the subject line because of space limitations on most printed forms; such references might include the names and dates of previous memos that have a bearing on this memo. If several items appear in the reference list, number them for easy reference in the body of the memo (see LETTERS).

Some organizations omit the From line and place an author's signature block at the end of the memo. Other organizations retain the From line but add the author's initials at the end of the memo. Titles following the author's name or initials are usually unnecessary but can be used.

The content of the subject line should be specific enough to tell readers exactly what the memo is about. The subject line may therefore include dates, invoice numbers, project information, loan agreement numbers, and other similar information. (A specific enough subject line may make a reference line unnecessary.) If the subject line extends beyond one line, the information should be single spaced and centered:

Subject: Revisions of the Payment Clause Loan Agreement 5676-34

Short reference lines or blocks can appear two lines below the date if the date appears by itself just right of the center of the page. Extensive references need to have their own lines, usually before or after the *Subject* line:

1. F. H. Howell, "Testing of the Wing Plate Assembly," May 18, 1990.
2. J. K. Jameson, "Design Options in the Wing Plate Assembly," March 22, 1990.

Numbering references helps writers refer to the references later in the text:

> Reference 1 notes that all wing plate assemblies have passed inspection this year. However, reference 2 indicates that design modifications must be undertaken to improve reliability.

The names of both the sender and the receiver do not require courtesy titles (*Mr., Mrs., Ms.,* or *Miss*), but *Dr.* is sometimes used. Names should be as complete as possible even if the sender and receiver are close friends. Long after the memo has been filed, future readers will probably not know whom Hank or Sue refers to, and the names could be important.

The subject line should be as specific as possible (see HEADINGS):

this

Subject: Recommendation to Test Two Methods of Lowering Salt Content

not this

Subject: Salt Content Tests

---

this

Subject: The Sales Decline in the Northern Region

not this

Subject: Northern Region Sales

The Body

Paragraphs in the body of the memo are usually single-spaced with a double space between them. These paragraphs may or may not be indented (5 to 10 spaces). Both the indented and block forms are correct and usually acceptable; however, your company may have a preferred style.

Headings and lists are important devices, especially when a memo is more than a page or two long. See HEADINGS and LISTS.

Memos

The Signature Line

Traditional memos have no signature line. The author's name appears after *From* in the heading.

Recently, however, many writers have begun signing their initials or their whole names two lines below the final line of the text. The name or initials may be typed, but they may also be handwritten.

Rarely do such signature lines contain titles, probably because the people within a company already know job titles or can easily look them up in a directory.

Reference Initials

Reference initials in memos usually contain only the typist's initials. These initials appear either two lines below the signature line or two lines below the final line of text (if the memo has no signature line). The initials are usually in lowercase letters:

jtk

If the reference initials also contain the author's initials, then they would precede those of the typist and would follow one of these forms:

GLK/jtk GLK:jtk glk:jtk

When someone other than the sender writes the memo, the sender's initials come first, then the writer's initials, and then the typist's initials:

GLK/TER/jtk GLK:TER:jtk

Memo (Printed Form)

M. L. Abrams
Page 2
March 15, 1989

The body of the memo has single-spaced paragraphs with one blank line between paragraphs. Paragraphs may appear in block form (no indentation) or with indentation (usually five spaces).

<u>Headings and Lists</u>

Headings are always valuable, but they are mandatory if the memo becomes two or more pages long. Lists can help even a one-page memo. See LISTS for a discussion of the different kinds of lists.

The heading for continued pages should contain the addressee's name, the date, and the page number. An optional form to the block pattern shown above is:

M. J. Abrams -2- March 15, 1989

The reference initials appear flush with the left margin and are two lines below the writer's initials or signature or two lines below the text (if the writer's initials or signature are omitted).

An attachment notation appears immediately below and flush with the reference initials. The number of attachments appears within parentheses, as shown below.

The memo ends with the cc list of those secondary readers receiving copies. A bcc (blind courtesy copy) list can also appear if the primary readers are not supposed to know or do not need to know the complete circulation list. The bcc list appears only on the copies, not on the original (see LETTERS).

J.A.

bop
Attachments (2)

cc Sidney White
Blake James
Sharon Billig

The Attachment Notation

Attachment notations are not very common in memos. If used, they appear on the line immediately below the reference notation:

GLK/jtk
Attachments (3)

In some very technical memos with a number of attachments (such as maps or charts), the attachments may be listed at the bottom of the memo following the attachment notation.

Courtesy Copy Notations

If used, cc (courtesy copy or carbon copy) notations appear two lines below the reference or attachment notations. The form varies:

cc
cc:
Copy to
Copies to

Memos sent to a large number of readers often have a distribution list instead of a courtesy copy list. The word *Distribution* appears in the heading following *To. Distribution* also appears instead of *cc* in the courtesy copy notation, and following *Distribution* is a list of the names and (if appropriate) departments of those people who should receive copies of the memo.

Only occasionally do bcc (blind courtesy copy) lists appear on memos. Blind courtesy copy lists appear only on the copies and not on the original memo.

If used, the bcc list appears two lines below the cc list.

See SPACING.

Metrics

Metric units of measurement are now used worldwide by scientists in the physical and biological sciences. The most precise version of the metric system is the International System of Units or SI (from the *Système international d'unités*) .

Despite its widespread acceptance, SI has not been adopted by all U.S. firms and government agencies. Retooling to metric standards has been a slow and costly process, and redrafting existing maps and design layouts has been unfeasible.

Nevertheless, SI is accepted internationally and uses unambiguous symbols. It is, therefore, the preferred system of measurement for all sciences and many areas of engineering.

1. Use the following base units and their SI symbols:

length	meter (m)
mass	kilogram (kg)
capacity	liter (L)
time	second (s)
current	ampere (A)
thermodynamic temperature	kelvin (K)
amount of substance	mole (mol)
luminous intensity	candela (cd)
plane angle	radian (rad)
solid angle	steradian (sr)

Table 1. SI-Derived units with special names

Quantity	Name	Symbol	Expressed in SI Units
absorbed dose of ionizing radiation	gray	Gy	J/kg
activity of radionuclides	becquerel	Bq	s^{-1}
electric capacitance	farad	F	C/V
electric conductance	siemens	S	A/V
electric potential, potential difference, electromotive force	volt	V	W/A
electric resistance	ohm	Ω	V/A
energy, work, quantity of heat	joule	J	N·m
force	newton	N	$m{\cdot}kg/s^2$
frequency	hertz	Hz	s^{-1}
illuminance	lux	lx	lm/m^2
inductance	henry	H	Wb/A
luminous flux	lumen	lm	cd·sr
magnetic flux	weber	Wb	V·s
magnetic flux density	tesla	T	Wb/m^2
power, radiant flux	watt	W	J/s
pressure, stress	pascal	Pa	N/m^2
quantity of electricity, electric charge	coulomb	C	s·A

2. Do not capitalize or italicize SI symbols, except those derived from proper names (e.g., A and K) and except for L for liter. The symbols do not change in the plural and are never followed by a period:

46 m (*not* 46m)	6 K
1 kg	6 kg
15 s	22.5 cd

Note 1: Use the metric abbreviations only when the metric unit follows a number. If the metric unit appears without a number, spell it out:

We measured 2 kg of salt.

but

We had several kilograms of salt.

Note 2: Wherever possible, choose SI units so that the numerical values will be between 0.1 and 1000:

54 m (*not* 54 000 mm)
3.6 mm (*not* 0.0036 m)

Table 2. SI-Derived units with no special names

Quantity	Description	Expressed in SI Units
acceleration—linear	meter per second squared	m/s^2
—angular	radian per second squared	rad/s^2
area	square meter	m^2
concentration (of amount of substance)	mole per cubic meter	mol/m^3
current density	ampere per square meter	A/m^2
density, mass density	kilogram per cubic meter	kg/m^3
dynamic viscosity	pascal second	Pa·s
electric charge density	coulomb per cubic meter	C/m^3
electric field strength	volt per meter	V/m
energy density	joule per cubic meter	J/m^3
heat capacity, entropy	joule per kelvin	J/K
heat flux density, irradiance	watt per square meter	W/m^2
luminance	candela per square meter	cd/m^2
magnetic field strength	ampere per meter	A/m
molar energy	joule per mole	J/mol
molar entropy, molar heat capacity	joule per mole kelvin	J/(mol·K)
moment of force	newton meter	N·m
permeability	henry per meter	H/m
permittivity	farad per meter	F/m
specific energy	joule per kilogram	J/kg
specific heat capacity, specific entropy	joule per kilogram kelvin	J/(kg·K)
specific volume	cubic meter per kilogram	m^3/kg
speed—linear	meter per second	m/s
—angular	radian per second	rad/s
surface density of charge, flux density	coulomb per square meter	C/m^2
surface tension	newton per meter	N/m
thermal conductivity	watt per meter kelvin	W/(m·K)
volume	cubic meter	m^3
wave number	1 per meter	m^{-1}

3. Use a point (period) as the decimal marker, and use spaces to separate long numbers into easily readable groups of three:

45 671.378 34
0.634 701

Note 1: When only four numbers appear on one side of the decimal, the space is optional but not preferred:

5.7634 *or* 5.763 4
8764 *or* 8 764

Note 2: In many foreign countries, writers use a comma as the decimal marker. If you are writing for a foreign journal or publisher, you may need to use a comma as the decimal marker:

5,763
0,634
3,1415

See Decimals and Periods.

4. Some SI-derived units have special names:

See table 1 on the previous page.

5. Some SI-derived units have no special names:

See table 2.

Metrics

6. Use the table of prefixes to form the names and symbols of multiples and submultiples of SI units:

See table 3.

NOTE 1: Without using a space or a hyphen, attach the prefixes directly to the SI base unit: kilogram, millisecond, gigameter, etc. Similarly, the abbreviations for the prefixes attach directly to the abbreviation for the SI units: cm, Mg, mK, etc.

NOTE 2: Do not use two or more of the prefixes to make compounds of the SI units. Write ns (nanosecond), not mμs (millimicrosecond).

NOTE 3: Although kilogram is the base unit for mass, the prefixes are added to gram (g), not kilogram (kg).

Table 3. Prefixes and their symbols for SI units

MULTIPLYING FACTOR			PREFIX	SYMBOL
1 000 000 000 000 000 000	=	10^{18}	exa	E
1 000 000 000 000 000	=	10^{15}	peta	P
1 000 000 000 000	=	10^{12}	tera	T
1 000 000 000	=	10^{9}	giga	G
1 000 000	=	10^{6}	mega	M
1 000	=	10^{3}	kilo	k
100	=	10^{2}	hecto	h
10	=	10^{1}	deca	da
0.1	=	10^{-1}	deci	d
0.01	=	10^{-2}	centi	c
0.001	=	10^{-3}	milli	m
0.000 001	=	10^{-6}	micro	μ
0.000 000 001	=	10^{-9}	nano	n
0.000 000 000 001	=	10^{-12}	pico	p
0.000 000 000 000 001	=	10^{-15}	femto	f
0.000 000 000 000 000 001	=	10^{-18}	atto	a

7. Some non-SI units are still permissible within SI:

See table 4.

Table 4. Non-SI units permissible within SI

QUANTITY	NAME	SYMBOL	DEFINITION
area	hectare	ha	1 ha = 1 hm^2 = 10 000 m^2
mass	ton, tonne	t	1 t = 1 000 kg = 1 Mg
plane angle	degree	°	1° = (π/180) rad
	minute	′	1′ = (π/10 800) rad
	second	″	1″= (π/648 000) rad
temperature	degree Celsius	°C	0°C = 273.15 K However, for temperature intervals 1°C = 1 K
time	minute	min	1 min = 60 s
	hour	h	1 h = 3600 s
	day	d	1 d = 86 400 s
	year	a	
volume	liter	l or L	1 l = 1 dm^3

8. Avoid certain metric units that have been replaced by SI units:

See table 5.

9. Use table 6 to convert SI units into the common units of measure still widely used in the United States.

Table 5. Metric units replaced by SI units

QUANTITY	NAME	SYMBOL	DEFINITION
absorbed dose of ionizing radiation	rad	rad	1 rad = 10 mGy = 10 mJ/kg
activity	curie	Ci	1 Ci = 37 GBq = 37 ns^{-1}
area	are	a	1 a = 100 m^2
	barn	b	1 b = 100 fm^2
conductance	mho	mho	1 mho = 1 S
energy	calorie	cal	1 cal = 4.1868 J
	erg	erg	1 erg = 0.1 μj
force	kilogram-force	kgf	1 kgf = 9.806 65 N
	kilopound	kp	1 kp = 9.806 65 N
	dyne	dyn	1 dyn = 10 μN
illuminance	phot	ph	1 ph = 10 klx
length	angstrom	Å	1 Å = 0.1 nm
	micron	μ	1 μ = 1 μm
	fermi	fm	1 fermi = 1 femtometer = 1 fm
	X unit	—	1 X unit = 100.2 fm
luminance	stilb	sb	1 sb = 1 cd/cm^2
magnetic field strength	oersted	Oe	1 Oe corresponds to $\frac{1000}{4\pi}$ A/m
magnetic flux	maxwell	Mx	1 Mx corresponds to 0.01·μWb
magnetic flux density	gauss	Gs. G	1 Gs corresponds to 0.1 mT
magnetic induction	gamma	γ	1 γ = 1 nT
mass	metric carat	—	1 metric carat = 200 mg
	gamma	γ	1 γ = 1 μg
pressure	torr	torr, Torr	1 torr = 1.333 22 x 10^2 Pa
viscosity			
—dynamic	poise	P	1 P = 1 dyn·s/cm^2 = 0.1 Pa·s
—kinematic	stokes	St	1 St = 1 cm^2/s
volume	stere	st	1 st = 1 m^3
	lambda	λ	1 λ = 1 μl = 1 mm^3

Metrics

Table 6. Metric values and their equivalents

Length

Myriameter (obs.)	10,000 meters	6.2137 miles
Kilometer	1,000 meters	0.62137 mile
Hectometer	100 meters	328 feet 1 inch
Dekameter	10 meters	393.7 inches
Meter	1 meter	39.37 inches
Decimeter	0.1 meter	3.937 inches
Centimeter	0.01 meter	0.3937 inch
Millimeter	0.001 meter	0.0394 inch

Area

Hectare	10,000 square meters	2.471 acres
Are	100 square meters	119.6 square yards
Centiare	1 square meter	1,550 square inches

Weight

Name	Number of grams	Volume of water corresponding to weight	Avoirdupois weight of water
Metric ton, millier or tonneau	1,000,000	1 cubic meter	2,204.6 pounds
Kilogram or kilo	1,000	1 liter	2.2046 pounds
Hectogram	100	1 deciliter	3.5274 ounces
Dekagram	10	10 cubic centimeters	0.3527 ounce
Gram	1	1 cubic centimeter	15.432 grains
Decigram	.1	0.1 cubic centimeter	1.5432 grains
Centigram	.01	10 cubic millimeters	0.1543 grain
Milligram	.001	1 cubic millimeter	0.0154 grain

Capacity

Name	Number of liters	Metric cubic measure	United States measure	British measure
Kiloliter or stere	1,000	1 cubic meter	1.308 cubic yards	1.308 cubic yards
Hectoliter	100	0.1 cubic meter	2.838 bushels 26.417 gallons	2.75 bushels 22.00 gallons
Dekaliter	10	10 cubic decimeters	1.135 pecks 2.6417 gallons	8.80 quarts 2.200 gallons
Liter	1	1 cubic decimeter	0.908 dry quart 1.0567 liquid quarts	0.880 quart
Deciliter	.1	0.1 cubic decimeter	6.1023 cubic inches 0.845 gill	0.704 gill
Centiliter	.01	10 cubic centimeters	0.6102 cubic inch 0.338 fluid ounce	0.352 fluid ounce
Milliliter	.001	1 cubic centimeter	0.061 cubic inch 0.271 fluid dram	0.284 fluid dram

Common Measures and Their Metric Equivalents

Common measure	Equivalent
Inch	2.54 centimeters
Foot	0.3048 meter
Yard	0.9144 meter
Rod	5.029 meters
Mile	1.6093 kilometers
Square Inch	6.452 square centimeters
Square foot	0.0929 square meter
Square yard	0.836 square meter
Square rod	25.29 square meters
Acre	0.4047 hectare
Square mile	259 hectares
Cubic inch	16.39 cubic centimeters
Cubic foot	0.0283 cubic meter
Cubic yard	0.7646 cubic meter
Cord	3.625 steres
Liquid quart, United States	0.9463 liter
Dry quart, United States	1.101 liters
Quart, imperial	1.136 liters
Gallon, United States	3.785 liters
Gallon, imperial	4.546 liters
Peck, United States	8.810 liters
Peck, imperial	9.092 liters
Bushel, United States	35.24 liters
Bushel, imperial	36.37 liters
Ounce, avoirdupois	28.35 grams
Pound, avoirdupois	0.4536 kilogram
Ton, long	1.0160 metric tons
Ton, short	0.9072 metric ton
Grain	0.0648 gram
Ounce, troy	31.103 grams
Pound, troy	0.3732 kilogram

Modifiers

Modifiers are words or groups of words that describe or limit other words. Modifiers include adjectives, adverbs, prepositional phrases, nouns used as adjectives, and clauses that function as adjectives or adverbs:

> The **entire** proposal had **excellent** graphics. (*adjectives*)
>
> The manager **eventually** explained the reasons for his disapproval. (*adverb*)
>
> The pump **next to the intake line** was serviced last month. (*prepositional phrase*)
>
> The Sky Aviation proposal, **which scored second in technical merit**, had some interesting innovations. (*adjectival clause*)
>
> The ventilation fan was replaced **because its peak circulation volume fell short of our needs**. (*adverbial clause*)

See ADJECTIVES, ADVERBS, NOUNS, PREPOSITIONS, and CONJUNCTIONS.

Writers and editors usually depend on their ears to tell them where a modifier should appear in a sentence. Essentially, however, modifiers should be as close as possible to the words they modify. If they aren't, readers might misinterpret the sentence. The most common sentence problems associated with modifiers result from dangling or misplaced modifiers.

Dangling Modifiers

Modifiers dangle if they do not seem to be related to anything in the sentence or if they are not placed near enough to the words they modify to seem attached to those words. Modifiers dangle when they float, unattached, in a sentence.

Dangling modifiers can be adjectives, adverbs, prepositional phrases, infinitive verbs, appositives, or clauses. Quite often, dangling modifiers are participial phrases, usually beginning with a present participle (such as *knowing*):

> Knowing that standard 3/4-inch pipe was too small, the specifications included provisions for larger pipe.

The phrase beginning with *knowing* seems to modify the noun *specifications*, but, clearly, specifications cannot know anything. The phrase must modify a human being to make logical sense, but no humans are mentioned in the sentence, so the modifier dangles.

Whenever you open a sentence with an action stated with an *-ing* verb (present participle) or *-ed* verb (past participle) and do not follow it with the name of the person doing the action, you will have a dangling modifier (sometimes called a dangling participle):

> *this*
>
> After discussing interest rate trends, we decided to refinance our present loan.
>
> *not this dangling modifier*
>
> After discussing interest rate trends, the decision was made to refinance our present loan.

> *this*
>
> Having analyzed the technical problems, she recommended routing the feed-forward signal through a broadband transmitter.
>
> *or this*
>
> An analysis of the technical problems led researchers to suggest routing the feed-forward signal through a broadband transmitter.
>
> *not this dangling modifier*
>
> Having analyzed the technical problems, the recommendation was to route the feed-forward signal through a broadband transmitter.

---

1. Ensure that modifiers, particularly those expressing action, have a clear noun to modify and are placed as close as possible to that noun (preferably just before it):

> *this*
>
> Having missed our connecting flight, we discovered that no later flights were going to Albuquerque.
>
> *not this dangling modifier*
>
> Having missed our connecting flight, no flights later that day were going to Albuquerque. (*Who missed the flight?*)

> *this*
>
> While reviewing the figures, we discovered many errors.
>
> *not this dangling modifier*
>
> While reviewing the figures, many errors became apparent. (*Who reviewed the figures?*)
>
> *nor this dangling modifier*
>
> Many errors became apparent while reviewing the figures.

NOTE 1: Dangling modifiers do not necessarily introduce the sentence; they can appear anywhere:

> The report was inaccurate, comparing it with the prior ones. (*Who compared it?*)

Modifiers

NOTE 2: Some introductory participles (usually ending in *-ing)* have become so common that they do not require clear words to modify:

> Considering your reluctance, you should not represent us before the Texas Railway Commission.
>
> Judging from the revised figures, the report will never be approved.

Misplaced Modifiers

Modifiers are misplaced when they do not appear in their customary place in a sentence. Readers often misread sentences in which the modifiers are misplaced:

> *this*
>
> The personnel manager told Hughes that the company no longer needed him.
>
> *not this misplaced modifier*
>
> Hughes was told that he was no longer needed by the personnel manager.

> *this*
>
> Your March 15 letter regarding the workover reached me today.
>
> *or this*
>
> Your letter regarding the March 15 workover reached me today.
>
> *not this misplaced modifier*
>
> Your letter regarding the workover of March 15 reached me today.

In both of these examples, the writer might not have intended what the "better" versions say, but the "better" versions are much clearer. Your goal as a writer should be to write so that you cannot be misunderstood. One way to achieve this goal is to ensure that modifiers appear where they should.

---

2. Ensure that modifiers appear either next to or as close as possible to the word or words modified:

> *this*
>
> The manager was interested only in production data.
>
> *not this misplaced modifier*
>
> The manager only was interested in production data. (*Does* only *modify* manager *or* data?)

See ADVERBS.

> The book on the shelf with all the samples is our only copy. (*Does the book or the shelf contain the samples?*)

> The report on geological formations in southern Utah that our manager studied was as up-to-date as possible. (*Did the manager study the report or the formations? The clause* that our manager studied *should appear immediately after* report *or immediately after* Utah. *The placement of the modifying clause conveys its meaning.*)

> *this*
>
> A computer program for estimating gradients has been written for the mainframe IBM in the Production Department.
>
> *not this*
>
> A computer program has been written for calculating estimates of the gradients on the mainframe IBM in the Production Department.

> *this*
>
> We are separately shipping the faulty circuit board.
>
> *or this*
>
> The circuit board that failed is being shipped separately.
>
> *not this*
>
> We are shipping the circuit board that failed under separate cover. (*Was it okay until you shipped it separately?*)

NOTE 1: If a modifier refers to two nouns, it should appear with the first noun mentioned:

> *this*
>
> The land is rocky on the west side of the allotment and somewhat less rocky on the east side.
>
> *not this*
>
> The land is rocky on the west side and somewhat less rocky on the east side of the allotment.

NOTE 2: Unmodified nouns might need an article *(a, an,* or *the)* or an adjective to clarify their meaning:

> *this*
>
> The secretary and the treasurer attended our meeting.
>
> *not this*
>
> The secretary and treasurer attended our meeting. (*Is* the secretary and treasurer *one person or are they two people?*)

Nouns

Nouns signify persons, places, things, and ideas. Even more significant, perhaps, nouns are the main words in a variety of noun phrases:

a **bottle**

the comprehensive **report**

a slowly changing **pattern**

some **tomatoes** for lunch

the young **engineer** who works next door

Noun phrases, in turn, become key building blocks in the English sentence. Within a sentence, a noun phrase can be a subject, an object, or a complement:

The proposed electrical changes will be expensive. *(subject)*

The engineer designed **two holding ponds**. *(object)*

The applicant was **the person who was busily filling out forms**. *(complement)*

Noun phrases can also complete a prepositional phrase by becoming the object of the preposition:

near **the fuel storage tank**
beyond **the property line**
at **the amount we requested**

1. Distinguish between count and non-count nouns.

Count nouns can be counted individually—people, posts, ducks, pencils. Non-count nouns cannot be counted individually—honey, gasoline, air, hospitality.

Count nouns can be either singular or plural:

a bottle/two bottles
every desk/six desks
neither proposal/three proposals
each pump/30 pumps
either ox/five oxen

Non-count nouns are collective in meaning, not singular or plural:

furniture/some furniture
meat/most meat
wheat/less wheat
hospitality/more hospitality
warmth/some warmth

See Plurals and Agreement.

Count and non-count nouns accept different modifying words.

Count nouns:

many fewer animals (*not* less animals)

three fewer pumps (*not* less pumps)

fewer gallons of gasoline (*not* less gallons)

Non-count nouns:

greater warmth (*not* seven warmths)

less gasoline (*not* fewer gasolines)

more hospitality (*not* three hospitalities)

Native speakers of English usually choose the proper modifying words unconsciously. Only occasionally do they make mistakes: *The zoo had less animals than we expected.* Because *animals* can be counted, the proper modifier is *fewer*: *The zoo had fewer animals than we expected.*

Many nouns can belong to either type, but their meanings change:

She's had many odd experiences. *(count)*

This job requires experience. *(non-count)*

The talks will take place in Cairo. *(count)*

He dislikes idle talk. *(non-count)*

2. Use collective nouns and the names of companies as either singular or plural.

Collective nouns are nouns that signify groups of people or things: *staff, team, family, committee, majority, crew, squad,* etc.:

The committee has met, and it has rejected the amendment. *(singular)*

The committee have met, and they have rejected the amendment. *(plural)*

The majority has made its viewpoint clear to the candidate. *(singular)*

The majority have made their viewpoint clear to the candidate. *(plural)*

Company names are similar to collective nouns because they both can be either singular or plural:

Sky Aviation has submitted its proposal. *(singular)*

Sky Aviation had their annual report sent to all stockholders. *(plural)*

See Agreement.

3. Distinguish between common and proper nouns:

Common Nouns

a company	the professor
three lines	the avenue
some paper	a river
an idea	our dentist

Proper Nouns

Acme Glass Company
Professor Thomas Miles
Second Avenue
the Mississippi River
Dr. John Wray

Note: Proper nouns are capitalized, and common nouns are not. For more information, see Capitals, Titles, and Adjectives.

Numbering Systems

Numbering systems are used with outlines, tables of contents, and headings to display a document's organization and allow readers easy access to parts of the document. The two basic numbering systems are the traditional outline system and the decimal system. See OUTLINES.

Traditional System

Traditional outlines use the following numbering and lettering conventions:

1. Uppercase Roman numeral
2. Capital letter
3. Numeral
4. Lowercase letter
5. Numeral in parentheses
6. Lowercase letter in parentheses
7. Numeral with right parenthesis
8. Lowercase letter with right parenthesis

Here, along with the standard indentations, is the traditional system:

```
I.
    A.
        1.
            a.
                (1)
                    (a)
                        1)
                            a)
```

Some authorities (e.g., *The Chicago Manual of Style,* 13th edition, p. 247) prefer a different, but similar, system of subordination.

Decimal System

In the decimal system, successive decimal points indicate levels of subordination:

```
1.0
    1.1
        1.1.1
        1.1.2
        1.1.3
            1.1.3.1
            1.1.3.2
2.0
    2.1
    2.2
        2.2.1
        2.2.2
```

1. Use the traditional system in most cases where you want to show multiple subordination levels, but use the decimal system for very lengthy documents.

The decimal system is preferable in very lengthy documents with a multitude of numbered subsections and in any document with so many major headings that the Roman numerals would become large enough to create confusion among those readers unfamiliar with Roman numerals.

However, with more than four or five levels of subordination, the decimal system is less desirable because readers cannot easily comprehend the text's logical structure. See TABLES OF CONTENTS and OUTLINES.

Numbering Systems and Punctuation

In the traditional system, a period or a single right parentheses always follows the outline number or letter:

```
I. First-order heading
    A. Second-order heading
        1. Third-order heading
            a. Fourth-order heading
                (1) Fifth-order heading
                    (a) Sixth-order heading
                        1) Seventh-order heading
                            a) Eighth-order heading
```

In the decimal system, two or more spaces follow the number. No punctuation is used after the number:

```
1.0 First-order heading
    1.1 Second-order heading
    1.1.1 Third-order heading
    1.1.2.1 Fourth-order heading
    1.1.2.1.1 Fifth-order heading
    1.1.2.1.1.1 Sixth-order heading
```

or

```
1.0 First-order heading
    1.1 Second-order heading
        1.1.1 Third-order heading
            1.1.2.1 Fourth-order heading
                1.1.2.1.1 Fifth-order heading
                    1.1.2.1.1.1
```

See HEADINGS and LISTS.

Numbers

Numbers can be written out or can appear as figures, depending on the size of the number, what it stands for, and how exact it is. The stylistic conventions for number usage vary, so you will find conflicting suggestions from one dictionary or style guide to the next. The recommendations that follow are based on the current standard practice for technical and scientific writing.

1. Use numerical figures for any number expressing time, measurement, or money:

3 a.m.
$15
45 ft
1 in.
8 cm
34.17 m

Measurement includes length, weight, volume, velocity, and even unusual measurement terms, such as *barn*, which in nuclear physics is used to express atomic cross sections in area equal to 10^{-24} square centimeter.

Figures are easier to read and are remembered more accurately and longer than their spelled-out versions. Rules 2 through 12, which follow, present, however, instances where rule 1 may not apply.

2. Write out numbers if they are below 10. If they are 10 or above, use figures:

five systems
15 systems
three mission capabilities
14 mission capabilities
two technicians
22 technicians

Note 1: Regardless of the number's size, use figures if they are followed by a unit of measurement (see rule 1):

5 pounds
2 yards
1 kilometer

Note 2: In nontechnical writing, writers often write out numbers less than 100—for example, thirty-five, seventy-one, eighty-nine. Note the hyphens in these written-out forms. See Hyphens. Writing out numbers less than 100 avoids overemphasizing double-digit numbers in nontechnical documents, which typically contain few numbers.

3. Write out numbers that begin a sentence:

Twelve inches from the centerline are two slots for plate fins.

Four years ago, we initiated an IR&D study of argon-atmosphere braze furnaces.

These two examples do not use figures even though they are followed by units of measurement. Rule 3 overrules rule 1.

4. Rewrite sentences beginning with a very large number:

not this

363 times a second the oscillator receives a signal from the bit generator.

nor this

Three hundred sixty-three times a second the oscillator receives a signal from the bit generator.

this

Every second, the oscillator receives 363 signals from the bit generator.

5. Use figures to express approximations that are based on experience, evidence, or both:

about 3,000 samples
approximately 60 applicants
roughly 2 cubic feet per second
over 3 million orders this quarter

Note: While some editors would retain the written out forms in the above example, others (notably the *U.S. Government Printing Office Style Manual)* prefer numerals with such words as *nearly, about, around,* and *approximately.* Use your judgment. Figures convey a greater sense of precision than words. Thus figures may seem to contradict the idea of approximating.

6. Write out approximations that are obvious exaggerations for effect:

That computer is not worth two cents.

The boss received a thousand telephone calls today.

His mother told him a million times to clean up that mess.

7. Use a combination of letters and figures for very large round numbers (1 million or greater):

We have invested over $45 million on laser research in the last 5 years.

Our annual IR&D budget exceeds $16 million.

Numbers

8. Be consistent.

Treat numbers of the same type equally within a sentence, paragraph, or section. However, **never** begin a sentence with a figure.

this

Unit A will require 5 outlets; Unit B, 17 outlets; Unit C, 9 outlets; and Unit D, 14 outlets.

not this

Unit A will require five outlets; Unit B, 17 outlets; Unit C, nine outlets; and Unit D, 14 outlets.

---

this

Seven of the stations carry 39 spare controllers. The other 14 stations carry only 8 spares.

not this

7 of the stations carry 39 spare controllers. The other 14 stations carry only eight spares.

nor this

Seven of the stations carry thirty-nine spare controllers. The other fourteen stations carry only eight spares.

nor this

Seven of the stations carry 39 spare controllers. The other fourteen stations carry only 8 spares.

The sentence cannot begin with a figure, so *seven* must be written out. The *14 stations* uses figures because 14 is greater than 9; so the two references to *stations* cannot be consistent. The number *39* is too large to write out, so both of the numbers referring to spare controllers are written as figures, although *8* is less than 10.

9. Use figures for quantities containing both whole numbers and fractions:

The proposal calls for 8½- by 11-inch paper.

See FRACTIONS.

10. Always use figures for percentages and decimal fractions:

The rectangular fins are 0.07 in. high.

The maximum core diameter is 2.54 mm.

The tests require an 8 percent solution.

NOTE: In the last example, *8%* would also be acceptable, although many style guides prefer that writers use the percent sign only in tables and visual aids. In accounting and other financial documents, the percent sign is common in text. See SIGNS and SYMBOLS.

11. Always use figures for dates:

June 14, 1989
14 June 1989
the 14th of June 1989
June 1989

NOTE: If you use the preferred style (month-day-year, as shown in the first example above), always separate the day and year with a comma. The second example shows the alternate style: day-month-year, with no punctuation.

The third example is wordy but still acceptable in some contexts, such as in legal documents.

If you write only month and year (as in the last example above), use no punctuation. Separating the month and the year is unnecessary. See COMMAS.

12. Form the plural of a number expressed as a figure by adding a lowercase *–s:*

before the 1970s
temperatures well into the 200s
the 5s represent actual strikes

NOTE: Plurals of numbers written out are formed like the plurals of other words:

in the twenties
groups of threes or fours

See PLURALS.

13. Use a comma to separate groups of three digits:

55,344,500
10,001
9,999
678

NOTE 1: In some technical fields, the preferred style is to omit the comma separating digits in numbers only four digits long:

5600
9999

NOTE 2: A practice outside the United States is to use a space instead of a comma to separate groups of three digits:

7 143
98 072.1
1 742 600 503

See METRICS.

Organization

Organization is the key writing principle. If you organize your documents well, you almost surely will have successful documents—even if you violate other writing principles. But if your documents are poorly organized, nothing can save them.

The ideas presented in a document should be structured in a natural but emphatic sequence that conveys the most important information to readers at the most critical times.

The principles of organization differ slightly from document to document, depending on the type of document, the readers, the content, and the writer's purpose. Nevertheless, logic and common sense dictate that a well-organized document must have certain features:

- The ideas in the document must be clear and sensible, given the subject, and comprehensible, given the readers.
- The document should conform to the readers' sense of what the most important points are and of how these points are arranged.
- The document should announce its organizational scheme and then stick to it.

Letters, memos, and reports differ somewhat in their organizational patterns, mostly because their readers differ. See LETTERS, MEMOS, and REPORTS.

Readers of letters are typically outside of the company or agency sending the letter. Their relationship to the writer is therefore more distant, and consequently more formal, than the relationship between the writer and others within the writer's company. See LETTERS.

Readers of memos, on the other hand, are typically from within the writer's company or agency and share various assumptions, experiences, and knowledge—all of which tend to make memos less formal than letters. See MEMOS.

The distance and formality between writer and reader affect organization in several ways. The greater the distance, the more the need to set up (introduce and perhaps explain) the ideas in the document. The greater the distance, the greater the need to substantiate information that might be subject to differing interpretations. The more formal the document, the more the writer must consider format traditions and reader expectations in organizing material.

Reports, technical or otherwise, often have prescribed organizations. Scientific report organization is based on a long tradition in the sciences. The organization of such reports is strictly prescribed, and writers have very few options in varying that organization. Technical (but nonscientific) reports offer somewhat more latitude, but even there some companies have strict guidelines on organizing technical reports.

Within the limitations imposed by tradition, logic, and audience, writers must carefully consider how to arrange their ideas and supporting data so that the document serves its purpose and satisfies the readers' needs. The principles listed below suggest how you can accomplish these tasks.

See LETTERS, MEMOS, REPORTS, and ELECTRONIC MAIL.

1. Organize information according to your readers' needs.

How you organize information depends on your readers. You might organize the same information differently for different readers, depending on their needs and your purpose in writing to them. Here, for instance, is the text of a short letter written to the test director of a laboratory:

> We request the following tests on the dry field cement samples that we shipped on July 20 to Mr. J. F. Springer of your laboratory:
>
> - Thickening time
> - Rheology
> - High temperature-high pressure fluid loss
> - 12- and 24-hr compressive strength
>
> Davidson-Warner, a cementing company, has been using this cement in our Mt. Hogan Field. On July 17, they experienced a cementing failure while setting a string of 3½-in. casing at 11,323 ft in our Hogan BB-62 well. They pumped 688 barrels of cement and 78 barrels of displacement fluid before halting displacement when the pressure increased to 5,000 psi.
>
> To facilitate your testing, we have attached pertinent well logs, cement data, and a copy of Davidson-Warner's laboratory blend test results. Please submit your findings to me at your earliest convenience.

Organization

This letter begins, appropriately enough, with a request. The writer wants something of the reader. Establishing what the writer wants makes sense as an opening statement. The specific details concerning the cementing failure do not appear until the middle paragraph because this particular reader will not need to know this information except as background for conducting the tests. The details of the cementing failure are less important than a list of the tests the writer is requesting.

However, if the document had been written to the production engineer who will now be responsible for this well, it might have begun like this:

> The Hogan BB-62 is currently shut in because of a cementing failure that occurred on July 17. The regional office would like us to return this well to production by July 28.
>
> On July 15, this well was shut in to allow Davidson-Warner to set a new string of 3½-in. casing from 10,500 ft to 11,890 ft. While setting the string at 11,332 ft, they halted displacement when the pressure increased to 5,000 psi. Before stopping, they had pumped 688 barrels of cement and 78 barrels of displacement fluid. They left approximately 35 barrels of cement in the casing (with a cement top at 8,992 ft).
>
> Wiley Laboratories has been asked to test dry field samples of the cement. In the meantime, AGF Cement has been contracted to finish setting the string. They will be onsite no later than July 25. You should plan to be present.
>
> Mt. Hogan Field production figures are down 4.3 percent in July, primarily due to this cementing failure. The regional production manager has asked that we resume full production by July 28. If you need assistance, call me at 555–6666.

This memo is written from supervisor to subordinate. Its tone is obviously different (more forceful, more directive) than the letter written to the laboratory. The organization of ideas is also very different.

The memo to the engineer begins with a statement of fact (a set-up), followed by a deadline. As in the first letter, the details of the cementing failure appear in the middle, but in this second example, the details lead to an amplification of the implied directive that appears in the opening paragraph. The memo closes with a compelling reason for action (production figures down) and a reminder of the deadline.

As you organize a document, always consider what information your readers need from you. In the examples above, the test director at Wiley Laboratories will not care that Davidson-Warner left 35 barrels of cement in the casing. The engineer will not care that the dry field samples were shipped to Mr. Springer. Each document above reflects those concerns that its readers will care most about.

The data and ideas that you include in a document and the way you organize these data and ideas depend on (1) whom you are writing to and (2) why you are writing to them.

---

2. Group similar ideas.

Separating similar ideas creates chaos. In the examples above, the details concerning the cementing failure appear in the same place. If they had been scattered, the effect could have been devastating for readers:

> The Hogan BB-62 is currently shut in because of a cementing failure that occurred on July 17. Wiley Laboratories has been asked to test dry field samples of the cement.
>
> On July 15, this well was shut in to allow Davidson-Warner to set a new string of 3½-in. casing from 10,500 ft to 11,890 ft. Please try to return this well to production by July 28. AGF Cement has been contracted to finish setting the string. Before stopping, Davidson-Warner had pumped 688 barrels of cement and 78 barrels of displacement fluid. AGF Cement will be onsite no later than July 25.

As this demonstration shows, separating related ideas creates confusion and jars readers.

---

3. Place your most important ideas first.

A frequent problem with business and technical writing is the tendency to lead **to**, rather than **from**, major ideas. Many writers believe that they have to build their case, that skeptical readers will not agree with their conclusions unless they first demonstrate how they arrived at those conclusions. This tendency results in documents that are unemphatic, difficult to follow, and filled with unnecessary detail.

The strongest part of a document is its beginning. Readers typically pay more attention at the beginning because they are discovering what the document is about. The beginning, then, is the most emphatic part of the document by virtue of its position. Because the beginning is so strong, you should begin with the most important ideas in the document—and then support those ideas by presenting your evidence afterwards.

The Scientific Format. Many of those writers who tend to lead down to their major ideas have been schooled in the scientific method. According to the scientific method, one presents the facts, observations, and data that lead to and support a conclusion. The strength of this method is that it presents a series of steps that culminates in an **inevitable** conclusion. Therefore, the steps are as important as the conclusion.

In some scientific reports (notably those written from one scientist to another), an organizational scheme based on the scientific method is desirable:

Abstract

Summary

Introduction

Materials and Methods

Results and Discussion

Fact 1
Fact 2
Fact 3
Fact 4

(therefore)

Conclusions

Recommendations (optional)

Summary (optional)

This format is acceptable only if readers will be as interested in the process of arriving at the conclusions as they are in the conclusions themselves. When readers are more interested in the conclusions, follow the managerial format.

The Managerial Format. The managerial format is the reverse of the scientific format. Managers (and most other nonscientific readers) are far more interested in the conclusions than they are in the steps leading to them. This is not to say that these readers will not want to see the conclusions supported—only that they will want the conclusions before the results and discussion:

Summary/Executive Summary

Introduction

Conclusions (and Recommendations)

(because of)

Results

Fact 1
Fact 2
Fact 3
Fact 4

Having the conclusions early in the report facilitates reading because the reader is given a perspective from which to understand the facts and data being presented. Furthermore, busy managers often know the background and tests that have led to the conclusions.

You should follow the managerial format in all documents except scientific documents written for scientific peers.

See Reports.

Note 1: The principle of emphasis through placement extends to all documents and all sections of documents. Your most important ideas should appear at the beginning of your documents and of individual sections. The most important idea in most paragraphs should appear in the opening sentence. The most important words in a sentence typically come at the beginning of the sentence. See Paragraphs and Sentences.

Note 2: A corollary to note 1 is that you should always subordinate detail. Place it in the middle of sentences, paragraphs, sections, and documents. Detail includes data, explanation, elaboration, description, analyses, results, etc.

Note 3: In lengthy documents, begin **and** end with important ideas.

The lengthier a document becomes, the more crucial this rule is. Readers of long passages need to be introduced to the subject, learn the most important points early, receive the supporting detail and explanation, and then have it all wrapped up in a tidy closing statement that reiterates the important points.

An adage regarding oral presentations (but applicable to writing) is that you should tell 'em what you're gonna tell 'em, tell 'em, and then tell 'em what you told 'em. See Repetition.

See Reports and Emphasis.

Organization

4. Keep your set-ups short.

Sometimes you cannot begin by stating your most important idea because the reader either will not understand it or will not accept it. If such is the case, you need to set up the most important idea by providing introductory information meant either to inform readers or to persuade them.

A fundamental of organization in business and technical writing is to keep your set-ups short. Do not delay your major ideas any longer than necessary.

When you give people positive information (i.e., when you say "yes" to them), you should give them the positive information right away. They want to hear it, and hearing it will make them more receptive toward you and the rest of the information you provide.

However, when you give readers negative information (when you say "no" to them), giving them the negative information first will put them off, and they will not be receptive to what follows. Moreover, they might become antagonistic toward you and might believe that you have made the negative decision precipitously.

Therefore, you should say "no" to readers only after you have set them up for it. Be careful, however, not to delay the "no" too long. Keep your set-ups short, as in the following example:

> I have been asked to reply to your request for additional compensation following approval of your Engineering Change Order dated March 3.
>
> As you know, a Health Department inspector ordered the design changes, and our contract states that all design changes required for safety reasons are warranted under the contractor's bond. Therefore, additional compensation would be inappropriate at this time.

The first sentence sets the stage. The second provides brief rationale for the decision. The third states the decision. The two-sentence set-up in this example makes the decision more palatable than if the writer had begun by saying: *"We will not be providing the additional compensation you requested."*

See INTRODUCTIONS.

5. List items in descending order of importance.

Readers typically assume that information in lists appears in descending order of importance: most important listed item first, least important item last.

Numbering and lettering systems reinforce this assumption. We all know that being number 1 is better than being number 6. We know from school that an A is better than an F. Rightly or wrongly, we assume a natural ranking of items. Therefore, writers should list items in descending order of importance.

If you wish to create a list in which items are equally important, use bullets or dashes instead of numbers or letters, and state that the listed items are equal.

See LISTS.

6. In long or complex documents, preview your most important ideas and your major content areas, and review (summarize) major points at the end of sections.

In longer documents, you must establish the structural framework of the documents. If you don't, readers may be overwhelmed by the document's size or complexity. Opening previews and concluding reviews are essential if you want readers to grasp your major points.

See INTRODUCTIONS, SUMMARIES, REPORTS, and REPETITION.

Even mechanical or routine features of a document can help readers understand its content. For example, a detailed, quite specific table of contents can almost be a summary of the document. In some special types of documents, the table of contents is supplemented by a matrix outlining where in the document each requirement or issue is addressed. Such a matrix is especially helpful in proposals, where the writer must respond to every one of the client's requirements. See TABLES OF CONTENTS.

Summaries and introductions are ideal devices for previewing content, but you can also preview content in opening paragraphs.

Generally, however, when the preview refers to itself as a preview, it is obtrusive. Your preview should sound natural and should be unobtrusive:

this

The Hamerling Study (March-October 1979) found that predators have played only a minor role in the recent population decline of the cutthroat trout. Far more serious impacts on this species are a degraded watershed, temperature increases, and deforestation.

Together, these environmental changes have reshaped the cutthroat trout's habitat, perhaps beyond the species' ability to adapt.

not this

This report discusses the results of the Hamerling Study (March-October 1979), which found that predators have played only a minor role in the recent population decline of the cutthroat trout. The first section concerns the quality of the watershed, which has declined significantly since 1965.

Following that section is a discussion of the role of climate changes, particularly a 2-degree increase in temperature throughout the study area. In section 3, the report notes the effect of deforestation in one part of the study area. In its concluding section, the report discusses the combined impact of watershed degradation, climate changes, and deforestation. As the report notes, these changes have reshaped the cutthroat trout's habitat, perhaps beyond the species' ability to adapt.

The first (preferred) version amounts to a summary of the report. It could actually appear in the summary, become part of an abstract, or open the introduction. It could even appear in all three places.

---

7. Discuss items in the same order in which you introduce them.

When you introduce items, you should discuss them in the same order later. Saying that you are going to talk about A, B, and C, and then beginning with B violates the readers' sense of order. Follow these examples:

The three greatest influences on cutthroat trout population are *a degraded watershed, temperature changes,* and *deforestation.*

The watershed has been declining in quality since 1965 when . . .

Temperature changes over the last 5 years have resulted in a 2-degree . . .

Deforestation through the study area has also affected . . .

---

this

The acquisition improved our *cash flow* while providing significant tax advantages and allowing us to capitalize expenses. Prior to the takeover, we had negative *cash flow* on several . . .

not this

The acquisition improved our *cash flow* while providing significant tax advantages and allowing us to capitalize expenses. Prior to the takeover, our *expenses* were not capitalized . . . .

This example demonstrates a subtle but important use of organization. The writer introduces three ideas: cash flow, taxes, and expenses. To be consistent with the order in which these ideas were introduced, the writer must follow the introductory statement with cash flow, not taxes or expenses, as occurs in the final version.

---

8. Use headings, transitions, key words, and paragraph leads to provide cues to the document's organization.

Throughout documents, you should signal organizational shifts or changes in direction by using headings, transitions, repeated key words, and opening or closing statements in paragraphs.

Headings are especially useful when you need to signal abrupt changes in direction, such as the transition from one topic to another (unrelated) topic. If the shifts are too radical, you cannot easily indicate them in text.

Transitions and repeated key words provide for smoother changes in direction and are useful between sentences and paragraphs, as in the example below. Note how the bolded words indicate organizational patterns and shifts in direction:

The coal seam trends northwesterly for approximately 9,500 meters before pinching out on a fault line. **However**, seismic evidence suggests that **another** seam of coal extends from a point 75 meters downdip of the pinchout. This **second** seam appears to trend northerly for another 5,000 meters. **Together**, these seams represent a sizeable reserve of recoverable coal, **but** initiating mining operations will still be extremely **difficult**.

The biggest **difficulty** is landowner resistance to strip mining . . . .

See HEADINGS, KEY WORDS, OUTLINES, PARAGRAPHS, and TRANSITIONS.

Outlines

Outlines are convenient tools for the schematic organization of material. See ORGANIZATION.

Preliminary or draft outlines help writers determine early in the writing process, usually before the document is written, whether the content is logical and complete. Preliminary outlines do not have to be neat or accurately numbered.

Final outlines (which usually form the table of contents) display the overall structure of the content. Final outlines may or may not be numbered. If they are numbered, they typically use either the traditional format (1/A/1/a, etc.) or the decimal format (1.0/1.1/1.1.1, etc.). See NUMBERING SYSTEMS.

Traditional Outlines

Traditional outlines are those using the following numbering and lettering system:

```
        TITLE
I.   First-level division
     A. Second-level division
        1. Third-level division
           a. Fourth-level division
              (1) Fifth-level division
                  (a) Sixth-level
                      division
II.  First-level division
     A. Second-level division
     B. Second-level division
```

NOTE 1: Some writers and editors prefer *a)* instead of *a.* to indicate a fourth-level division.

NOTE 2: Because Roman numerals vary in length, they are customarily aligned according to the period, not the length of the numeral:

```
  I.
 II.
III.
```

Decimal Outlines

```
        TITLE
1.0 First-level division
    1.1 Second-level division
        1.1.1 Third-level division
              1.1.1.1 Fourth-level
                      division
    1.2 Second-level division
        1.2.1 Third-level division
              1.2.1.1 Fourth-level
                      division
2.0 First-level division
```

NOTE: A variation of the decimal format uses hundreds and tens. This format is not widely used, perhaps because it is less flexible than the decimal and traditional formats:

```
        TITLE
100 First-level division
    110 Second-level division
        111 Third-level division
        112 Third-level division
    120 Second-level division
200 First-level division
```

1. Avoid outlines with more than five levels of subordination.

Subordination refers to the number of successive subdivisions. The more intricate and involved the subdivisions become, the harder it is for readers to grasp and remember the organizational scheme. When the level of subordination reaches six or seven levels, readers will not be able to comprehend the successive subdivisions. Even in outlines that you create only for yourself, too many subdivisions will cause confusion.

2. Do not make your outlines too brief.

Brevity may be the soul of wit, but too brief an outline will not allow you to explore the content sufficiently, and it will not assist readers in understanding your organizational scheme:

```
  I. Intro
 II. The Problem
III. Options
 IV. Analysis
  V. Conclusions
 VI. Further Work
```

This outline has sparse (indeed, cryptic) titles and no subdivisions. In effect, it provides nothing beyond a vague sense of general direction. Fleshing out this outline will help the writer think much more carefully about the exact content needed and about the logic and the arrangement of ideas.

See HEADINGS for a discussion of informative headings and CAPTIONS for a description of action captions. Also, see ORGANIZATION.

3. Maintain parallel structure in formal outlines.

Each division heading and each subheading should be grammatically parallel with items at the same level of heading. So if you use *–ing* verb forms for some headings at one level, use *–ing* verb forms for all headings at that level:

this

2.1.1 Preparing for the trial run
2.1.2 Checking safety procedures
2.1.3 Conducting the trial run
2.1.4 Determining preliminary findings

not this

2.1.1 Preparing for the trial run
2.1.2 Checking safety procedures
2.1.3 The trial run itself
2.1.4 Preliminary findings

In many cases, parallelism allows writers to avoid repeating words that occur within all headings at the same level:

this

2.8.1 Test results

2.8.1.1 DOD
2.8.1.2 Acme Testing Laboratory
2.8.1.3 Conair Environmental Labs

not this

2.8.1 DOD test results
2.8.2 Test results from the Acme Testing Laboratory
2.8.3 Test results from Conair Environmental Labs

4. If possible, design your outline so that each subdivision has at least two points.

If a subdivision has only one subpoint in it, then the subpoint should become the subdivision heading:

this

3. Overhead rates

4. Labor issues

not this

3. Cost analysis

   a. Overhead rates

4. Labor issues

In the second example above, the subdivision for *overhead rates* has but a single point. If the cost analysis consists of nothing more than overhead rates, why list cost analysis as an activity? The first example properly recognizes that the cost analysis is nothing more than a determination of overhead rates.

5. Use an outline to check the logical consistency and basic organization of a piece of writing.

If an outline is not parallel and is not logical, then the document based on the outline is likely to be chaotic. See ORGANIZATION and TABLES OF CONTENTS.

Paragraphs

aragraphs are visual and logical signals to readers.

As visual signals, paragraphs help readers to perceive divisions within a document. The typographical devices used to show the divisions include indentation, blank lines above and below paragraphs, and paragraph numbers. Without visual paragraphing, texts would be a mass of undifferentiated sentences.

As logical signals, paragraphs reflect the major divisions and subdivisions in content within a document. In good writing, the transition from topic to topic is reflected in the transition from paragraph to paragraph. Each major topic has its own paragraph (and sometimes more than one), and each paragraph concerns only one topic.

A Case Study in Paragraphing

Some writers dump everything they can think of about a topic into a single paragraph. Then when a paragraph becomes long enough (by whatever standard), these writers pause, indent, and start another paragraph. This sort of paragraphing is neither logical nor effective, as the following example illustrates:

> Oxides of nitrogen include nitrogen dioxide (NO_2) and nitric oxide (NO). NO_2 is a pungent gas that causes nose and eye irritation and pulmonary discomfort. NO is converted to NO_2 by atmospheric chemical reaction. Both NO and NO_2 participate in photochemical reactions leading to smog. Sulfur dioxide (SO_2) is a colorless and pungent gas that causes irritation to the respiratory tract and eyes and causes bronchoconstriction at high concentrations. Hydrocarbons react with NO or NO_2 and sunlight to form photochemical oxidants or smog. Health effects include irritation of the eye, nose, and throat. Extended periods of high levels of oxidants produce headaches and cause difficulty in breathing in patients suffering from emphysema.

What did the writer of this paragraph want to accomplish? Is the first sentence on NO and NO_2 an accurate reflection of the rest of the content? How do the other facts and points in the paragraph fit together? Can readers see a definite pattern or structure to the facts?

These and similar questions suggest several remedies:

- Shorten the paragraph and focus on only one topic.
- State this topic in the opening sentence.
- Supply organizational cues in the opening sentence and, as appropriate, in later sentences.

By applying these remedies, we can improve the paragraph as follows:

> Nitrogen oxides, hydrocarbons, and sulfur dioxide—these constituents of smog can cause health problems. Nitrogen dioxide (NO_2) is a pungent gas that causes nose and eye irritation and pulmonary discomfort. Hydrocarbons that react with NO_2 or with nitric oxide (NO) and sunlight form photochemical oxidants that can irritate the eyes, nose, and throat. Extended exposure to high levels of oxidants can produce headaches and cause persons with emphysema to have trouble breathing. Sulfur dioxide (SO_2) is a colorless and pungent gas that irritates the eyes and respiratory tract and, at high concentrations, can cause bronchoconstriction.

This paragraph might also be revised to focus on a single health problem, such as eye irritation. If so, eye irritation would become the focus of the opening sentence. Then all succeeding sentences would relate to eye irritation.

The original paragraph might also be broken into separate paragraphs that discuss each type of pollutant. We can't know which approach is correct unless we know the context in which the revised paragraph will appear and the purpose of the document as a whole. See ORGANIZATION.

---

1. Limit paragraphs to a single topic or major idea.

Ensure that your paragraphs focus on a single topic or idea. When you go to a new topic, start a new paragraph. If your paragraph on a single topic becomes too long, start a new paragraph at a logical point and have two (or more) paragraphs dealing with the same topic. When such is the case, you normally focus each paragraph on a subtopic related to the overall topic.

---

2. Do not allow paragraphs to become too long.

Quantifying paragraph length is difficult, but in business and technical writing, paragraphs exceeding 150 to 175 words should be rare. Most paragraphs will consist of three to six sentences. If a single-spaced paragraph goes beyond one-third of a page, it is probably too long.

A double-spaced paragraph should not exceed half a page in length.

The document's format should influence paragraph length. If a document has narrow columns (two or three to the page), then paragraphs should be shorter, perhaps on the average no more than 125 words. If a document uses a full page format (one column), then average paragraph length can reach 175 words.

Length is therefore a function of appearance and visual relief. Almost all readers have difficulty with dense pages of print, no matter how well written and logically organized the text may be. Remember that paragraphs are visual devices meant to make reading easier, so keep them shorter rather than longer.

3. Vary the length of your paragraphs.

A document containing paragraphs of uniform length would be dull and difficult to read. For the sake of variety and to stimulate reader interest, you should vary the length of your paragraphs, especially in documents longer than one page.

The length of successive paragraphs will of course depend on content. The logic of the material will dictate, at least to some extent, where paragraphs can logically begin and end, but you still have a great deal of latitude.

A particularly involved point may require lengthy explanation and two or three examples. If so, you might state the point and explain it in one or two paragraphs and then make each example a separate paragraph. Dividing the topic in this fashion is especially desirable in a double- or triple-column page format.

Your paragraph stating the main point could be relatively short. Short paragraphs usually draw attention to themselves, so they are useful for stating major ideas. The explanatory paragraph should be much longer. The paragraphs providing the examples should vary in length, with the most important example appearing in the longest paragraph.

Are single-sentence paragraphs acceptable?

Yes. A common misconception about paragraphing is that single-sentence paragraphs somehow violate a principle of writing. In fact, single-sentence paragraphs are very emphatic, especially if they are surrounded by longer paragraphs. You should take care not to use single-sentence paragraphs too often, however. Too many single-sentence paragraphs and you have no paragraphs. Use them judiciously. See EMPHASIS.

4. Ensure that the opening sentence of every primary paragraph accurately reflects the content of that paragraph and any following secondary paragraphs.

Primary paragraphs introduce an idea. Secondary paragraphs develop and support that idea. All primary paragraphs should have an opening sentence that introduces the content of the primary and any following secondary paragraphs. This opening sentence is called a topic sentence.

The opening sentence should establish a key word or phrase that indicates the paragraph's topic. If your paragraph will focus on health problems, then the opening sentence should contain at least two key words: *health* and *problems*. These key words help establish the paragraph's viewpoint, which is often called its thesis. The three examples below each have a topic sentence that announces the thesis of the paragraph:

> Timber sales along the Graveny ridge have substantially increased erosion. From 1972 to 1983, the Forest Service conducted four timber sales that . . .

> MOGO's reservoir study of May 1984 indicates that remaining recoverable reserves exceed previous estimates by over 66 percent. Seismic data gathered in conjunction with the study . . .

> The Packaging Department examined the problem and recommends replacing our standard cardboard containers with molded plastic wrap. The plastic is applied from a hot roller after the cases . . .

Secondary paragraphs do not begin with topic sentences. In a technical report discussing a series of tests, for instance, the results section of the report might have several paragraphs opening as follows:

> Test 1, series 1, involved decreasing eluants by 0.4 cm^3/hr and noting pH changes occurring as the solution was heated to 250 degrees F . . . .

Paragraphs

> During test 1, series 2, eluants were removed altogether, and the solution was subjected to pressure variations during heating . . . .

These paragraphs develop and support the thesis that was established in a topic sentence in a previous primary paragraph.

As readers, we should expect the first secondary paragraph to focus entirely on test 1, series 1. Any information in that paragraph that is not related to test 1, series 1, does not belong there. Similarly, the second secondary paragraph should focus on test 1, series 2.

Open every primary paragraph with a topic sentence that states the thesis of that paragraph and any following secondary paragraphs.

See ORGANIZATION.

---

5. Organize paragraphs logically.

The structure of the ideas within a paragraph should be logical. Furthermore, the paragraph structure should be obvious to readers.

Sometimes this structure follows a classic organizational pattern: chronological, whole to parts, problem to solution, cause to effect, most important to least important, general to specific, and so on. Sometimes the structure follows some logic that is inherent to the subject. A paragraph on drilling rig problems, for instance, might be organized according to a series of problems that relate to each other in some way that uninformed readers would not perceive.

The paragraph below is paraphrased from Charles Darwin's *Origin of Species.* It demonstrates a classic organizational pattern: general to specific. Note that the opening sentence is a topic sentence and that the three succeeding sentences substantiate Darwin's thesis:

> Without exception, every species naturally **reproduces** at so high a **rate** that, if not destroyed, the earth would soon be covered by the progeny of a single pair. Even **slow-breeding** man has **doubled** in 25 years, and at this **rate**, in less than 1,000 years, there would literally not be standing room for his progeny. Linneaus has calculated that if an annual plant **produced** only two seeds—and no plant is so **unproductive**—and their seedlings next year **produced** two, and so on, then in 20 years there should be 1,000,000 plants. The elephant is reckoned the slowest **breeder** of all animals, and I have taken some pains to estimate its minimum **reproductive rate**; it will be safest to assume that it begins **breeding** when 30 years old, and goes on **breeding** till 90 years old, bringing forth six young in the interval, and surviving till 100 years old; if this be so, after 750 years there would be nearly 19,000,000 elephants alive, descended from the first pair.

---

6. Use key words and other devices to ensure that paragraphs are coherent.

Coherence refers to the cohesiveness of a paragraph's sentences. In a coherent paragraph, the sentences seem to "stick together"—they all clearly belong in the paragraph and are logically connected to one another.

In the preceding paragraph example, the boldfaced key words indicate one of the most common methods of achieving coherence: repeating key words. The key words in the Darwin paragraph form a clear link between sentences. As you read the paragraph below, note the lack of coherence:

> A great number of apparatus are available today for field work in the broad sense, including gas-chromatographs, as well as infrared, electrochemical, and other analyzers. In connection with the early prediction of possible pollutants and the assessment of natural discharge prior to the development of geothermal resources, however, hydrogen sulfide and volatiles such as ammonia, mercury, and arsenic are the major concern. Under the conditions prevailing before industrial development, preliminary evaluation and prediction of the discharge of such chemicals depends to a sizeable extent on water analyses. Surveying mercury content in air might deserve consideration; however, it is not discussed here, as mercury determination in soil is likely to be a valid substitute for it.

The opening sentence to this paragraph suggests that the paragraph will discuss the apparatus available for field work, particularly those apparatus listed. However, this equipment is never again discussed. The second, third, and fourth sentences seem loosely connected, but the paragraph never "gels"; it never seems to be focused on a single topic. In short, the paragraph is incoherent.

You can achieve coherence by opening with a topic sentence, by using a clear organizational scheme, by repeating key words, by using transitional words (such as *however, furthermore, consequently, next, then, additionally,* etc.), and by using pronouns to link sentences to the major idea or theme of the paragraph. See ORGANIZATION, KEY WORDS, TRANSITIONS, and PRONOUNS.

7. Emphasize the important ideas within a paragraph.

The opening and closing sentences of a paragraph tend to be the most emphatic sentences in the paragraph simply by virtue of their position. Readers pay more attention to those sentences than to the sentences that fall in the middle of the paragraph. Therefore, you should try to place your most important ideas in those sentences.

The Darwin paragraph on the preceding page opens with a clear statement of Darwin's thesis. The opening sentence is the strongest sentence in the paragraph, and Darwin has wisely used it to state his most important idea. The closing sentence is also strong, and Darwin uses it to give his best example. If his thesis is true of the elephant, which is the **slowest** breeder of all animals, then it must also be true of every other species.

8. Provide transitions between paragraphs.

In most well-written documents, the information flows from paragraph to paragraph. To achieve this effect, you must provide smooth transitions between paragraphs.

Writers can set up transitions by previewing content. If you announce, for instance, that you will be discussing five topics and then list those topics, you have set up a progression that the reader will expect. As you move from topic to topic, the transitions will be automatic:

> The first topic concerns . . .
>
> Likewise, the second topic . . .
>
> The third topic . . .
>
> However, the fourth topic . . .
>
> Finally, the fifth topic . . .

As you can see, these paragraph openings also use some transitional words to make the transition, but merely moving to and announcing the next topic is sufficient.

Sometimes you can create the transition between paragraphs by using key words to connect the closing sentence of one paragraph and the opening sentence of the next:

> . . . because deep **salt domes** usually occur as a result of normal **faulting.**
>
> Thrust (reverse) **faults**, on the other hand, are normally responsible for piercement **salt domes** . . .

In this excerpt, the first paragraph closes with a key word (*faulting*), a variation of which is repeated in the opening sentence of the next paragraph. The first paragraph concerns deep salt domes; the second concerns piercement salt domes. Repeating a variation of *faulting* helps make the transition.

In this example, the opening sentence of the succeeding paragraph makes the transition.

However, the transition could also be made by the closing sentence of the preceding paragraph:

> . . . because deep **salt domes** usually occur as a result of normal **faulting**. Thrust (reverse) **faults**, on the other hand, are normally responsible for **piercement salt domes.**
>
> **Piercement domes**, which are common along the Texas and Louisiana Gulf Coast, produce from traps caused when complex **faulting** forces a salt core upward through overlying sediments . . . .

In some documents, the information cannot easily flow from paragraph to paragraph because the paragraph topics are too disjointed. When such is the case, use headings, lists, and numbering systems to indicate the transition from one topic to another:

> . . . Reef-producing areas might or might not be obvious from overlying sediments.
>
> **Piercement Domes**
>
> Piercement domes, which are common along the Texas and Louisiana Gulf Coast, produce from traps caused when complex faulting forces a salt core upward through overlying sediments . . . .

See HEADINGS, LISTS, NUMBERING SYSTEMS, and TRANSITIONS.

9. If appropriate, break up or replace paragraphs with lists.

If a paragraph consists of a long series of items or if a paragraph contains such a series, consider replacing the paragraph with a displayed list. Lists are more emphatic than paragraphs, so if you want to emphasize the series of items, display it. See LISTS.

Parallelism

Parallelism is essentially a convention of sentence construction. The principle behind it is that similar ideas should be expressed in a similar fashion, thereby demonstrating their similarity and making reading easier. The following sentence is not parallel:

> The analysis will include organizing, dividing, and assessment of turnaround functions.

The sentence verb *include* is followed by three key words: *organizING, dividING,* and *assessMENT*. These three words appear in series. They are equal in purpose and use in the sentence. Therefore, they should have the same grammatical form:

> The analysis will include organizing, dividing, and assessing turnaround functions.

1. Ensure that two or more parts of speech behaving similarly in a sentence or coordinated (connected) in some way are parallel in construction.

Parallelism applies not only to verbs, but also to nouns, adjectives, phrases, and every other part of a sentence:

> The Interface Team will be responsible **for integrating** the functional units developed by the QA Team and **for executing** the model test matrix.

> Applying **abstraction**, **partition**, and **projection** to the system development process results in the traditional top-down view of the software engineering process.

> Figure 2.2-1 shows the documentation relationships: **where things happen, why things happen,** and **how things can be changed.**

> Multilevel training was necessary to meet the needs of **managers, designers**, and **programmers**.

> A final report was prepared, **describing** the case study process and **referencing** the documents containing the code.

2. Make items in lists parallel.

Parallelism is especially important in lists. A list, whether displayed vertically on the page or embedded within a paragraph, is a series. To make it parallel, each item should be constructed similarly and should begin with the same kind of word (noun, verb, etc.):

> This file will include the following items:
>
> 1. Problem headings
> 2. Database specifications
> 3. Reporting intervals
> 4. Restart options
> 5. Level of detail options
> 6. Links to report macros

The following list is also parallel (each item completes the sentence started by the introductory statement). Note that each item begins with the same kind of verb:

> The study concluded that the ATAC fighter must:
>
> 1. Have a long-range, high-payload capability.
> 2. Be flexible in mission and payload design.
> 3. Be survivable against A-A and S-A threats.
> 4. Be maneuverable in the F-15/ F-16 class.

NOTE: This example has several variations. Many authorities would insist on a different lead-in sentence (one with a complete grammatical structure):

> A study concluded that the ATAC fighter must have these features:

See COLONS, CONJUNCTIONS, and LISTS.

Parentheses

Parentheses are used to insert (in an emphatic way) material into a sentence. Dashes—which are more emphatic than parentheses—are also used to insert material. Commas, which are also used to insert material, are less emphatic than either dashes or parentheses.

Using parentheses appropriately and effectively is an art. The following rules will help you develop this art.

1. Parentheses enclose explanatory sentences within a paragraph:

> Only the total systems approach can deal with the tradeoff in performance between the weapon and the aircraft platform. Existing beyond-visual-range air-to-air missiles are inhibited, for instance, by the lack of an effective IFF system. The total systems approach, with its full range of analysis tools, may be the only acceptable means of evaluating tradeoffs prior to the detail design phase. (The discussion of IFF design under Targeting Systems on p. 89 reveals how we solved the problem cited above.)

2. Parentheses enclose references, examples, ideas, and citations that are not part of the main thought of a sentence:

> Our Level 6 analysis (see figure 9.4) illustrates how a single multi-mission destroyer can contribute to task force operations.

> Our design accounts for all environmental factors that may affect sensitivity (smoke, terrain, weather, and physical damage).

> Affordability (cited in the RFP as a primary concern) was the guiding principle behind our application of new technologies.

> Our previous state-of-the-art survey (conducted over a 3-month period in 1987) suggested that RDF SOPs were not current.

> The most recent research (Smithson 1988) revealed pollution problems from nearby gasoline storage tanks.

See CITATIONS.

Parentheses, Commas, and Dashes

Commas and dashes also enclose explanatory ideas. Commas are less emphatic than parentheses; dashes are more emphatic. Note how emphasis progressively increases in the following examples:

> Cost analyses using both parametric and detail O&S cost methodologies helped us determine the right support systems.

> Cost analyses, using both parametric and detail O&S cost methodologies, helped us determine the right support systems.

> Cost analyses (using both parametric and detail O&S cost methodologies) helped us determine the right support systems.

> Cost analyses—using both parametric and detail O&S cost methodologies—helped us determine the right support systems.

See COMMAS and DASHES.

3. Parentheses enclose numbers in a paragraph list:

> The operational characteristics we will discuss below are (1) manning, (2) training, and (3) providing required support.

See LISTS.

4. Parentheses enclose acronyms, abbreviations, definitions, and figures that have been written out:

> The CARP (Capital Area Renovation Project) is adequately funded as long as the contractor trims costs by using off-the-shelf materials wherever possible.

> United's South Fork Mine can deliver over 20,000 dwt (deadweight tons) of ore every month.

> Artesian water (water naturally confined in the ground under pressure) is the primary source for the city's culinary use.

> By the project deadline date, Northrop will deliver fifty (50) centrifugal pump assemblies to the San Diego facility.

See ABBREVIATIONS and ACRONYMS.

NOTE: The practice of writing out numbers and enclosing the figure in parentheses is not necessary except in legal, contractual, or requisition documents. Do it only when you need to protect against unauthorized alteration of numbers in a document.

See NUMBERS.

Parentheses

Parentheses and Brackets

Brackets are, in effect, parentheses. They enclose incidental or explanatory words and phrases within parentheses or within quoted material:

> The environment and activities of opposing forces may change the capabilities of a particular sensor (see appendix 4, Battlefield Adaptability Requirements, for a fuller discussion of RGS [Remote Ground Sensing] and ground-based sensor limitations).

> Your original letter stated: "Our onsite project coordinator [Walt Petersen] will be responsible for maintaining the Schedule of Deliverables."

See BRACKETS.

Parentheses and Periods

If the entire sentence is enclosed by parentheses, the period at the end of the sentence goes inside the closing parentheses:

> (See appendix 2 for the complete test results.)

If only part of a sentence is enclosed by parentheses and the closing parenthesis occurs at the end of the sentence, the period goes outside the closing parenthesis:

> Hydrostatic and thermostatic monitors ensure system equilibrium (see figure 5-15 for monitor locations).

See PERIODS.

Parentheses and Question Marks

Question marks come inside parentheses when they are part of the parenthetical (added) information:

this

> The project deadline (April 1?) is never stated in the Statement of Work.

not this

> The project deadline (April 1)? is never stated in the Statement of Work.

See QUESTION MARKS.

Periods

Periods primarily indicate a break or a full stop in a text. At the end of a spoken sentence (signaled by a period), the voice drops and the speaker takes a breath.

1. Periods follow statements, commands, indirect questions, and questions intended as suggestions:

Statements

The workover plan was finished.

Tomorrow we will visit the mine site.

Mr. Smythe owes OP&L $75.

Commands

Stop working on the project now.

Please help us tomorrow.

Redesign the pump housing to accommodate the larger intake pipe.

Indirect Questions

I wonder how he managed the project.

Jane Greer asked whether we would approve the budget.

Questions Intended as Suggestions

Will you please return the forms by a week from Monday.

Would you let me know if you have any questions.

2. Periods follow numerals or letters marking a list, but periods need not follow the items listed unless they are full sentences (see rule 1 above):

a. A larger pump

b. An extra ventilation fan

c. A heavy duty circuit breaker

---

1. The cost is 50 percent greater than was budgeted.

2. Materials were not equal to those specified.

3. Installation procedures were violated.

NOTE: You may need a period to end a list that continues the syntax established in its lead-in sentence:

We tested the procedure by

1. increasing the flow,
2. decreasing the temperature, and
3. contaminating the water.

This pattern of continued syntax and punctuation is much rarer than it used to be. See LISTS.

3. Periods separate integers from decimals:

4.567
327.5
1,456.25

NOTE: In some foreign countries, a comma separates integers from decimals and spaces separate groups of three numerals in longer numerals:

4,567

56 764,534 45

See METRICS.

4. Use a period with run-in headings, but not with displayed headings:

Two Options. The first option is to discontinue the testing until safety procedures are developed. The second option . . .

This same heading would have no following period if it appeared on its own line:

Two Options

The first option is to discontinue the testing until safety procedures are developed. The second option . . .

NOTE: You can also use run-in headings with dashes, colons, or no punctuation. But be consistent. Once you've established a pattern, use it throughout a document.

See HEADINGS.

5. Periods follow some abbreviations:

10 a.m.	6 p.m.
A.D. 1910	225 B.C.
U.S.A.	Mr./Mrs./Ms.
e.g.	S. Pugh
Dr. William Lange	U.K.
	i.e.

NOTE: Many abbreviations no longer require periods, especially names of fraternal organizations, government agencies, corporations, and colleges and universities:

BPOE	BLM
DOE	GM
UCLA	LSU

See ABBREVIATIONS and PARENTHESES.

Photographs

Photographs convey realism and authenticity. They are the most persuasive kind of visual aid because readers tend to trust the exactness and realism of photographs.

If you want to show readers what **is**, use a photograph (see figure 1). If you want to show readers what **is possible**, use a drawing (see figure 2).

The principles of photographic composition are beyond the scope of this section, but we can present a few basic principles for you to use in creating, selecting, and placing photographs in your documents. For example, one principle of drafting documents is to call out (label) only one item that occurs many times on a drawing and note this convention by enclosing the word *typical* underneath the callout. For general information about photographs as visual aids, see VISUAL AIDS. See also CHARTS, GRAPHS, ILLUSTRATIONS, and TABLES.

Figure 1. Hydraulic Cylinder. *The hydraulic cylinder can be replaced in less than 15 minutes by a trained mechanic, thus reducing downtime and maintenance expense.*

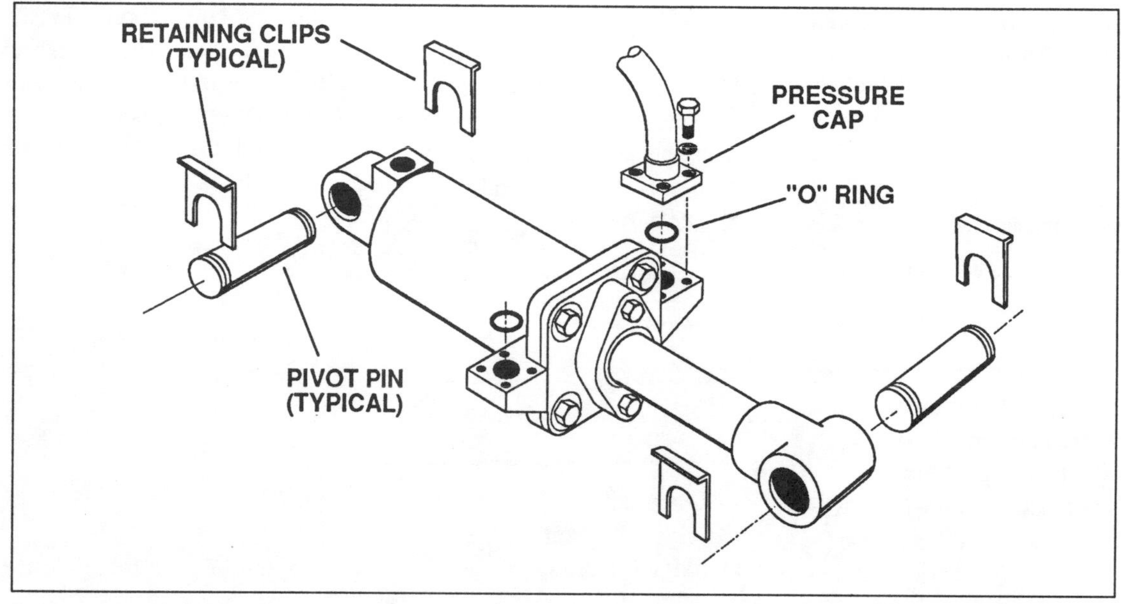

Figure 2. Hydraulic Cylinder. *To reduce downtime and maintenance expense, the hydraulic cylinder has knock-out pins and O-ring pressure fittings that make a 15-minute replacement possible.*

1. Ensure that each photograph has a principal point of interest.

Each photograph must have a principal point of interest. Create the photograph so that your readers' eyes are led naturally and immediately to the point of interest. To accomplish this, your photograph must be simple and uncluttered (see figure 3).

To establish the central point of interest, ensure that the photograph is taken from an angle that maximizes the effective coverage of the object. The same object can be photographed from a variety of angles, so choose the angle that best focuses on the object of interest and that best shows what you want the photograph to show.

Figure 3 focuses on the navigational unit, and the angle for the photograph (shooting up from ground level) eliminates potentially distracting details from the ground near the object. Also, the mountains in the background are sufficiently far away that the navigational aid continues to be the central point of interest.

Figure 4 is cluttered and thus not effective. Readers see the ship in the foreground, maybe some of the ship in the background, two cranes, a radar tower, a buoy, and mountains in the background. The crane dominates the picture, but the foreground ship might well be the focus of the picture.

Figure 3. Self-Contained Air-Navigational Unit. *One person can transport, assemble and disassemble, and operate this beacon unit.*

Figure 4. A Ship or a Crane or What? *The clutter in the photograph distracts the readers from quickly and surely seeing a single effective point of interest.*

2. Ensure that photographs are simple and uncluttered. If necessary, airbrush or crop photographs to eliminate distracting detail.

Each photograph should have a single central subject. Eliminate everything in the photograph that does not contribute or relate to that central subject.

In figure 5 the extraneous material present in figure 4 has been removed, making the view of the crane and the ship stand in sharp focus. Figure 5 is a much better photograph than figure 4.

Figures 6 and 7 provide a second illustration of the value of eliminating clutter. The laundry press in figure 6 is the central figure, but the unnecessary detail in the picture is distracting. In figure 7 the background detail has been airbrushed out. Also, overall contrast has been enhanced by retouching.

3. Ensure that photographs are taken from a proper angle of view and from the proper distance.

Take photographs from an angle that maximizes your readers' focus on the principal point of interest and minimizes surrounding detail. Figure 3 focuses on the navigational unit, and the angle for the photograph (shooting up from ground level) eliminates potentially distracting details. If the photographer had taken the picture from above the unit, the ground vegetation in the background could have interfered with the sharp outline of the equipment and its stand.

Figure 5. The On/Off Loading Crane.
The newly designed crane can load or unload a 6-week supply of food and materiel in 12 hours.

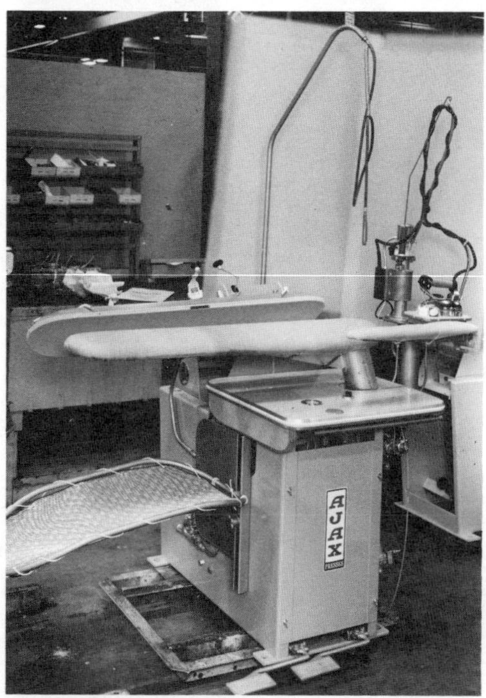

Figure 6. Ajax Laundry Press (Before).
This press features a built-in spray gun and hand iron for detailed finishing.

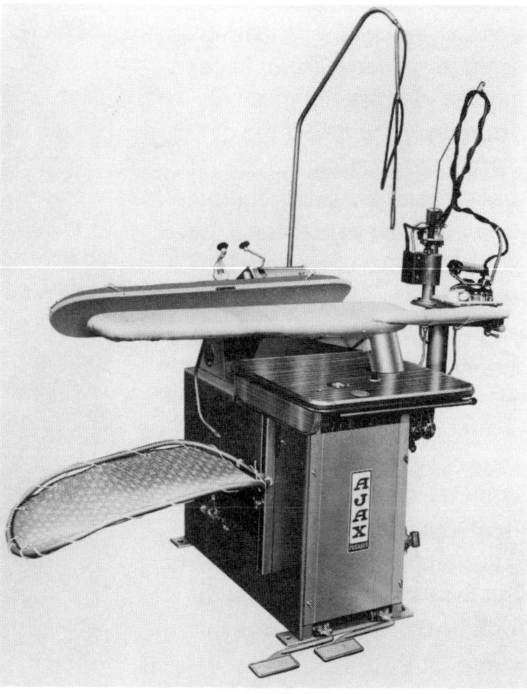

Figure 7. Ajax Laundry Press (After).

If you need to, climb a tree or crawl on the ground to get the right angle. In most cases, avoid straight-on, one-sided views. Showing two or three sides of an object gives more information.

If a subject lends itself to a vertical format, orient the camera accordingly. In general, closer is better. Close shots automatically eliminate much background and promote a focus on the subject. Also, avoid aligning your subject with distracting background objects, such as trees growing behind someone's head.

Sometimes, to eliminate distracting, nonessential detail and to highlight some feature, you might have to take the photograph from a new angle or from a different distance. Sometimes you might have to clean up an area around the object you are shooting.

Before you take your photograph, consider what the photograph is intended to show, what the reader should be focusing on, and whether the objects visible through the lens are appropriate. Figure 8 was taken from an angle that reveals three faces of the object: top, side, and near end. It shows the most important fittings and labels. Because it is made of light-colored materials, it was photographed against a dark background for better contrast.

Figure 9 shows one acceptable use of a straight-on shot. Showing control location and legibility of labels is more important than showing box depth or pushbutton height.

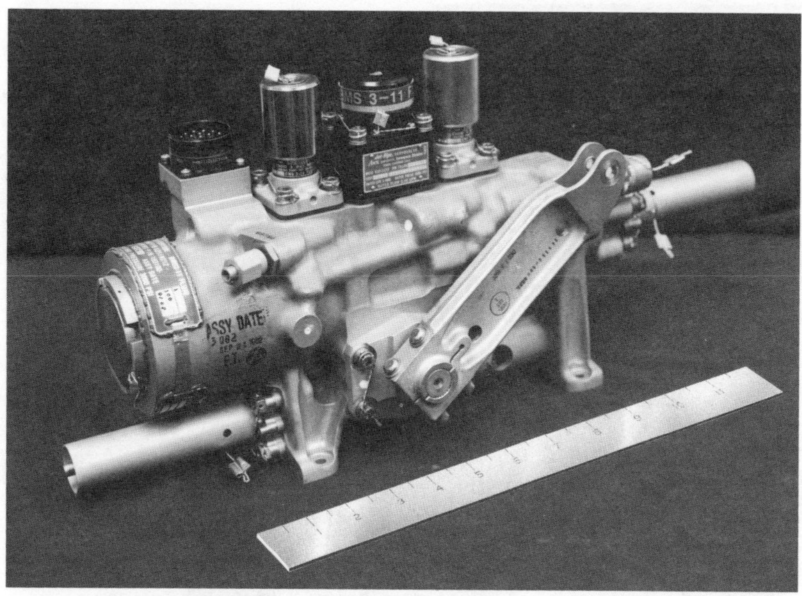

Figure 8. Servo Controller. *This aircraft flight control servo unit has redundant hydraulics and electromechanical override for maximum reliability.*

As you take the picture and as you crop it, do **not** center the subject. Place it slightly off center, usually in one of four places—as shown in figure 10, which illustrates the intersection of thirds.

Start by placing your subject on one of the two vertical lines, then move the center up or down to one of the two horizontal lines to decide where it best fits. Notice that on figure 11 the navigational unit is located toward the left-lower intersection. This picture also has an appropriate background subject.

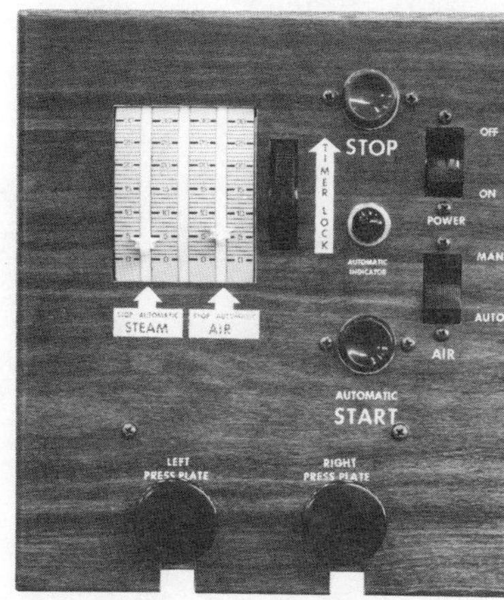

Figure 9. Control Station. *A mechanical programmer allows optional automatic cycling.*

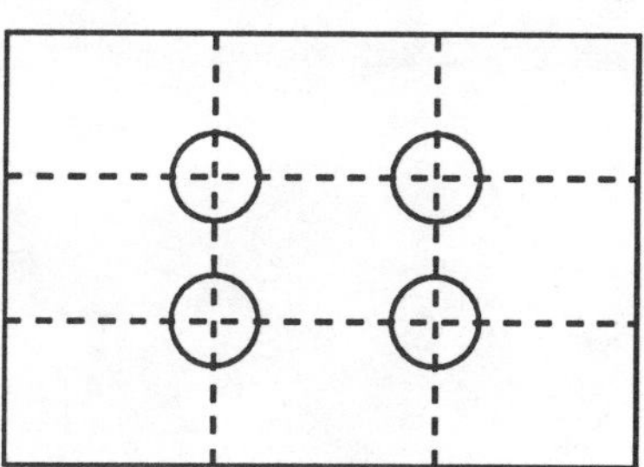

Figure 10. The Intersection of Thirds. *Place the center of interest of your photographs on one of the circles.*

4. Ensure that photographs have sufficient contrast and are in focus.

Proper separation of light and shadow (contrast) makes for a good black-and-white photograph (see figure 12). If the contrast is not sufficient, readers might not be able to distinguish the shapes and details of the objects photographed. If the photograph has too much contrast, detail will be lost and the photograph will look too sharp, even unrealistic.

Proper contrast occurs when the photograph shows a clear range of tones: crisp whites, distinct shades of gray, and deep blacks. Figure 13 is overexposed; everything is light and bright, slightly out of focus, poorly framed, and badly cropped.

Figure 11. Portable Navigational Unit. *Our navigational unit has been used successfully in battlefield conditions to direct C-130 supply operations.*

Figure 12. Concrete Batch Plant. *Aggregate moves from the first structure (background) into the second structure (foreground), where cement is added, mixed, and then loaded into trucks.*

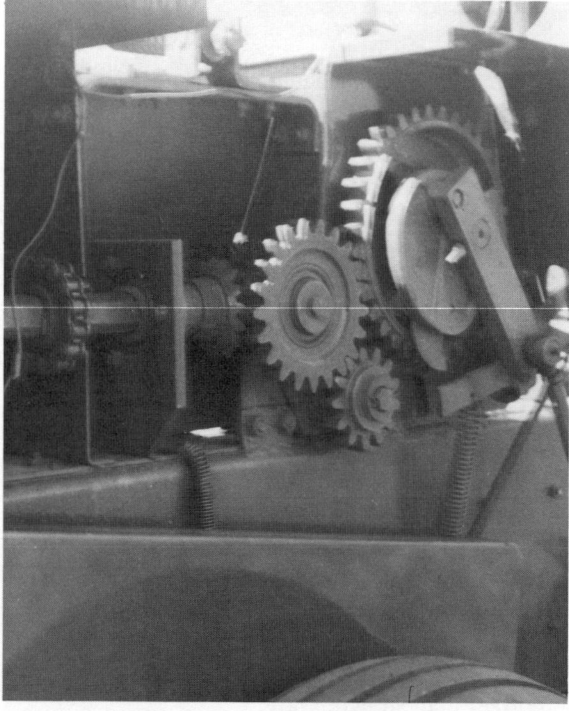

Figure 13. Some Gears and a Wheel. *This photograph is an excellent example of a bad example.*

5. Establish the size and proportion of the objects by using scales or by including objects in the photograph that permit scale comparisons.

Place a scale device in or on the pictures so that the readers have a sense of size. You might include a vehicle, a person, a hammer, or some other familiar object that creates a sense of proportion and size (see figure 14). Or as an option, print an actual scale or ruler beside a photograph.

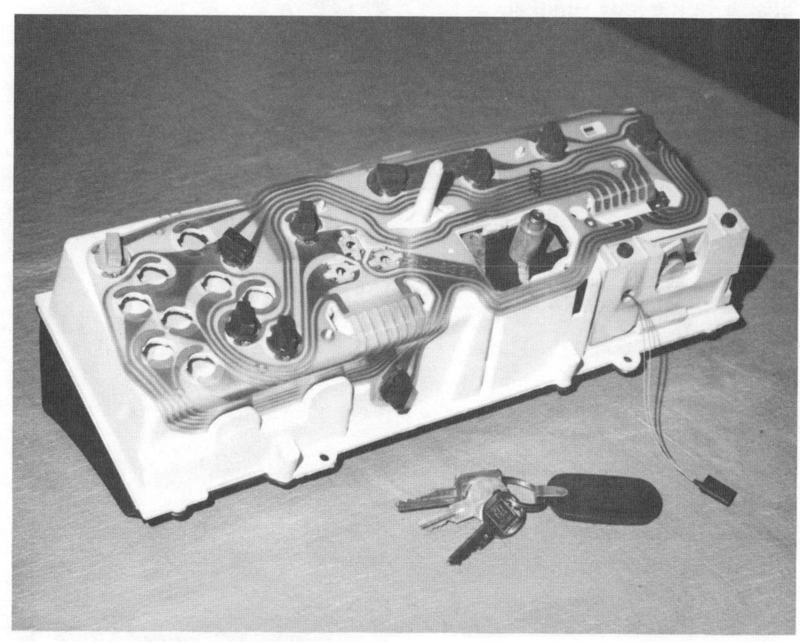

Figure 14. Instrument Cluster. *Printed circuits eliminate much wiring on the rear of this automobile instrument cluster.*

Photographs taken outside of the normal range of our visual experience must be placed into perspective. Photographs taken extremely close up or extremely far away might be difficult for readers to grasp because they lack perspective. Without perspective, readers might interpret a closeup of the hair on a man's arm as a bizarre forest and a closeup of fabric as a net made of thick ropes.

To maintain proper proportion, use a telephoto lens for closeups. Avoid fisheye lenses because they extremely distort proportion. Don't photograph a long, narrow object from near one end; this will cause excessive foreshortening (the railroad-track effect). As figure 15 illustrates, changing the angle and distance could change a viewer's grasp of the size and the proportion of the bucket loader; the angle in figure 15, for example, makes the rear end seem to be more massive than the other end.

Figure 15. Front-End Loader. *The supercharged diesel engine in this bucket loader provides ample power for loading rock and reinforced concrete.*

Do not stint on film. Professional photographers know that shooting many frames is cheaper in the long run than returning for reshooting. Take many shots from different angles the first time. Then select the best shots.

6. Place a north arrow and a scale device on geographical photographs.

Place a north arrow on all photographs that show geographical scenes (see figures 16 and 17). Photographs of geologic features are especially difficult for readers to interpret unless the photograph includes a vehicle, a person, or some other familiar object that permits a scale comparison.

Figure 16. A Piece of the Rock or All of It. *This 4-foot high boulder could be mistaken for a 1500-foot cliff. Try to locate the automobile key on the face of the rock.*

Figure 17. Jordanelle Dam Construction Site. *Patches of bare rock that will be left and right anchorpoints for the Jordanelle Dam are visible, just below and left of center, in this view looking downstream over the to-be-flooded Hailstone Junction on Highway 40, southwest toward Heber Valley and Provo Canyon.*

Plurals

Plurals of most nouns and pronouns are signaled by their spelling. Such changes are no problem if they follow the regular pattern: an *–s* or an *–es* added to the singular form makes the plural form:

report + s	=	reports
book + s	=	books
church + es	=	churches
tax + es	=	taxes

Problems arise when the plural does not follow the regular pattern:

mouse	mice
datum	data
chassis	chassis
fungus	fungi
matrix	matrices
I	we
he, she, it	they

The following discussion covers these and other irregular plurals. The best guide, however, is a good recent dictionary. See REFERENCES.

See NOUNS and SPELLING.

1. Use the following list to determine the plurals of many irregular forms, especially those technical terms borrowed from Latin or other languages:

addendum, addenda
agendum, agenda
alga, algae
alumnus, alumni (*masc.*)
alumna, alumnae (*fem.*)
antenna, antennas (antennae, *zoology*)
appendix, appendixes (*or* appendices)
axis, axes
basis, bases
cactus, cactuses
calix, calices
cicatrix, cicatrices
Co., Cos.
coccus, cocci
consortium, consortia
crisis, crises
criterion, criteria
curriculum, curriculums (*or* curricula)
datum, data
desideratum, desiderata
ellipsis, ellipses
equilibrium, equilibriums (equilibria, *scientific*)
erratum, errata
executrix, executrices
focus, focuses
folium, folia
formula, formulas
fungus, fungi
genus, genera
gladiolus (*singular and plural*)
helix, helices
hypothesis, hypotheses
index, indexes (indices, *scientific*)
lacuna, lacunae
larva, larvae
larynx, larynxes
lens, lenses
locus, loci
madam, mesdames
matrix, matrices
medium, mediums (*or* media)
memorandum, memorandums (*better* memo, memos)
minutia, minutiae
nucleus, nuclei
oasis, oases
octopus, octopuses
opus, opera
parenthesis, parentheses
phylum, phyla
plateau, plateaus
radius, radii
radix, radixes
referendum, referendums
septum, septa
seta, setae
stimulus, stimuli
stratum, strata
stylus, styluses
syllabus, syllabuses (*or* syllabi)
symposium, symposia
synopsis, synopses
terminus, termini
testatrix, testatrices
thesaurus, thesauri
thesis, theses
thorax, thoraxes
vertebra, vertebras (vertebrae, *zoology*)
virtuoso, virtuosos
vortex, vortexes

NOTE 1: Many of the above forms now have regular plurals (*appendix, appendixes* or *memorandum, memorandums*). However, some editors still prefer the irregular forms (usually based on the word's origin in Latin or another language: *appendices, memoranda*). The longer a word is in English, the stronger the tendency is to make the plural conform to the regular English pattern (adding an *–s* or *–es* to the singular form).

NOTE 2: Though many of these words come from other languages, they are now sufficiently English and do not need underlining or italics. See UNDERLINING and ITALICS.

2. In compound terms add the plural ending (usually *–s* or *–es*) to the most significant word:

attorneys at law
bills of fare
brothers-in-law
comptrollers general
daughters-in-law
goings-on
grants in aid
lookers-on
reductions in force
surgeons general

assistant chiefs of staff
assistant surgeons general

assistant attorneys
deputy judges
lieutenant colonels
trade unions

hand-me-downs
higher-ups
pick-me-ups

3. Nouns ending in *o* preceded by a consonant usually add *–es* for the plural:

echo, echoes
veto, vetoes
potato, potatoes

EXCEPTIONS: This rule has many exceptions, so if in doubt, check a good dictionary. See REFERENCES.

Plurals

Here are some of the common exceptions:

dynamo, dynamos
Eskimo, Eskimos
ghetto, ghettos
halo, halos
indigo, indigos
magneto, magnetos
octavo, octavos
piano, pianos
sirocco, siroccos
two, twos
zero, zeros

4. The coined plurals of abbreviations, titles, figures, letters, and symbols require an –*s* and sometimes an apostrophe plus an –*s*:

OK's
ABC's
CODs or COD's
the three Rs
SOS's
g's
1 by 4's

NOTE: Use the apostrophe only if necessary. Save the apostrophe to show possession, as in *John's hat*. The trend is for the apostrophe to vanish, leaving the simple –*s* signal that the item is a plural. See APOSTROPHES.

5. Plurals of pronouns, when they exist, are likely to be very irregular:

I	we
you	you
he, she, it	they

See PRONOUNS.

Possessives

Possessives are those forms of nouns and pronouns that show ownership or, in some cases, other close relationships:

Ownership

IBM's service booklet
Mr. Vaughan's store
his store
Susan's desk
her desk
Lewis' report
the engineer's schedule
the Lewises' house

Other Relationships

the book's cover
its cover
the corporation's support
his lawyer's consent
the captain's story
a summer's day
a day's absence
a doctor's degree

NOTE: Noun possessive forms routinely require an apostrophe or an apostrophe plus an *–s*. See APOSTROPHES.

---

1. Distinguish between true possessives and descriptive terms:

Possessives (whose . . .)

Exxon's reply
the employee's record
Oregon's laws
the Smiths' house

Descriptive Terms (what kind of . . .)

an Exxon reply
the employee record
Oregon laws
the Smith house

NOTE 1: Either form of the above phrases is correct, so decide which form you prefer and then be consistent within the same document.

NOTE 2: The names of countries, governmental units, and organized groups ending in *–s* usually do not require apostrophes:

United States plan
Massachusetts statutes
Mineworkers court case
United Nations publication

---

2. For singular nouns not ending in *–s* and for plural nouns not ending in *–s*, form the possessive by adding an apostrophe plus an *–s*:

the cat's paw
Anne's statement
a man's coat
men's coats
an accountant's books
the children's payments

---

3. For both plural nouns and singular nouns ending in *–s* or an *–s* sound, the possessive form requires only an apostrophe:

General Dynamics' proposal
Sears' 4th Quarter Report
Penneys' reaction
the boss' idea
James' speech

NOTE: Some editors and writers prefer to add both an apostrophe and an *–s*, especially if the new word has an extra syllable:

General Dynamics's proposal
the actress's script
the boss's idea
James's speech

---

4. Add an apostrophe plus an *–s* to the end of personal and organizational names showing possession:

Sears & Roebuck's policy

Charles F. Shook's decision

the Odd Fellows's initiation (*or* Odd Fellows' initiation)

Dewey, Cheatum, and Howe's corporate policy

NOTE: Corporate and organizational practices vary, so, if possible, check the letterhead or other correspondence for exceptional cases:

American Bankers Association
Steelworkers Union
Investors Profit Sharing

---

5. Possessive forms of personal pronouns and of the relative pronoun *who* do not require an apostrophe:

My secretary had mine.

Your supervisor had hers.

The company lost its comptroller.

We refused to pay for ours.

They lost theirs when the market fell.

He mentioned his.

Whose report is this?

NOTE 1: These are the possessive forms of personal pronouns: *my/mine, your/yours, his, her/hers, its, our/ours, their/theirs.* In cases with two forms, the first form must come before the noun it possesses and the second form comes after the verb, with its noun implied:

They were her ideas.

The ideas were hers.

Possessives

NOTE 2: Distinguish between possessive forms without apostrophes and contractions with apostrophes:

The pump had lost its cover.

We decided that it's (*it is*) time to redrill.

He had changed his job recently.

He's changing his job.

Whose idea was this?

Who's going to be at the meeting?

See APOSTROPHES.

6. Possessive forms of indefinite pronouns require apostrophes:

anyone else's task
one's ideas
the other's notion
the others' schedules
anybody's recommendation
someone else's job

7. Possessives sometimes occur without a following noun:

My ideas are like Sue's.

His nose is like a bloodhound's.

I'll be at Jim's.

She was at the doctor's.

IBM's is good, but Apple's is better.

NOTE: Large, established companies sometimes violate the usual rule (singular form plus an apostrophe and an *–s*):

We conducted a survey at Macys. (*or* Macys')

Harrods is splitting its stock.

8. A possessive modifies an *–ing* form of a verb used as a noun:

Bill's speaking to my boss helped.

I objected to his working on the rig overnight.

I admired Sue's planning.

Prepositions

Prepositions are words that connect or relate nouns and pronouns to preceding words and phrases:

> The engineer moved **from** his desk.
>
> The plans **for** the new substation have yet to be completed.
>
> The case **against** her became even more convincing.
>
> There is truth **in** what you say.
>
> The firm submitted a summary **of** the specifications.

The simple prepositions are *at, by, in, on, down, from, off, out, through, to, up, for, of,* and *with.* More complex, even phrasal, prepositions also exist: *against, beneath, in front of, on top of, on board (of), outside of, according to, on account of, by means of,* etc.

Although they number less than a hundred, prepositions are essential words in English. Most normal sentences contain one or more prepositions.

1. Do not be overly concerned if you end a sentence with a preposition.

For over a thousand years English has had normal sentences that ended with prepositions:

> That's something we can't put up with.
>
> The Universal acquisition is the most difficult deal we've gotten into.
>
> This is the report I've been telling you about.
>
> She's the accountant you spoke to.
>
> This project is the one that you objected to.

Winston Churchill was once corrected for ending a sentence with a preposition, and he supposedly replied, "That is the sort of English up with which I will not put."

As Churchill's witty reply indicates, many English sentences sound awkward if you try to avoid ending them with prepositions:

> *not*
>
> The Universal acquisition is the most difficult deal into which we've gotten.
>
> This is the report about which I told you.
>
> She is the accountant to whom you spoke.
>
> This project is the one to which you objected.

Make your sentences as simple, smooth, and direct as possible, and don't worry about such misconceptions as not ending a sentence with a preposition. The fact is, a preposition is a fine word to end a sentence with.

2. You can sometimes omit prepositions without changing the meaning of the sentence:

> All (of) the engineers visited the site.
>
> We moved the pipe off (of) the loading dock.
>
> The filing cabinet is too near (to) the door.
>
> We met (at) about 8 p.m.
>
> Where are they (at)?

In each of the above sentences, the preposition within parentheses is unnecessary. In the last sentence, *at* is both unnecessary and incorrect.

Generally, native speakers of English can be guided by their innate sense of what constitutes smooth and clear uses of prepositions.

See MODIFIERS.

3. Distinguish between the prepositions *between* and *among.*

Between usually refers to two things, while *among* refers to more than two things. However, *between* can also refer to more than two things if each of the things is compared to all the others as a group:

> The judge divided the land between the two parties. (*not* among)
>
> The judge divided the land among a dozen parties. (*not* between)
>
> We had trouble deciding between the two pumps. (*not* among)
>
> We carefully analyzed the differences between the six alternatives. (*or* among)
>
> We had trouble deciding among all the possible small trucks. (*or* between)

See WORD PROBLEMS.

Pronouns

Pronouns are words that take the place of more specific nouns or noun phrases:

George completed the drawings.
He completed the drawings.

The young engineer spoke up.
She spoke up.

John's survey was efficient.
His survey was efficient.

First State Bank went bankrupt.
It went bankrupt.

John, Sue, Esther, and George left the party early.
They left the party early.

Who completed the drawings?
(Who = *somebody unknown*)

The man hit himself.
We ourselves paid for the damage.

The bid and the interest were issues.
Those were issues.

John, Sue, Esther, George, etc., left the party early.
Everyone left the party early.

As the above examples indicate, pronouns include several types of words: **personal** pronouns (*he, she, his, they,* etc.), **interrogative** and **relative** pronouns (*who, that,* and *which*), **reflexive** and **intensive** pronouns (*himself, ourselves,* etc.), **demonstrative** pronouns (*this, that, these,* and *those*), and **indefinite** pronouns (*everyone, anybody, someone,* etc.).

Personal Pronouns

Personal pronouns are those that commonly replace the names of individuals or objects: *I, we, you, he, she, it,* and *they*:

- *I* and *we* are first person pronouns—that is, they are used for the person(s) speaking.
- *You* (singular and plural) is the second person pronoun—that is, it is used for person(s) spoken to.
- *He, she, it,* and *they* are third person pronouns—that is, they are used for persons or objects spoken about.

Most personal pronouns also have different forms for the singular and the plural, for different uses in sentences, and for possessives. The table on this page summarizes these different forms of the personal pronouns.

Personal Pronouns

			Subjective Case	Objective Case	Possessive Case
1st Person	Singular		I	me	my/mine
	Plural		we	us	our/ours
2nd Person	Singular		you	you	your/yours
	Plural		you	you	your/yours
3rd Person	Singular	Masculine	he	him	his
		Feminine	she	her	hers
		Non-human	it	it	its
	Plural		they	them	their/theirs

While the differences between the singular and plural forms are obvious, the differences between the cases are often confusing. Different cases (pronoun forms) have different uses in sentences:

I surveyed the site. (I *is the subjective case.*)

The committee quizzed me. (Me *is the objective case.*)

My report was too long. (My *is the possessive case—the one that comes before its noun.*)

The report is mine. (Mine *is the possessive case—the one that follows its noun.*)

See PLURALS.

1. Use personal pronouns in business and technical documents to establish a personal, human tone.

Pronouns—especially *I* and *you*—establish the identities of the writer and the reader. Such pronouns bring a human tone to a letter or memo:

this

- Based on my review, I recommend that you sell your MOGO stock and buy Sky Aviation stock.

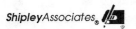

not this

Based on a careful review, the sale of your MOGO stock is recommended. Sky Aviation would be a good replacement stock.

See TONE.

2. Use subjective case pronouns for the subject of a verb or when the pronoun follows a form of *be (am, is, are, was, were, be, been)*:

Subject of a Verb

Jan and I analyzed the blueprints.

We discussed the design options.

You were omitted from the roll.

He called two colleagues.

She and her employee came to the 11 a.m. meeting.

It was a poor choice.

They and Harold met about the legal problem.

NOTE: In cases where a pronoun and a noun are both subjects of the same verb, you can test the pronoun by removing the noun. In the sentence *She and her employee came to the 11 a.m. meeting*, no one would read it as follows: *Her came to the 11 a.m. meeting*. So *she* is the correct pronoun.

Following a Form of Be

The engineer chosen was she.

The contractor who won is he.

Was it they who called?

It could have been I.

NOTE: Pronouns following forms of *be* often sound strange:

It is I.

This is she.

Normally, objective case pronouns follow verbs: *It is me* or *This is her*. These sentences are acceptable in informal speech, which is where they ordinarily would appear anyway. In formal speech and in most writing, the subjective case forms are correct. (Of course, if your sentence sounds stiff or strange, rephrase it to avoid the problem. You could say *I am here* instead of *It is I*.

3. Use objective case pronouns when the pronoun is the object of a verb or the object of a preposition:

Object of a Verb

The committee chose her.

Carol did not include Jane and him.

The pollution affected them.

The President contacted Harry and me.

NOTE: When a noun and a pronoun both follow a verb, you can check the pronoun by omitting the noun. So *The President contacted Harry and me* becomes *The President contacted me*. Few people would be comfortable with *I*, which is the wrong pronoun, but many speakers often use *I* when a noun comes before it: *The President contacted Harry and I*. This sentence is incorrect.

Object of a Preposition

Frank walked by her.

The team studied with me.

On account of me, the project ended.

The proposed schedule depended on Jane and her.

Acme Inc. worked against Jason and me.

NOTE: In the last two sentences, you can test for the correct pronoun by removing the noun that comes between the preposition and the pronoun. (Wrong: *The proposed schedule depended on she. Acme Inc. worked against I.)*

4. Use possessive cases correctly:

That was her report.
The report was hers.

The problems were ours, not yours.
They were our problems, not your problems.

I rejected your arguments.
The arguments were yours, not mine.

NOTE 1: In cases where two possessive forms exist for a single pronoun, the simple form (without an *–s)* comes before the noun; the other form (with an *–s)* follows a form of *be (am, is, are, was, were, be, been)*. *His* and *its* have only a single form.

NOTE 2: Do not confuse the possessive pronouns with simple contractions. Possessive pronouns do not have apostrophes; contractions have apostrophes:

Possessive Pronoun	Contraction
its	it's
his	he's
their/theirs	they're
your/yours	you're

See POSSESSIVES.

Pronouns

5. Choose pronouns so that they agree with their antecedents in number, in gender, and in case:

Agreement in Number

The men worked on the design plan all night, but they were unable to finish. (men *[antecedent]* = *plural;* they = *plural)*

Cheryl Higgins prepared a revised safety procedure, but she failed to get managerial approval. (Cheryl Higgins *[antecedent]* = *singular;* she = *singular)*

Agreement in Gender

Sidney Brown was eager to take his first actuarial exam. (Sidney *[antecedent] can be either male or female, so the pronoun is a key sign of which is intended. Often the female spelling is* Sydney.)

NOTE: When the antecedent is an indefinite pronoun, writers often don't know whether to use a singular or plural pronoun, much less a male or female pronoun:

Everyone should arrange their (his *or* her?) desk before leaving.

Everybody is responsible for their (his *or* her?) own time cards.

The forms with *their* have become more acceptable in speech, even though *everyone* and *everybody* are usually considered singular pronouns. To avoid any sexist language and to eliminate the clumsy *his* or *her*, the best option would be to rewrite the sentences as plurals:

All employees should arrange their desks before leaving.

All clerks and secretaries are responsible for their own time cards.

See AGREEMENT, SEXIST LANGUAGE, and the discussion below of indefinite pronouns.

Agreement in Case

Betty argued with them—especially Susan and him. (them = *objective case;* him = *objective case*)

Interrogative and Relative Pronouns

Interrogative and relative pronouns are similar in their uses, and some interrogative pronouns are identical to the main relative pronouns: *who, whom, whose,* and *which.* Relative pronouns also include *that, whoever, whomever, whatever, why,* and *where.* Interrogatives also include *what*, which is not a relative form.

Many interrogative and relative pronouns have only one form, but *who* changes its form just as the personal pronouns do:

Subjective case: who, whoever

Objective case: whom, whomever

Possessive case: whose

That and the other relative and interrogative forms do not change to reflect the different cases.

6. For interrogative and relative *who*, use the subjective case for subjects and following a form of *be*; use the objective case for objects of verbs and prepositions:

Subjective Case

Who is the project engineer?

Whoever writes the report gets all the credit.

The agent who spoke to us was courteous.

The supervisor determined who would be the representative.

The representative is whoever has the most years of service.

Objective Case

Whom did you nominate?

Whom did you wish to speak to? *Or:* To whom did you wish to speak?

Whomever you nominate, we'll find someone to balance the ticket.

The man whom you spoke to is our president.

NOTE 1: The first two examples under the objective case sound almost too formal, even stiff. Most speakers of English are more comfortable if a subjective *who* begins the sentence or question. For this reason, two other versions of these questions are acceptable in informal, spoken English:

Who did you nominate?

Who did you wish to speak to?

Similarly, even with non-questions, subjective *who* sometimes replaces more correct *whom*:

Whoever you nominate, we'll find someone to balance the ticket.

These informal forms with *who* or *whoever* are incorrect in writing even though acceptable in informal speech.

NOTE 2: Deciding on the correct case is especially difficult when the relative pronoun is part of a complex sentence. The trick is to isolate only the clause containing the relative pronoun:

who wants to study chemistry

whom the proposal team chose

whoever is the top candidate

These are correct uses of *who* and *whom*, so you can insert them into any sentence, and they'll be correct:

> John, who wants to study chemistry, is our lab technician.
>
> We left with Sandra, whom the proposal team chose.
>
> Whoever is the top candidate will be our speaker.
>
> We planned to interview whoever is the top candidate.

So to decide on the case of a troublesome use of *who* or *whom*, try to isolate the clause containing the relative pronoun (underlined below):

> We decided to abandon the direction established by the geologist <u>who/whom we first talked to</u>.

The proper form then is *whom*, used as the object of the preposition *to*.

NOTE 3: Adjective clauses introduced by a relative pronoun are often difficult to punctuate. The simplest rule is to enclose such clauses with commas when they are nonessential:

> Jack Craven, who is our project coordinator, has been with the company for 15 years.
>
> We presented the proposal to the team from AirFlo Inc., which is a firm based in Denver.

When the clauses are essential, no commas are required:

> The proposal that we sent to the Department of Transportation has been canceled. (*Without the clause* that we sent to the Department of Transportation, *the sentence would not be clear to most readers, especially if more than one proposal were possible.)*
>
> The Governor proposed banning all autos that did not have a safety inspection. *(The clause* that did not have a safety inspection *is essential to the meaning.)*

See COMMAS.

Reflexive and Intensive Pronouns

Reflexive and intensive pronouns are identical in appearance: Both end in *–self* (singular) or *–selves* (plural). Personal pronouns have reflexive and intensive forms: *myself, ourselves, yourself, yourselves, himself, herself, itself,* and *themselves.*

Reflexive pronouns "reflect" back to a noun mentioned earlier in the same sentence:

> George injured himself.
>
> The team quarreled among themselves.
>
> Amy cut herself.
>
> The dog licked itself.

Intensive pronouns usually follow the nouns they intensify:

> George himself was injured.
>
> The team themselves were arguing.
>
> Amy herself ran the errand.
>
> I myself checked on the data.

---

7. Avoid the unnecessary use of intensive/reflexive forms when an ordinary personal pronoun would suffice:

> With our permission, Jeff became the spokesman for Jim and myself. (*better:* Jim and me)
>
> John and myself are both uncomfortable with the proposal. (*better:* John and I)

Demonstrative Pronouns

Only four demonstrative pronouns exist:

	Singular	Plural
"near"	this	these
"far"	that	those

Demonstrative pronouns sometimes appear before a noun and sometimes they can replace the noun or noun phrase entirely:

> This design plan has problems.
>
> This has problems. (*This sentence assumes that the reader or listener knows what the word* this *refers to.)*
>
> That proposal for the DOE demonstrates effective graphics.
>
> That demonstrates effective graphics.

---

8. Avoid vague uses of demonstrative pronouns (usually when the pronoun is used without the noun it is describing):

> This is something to consider. (*better:* This shortfall in payments is something to consider.)
>
> These are difficult. (*better:* These exercises are difficult.)

NOTE: Such vague sentences are particularly annoying when, for example, a *this* refers back to an entire sentence or several things in a sentence:

> *not this*
>
> The travel plans were a jumble and even turned out to be beyond our budget. This meant that we could not make connections as planned.
>
> *this*
>
> The travel plans were a jumble and even turned out to be beyond our budget. The jumble (*or* This jumble) meant that we could not make connections as planned.

Pronouns

Indefinite Pronouns

Indefinite pronouns include a number of words that have unspecified or vague meanings, usually because the writer or speaker does not want to identify or can't identify the person(s) or thing(s) referred to. These sentences illustrate some of the common indefinite pronouns:

> **Everyone** should proofread the report before we send it out.
>
> We cleaned out **everything** before vacating the office.
>
> **Both** were involved in the design tests last summer.
>
> We determined that **somebody** had changed the entry code in the computer.
>
> The procedures required that **anyone** leaving the security area sign and note the date and time.
>
> **Nobody** had a pass to be on the construction site after normal work hours.

A List of Indefinite Pronouns

everyone	everything
everybody	every
each	all
both	
someone	something
somebody	somewhere
some	another
one	
anyone	anything
anybody	anywhere
either	any
no one	nothing
nobody	nowhere
none	neither
many	few
several	others
more	most

NOTE: Many of these indefinite pronouns can act very much like adjectives:

> Several books were stolen from our library.
>
> Most participants would want to attend the final session.
>
> *or*
>
> Several were stolen from our library.
>
> Most would want to attend the final session.

---

9. Indefinite pronouns used as subjects should agree in number with their verbs:

> Anyone likes to receive a positive performance review. (Anyone = *singular;* likes = *singular)*
>
> Several were contacted before we chose a final candidate. (Several = *plural;* were = *plural)*
>
> All of the sugar was tainted. (All of the sugar = *singular;* was = *singular)*
>
> All of the employees were notified of the new vacation policy. (All of the employees = *plural;* were = *plural)*

NOTE: Sometimes the indefinite pronoun, even though considered grammatically singular, requires a plural pronoun:

> Everyone should abandon their attempt to discover the error.

Strict editors would argue that *everyone* is singular and *their* is plural, so traditionally the correct form has been this version:

> Everyone should abandon his attempt to discover the error.

Feminists and others have criticized this version as being sexist because females are ignored. One option would be to replace *his* with *his or her*. A more reasonable option is to rewrite the sentence so that it is clearly plural:

> All engineers should abandon their attempts to discover the error.

See AGREEMENT and SEXIST LANGUAGE. Also see the discussion above of personal pronouns.

Punctuation

Punctuation marks are as much a part of language as words. Like words, punctuation is a code that allows writers to communicate with readers who know the code.

Like words, punctuation rules (conventions) are not firm, fixed, and unchanging. The rules are evolutionary, but about 95 percent of the rules are relatively fixed and not debated as, for instance, the rule that requires the comma in *June 15, 1989*.

Punctuation rules are subject to tradition and local usage. The rules differ slightly from industry to industry and from publication to publication. The punctuation style that one publisher prefers might differ slightly from the style of another publisher.

Writers who use every permissible mark of punctuation follow a **mandatory** (formal) style. Writers who omit optional punctuation follow an **optional** (informal) style. Other terms can be and have been used to describe these two styles of punctuation: conservative vs. liberal and closed (close) vs. open.

The following examples illustrate the differences between the mandatory and optional styles.

Example 1: Commas in a Series

Writers following the optional style usually omit the comma before the *and* joining the last two items in a series:

> We requested employment figures for 1986, 1987 and 1988.

> The report analyzed the possible market in 1989-1990, the projected labor costs and the supply of raw materials.

Writers following the mandatory style always include the comma before the *and* joining the last two items in a series.

In some sentences, the comma before the *and* is not necessary, but in some sentences, omitting the comma can create ambiguity:

> The maintenance people replaced the rocker arm bracket, hinge pin and wheel assembly.

Are the hinge pin and the wheel part of the same assembly? A comma after *pin* clearly signals that the three items are separate:

> The maintenance people replaced the rocker arm bracket, hinge pin, and wheel assembly.

Because clarity and precision are so important in technical and scientific writing, we recommend that writers adopt the mandatory style and retain the comma before the *and* in a series.

Example 2: Commas in Dates

Punctuating the day, month, and year is usually simple and straightforward. A comma separates the day and the year:

> June 15, 1990

What happens, however, when the date appears in the middle of a sentence?

> We moved on June 15, 1990 into our new office.

Writers following the optional style would not insert a comma after *1990*. Writers following the mandatory style would add a comma after *1990*:

> We moved on June 15, 1990, into our new office.

Both versions are "correct." Both are acceptable because the presence or absence of the comma after *1990* does not affect clarity.

---

1. Use the mandatory style for most technical, scientific, and legal documents.

The mandatory style allows for more precision and can help you avoid ambiguity, so we recommend it.

We also recommend it for any formal or critical documents. In letters and memos to familiar readers, however, you might wish to follow the optional, less formal style.

Mandatory/Optional Punctuation

The following rules are those that allow for optional punctuation. Writers following the optional style might omit punctuation in the cases cited below except when clarity would suffer. If omitting punctuation would make the writing less clear, more ambiguous, or at all confusing, then use the appropriate mark of punctuation.

—Use an apostrophe and an *–s* to form the singular possessive of words of more than one syllable ending in *–s*:

> Harris's report
> Davis's plan

Punctuation

OPTIONAL STYLE: These possessive forms would be *Harris'* and *Davis'*. Note that the apostrophe is not optional.

—Use a comma before a coordinate conjunction to separate two independent thoughts, even when they are quite short and simple:

The plan was finished, and the budget calculated.

OPTIONAL STYLE: You would omit the comma after *finished.*

—Use a comma before the *and* that joins the last two items in a series:

We ordered two water pumps, a fan, and three replacement belts.

OPTIONAL STYLE: You would omit the comma after *fan.*

—Use a comma to enclose parenthetical expressions, even very short ones such as *thus*:

He was, thus, surprised by the answer.

OPTIONAL STYLE: You would omit both commas around *thus.*

—Use a comma after introductory phrases and clauses, even when they are very short and simple:

After we wrote the report, we submitted it.

OPTIONAL STYLE: You would omit the comma after *report.*

—Use a comma after the year in a date and the state in an address when either appears in the middle of a sentence:

The time sheets for July 6, 1990, show no overtime.

His speech in Joplin, Missouri, was most forgettable.

OPTIONAL STYLE: You would omit the commas after *1990* and *Missouri.*

—Use hyphens to form compound words that modify other words:

We will install a high-tension line above the Bradley overpass.

OPTIONAL STYLE: You would omit the hyphen between *high* and *tension.*

—Use periods after all abbreviations, including the names of government agencies, colleges and universities, and private organizations:

I.B.M.

S.U.N.Y. (State University of New York)

N.A.A.C.P.

OPTIONAL STYLE: You would omit the periods in these and most other abbreviations.

—Use a semicolon along with a coordinate conjunction to join independent clauses or complete thoughts that already contain a comma, even if they are clear without the semicolon:

Although new rain gauges helped us monitor total precipitation, we could not have anticipated the heavy spring runoff; and the resulting floods caused considerable damage to the watershed.

OPTIONAL STYLE: You would use a comma after *runoff,* not a semicolon.

For further information on commas, periods, semicolons, colons, dashes, and other marks of punctuation, see the alphabetical entries elsewhere in this *Style Guide.*

Question Marks

Question marks in English, unfortunately, are placed at the end of sentences. Spanish, to make reading easier, places an upside-down question mark at the beginning and a right-side-up question mark at the end of question sentences.

1. Use question marks to indicate direct questions:

> Will analysis modeling be required?

NOTE 1: Use a separate question mark for each in a series of incomplete or elliptical questions:

> When will the preliminary targeting studies be due? In 30 days? 60? 90?

NOTE 2: Use question marks at the end of statements written as declarations but intended as questions:

> These are the final figures?
>
> Regulating the supply pressure was the only realistic solution?

NOTE 3: Do *not* use question marks for indirect questions or for statements written as questions but intended as courteous requests:

> During our preliminary design studies, we asked whether the weapon parameters would be an integrated part of the overall system requirements. (*The underlined clause is an indirect question. Its phrasing is not identical to a direct question.*)
>
> Will you please forward five copies of DD Form 1425.

See PERIODS.

2. Use question marks to indicate questions within a sentence:

> Your project managers have the authority, don't they, to reallocate resources based on changing needs?

NOTE 1: When the question follows an introductory statement, capitalize the first word of the question and use a question mark:

> The remaining question is, Can shortfalls in determining performance results be quantified with the Phase 2 synthesis procedure?
>
> Today's manufacturer asks, How can Q&A expenses be distributed across project and functional lines?

NOTE 2: If the question precedes a concluding sentence remark, the question mark goes after the question, and the sentence remark begins with a lowercase word:

> Which mission would prove most productive? was the remaining question.

3. Use question marks within parentheses to indicate doubt:

> CAD/CAM was first investigated at MIT in 1964(?).

Question Marks with Other Punctuation

4. Place question marks inside of quotation marks, parentheses, or brackets only when they are part of the quoted or parenthetical material:

> During the preproposal conference, an Allied representative asked, "Does the Statement of Work represent a minimal subset of requirements?"
>
> What did the contacting officer mean when she said, "The Statement of Work is the minimal subset of requirements"?
>
> When did she ask, "Who is the project manager?"
>
> The engineering program includes analysis, design, testing (fabrication?), and integration of the unit into the helicopter.
>
> Doesn't the Program Plan call for Task F completion no later than 75 days ARO (August 17)?

See PARENTHESES, BRACKETS, and QUOTATION MARKS.

Quotation Marks

Quotation marks have multiple uses. The most common use (enclosing direct quotations) gives them their name. In earlier centuries, quotation marks did not exist and the reader could not tell easily the writer's words from the quoted words. Today, the conventions for using quotation marks are well established.

1. Use quotation marks to enclose direct quotations:

The RFP says, "All pages in the proposal must be numbered."

Direct quotations include the actual words and phrases from a document or from a person speaking.

Indirect quotations do **not** take quotation marks:

The RFP says that all pages in the proposal have to be numbered.

Indirect quotations do not give every word and phrase in the direct quotation. Often an indirect quotation is only a paraphrase:

The RFP says that we should number all pages in the proposal.

See QUOTATIONS.

NOTE 1: Long quotations have two equally acceptable conventions: (1) They may be enclosed by quotation marks, or (2) they may be indented from both the left and right margins (in which case they do **not** require quotation marks). If quotation marks are used and the quotation extends for more than one paragraph, quotation marks should appear at the beginning and ending of the entire quotation and at the beginning of each new paragraph within the quotation.

NOTE 2: Single quotation marks are used to indicate a quotation within a quotation:

According to the NASA report, "National Aerodynamics argued for a 'differential scale of evolution.'"

2. Use quotation marks to indicate the title of an article, section, volume, and other parts of a longer document:

The contracting officer must approve all items specified under "Special Equipment" in the cost proposal.

This volume must include a completed and signed Standard Form 33, "Solicitation, Offer, and Award."

See TITLES.

3. Use quotation marks to indicate that a word is used in a special or abnormal sense:

The 1990 study suggested that NASA's definition of "suitability" contradicts the goals of the program.

Only in English do "thin chance" and "fat chance" mean the same.

NOTE: Italics (or underlining) can replace quotation marks when you want to refer to a word as a word:

In the contract, *boundaries* refers only to those property lines surveyed after July 1990.

See ITALICS and UNDERLINING.

Quotation Marks with Other Punctuation

4. Always place periods and commas inside of closing quotation marks:

We have completed the section entitled "Representations, Certifications, and Acknowledgements."

The logarithmic decrease of the differential threshold is sometimes mistakenly called "Fechner's law."

NOTE: This convention seems illogical, but it is now standard in the United States. The convention developed because printers wanted to put the smaller periods and commas inside of the closing quotation marks for a cleaner appearance on the page.

British usage places commas and periods inside or outside the quotation marks, depending on whether they are or are not part of the quotation.

5. Always place semicolons and colons outside of closing quotation marks:

The corporation's experience belongs under "Related Experience"; the project manager's experience belongs under "Resumes of Key Personnel."

Include the following under "Manhours and Materials":

a. Work statement tasks

b. Estimated completion schedule

c. Materials/equipment required

6. Place dashes, exclamation marks, and question marks inside of quotation marks if they are part of the quotation; otherwise, place them outside of quotation marks:

The section entitled "Personnel Qualifications"—the only part of the proposal where we can address the team's APL experience—is restricted to five pages.

He said, "Can we improve the unload utilities without losing the language interface?"

See QUESTION MARKS and SPACING.

Quotations

Quotations are an effective tool when you have to refer persuasively to data and conclusions from another document.

When you quote from another document, be careful not to misrepresent the content and the intent of the original passage. The following rules are suggestions. You must judge for yourself if you are accurately representing the original document.

1. Quote only the key or relevant passages:

> Your letter made an excellent case for the "procedural lapse" that caused the double billing to your account.
>
> In the analysis of the data, Jameson (1989) argues for three "equally persuasive hypotheses."

NOTE 1: Sometimes only a two- or three-word phrase is sufficient to capture the flavor of the original document. Rarely do you need to quote whole sentences or paragraphs from the original document.

Long quotes distract the reader and often signal that the writer has not done the work necessary to boil the quoted document down to its essentials.

NOTE 2: As illustrated in the two examples above, all quoted words, phrases, and sentences should normally be enclosed by quotation marks. See QUOTATION MARKS.

NOTE 3: In cases where words are omitted from the middle of quoted material, an ellipsis signals that material has been omitted:

> Your letter made an excellent case for the "procedural lapse . . . and the sloppy record keeping" that caused the double billing of your account. (*The original read:* ". . . the procedural lapse when my account was opened and the sloppy record keeping ever since.")

See ELLIPSES.

2. Cite the sources for any quoted material—from words and phrases to whole sentences and paragraphs. See CITATIONS.

Inexperienced writers sometimes are careless in their citations.

No material from another source, especially copyrighted material, should ever appear in another document without full and adequate credit being given to the original author(s).

No reader should ever have to guess what is original and what the writer is borrowing from someone else. Both accurate citations and accurate use of quotation marks and ellipses can remove such uncertainties.

3. Distinguish carefully between direct and indirect quotations.

Direct quotations contain only the original words and phrases of the document being quoted.

Indirect quotations are a writer's summary of someone else's words. Some minor words may come from the original, but the writer has made significant changes. Even then, key words should appear within quotation marks.

Below is an original passage. Following it are examples of a direct quotation and an indirect quotation:

Original Passage

> Hank Stevens was over 30 minutes late three times during the week of November 3. He called in on one of these mornings, but we received no calls on the other two mornings. Although it is now November 15, he has given no satisfactory excuse or explanation of his lateness.

Direct Quotation

> According to Hank Stevens' supervisor, Hank has failed to give a "satisfactory excuse or explanation of his lateness" on three mornings during the week of November 3. Hank did call in one of the mornings, but he did not call in the other two mornings.

Indirect Quotation

> According to Hank Stevens' supervisor, Hank has not explained adequately his three instances of lateness during the week of November 3. Hank was over 30 minutes late in each case, and he only called in one time.

Quotations

NOTE 1: As this example illustrates, the direct quotation is often embedded in a passage that contains some indirect quotations. As rule 1 above indicates, you should quote only the pertinent words and phrases.

NOTE 2: Often the change from direct to indirect quotations involves a change in syntax and wording (especially in the pronouns):

Direct Quotation

"We need to receive your response by no later than January 15, 1990."

Indirect Quotation

MOGO Oil said that they must have our written response by January 15, 1990.

Direct Quotation

"I have been unable to locate the original data collected in 1976. The files seem not to have been moved when we moved in 1980 from the old building to our present building."

Indirect Quotation

Gene Sayers has been unable to find the original 1976 data. He suspects that the files were not moved in 1980 when we moved into our present building.

4. Use brackets to insert comments or corrections in quoted material:

"The measured length [8.35 feet] differs from the length specified in the specification."

"Ralph Stevenson [Stephenson] was the representative elected from Curry County."

See BRACKETS.

Redundant Words

Redundant words or phrases unnecessarily qualify other words or phrases.

For instance, in the expression *basic fundamentals*, the word *basic* is unnecessary because, by definition, all fundamentals are basic.

Past experience is redundant because for experience to be experience, it must have been acquired in the past. *Past history* is redundant for the same reason. You can't have present or future history. All history is past. However, *ancient history* and *recent history* are acceptable because they both refer to specific parts of the past.

1. Eliminate redundant words.

A fundamental of good writing style is to eliminate unnecessary words. Do not say *main essentials*. Just say *essentials*. Do not speak of the *final conclusion*. It is simply the *conclusion*. Documents are not *attached together*. They are simply *attached*.

See Wordy Phrases.

Redundancies and Emphasis

2. Use redundant words to emphasize or dramatize a situation or condition:

> Mailing the ramjet study by Friday is absolutely essential.

The only proper use of redundancies in writing is to emphasize. The expression *absolutely essential* is redundant because nothing can be more essential than *essential*. If you need to heighten the sense of urgency in a situation by exaggerating, then redundant words are acceptable. However, do **not** overuse redundancies for emphasis. The effect diminishes quickly. You can become so exaggerated in your style that readers pay less attention to your ideas. Too much emphasis becomes no emphasis.

See Emphasis and Gobbledygook.

A List of Redundancies

The following list of redundancies will help you identify those you habitually use. The redundant expression appears in the left column; in the right column are possible substitutes:

Absolutely complete	complete
absolutely essential	essential
absolutely nothing	nothing
accidentally stumbled	stumbled
a.c. current	a.c./alternating current
actual experience	experience
adequate enough	adequate/enough
advance forward	advance
advance planning	planning
aluminum metal	aluminum
and etc.	etc.
any and all	any/all
arrive on the scene	arrive
ask the question	ask
assembled together	assembled
attached hereto	attached
attach together	attach
Basic fundamentals	fundamentals
before in the past	before/in the past
betwixt and between	between
blue in color	blue
brief in duration	brief/quick/fast
Check up on	check
circle around	circle
close proximity	proximity
collect together	collect
combine together	combine
completely destroyed	destroyed
completely opposite	opposite
connect together	connect
consensus of opinion	consensus
consequent results	results
consolidate together	consolidate
continue on	continue
continue to remain	remain
contributing factor	factor
cooperate together	cooperate
couple together	couple
Desirable benefits	benefits
diametrically opposite	opposite
disappear from sight	disappear
disregard altogether	disregard
Each and every	each/every
early beginnings	beginnings
empty cavity	cavity
enclosed herewith	enclosed
endorse on the back	endorse
end product	product
end result	result
entirely destroyed	destroyed
equally as good	as good/equally good
exactly identical	identical
expired and terminated	expired/terminated
extremely immoderate	immoderate
Fast in action	fast
few in number	few
filled to capacity	filled
final completion	completion
final conclusion	conclusion
finally ended	ended
first beginnings	beginnings
following after	following/after
funeral obsequies	obsequies
fused together	fused
Heat up	heat
hidden pitfall	pitfall
hopeful optimism	hope/optimism
Important essentials	essentials
Joint cooperation	cooperation
join together	join
joint partnership	partnership
just exactly	just/exactly
Large in size	large
large-sized	large
lift up	lift
living incarnation	incarnation

Redundant Words

Redundant	Concise
Main essentials	essentials
melt down	melt
mingle together	mingle
mix together	mix
more preferable	preferable
mutual cooperation	cooperation
Necessary requisite	requisite
new innovation	innovation
One and the same	the same
one definite reason	one reason
one particular example	one example
one specific case	one case
Part and parcel	part
past experience	experience
period of time	period
personal friend	friend
personal opinion	opinion
pervade the whole	pervade
plan ahead	plan
plan for the future	plan
plan in advance	plan
postponed until later	postponed
presently planned	planned
prolong the duration	prolong
Qualified expert	expert
Really and truly	really
reason is because	reason is that/because
recur again	recur
red in color	red
reduce down	reduce
regress back	regress
remand back	remand
repeat again	repeat
resultant effect	effect
Same identical	same
seems apparent	seems/is apparent
separate and distinct	separate/distinct
shuttle back and forth	shuttle
single unit	unit
skirt around	skirt
small in size	small
small-sized	small
specific example	example
still continue	continue
still remains	remains
suddenly collapsed	collapsed
summer months	summer
surprising upset	upset
surrounding circumstances	circum-stances
surround on all sides	surround
Ten miles distant from	ten miles from
three hours of time	three hours
throughout the entire	throughout
throughout the whole	throughout
total of ten	ten
to the northward	north/northward
traverse across	traverse
true fact	fact
Ultimate end	end
universal the world over	universal
unsolved problem	problem
Visit with	visit
Ways and means	ways/means

References

References are essential because writers must constantly choose between different styles and different ways of saying something. References help writers make proper choices.

The *Shipley Associates Style Guide* will answer many of your stylistic questions and will help you to become a more effective writer. However, for further information, including far more exhaustive treatments of some stylistic issues, refer to the books listed below. These references are among the finest available in their special areas. Some of the references listed might not be in print currently, but they would be available in libraries. Often books go out of print while a new edition is in preparation.

Dictionaries

An up-to-date dictionary is an essential writer's tool. Besides providing correct spellings, a dictionary gives definitions, pronunciations, word origins, synonyms, and guidance on word usage.

Most of the dictionaries listed below are abridged dictionaries written for general readers as well as readers in the colleges and universities. The exception is *Webster's Third New International Dictionary of the English Language, Unabridged;* this dictionary was completed in 1961 and has been reprinted many times since. Although it is over 20 years old, this dictionary is still the best about American English.

Some general dictionaries are directed toward specific users. For example, the *Oxford Student's Dictionary of American English* has been prepared for non-English speaking students. The entries are brief and very clear, and special attention is given to simple idioms (phrases) that have special meanings.

The American Heritage Dictionary. 1982. 2d college ed. New York: Houghton Mifflin Company.

Hornby, A.S. *Oxford Student's Dictionary of American English.* 1983. New York: Oxford University Press.

Random House College Dictionary. 1984. New York: Random House, Inc.

Webster's Ninth New Collegiate Dictionary. 1988. 9th ed. Springfield, Massachusetts: G. & C. Merriam.

Webster's New World Dictionary. 1983. 2d college ed. New York: World Publishing Company.

Webster's Third New International Dictionary of the English Language, Unabridged. 1986. Springfield, Massachusetts: G. & C. Merriam.

Specialized Dictionaries

In addition to those dictionaries listed above, many professional groups or disciplines have specialized dictionaries that list the technical terms and jargon particular to their professional area. Following are a few of these specialized dictionaries.

Black's Law Dictionary. 1983. 5th ed. Henry Campbell Black. St. Paul, Minnesota: West Publishing Co.

Dictionary of Geological Terms. 1984. 3d rev. ed. Garden City, New York: Anchor Press.

A Dictionary of Mining, Mineral, and Related Terms. 1968. Ed. by Paul W. Thrush and the Staff of the Bureau of Mines. Washington: U.S. Department of the Interior, Bureau of Mines.

Glossary of Geology. 1987. 3d ed. Ed. by Robert L. Bates and Julia A. Jackson. Falls Church, Virginia: American Geological Institute.

The Illustrated Petroleum Reference Dictionary. 1985. 3d ed. Ed. by R. D. Langenkamp. Tulsa, Oklahoma: PennWell Publishing Company.

Langenkamp, R. D. 1984. *Handbook of Oil Industry Terms and Phrases.* 4th ed. Tulsa, Oklahoma: PennWell Publishing Company.

Mathematics into Type. Rev. ed. 1979. Providence, Rhode Island: Mathematical Society.

McGraw-Hill Dictionary of Scientific and Technical Terms. 1984. Ed. by Syvil P. Parker. New York: McGraw-Hill Book Company.

Schwarz, Charles F., Edward C. Thor, and Gary H. Elsner. 1976. *Wildland Planning Glossary.* USDA Forest Serv. General Technical Report, PSW-13. Pacific Southwest Forest and Range Experimental Station. Berkeley, California.

References

Webster's New Geographical Dictionary. 1988. Springfield, Massachusetts: G. & C. Merriam.

Spelling Guides

Spelling guides are alphabetized lists of words meant primarily for persons who need to check spelling or word division.

10,000 Medical Words: Spelled and Divided for Quick Reference. 1972. New York: McGraw-Hill Book Company.

20,000 Words: Spelled and Divided for Quick Reference. 1977. 7th ed. New York: McGraw-Hill Book Company.

Webster's Instant Word Guide. 1980. Springfield, Massachusetts: Merriam-Webster, Inc.

Webster's Medical Speller. 2d ed. 1987. Springfield, Massachusetts: Merriam-Webster, Inc.

Thesauruses

A thesaurus provides synonyms and often antonyms. Use a thesaurus when you need to find optional ways of expressing an idea, when you can't think of a word but know the word exists, or when the only word you can think of is not exactly correct and you need to find a more precise alternative. Do not use a thesaurus to find bigger words than the ones you can think of. In other words, don't try to sound impressive by finding and using big words. See GOBBLEDYGOOK.

The New Roget's Thesaurus in Dictionary Form. 1985. Ed. by Philip D. Morehead. New York: New American Library.

The Random House Thesaurus. 1987. Ed. by Jess Stein and Stuart B. Flexner. New York: Random House.

Roget's II: The New Thesaurus. 1988. New York: Houghton Mifflin Company.

Webster's New Dictionary of Synonyms. 1984. 2d ed. Springfield, Massachusetts: Merriam-Webster, Inc.

General Style Guides

The *Shipley Associates Style Guide* is a general style guide. However, it differs from those listed below in that it provides much more information about effective writing techniques and the writing process, and it provides models of effective letters, memos, and other documents.

General style guides are, next to an up-to-date dictionary, the best writer's resources. They usually cover punctuation, abbreviations, spelling problems, capitalization, and special signs and symbols. In addition, each of those listed below has special features. *The Chicago Manual of Style*, for instance, has a long discussion of printing and binding. The *United States Government Printing Office Style Manual* has special guidelines for Congressional publications and a fine chapter on word compounds.

The Chicago Manual of Style. 1982. 13th ed. Chicago: The University of Chicago Press.

Chicago Guide to Preparing Electronic Manuscripts for Authors and Publishers. 1987. Chicago: The University of Chicago Press.

The Complete Guide to Citing Government Documents. 1984. Diane L. Garner and Diane H. Smith. Betheseda, Maryland: American Library Association.

The Gregg Reference Manual. 1985. 6th ed. Ed. by William A. Sabin. New York: Gregg Division, McGraw-Hill Book Company.

Hutchinson, Lois. *Standard Handbook for Secretaries.* 1969. 8th ed. New York: McGraw-Hill Book Company.

The McGraw-Hill Style Manual: A Concise Guide for Writers and Editors. 1983. Ed. by Marie Longyear. New York: McGraw-Hill Book Company.

The Secretary's Handbook. 10th ed. 1988. Revised by Margaret D. Shertzer. New York: Macmillan Publishing Company.

United States Government Printing Office. 1984. *Style Manual.* Washington, DC: United States Government Printing Office.

References

Webster's Secretarial Handbook, 1983. 2d ed. Springfield, Massachusetts: Merriam-Webster, Inc.

Webster's Standard American Style Manual. 1985. Springfield, Massachusetts: Merriam-Webster, Inc.

Words into Type. 1974. 3d ed. Ed. by M. Skillin and R. Gay. Englewood Cliffs, New Jersey: Prentice-Hall, Inc.

Specialized Style Guides

Specialized style guides are those intended for a particular professional group. Despite their special audience, they usually also cover basic punctuation and other items of general interest.

American Chemical Society. 1978. *Handbook for Authors of Papers in American Chemical Society Publications.* Washington, DC: American Chemical Society.

American Institute of Physics. 1978. *Style Manual for Guidance in the Preparation of Papers.* 3d rev. ed. New York: American Institute of Physics.

American Medical Association, Scientific Publications Division. 1976. *Style Book and Editorial Manual.* 6th ed. Chicago: American Medical Association.

American Psychological Association. 1983. *Publication Manual.* 3d ed. Washington, DC: American Psychological Association.

Council of Biology Editors. 1983. *CBE Style Manual.* 5th ed. Betheseda, Maryland: Council for Biology Editors, Inc.

Swanson, Ellen. 1982. *Mathematics into Type: Copyediting and Proofreading of Mathematics for Editorial Assistants and Authors.* Rev. ed. Providence, Rhode Island: American Mathematical Society.

U.S. Geological Survey. 1978. *Suggestions to Authors of the Reports of the United States Geological Survey.* 6th ed. Washington, DC: Government Printing Office.

Webster's Legal Secretaries Handbook. 1981. Ed by Coleen K. Wilhgott. Springfield, Massachusetts: Merriam-Webster, Inc.

Zweifel, Frances W. 1988. 2d ed. *A Handbook of Biological Illustration.* Chicago: University of Chicago Press, Phoenix Books.

Grammar and Usage Handbooks

Grammar handbooks, especially those intended for college students, survey the principles of English grammar and provide many dos and don'ts for writers. The Harbrace and Random House grammar books listed below are only two of the many such current books available in bookstores.

Usage handbooks provide rules for the proper use of words. Such rules quite often reflect the writers' prejudices, so keep that in mind as you use such handbooks. The best and most comprehensive usage reference is *Webster's Dictionary of English Usage.* Published in 1989, it surveys the history of disputed usages and concludes each survey with a judgment (recommendation) regarding the dispute.

Baker, Sheridan Baker. 1984. *The Complete Stylist and Handbook.* 3d ed. New York: Harper & Row Publishers, Inc.

Bernstein, Theodore M. 1977. *The Careful Writer: A Modern Guide to English Usage.* New York: Atheneum.

Bernstein, Theodore M. 1984. *Miss Thistlebottom's Hobgoblins: the Careful Writer's Guide to the Taboos, Bugbears, and Outmoded Rules of English Usage.* New York: Simon and Schuster, Inc.

Bernstein, Theodore M. 1965. *Watch Your Language: A Lively, Informal Guide to Better Writing.* New York: Macmillan.

Copperud, Roy H. 1979. *American Usage and Style: The Consensus.* New York: Van Nostrand Reinhold & Company.

Evans, Bergan, and Cornelia Evans. 1957. *A Dictionary of Contemporary American Usage.* New York: Random House.

References

Follett, Wilson. 1966. *Modern American Usage: A Guide.* Edited and completed by Jacques Barzun and others. New York: Hill and Wang.

Fowler, Henry Watson. 1987. *Dictionary of Modern English Usage.* 2d rev. Ed. by Sir Ernest Gowers. Oxford: Oxford University Press.

The Handbook of Nonsexist Writing for Writers, Editors, and Speakers. 1988. Casey Miller and Kate Swift. 2d ed. New York: Harper & Row Publishers, Inc.

Harbrace College Handbook. 1986. 10th ed. Ed. by John C. Hodges and Mary E. Whitten. New York: Harcourt Brace Jovanovich, Inc.

Nicholson, Margaret. 1957. *A Dictionary of American-English Usage, Based on Fowler's Modern English Usage.* New York: Oxford University Press.

Random House Handbook. 1988. 5th ed. Ed. by Frederick Crews. New York: McGraw-Hill Book Company.

Webster's Dictionary of English Usage. 1989. Springfield, Massachusetts: Merriam-Webster, Inc.

Books on Writing

The following books cover writing, both as a process and as a final product. Strunk and White's book is perhaps the most famous and the most readable book of those listed, but the others are also valuable.

Flesh, Rudolf. 1986. *Art of Readable Writing.* Rev. ed. New York: Macmillan.

Lanham, Richard A. 1987. *Revising Business Prose.* 2d ed. New York: Macmillan.

Strunk, W., Jr., and E. B. White. 1979. *The Elements of Style.* 3d ed. New York: Macmillan.

Tichy, H. J. and Sylvia Fourdrinier. 1988. *Effective Writing for Engineers, Managers, Scientists.* 2d ed. New York: John Wiley & Sons.

Williams, Joseph M. 1989. *Style: Ten Lessons in Clarity and Grace.* 3d ed. Glenview, Illinois: Scott, Foresman and Company.

Zinsser, William Knowlton. 1985. *On Writing Well: An Informal Guide to Writing Nonfiction.* 3d ed. New York: Harper & Row Publishers, Inc.

Repetition

Repetition is sometimes considered a trait of poor writing. In fact, repetition can be a valuable emphasis technique. It can enhance the impact and readability of a document. But you must be careful not to repeat an idea too soon after stating it the first time, and when you repeat ideas, you should state them in a different way than you did originally:

this

In my opinion, the Rothskeller algorithm will not alleviate error detection inaccuracies. The mathematical model proposed does not adequately account for errors introduced by migrant electrons. These electrons interact randomly with bits and can change bit patterns in fundamental and disastrous ways. Superior error detection techniques not only must minimize the mushrooming effect of errors compounded by repetition of a bit sequence (which Rothskeller does very effectively) but also must account for random errors that may inadvertently be replicated hundreds of times.

The Rothskeller algorithm for random error detection identifies logical bit pattern inconsistencies and applies logic correction.

However, its identification strategies assume that errors will be of predictable types. Nonpredictable logic errors, caused by random migrant electrons, can go undetected. Therefore, I do not believe that the Rothskeller algorithm will effectively alleviate error detection inaccuracies.

The repeated idea (first and last sentences) is separated by lengthy discussion. Furthermore, the last sentence states the idea somewhat differently than it was stated originally. Someone reading the revised passage will be less likely to find the repetition obtrusive.

not this

In my opinion, the Rothskeller algorithm will not alleviate error detection inaccuracies. The mathematical model proposed does not account for errors introduced by migrant electrons. Therefore, I do not think that the Rothskeller algorithm will alleviate error detection inaccuracies.

This is poor repetition because the repeated idea (first and last sentences) is repeated too quickly, and the author uses virtually the same combination of words to state the idea both times.

Effective repetition of a fact or idea reinforces it in the reader's mind. The reinforcement emphasizes the idea and helps readers remember it.

See ORGANIZATION, EMPHASIS, and KEY WORDS.

---

1. Design documents with clean and deliberate repetition in mind.

As you design a document and organize your ideas, build in effective repetition. Consider repeating (1) key requests or recommendations, (2) major conclusions, and (3) most important or most convincing facts.

Most professionals in the world of work have more documents crossing their desks than they have time to read. Research shows that the majority of intended readers skim through the documents they receive. Rarely do they read the documents in depth, and almost never will they read something more than once. Consequently, you must convey your important ideas quickly and emphatically. Repeating key requests, recommendations, conclusions, and facts helps to ensure that skimming readers will not miss the most important ideas in your documents.

---

2. Use the inherent repetition in formal report structure to reinforce major ideas and to strengthen logic and impact.

Technical and other formal reports are structured for deliberate repetition. The writer's conclusions, for instance, typically appear in these sections of the report: abstract, executive summary, conclusions, and discussion. The recommendations will appear one way or the other in the abstract, executive summary, and perhaps the discussion. They will also appear in their own section.

Repetition in reports is deliberate. It allows readers to read selectively. Some readers will read the abstract and will not need to read further. Others will read the executive summary and perhaps the conclusions and recommendations sections. Still others will glance at the results section and then read through the discussion.

Because reports are deliberately repetitive, all of these readers will have encountered the major conclusions and recommendations. Those who read the major conclusions and recommendations more than once will have had those ideas reinforced. See REPORTS.

Repetition

3. Use repetition to emphasize the logic behind a discussion, especially when details are parallel in their intent.

Repetition of a key word or phrase indicates that a sequence of ideas is parallel:

> Skillful writers have a clear sense of purpose. Skillful writers are aware of their readers' wants, needs, and concerns. Skillful writers can choose between many stylistic options. In short, skillful writers focus their task and use the right techniques to create the right effect.

This kind of repetition is effective in emphasizing key points and limiting sentence length. (Imagine how difficult this passage would be to read if it were a single sentence.) Beware of using this kind of repetition too often, however. With much repetition, the effect diminishes and the writing begins to sound unnatural.

See PARALLELISM, KEY WORDS, and EMPHASIS.

Reports

Reports cover a broad range of business and technical documents, including formal reports, scientific reports (often published), corporate technical reports (following internal guidelines), progress reports, trip reports, laboratory and research reports, accident reports, memorandum reports, and financial reports.

Many of these reports are periodic documents that convey the status of a program, project, task, study, or other organizational effort. Other reports are written in response to specific needs and situations.

Some reports are more informal than others, but readers of reports generally expect to find certain information (summaries, conclusions, recommendations, analyses, supporting facts, etc.), and they expect the report's tone to be businesslike—not officious or bureaucratic, but objective, factual, and honest. See TONE.

Formal reports have traditional components, which are discussed below. For further information relevant to reports, see MEMOS, ORGANIZATION, and VISUAL AIDS.

Scientific Reports

Scientific reports are tightly controlled by scientific convention and tradition. Many scientific reports are published by professional groups and conferences, and many appear in technical or scientific journals. These professional organizations usually have explicit editorial guidelines that writers must follow.

The tradition of the scientific method dictates the format of most scientific reports:

Abstract

Introduction

Materials and Methods

Results and Discussion

Fact 1
Fact 2
Fact 3

(therefore)

Conclusions

Recommendations (if any)

Summary (optional)

This format is roughly chronological—moving from the problem to be solved, to the test design (including materials as well as methods), to the test results, to an analysis of the results, and finally to the conclusions.

This logical pattern roughly duplicates the process the scientist used while conducting the study. Ideally, readers should be able to duplicate the process themselves and reach the same conclusions.

In scientific reports, the process of arriving at the conclusions is generally as important as the conclusions themselves. And the pattern of the scientific report tends to reinforce the equal importance of process and conclusions. In doing so, however, it delays the conclusions, which many readers would consider the most important ideas in the report.

The logic behind scientific reports is inductive: *fact, fact, fact, fact (therefore) conclusions.* This pattern is effective, but it is also suspenseful—and that's the major drawback to the scientific format.

Most business and technical readers are too busy to be held in suspense. They want to know what's important right away. If they want to read a good mystery, they'll read Agatha Christie.

So avoid the scientific format unless you are a scientist writing for other scientists.

In fairness, we should note that reports of all kinds are typically divided into clearly marked sections, and most readers never read the entire report anyway. They read selected sections, depending upon their needs. Scientific reports do allow for conclusions to appear early: in the abstract, for instance, and often in the introduction. So if readers of scientific reports want to know the conclusions first, they go to the section entitled "Conclusions."

The inductive mode of thought behind the scientific format is contrary to the way most readers want to encounter information. For most readers you should use the far more common format found in standard technical reports.

Reports

Technical Reports

Technical and scientific reports often share many features, but technical reports usually differ from scientific reports in several crucial respects:

—They are distributed within an organization and are generally not formally published.

—They are intended for internal use only (many are even proprietary) or have a very limited distribution outside of the parent organization.

—Their readers are decisionmakers and others who need to have all of the important information (key findings, conclusions, and recommendations) right away and who may not be at all interested in how the writer arrived at that important information.

Technical report formats usually follow a managerial format, which emphasizes the conclusions and recommendations by placing them at the beginning of the report and subordinates the results and discussion:

Executive Summary

Introduction

Conclusions and Recommendations

(because of)

Results and Discussion

Fact 1
Fact 2
Fact 3

Summary (optional)

The managerial format opens with a summary (often called an executive summary) that presents a distillation of the report's most important ideas. Following the summary, writers often provide a list of conclusions and recommendations so that busy managers and supervisors have to read no further to discover the essence of the report.

The managerial format follows an inverted logic: *conclusion (based on) fact, fact, fact, fact.* If readers wish, they can read the facts to determine how the writer arrived at the conclusion. But they don't have to. They can read the conclusion alone and then go on to something else.

Decisionmakers are almost always part of the audience for technical reports, and they are usually the primary readers. So most technical reports should follow the managerial format.

Memorandum Reports

Memorandum reports are less formal and usually shorter versions of technical reports, although both types of reports may be very similar in content. Memorandum reports almost always follow the managerial format, but they usually do not include all of the components of a standard technical report. They do not, for instance, have covers, title pages, tables of contents, lists of figures, abstracts, and other formal sections required for either scientific or technical reports. These formal sections are necessary only when reports are widely circulated or published.

See MEMOS.

Parts of Reports

Scientific, technical, and some memorandum reports might include the following:

Letter of Transmittal
Cover
Abstract
Title Page
Preface or Foreword
Table of Contents
List of Figures
Body
Bibliography or List of References
Appendix

Letter of Transmittal

A letter of transmittal accompanies and introduces a report. It might explain what the report is about, why it was written, how it relates to previous reports or projects, what problems the writer encountered, why the report includes or excludes particular data, and what certain readers may find of interest.

A letter of transmittal can provide information that would not be appropriate in the report itself, especially sensitive or confidential information. Hence, different letters of transmittal may be written for different readers of the same report.

Letters of transmittal are usually brief. They tend to be less formal than the reports they transmit. However, the more formal the report, the more formal the letter of transmittal is likely to be.

Cover

Covers are appropriate on formal reports and on those intended for widespread or public distribution. The information on the cover is usually similar to the information found on the title page (see below). However, covers are usually well designed and often include artwork.

Abstract

An abstract is a very brief distillation of a report's content. It is intended to describe the report's content and sometimes to provide information about key findings, conclusions, and recommendations.

Some abstracts, especially those for published scientific reports, are primarily useful in data banks and library catalogues. Such abstracts will be printed in catalogues or bibliographies. Prospective readers should be able to determine from reading the abstract whether they would profit from reading the entire report.

Less formal abstracts often function as one-page summaries of corporate technical reports.

Actual summaries may be longer and include more information. In addition, summaries are part of the report and should not be separated from it. Abstracts, on the other hand, are not considered part of the report and should always be understandable in and of themselves.

Abstracts are usually either **descriptive** or **informative**. In either case, they present the key information in a brief paragraph or two (usually no more than about 250 words).

Descriptive Abstracts

Descriptive abstracts describe the content of the report but do not include interpretive statements, conclusions, or recommendations:

> The report analyzes the effects of caffeine on three groups of heart patients: (1) those with diagnosed hypertension and initial signs of heart trouble, (2) those using blood pressure medication but who have not had surgery, and (3) those having had heart surgery. The report discusses the correlation between caffeine and variations in blood pressure for these three groups.

This abstract describes the general scope of the research but does not provide results or conclusions.

Informative Abstracts

Informative abstracts are generally longer and more comprehensive than descriptive abstracts. Typically, they describe the research or project and summarize key results and conclusions:

> Caffeine, in moderate amounts (no more than two cups of coffee per day), has no significant impact on patients with heart problems (ranging from those with diagnosed hypertension to those having had actual heart surgery). Beyond two cups, however, the impacts become increasingly severe. Patients with recent heart surgery showed the most effects, including very high blood pressure and chest pains. Patients on blood pressure medication could cancel the effects of the medication by drinking more than two cups of coffee. Patients with diagnosed hypertension showed elevated blood pressure for up to 3 hours after drinking over two cups of coffee. In conclusion, the effects of caffeine increased substantially with every cup of coffee beyond the two-cup threshold.

In this (fictitious) informative abstract, readers interested in the subject can determine if they would want to read the full report. Informative abstracts provide key results and conclusions. Consequently, if the research techniques are obvious, knowledgeable readers may need no more than the abstract.

If you have a choice, always write an informative abstract.

See SUMMARIES.

Title Page

The title page can contain the following information:

- The title of the report
- The name of the person(s) writing the report
- The name of the person(s) for whom the report is prepared
- The date of submission
- The name of the division, group, or department, as well as the name of the organization
- A research number or other documentation aid
- A copyright notice and other special notations (such as ***SECRET*** or ***PROPRIETARY INFORMATION***)

Reports

Preface or Foreword

Prefaces or forewords (they are the same) generally appear only in formal or published reports—and often not even there. Informal and memorandum reports rarely include a preface or foreword.

If used, a preface or foreword can include the following:

> References to other researchers or reports to which the author is indebted
>
> Background information regarding the origin of the report—such as who requested it, who funded it, what the goals were, and so on
>
> Acknowledgment of contributors, including other researchers, managers, technicians, reviewers, editors, proofreaders, and so on
>
> Financial implications
>
> Observations regarding unusual conclusions or recommendations
>
> Miscellaneous personal comments about the contents, including areas for future study

Table of Contents

The table of contents is an outline of the report.

It helps readers understand the structure of the report and locate particular sections. It helps writers organize their thoughts (or check their organization).

A table of contents should contain enough second- and third-level headings to capture the actual content and approach of the chapters. Chapter headings by themselves are often too cryptic:

not this

I. Introduction
II. Preliminary Conditions
III. Governmental Controls

this

I. Introduction

- A. Corporate policy on experiments with animals
- B. Precedents for this research
- C. Guidelines and goals of this research

II. Preliminary Conditions

- A. Physiological profiles of the test animals
- B. Structure of control and experimental groups
- C. Checks and balances in the research procedures

III. Governmental Controls

- A. Documentation needed for report to the FDA
- B. External verification of results
- C. Legal penalties for failure to report

See TABLES OF CONTENTS.

List of Figures (or Tables or Maps)

A list of figures (or tables or maps) is necessary only if the report is extensive and contains many of these or other visual aids. See VISUAL AIDS.

If used, the list of figures appears following the table of contents and on a separate page. (NOTE: The table of contents should include the list of figures and its page number.) See TABLES OF CONTENTS.

Tables and figures are usually listed separately, so if you list tables, do so in a List of Tables.

Figures include charts, graphs, maps, photographs, and diagrams. If you have a large number of any particular type of figure, you can list them as separate types of visuals:

> List of Maps
> List of Charts
> List of Photographs

Number tables and figures (and other specific types of visuals) separately, and number them sequentially as they appear in the report. See CAPTIONS.

NOTE: If your report has large separate sections, you can number visuals sequentially within each section (see CAPTIONS).

Body

The body of a report can follow either the scientific format or the managerial format. (See the opening section of this discussion of reports, and also see ORGANIZATION.)

Scientific Organization

Abstract
Introduction
Materials and Methods
Results and Discussion
Conclusions
Recommendations (if any)
Summary (optional)

Managerial Organization

Executive Summary
Introduction
Conclusions
Recommendations
Materials and Methods (optional)
Results and Discussion
Summary (optional)

See Summaries and Organization.

Introduction

The introduction sets the stage. It normally includes the historical background of the report (and the project or program being reported) and establishes the scope of the report. The introduction may also define special terms and discuss the report's relation to other reports or research efforts.

Introductions also discuss the content and organization of the report. In other words, the introduction tells readers what the report contains and where to find it. In essence, the introduction is a road map.

If the report does not contain a preface, some of the items covered in the preface may also appear in the introduction:

—Person or group authorizing the research

—Contributors, especially other researchers

—Financial implications

—Noteworthy points about the conclusions and recommendations

—Other special items of interest

One major difference between an introduction and a summary is that the introduction does not contain the conclusions and recommendations. Another major difference is that a summary does not provide background information or lay out the structure of the report. See Introductions.

Materials and Methods

This section includes the materials and methods used during the experiment, study, or project. Limit this section to those materials and methods unfamiliar to knowledgeable readers. If the materials and methods are standard, you can mention them briefly in the introduction and then omit this section.

Results and Discussion

This section presents relevant data, discusses the meaning and significance of the data, makes inferences, and states the conclusions. If you have a lot of raw data to present, place it in an appendix and extract only the most important data to present in this section.

In some reports, especially formal scientific reports, the results are separate from the discussion.

Conclusion

This section brings together everything in the report and states your convictions. Every conclusion should grow out of information elsewhere in the report. Without such logical support, readers will justifiably feel that you have failed to accomplish the goals of the research.

Recommendations

Recommendations are suggestions for future actions—either managerial action or future research. Recommendations are almost always present in reports directed to corporate managers and supervisors.

In some cases, conclusions and recommendations are presented in a single section.

Summary and Executive Summary

Traditionally, the summary appeared at the end of the report. In the scientific format, the summary still appears at the end (if it appears at all). Its purpose at the end of a report is to "sum up" the major ideas presented, to remind readers what was important about what they read—the key findings, the conclusions, and any recommendations.

Summaries at the beginning of a report are becoming more

common. They are highly desirable in reports directed to managers and supervisors.

Quite often, this opening summary is called an "executive summary." The title indicates clearly how this summary is meant to be read and who is meant to read it. It opens the body of a report written in the managerial format. If well done, the executive summary includes everything a busy manager or supervisor needs to know to make a decision. The detailed results and data often appear only as an appendix. Consequently, a good executive summary in effect makes the rest of the report superfluous—and it should. If you are writing well, readers should not have to read beyond your summaries unless they have a particular need for the detail that follows.

The information in a summary must be consistent with information appearing throughout the body of the report. Furthermore, you should have nothing in the summary that does not also appear elsewhere in the report.

Summaries are always part of the body of a report. Abstracts, on the other hand, should always be able to stand by themselves.

See SUMMARIES.

Bibliography or List of References

A bibliography or list of references is necessary only in more formal reports or in reports with a number of references.

If you have only two or three references, cover them fully in the text:

> As George Stevens established in "The Life Cycle of the Toad" (*Animal Physiology*, X [March 1983] 234-237), toads have very low metabolic levels.

See CITATIONS and BIBLIOGRAPHIC FORM for full information on the use of parenthetical citations and for different ways to list bibliographic entries.

Appendix

The appendix is for information that is not properly part of the text or is too lengthy to be included in the text (voluminous data, computer programs, lengthy descriptions of methods, etc.).

If information in the appendix is of more than one kind, use two or more appendices, each identified by letter and title:

> Appendix A—Graphs
> Appendix B—Photographs
> Appendix C—Programs

Ensure that you always mention the appendices in the text. Where reference to an appendix would help readers, identify which appendix is appropriate and what the reader can expect to find there:

> Appendix E presents raw distillation data.
>
> For further information regarding these formulas, see appendix B1.
>
> The names and addresses of all of those who responded are listed in appendix H.

See APPENDICES/ATTACHMENTS.

Scientific/Technical Style

Scientists and technical specialists write and speak a different language. They do use many of the words and sentence patterns that nontechnical writers use, but their language is sufficiently different to be called a scientific or technical style. See STYLE.

Most obviously, scientists and technical specialists use technical terms: *joule, volt, electron, ion, protozoa, electroencephalogram, uterine tube, ethyl ethers, hypochlorous acid,* etc. Such terms have specific meanings and are generally foreign to lay readers. Often, lay readers consider such technical terms to be jargon because they do not readily know and perhaps cannot easily understand them. See JARGON.

Less obviously, scientists and technical specialists sometimes use common words in uncommon ways. Often, such uses are more confusing to lay readers than technical words, which lay readers expect to be foreign to their experience. Here are two examples of uncommon uses of common words:

> A continuous function in an *n*-dimensional vector space is considered **smooth** when the function has certain well-defined features.
>
> We were unable to calculate the **work** because the granite outcrop would not budge, even after a standard charge exploded in a hole drilled into its base produced a hairline fracture evident throughout the circumference of the **neck**.

In the first example, mathematicians have borrowed the intuitive notion of smoothness to describe an abstract mathematical concept. In the second example, physicists define *work* to be the effect when a force moves an object a certain distance. Without movement, work (according to the definition) has not taken place. Equally, *neck* describes that portion of an outcropping where the base of the outcropping most clearly resembles the border between the outcropping and the mass of rock from which the outcropping protrudes. The resemblance to a human neck is clear, but lay readers may not make the connection as readily as geologists.

Both technical terms and common words used in uncommon ways complicate scientific and technical writing. In both cases, lay readers may become lost, even when the writing is clear, concise, and logical. Therefore, if you are writing a scientific or technical document that is intended, at least in part, for lay readers, try to define technical terms (or don't use them), and avoid using common terms in uncommon ways.

If you are writing for scientific or technical readers, you must still try to make the writing as clear, concise, and logical as you can. Technical word usage may not hinder technical readers, but writing that is poorly organized, clumsily phrased, and inaccurately conceived will still be difficult if not impossible to read.

1. Make your use of technical and scientific terms appropriate for your readers.

Avoid unusual or overly technical terms if possible. If you cannot avoid them and your readers will not understand them, then define the terms. Do not use unfamiliar abbreviations unless your readers will understand them or unless you carefully explain the abbreviations first. See ABBREVIATIONS and ACRONYMS. Once you have established the terms and abbreviations, be consistent in your usage throughout the document.

Do not assume that your readers (**all** of your readers) know and understand your terms as you are using them. This is a trap.

First, rarely do all readers of a document have the same kind and level of technical background. You should always write for the lowest common denominator—that is, for the least technically sophisticated reader.

Second, even well-established technical terms, concepts, and abbreviations may be subject to dispute, so you may have to stipulate definitions so that your readers know exactly what you intended when you used a particular word.

One of the easiest ways to handle difficult or unfamiliar technical terms is to provide an informal definition when the terms first appear:

Scientific/Technical Style

A further health problem in many African countries results from filariasis, which means that the blood contains small threadlike worms.

or

The presence of small threadlike worms in the blood (called filariasis) is a further health problem in many African countries.

Third, scientists sometimes use different words to describe essentially the same thing, and this creates substantial confusion, even among scientific readers. Do not speak of *aspects* of a procedure in one paragraph, and then refer to the same concept as *elements* or *features* later.

2. Use concise, direct sentences.

Sentences are the building blocks of effective writing of any kind. However, they are especially important in writing that is inherently complicated and includes jargon. So strive to make your sentences clear, direct, and concise. See SENTENCES.

The principles of writing direct, concise sentences are summarized below. Elsewhere in this *Style Guide*, you will find each topic discussed in depth.

- **Choose active rather than passive sentences:**

this

We determined that the coefficient of friction varied most at extremely cold temperatures.

not this

It was determined that the coefficient of friction varied most at extremely cold temperatures.

See ACTIVE/PASSIVE.

- **Avoid wordiness:**

this

Our revised proposal presented further justification for development costs while offering to reduce our profit fee by 20 percent.

not this

Further justification for development costs, along with an offer for the 20 percent reduction of our profit fee, was presented in our revised proposal.

See WORDY PHRASES.

- **Use strong verbs:**

this

After lengthy study, we adjusted the effluent guidelines to accommodate projected economic hardships.

not this

After lengthy study, we made an adjustment of the effluent guidelines to effect greater accommodation with projected economic hardships.

See STRONG VERBS.

- **Avoid false subjects:**

this

Five-spot pattern recoveries are probably less efficient in sand trap reservoirs that have been depleted to within 15 percent of recoverable reserves.

not this

It is probable that five-spot pattern recoveries are less efficient in sand trap reservoirs that have been depleted to within 15 percent of recoverable reserves.

See FALSE SUBJECTS.

- **Use pronouns to make your writing more personal and direct:**

—Pronouns are appropriate when a scientific or technical writer is recommending something, drawing conclusions, or conveying deliberate decisions or choices:

The evidence suggests that this species is in fact indigenous to the Everglades. Therefore, I recommend broadening the scope of the USDA's habitat study before it writes the Los Puertos EIS.

The globule had a specific density of 6.78, more than twice what the OCS recovery team had estimated, so we concluded that zinc, not iron, was its major constituent.

Once we had analyzed the data from the pilot tests, we determined how to control temperature variations in succeeding tests.

—Some technical and scientific writing does not lend itself to first person pronouns. The historical description of a laboratory procedure, for instance, should not mention the person who performed the procedure unless the focus of the discussion is on that person and not the procedure. If the procedure itself is more important, do not use personal pronouns:

The ore sample is washed in a weak solution of hydrochloric acid. Next, the ore is cleansed thoroughly in a water bath and then dried in a heat chamber.

NOTE: If this passage appeared in a set of instructions, second person pronouns and imperative sentences would be appropriate:

Wash the ore sample in a weak solution (no more than 5 percent) of hydrochloric acid. Then you should clean the sample thoroughly in a water bath and dry it in a heat chamber.

or

Wash the ore sample in a weak solution (no more than 5 percent) of hydrochloric acid. Then clean the sample thoroughly in a water bath and dry it in a heat chamber.

The use of pronouns in technical writing has become more common in the last several decades, but don't overuse pronouns. Most scientific and technical writing is meant to convey information objectively, not to establish the writer's personality. If you are writing for the general public, however, use more pronouns and try to convey both clarity and warmth. For an example, read anything by Carl Sagan, Isaac Asimov, or Arthur C. Clarke, three successful scientific writers whose readers are primarily nontechnical. See PRONOUNS.

3. Design scientific and technical documents for visual impact and readability.

Visual appearance has become more and more important as a feature of good scientific and technical style. Well-conceived graphs, tables, and illustrations are essential if a document is to look fully professional.

In essence, the text supports the visuals, not the reverse. So time spent planning and designing visuals is critical for successful scientific and technical documents.

Below are some key principles of using visual aids. For a much more complete discussion, see VISUAL AIDS, CAPTIONS, CHARTS, GRAPHS, ILLUSTRATIONS, TABLES, MAPS, and PHOTOGRAPHS.

- Create your visuals before you write your text.
- Select visuals that are appropriate for your readers.
- Focus your visuals on key points and keep them simple and uncluttered.
- Introduce visuals before they appear in the text.
- Use clear, active captions on your visuals.
- Use emphatic devices (underlining, *italics*, **boldface**, shading, etc.) to emphasize important ideas in your visuals as well as your text.

See DESKTOP PUBLISHING.

4. Above all, be as accurate as possible.

Good scientific and technical writing is precise and accurate—in its facts, its references, its procedures, its analyses.

Check every detail. If your document mentions that the site of the project is southwest of Dry Gulch, then the map should not show the site to be northwest of Dry Gulch. Similarly, if you mention production data in the text, the same figures (rounded to the same significant figures) should appear in accompanying tables. Every detail in the document should be as accurate as the writer can humanly guarantee.

A single inaccurate figure or fact can destroy the credibility of a document and its writer.

NOTE: Some writers defend weasel wording or hedging by stating that we can't know anything for sure; therefore, we can make no absolute statements. According to them, we can never state a fact because we can't be sure that anything is irrevocably true. The words typically used to hedge are: *generally, usually, likely, possibly, notion, surmise, speculation, conjecture, indicate, suggest, appear, seem, believe,* etc.

If necessary, use such words to indicate honest doubt or uncertainty, but do not overdo them. If you are reasonably certain of something, say so. Weasel wording weakens your document and your image:

> *this*
>
> Gas reserves in the Mellencamp zone are probably significant.
>
> *not this*
>
> We believe that the evidence favors an interpretation that gas reserves in the Mellencamp zone are likely to be potentially significant.

Semicolons

Semicolons have two primary functions—linking thoughts and separating thoughts.

1. Semicolons link complete thoughts that could otherwise stand alone as separate sentences:

> Western Aeronautics has completed more than 15 avionics contracts in the last 5 years; in 11 of those contracts we used CAD/CAM techniques to minimize development costs and improve both reliability and performance.

Typically, the complete thoughts linked by a semicolon are equal in structure and importance. Writers could separate the complete thoughts with a period and create two sentences; however, the semicolon shows a closer relationship between the thoughts than a period does. The semicolon says, "These thoughts are closely related."

NOTE 1: Semicolons used to link complete thoughts do not require conjunctions (transitional or connecting words like *however, consequently, furthermore,* and *thus):*

> Detailed trade studies helped us determine the relative importance of the various technologies in designing a supersonic cruise fighter; similar performance studies helped us evaluate the trade study findings in air-to-air operations in a simulated combat environment.

> High maneuverability was our primary design consideration; our secondary considerations included short take-off and large payloads.

NOTE 2: The following transitional words and phrases can be used with semicolons if the writer needs to indicate or clarify the relationship between the thoughts before and after the semicolon: *accordingly, consequently, for example, for instance, further, furthermore, however, indeed, moreover, nevertheless, nonetheless, on the contrary, on the other hand, therefore, thus:*

> We use aircraft geometry to generate survivability parameters such as radar signature; furthermore, we add performance, weapons, and avionics characteristics from the developed aircraft design to evaluate military effectiveness. *(Note the comma following* furthermore.)

> The SDC is a multiterminal facility dedicated to a variety of projects; however, its size and flexibility, coupled with strict management controls, guard against fragmentation and crossover.

NOTE 3: Do **not** use the shorter conjunctions *(and, but, or, for, nor, so,* and *yet)* with semicolons; use these simple conjunctions only when linking two complete thoughts with a comma.

However, if the complete thoughts are lengthy and already contain commas, then use a semicolon with these shorter conjunctions to join the two complete thoughts:

> The committee began its scrutiny of the preliminary design study, which General Avionics submitted upon just two weeks' notice; and they found that the transformational analyses, although obviously hurried, were still superior to those of other designers who had had much more time.

See COMMAS, CONJUNCTIONS, and TRANSITIONS.

2. Semicolons separate items in series when one or more of the items has a comma:

> Our cost breakdown demonstrates our cost consciousness; our commitment to low overhead, especially through our direct contract-costing procedures; and our desire to minimize risk by using proven resources.

Without the semicolons to separate each major item in the series, readers might not understand how many items the series contains. The need for clarification varies from sentence to sentence. Sometimes it is not crucial; sometimes it is:

> Our avionics designs incorporate state-of-the-art subcomponents, including dual Intel 86000 microprocessors; Marquette frequency stabilizers, the most advanced anti-ECM devices currently available; and Barnett Industries' redesigned RFX regulators.

If the three items in this series had been separated with commas, the purpose of the phrase *the most advanced anti-ECM devices currently available* would not be clear. It would seem to be a fourth item in the series, although its true purpose is to describe the Marquette frequency stabilizers. The semicolons clarify its purpose in the sentence.

See COMMAS.

Sentences

Sentences are the building blocks of thought. Without sentences and the context in which they appear, communication would be impossible.

Sentences are fundamental to language, yet they are hard to define. *Webster's New Collegiate Dictionary* says that a sentence is a "grammatically self-contained speech unit." Many teachers would call it "a complete thought" and perhaps add that it usually contains, as a minimum, a subject and a verb. That definition would seem to rule out the following, all of which are sentences:

> Yes.
> No.
> Maybe.
> Stop.
> Hello.
> Me?
> When?
> Where?
> Why?
> How?
> OK.
> Oh!

All written sentences begin with a capital letter and end with a mark of punctuation, usually a period but sometimes a question mark or exclamation point. This convention applies to all sentences, even those with only one word and those in which words that are understood have been left out.

Most sentences are longer than one word and do include both the subject and the verb:

> The invoice was late.
>
> Because the invoice was late, we could not include it in accounts payable for November.
>
> When did the invoice arrive?
>
> It arrived late.
>
> The invoice, which was late, missed the deadline for November accounts payable.
>
> The invoice was late, so we could not include it in November accounts payable.
>
> Next time, send us the invoice promptly.
>
> What happened with the late invoice was that we could not include it in November accounts payable.

In some cases, parts of the sentence are understood but not stated:

> Too late. (The invoice was too late.)
>
> Late again! (The invoice was late again!)

These examples reveal several things about sentences. First, they are self-contained, although they might rely heavily on something said earlier (or later) for readers to fully comprehend them. Second, they consist of a meaningful word or group of words. A word constituting a sentence does not have to be a particular kind of word, nor does it have to be meaningful in normal contexts. *OK* and *Yes* are clearly self-contained expressions, but *String* could also be a sentence:

> What did you use to secure the box?
>
> String. (I used string. *The* I used *is understood.)*

Single verbs can also function as sentences:

> What do you suggest I do during lunch?
>
> Run. (I suggest that you run.)

So, must sentences express complete thoughts to be sentences? Yes, although the completeness of the thought usually depends on the context in which the sentences appear. For an utterance to be a sentence, it must either state or imply a complete thought, given its context.

Must sentences contain a subject and a verb to be sentences? Yes and no. Sentences do have a grammatical structure, including a subject and a verb, but either or both can be understood:

> When should I leave?
>
> Now. (You should leave now. *In this sentence, the subject* [you] *and the verb* [should leave] *are both understood.)*

Sometimes the subject and/or verb are complicated and don't convey the primary meaning or central thought in the sentence:

> What happened with the late invoice was that we could not include it in November accounts payable.

The subject is *What happened with the late invoice*. The verb is *was*. The subject is a complicated noun clause, and the main meaning is not in the main verb, but in the final clause: *that we could not include it in November accounts payable.*

Still, in most business and technical writing, sentences do have a subject and verb, even if these grammatical slots are filled with many words and have complex grammatical relationships.

Perhaps because sentences are difficult to define, most grammar handbooks settle for two fairly simple, yet practical, systems for cataloguing sentences:

Sentences

- Purpose or Intent
  - —Declarative Sentences
  - —Interrogative Sentences
  - —Exclamatory Sentences
  - —Imperative Sentences
- Grammatical Structures
  - —Simple Sentences
  - —Compound Sentences
  - —Complex Sentences
  - —Compound-Complex Sentences

Purpose or Intent of Sentences

1. Use declarative sentences to make statements of fact and opinion. Usually such sentences follow the subject-verb word order, and they end with a period:

> We reviewed the report.
>
> Because of the detailed analyses involved, our review of the report is likely to take several days.
>
> The report is only five pages long.
>
> The report, which is only five pages long, will still take several days to review because the analyses are lengthy.

2. Use interrogative sentences to ask questions. Interrogative sentences usually begin with a question word *(who, which, where, when, why,* and *how)* or with a verb:

> Who is the engineer in charge?
>
> Which plan is likely to be approved?
>
> When will the construction project end?
>
> How often do they propose to inspect the site?
>
> Have you filled in all the necessary forms?
>
> Were the construction specifications adequate?

3. Use exclamatory sentences to make strong assertions or surprising observations. Exclamatory sentences usually end with an exclamation point:

> What a surprising conclusion!
>
> That's wrong!
>
> What a field day for the lawyers that will be!
>
> Oh, I doubt that!

NOTE: Exclamatory sentences often have grammatical structures very different from normal declarative sentences. In fact, they may be only a word or two long:

> No!
>
> How surprising!
>
> A shame!

4. Use imperative sentences to give directions or commands. Imperative sentences usually begin with a verb and end with a period (although an exclamation point is also occasionally possible):

> Move the recycling pump to the second floor.
>
> Adjust the flange on the steam connection to prevent leakage.
>
> Do not submit the pink copy of this form!
>
> Stop. *(or* Stop!)

Grammatical Structures of Sentences

Sentences have four grammatical structures—simple, compound, complex, and compound-complex. These four structures, however, can be formed into an infinite number of unique sentences.

Simple Sentences. Simple sentences are sentences that express one complete thought. Essentially, they contain a single subject and a single verb, although both subject and verb may be compound:

> The pump failed. *(single subject and verb)*
>
> The new steam pump failed after only 3 weeks of service. *(single subject and verb)*
>
> We analyzed the blueprints. *(single subject and verb)*
>
> James Hawkins and I analyzed the blueprints for the new maintenance facility. *(compound subject, single verb)*
>
> James Hawkins and I analyzed and revised the blueprints for the new maintenance facility. *(compound subject and compound verb)*

NOTE 1: As indicated above, simple sentences can contain compound subjects, such as *James Hawkins and I,* and compound verbs, such as *analyzed* and *revised.* Although compound, such subjects and verbs form a single unit, at least for the purpose of the sentence in question, so the sentence is still considered simple.

NOTE 2: A quick test for a simple sentence is that you cannot logically break the sentence at any point and come up with two other simple sentences. For example, the following simple sentence, even with compound subject and compound verb, cannot be broken into two simple sentences, so the sentence is a single, simple unit:

> My supervisor and I joked about the assignment and then worked on ways to accomplish it.

Compound Sentences. Compound sentences are essentially a union of two or more simple sentences. These simple sentences are usually linked by one of the simple coordinating conjunctions: *and, but, or, nor, for, yet,* and *so.*

> The project was expensive, and management still hadn't decided to proceed with it.

> Our supervisor wanted to increase office productivity, but the turnover in personnel made such an increase unlikely.

See COMMAS and CONJUNCTIONS.

Sometimes the simple sentences are linked by a semicolon or by a semicolon and a conjunctive adverb:

> The data confirmed our initial assumptions about the problems in prototype production; with these problems, the project will almost certainly exceed the budget.

> The surveying was to have been completed by October 15; however, construction must start on or before November 15.

See SEMICOLONS and CONJUNCTIONS.

NOTE 1: A quick test for a compound sentence is to see if you can divide the sentence into two or more simple sentences:

> The surveying was to have been completed by October 15. Construction must start on or before November 15.

NOTE 2: Sometimes three or more simple sentences can combine into a compound sentence:

> The site was ready, the construction crew was ready, and the materials were ready, but the weather was not cooperative.

Complex Sentences. A complex sentence is a simple sentence with a dependent (subordinate) clause attached to it. The dependent clause can appear in front of the main clause (the otherwise simple sentence), in the middle of the main clause, or behind the main clause.

Here are some dependent clauses:

> Although our bid was the lowest . . .

> . . . who was the most expensive candidate . . .

> . . . because the tailings pile is virtually inert.

Adding a simple sentence to each of these dependent clauses forms a complex sentence:

> Although our bid was the lowest, another contractor had more experience.

> Cameron Blake, who was the most expensive candidate, did have the most impressive credentials.

> Reclamation of the mine site will be difficult because the tailings pile is virtually inert.

NOTE 1: A test for a complex sentence is to separate the dependent clause and the main clause (simple sentence). This test will work for the sentences above, but not for this sentence:

> What Jack wanted to discuss with us became clear once the meeting got under way.

What Jack wanted to discuss with us is a noun clause that functions as the subject of the sentence. Trying to separate it from the rest of the sentence would result in two sentence fragments, neither of which can stand alone. Although this sentence fails the test, it is still a complex sentence.

NOTE 2: Dependent clauses are usually introduced by these words:

- Subordinate Conjunctions

  Because, since, although, even though, after, before, so that, while, when, etc.

  See CONJUNCTIONS.

- Relative Pronouns

  Who, whom, whose which, that, whoever, whomever, why, when, where, etc.

  See PRONOUNS.

Compound-Complex Sentences. Compound-complex sentences are a combination of the two previous sentence types. They are both compound and complex. Therefore, a compound-complex sentence has two attached independent clauses—a compound sentence (two simple sentences attached to each other)—and at least one dependent clause:

> Because the firm's manufacturing capacity could not be increased rapidly enough, they were unable to fill their orders; consequently, competitors gained a significant foothold on the market.

NOTE: Because this sentence is compound, the semicolon separates two independent clauses, each of which could stand alone as a complete thought. The introductory dependent clause beginning with *because* makes the sentence complex.

Sentence Length and Readability

All readability formulas include sentence length as one measure of the readability of a piece of writing. A formula usually asks you to determine the average sentence length in the document or passage. Some authorities argue that average sentence length for any level of reader should be kept below some maximum (15 to 20 words). For younger or less sophisticated readers, the average sentence length should be even less (8 to 12 words, depending on how young the readers are).

Sentence length is one important factor in readability. Readers have to read, comprehend, remember, and interpret information sentence by sentence. The longer a sentence, the more they have to hold in their minds to comprehend, remember, and interpret the thought being expressed. Long sentences place an unnecessary burden on readers.

Another factor in readability is sentence syntax (structure). Long sentences can still be easily readable if they are constructed so that the sentence is easy to follow and easy to understand:

> We accepted the bid from the Cranston Construction Company—although it was the highest bidder—because (1) it has the manpower and equipment to start the project immediately, (2) its personnel are experienced in this type of construction, (3) it has the necessary permits in hand, (4) it is a local company using local resources, and (5) its management was willing to post a substantial performance bond.

This 67-word complex sentence is long but readable because it states its central point immediately: We accepted the bid from Cranston. The dependent clause enclosed by dashes clearly states a fact contrary to our expectations: Cranston was the highest bidder. We don't expect the contract to go to the highest bidder, and we wonder why Cranston received the award. So the numbered list provides the rationale for the decision. The numbering of the list helps clarify the syntax.

However, long sentences must be written this clearly to be readable. If your average sentence becomes too long and you do not have the skill to structure each sentence with great clarity, then your writing will be difficult, if not impossible, to read. See STYLE.

---

5. Limit sentence length to about 20 words for typical business and technical writing.

The 20-word average is based on readability experiments and studies that reinforce the discussion of sentence length presented above. Obviously, in arriving at a 20-word average, you will have some longer sentences and some shorter sentences.

Longer sentences were acceptable many years ago. Writers in the 19th century produced some mammoth sentences. Today, the trend is toward short, concise sentences intended for busy readers who don't have the time for or the interest in long-winded prose. The short sentence is the better sentence.

---

6. Use a variety of sentence types and sentence lengths.

Writing that is uniform is tedious. Make some sentences long and some short. Make most of them moderate in length. Remember that long sentences are useful for presenting involved concepts and for elaborating on a point that requires some thought. Short sentences are useful for stating clear, crisp thoughts.

Short sentences are naturally emphatic. Long sentences are not.

Create variety, too, in your choice of sentence types. Use mostly simple sentences, but do not avoid the compound, complex, and compound-complex sentences. Compound and complex sentences are very useful for expressing related ideas. If you use only simple sentences, you will be producing Dick-and-Jane writing. Compound and complex sentences lend themselves to the expression of related, connected, contrasting, and sequential thoughts.

7. Strive to make all sentences direct.

Keep the syntax (structure) of the sentence as uncomplicated as possible. You can do this by keeping the subject as close as possible to the verb; by keeping modifiers as close as possible to the words they modify; and by using conjunctions and transitions to show progress, sequence, connection, and contrast. See TRANSITIONS, PRONOUNS, MODIFIERS, ADJECTIVES, ADVERBS, NOUNS, VERBS, and CONJUNCTIONS.

As you write or revise sentences, ask yourself, "What is the single, central concept I am trying to express in this sentence?" In other words, "What is the point?" State that point clearly and directly, regardless of the sentence type or length.

Sexist Language

Sexist language is an integral part of our language. English from its earliest history has often marked words as either male or female (and even sometimes neuter). Pronouns are the commonest surviving examples: *he, him, his* vs. *she, her, hers* vs. *it, its*. A number of nouns also have different male and female forms: *waiter/waitress, stewardess/steward, heir/heiress, countess/count, host/hostess, actress/actor, usher/usherette*. And some words used for everyone seem to include only males: *mankind, layman, manpower*, and so on.

Many such distinctions, called gender distinctions, have become objectionable, especially in recent years with the debate about equal rights for women. So, many publishing firms and most writers routinely remove unnecessary and often objectionable gender distinctions from published writing. This trend is the basis for the following rules, most of which require little effort from writers.

---

1. Do not use words that unnecessarily distinguish between male and female:

These	Not these
flight attendant	stewardess
people, humans	mankind
work force	manpower
layperson	layman
employee	workman
heir	heiress
serving person	waitress

NOTE 1: The use of female forms such as *waitress* and *heiress* has declined. *Heir* now includes both male and female; *waiter* still has male echoes, but these may fade soon. The best advice is to be sensitive to this issue and then to use female forms only when you have a definite need to signal a gender difference.

NOTE 2: Historically the word *man* (especially used in compound words like *layman)* could include both males and females; its closest modern equivalent would be, for instance, the indefinite pronoun *one* or *person*. This historical meaning has however been forgotten, so much so that many women now argue that they are silently being left out when compounds with *man* are used.

---

2. Avoid unnecessary uses of *he, him,* or *his* to refer back to such indefinite pronouns as *everyone, everybody, someone,* and *somebody.*

The problem sentences are often ones where the indefinite pronouns introduce a single person and then a later pronoun refers to that person:

> Everyone should take (his? her?) coat.
>
> Someone left (his? her?) report.

Unless we clearly know who *everyone* and *someone* refer to, we cannot pick the proper singular pronoun. We thus have to choose among several options:

—Make the sentences plural, if possible:

> All employees should take their coats.

—Remove the pronoun entirely:

> Someone left a (*or* this) report.

—Use both the male and female pronouns:

> Each employee should take his or her report.
>
> Someone left his or her report.

—Use the plural pronoun *their* (or maybe *they* or *theirs):*

> Each employee should take their coat.
>
> Someone left their report.

NOTE: This last option is fine for informal or colloquial speech, but most editors and writers would object to the use of the plural pronouns to refer back to the singular *everyone* and *someone.*

See PRONOUNS and AGREEMENT.

---

3. Avoid unnecessary uses of *he, him, his* or *she, her, hers* when the word refers to both males and females:

> *not these*
>
> A secretary should set her (his?) priorities each day.
>
> The engineer opened her (his?) presentation with an overhead transparency.
>
> A writer should begin his (her?) outline with the main point.

As with rule 2, writers have several options:

—Change the sentences to plurals:

> Secretaries should set their priorities each day.
>
> Writers should begin their outlines with the main point.

—Remove the pronouns:

> The engineer began the presentation with an overhead transparency.
>
> A secretary should set firm priorities each day.

NOTE: A third option is to use the phrase *his or her,* but this becomes clumsy in a text of any length, so it is better to use one of the two options given above.

4. Avoid the traditional salutation *Gentlemen* if the organization receiving the letter includes males and females.

The best option is to use one of the following:

> Ladies and Gentlemen:
>
> Gentlemen and Ladies:

If the letter is going to a single person whose name you do not know, then use these forms:

> Dear Sir or Madam:
>
> Dear Director:
>
> Dear Personnel Manager:

NOTE: In recent years a number of unusual salutations have appeared, but you should avoid them:

> Dear Gentlepersons:
>
> Dear Gentlepeople:
>
> Dear People:
>
> Dear Folks:

See LETTERS.

5. Do not substitute *s/he, he/she, hisorher,* or other such hybrid forms for standard personal pronouns.

These hybrid forms are unpronounceable and are not universally accepted by English users, so avoid them. Instead, either remove pronouns or change the sentences to plurals, as suggested under rule 3. Where you must use singular personal pronouns, use *he and she, his or her,* or *him and her.*

6. Do not call adult females *girls,* especially in a business or technical situation.

Referring to adult females as *girls* is no longer acceptable to most people except in contexts (typically humorous) in which it would also be appropriate to refer to adult males as *boys.* Labeling women as *girls* in serious (or even casual) conversation indicates a bias (intentional or otherwise) that is inappropriate in the business and technical community.

Signs and Symbols

Signs and symbols are increasingly important in scientific and technical writing. So the signs and symbols used in scientific and technical documents should be standard, and you should ensure that your use of signs and symbols is consistent within a document.

---

1. Choose standard signs and symbols, and ensure that readers understand them.

Some symbols are so well known that you don't need to explain them, regardless of where they appear: =, +, –, $, %, x, ±, and ÷.

Other symbols require an explanation, either in notes at the bottom of a table or in a separate list of signs and symbols for a specific text.

---

2. Limit signs and symbols to tables, figures, and other visual aids; avoid them in the text itself.

EXCEPTION: Some very common symbols, such as the percent sign (%), may be used in texts written for a specific group of readers. Accounting documents, for instance, routinely refer to percentages. Writing out *percent* rather than using the symbol (%) is both time consuming and unnecessary. Similarly, chemical symbols are appropriate in documents written for people who know and understand the symbols, but such symbols are inappropriate in business documents and technical documents intended for nonchemists.

---

3. No space appears on either side of the signs +, –, ±, x and ÷:

C+D　　245±5
675–41　　84÷12
7x12

EXCEPTION: When the x is used to mean "crossed with" (as in plant or animal breeding) or to indicate magnification, a space appears on each side of the symbol:

Early Roma x Big Girl
x 20 (magnification)

NOTE: A space does appear on either side of the equals sign:

x+y = 4

See MATHEMATICAL NOTATION.

Common Signs and Symbols

Chemical

Element	Symbol	Atomic number	Atomic weight[1]
Actinium	Ac	89	227.0278
Aluminium	Al	13	26.98154
Americium	Am	95	(243)
Antimony (Stibium)	Sb	51	121.75
Argon	Ar	18	39.948
Arsenic	As	33	74.9216
Astatine	At	85	(210)
Barium	Ba	56	137.33
Berkelium	Bk	97	(247)
Beryllium	Be	4	9.01218
Bismuth	Bi	83	208.9804
Boron	B	5	10.81
Bromine	Br	35	79.904
Cadmium	Cd	48	112.41
Caesium	Cs	55	132.9054
Calcium	Ca	20	40.08
Californium	Cf	98	(251)
Carbon	C	6	12.011
Cerium	Ce	58	140.12
Chlorine	Cl	17	35.453
Chromium	Cr	24	51.996
Cobalt	Co	27	58.9332
Copper	Cu	29	63.546
Curium	Cm	96	(247)
Dysprosium	Dy	66	162.50
Einsteinium	Es	99	(252)
Erbium	Er	68	167.26
Europium	Eu	63	151.96
Fermium	Fm	100	(257)
Fluorine	F	9	18.998403
Francium	Fr	87	(223)
Gadolinium	Gd	64	157.25
Gallium	Ga	31	69.72
Germanium	Ge	32	72.59
Gold	Au	79	196.9665
Hafnium	Hf	72	178.49
Helium	He	2	4.00260
Holmium	Ho	67	164.9304
Hydrogen	H	1	1.00794
Indium	In	49	114.82
Iodine	I	53	126.9045
Iridium	Ir	77	192.22
Iron	Fe	26	55.847
Krypton	Kr	36	83.80
Lanthanum	La	57	138.9055
Lawrencium	Lr	103	(260)
Lead	Pb	82	207.2
Lithium	Li	3	6.941
Lutetium	Lu	71	174.967
Magnesium	Mg	12	24.305
Manganese	Mn	25	54.9380
Mendelveium	Md	101	(258)
Mercury	Hg	80	200.59
Molybdenum	Mo	42	95.94
Neodymium	Nd	60	144.24
Neon	Ne	10	20.179
Neptunium	Np	93	237.0482
Nickel	Ni	28	58.69
Niobium	Nb	41	92.9064
Nitrogen	N	7	14.0067
Nobelium	No	102	(259)
Osmium	Os	76	190.2
Oxygen	O	8	15.9994
Palladium	Pd	46	106.42
Phosphorus	P	15	30.97376
Platinum	Pt	78	195.08
Plutonium	Pu	94	(244)
Polonium	Po	84	(209)
Potassium (Kalium)	K	19	39.0983
Praseodymium	Pr	59	140.9077
Promethium	Pm	61	(145)
Protactinium	Pa	91	231.0359
Radium	Ra	88	226.0254
Radon	Rn	86	(222)
Rhenium	Re	75	186.207
Rhodium	Rh	45	102.9055
Rubidium	Rb	37	85.4678
Ruthenium	Ru	44	101.07

Signs and Symbols

Element	Symbol	Atomic number	Atomic weight[1]
Samarium	Sm	62	150.36
Scendium	Sc	21	44.9559
Selenium	Se	34	78.96
Silicon	Si	14	28.0855
Silver	Ag	47	107.8682
Sodium (Natrium)	Na	11	22.98977
Strontium	Sr	38	87.62
Sulfur	S	16	32.06
Tantalum	Ta	73	180.9479
Technetium	Tc	43	(98)
Tellurium	Te	52	127.60
Terbium	Tb	65	158.9254
Thallium	Tl	81	204.383
Thorium	Th	90	232.0381
Thulium	Tm	69	168.9342
Tin	Sn	50	118.69
Titanium	Ti	22	47.88
Tungsten (Wolfram)	W	74	183.85
(Unnilhexium)	(Unh)	106	(263)
(Unnil-pentium)	(Unp)	105	(262)
(Unnil-quadium)	(Unq)	104	(261)
Uranium	U	92	238.0289
Vanadium	V	23	50.9415
Xenon	Xe	54	131.29
Ytterbium	Yb	70	173.04
Yttrium	Y	39	88.9059
Zinc	Zn	30	65.38
Zirconium	Zr	40	91.22

[1]These atomic weights apply to elements as they exist naturally on Earth and to certain artificial elements. Values in parentheses are used for radioactive elements whose atomic weights cannot be quoted precisely without knowledge of the origin of the elements. The value given is the atomic mass number of the isotope of that element of longest known half life.

Electrical

ℛ reluctance
↔ reaction goes both right and left
↕ reaction goes both up and down
↕ reversible
→ direction of flow; yields
→ direct current
⇆ electrical current
⇆ reversible reaction
⇄ reversible reaction
⇆ alternating current
⇄ alternating current
⇌ reversible reaction beginning at left
⇋ reversible reaction beginning at right
Ω ohm; omega
MΩ megohm; omega
μΩ microohm, mu omega
ω angular frequency, solid angle; omega
Φ magnetic flux; phi
Ψ dielectric flux; electrostatic flux; psi
γ conductivity; gamma
ρ resistivity; rho
Λ equivalent conductivity
HP horsepower

Geologic Systems

J Jurassic
T̶R Triassic
P Permian
P Pennsylvanian
M Mississippian
D Devonian
S Silurian
O Ordovician
Є Cambrian
pЄ Precambrian
C Carboniferous
Q Quaternary
T Tertiary
K Cretaceous

NOTE: These standard letter symbols are used by the Geological Survey on geologic maps. Capital letter indicates the system, and one or more lowercased letters designate the formation and member where used.

Mathematical

— vinculum (above letters)
∻ geometrical proportion
∸ difference, excess
∥ parallel
∥s parallels
∦ not parallels
| | absolute value
· multiplied by
: is to; ratio
÷ divided by
∴ therefore; hence
∵ because
∷ proportion; as
≪ is dominated by
> greater than
⊏ greater than
≥ greater than or equal to
≧ greater than or equal to
⋛ greater than or less than
≯ is not greater than
< less than
⊐ less than
⋚ less than or greater than
≮ is not less than
⋖ smaller than
≤ less than or equal to
≦ less than or equal to
≧ *or* ≥ greater than or equal to
⋜ equal to or less than
⋜ equal to or less than
≰ is not greater than equal to or less than
⋝ equal to or greater than
≱ is not less than equal to or greater than
⊥̲ equilateral
⊥ perpendicular to
⊢ assertion sign
≐ approaches
≐ approaches a limit
≚ equal angles
≠ not equal to
≡ identical with
≢ not identical with
𝍸 score
≈ *or* ≒ nearly equal to
= equal to
∼ difference
≃ perspective to
≅ congruent to approximately equal
≏ difference between
≎ geometrically equivalent to
⊂ included in
⊃ excluded from
⊂ is contained in
∪ logical sum or union
∩ logical product or intersection
√ radical
√ root
²√ square root
³√ cube root
⁴√ fourth root
⁵√ fifth root
⁶√ sixth root
π pi
ε base (2.718) of natural system of logarithms; epsilon
∈ is a member of; dielectric constant; mean error; epsilon
+ plus
+ bold plus
− minus
− bold minus
/ shill(ing); slash; virgule
± plus or minus
∓ minus or plus
× multiplied by
= bold equal
number
℔ per
% percent
∫ integral
| single bond
╲ single bond
╱ single bond
‖ double bond
⑊ double bond
⫽ double bond
⬡ benzene ring
∂ *or* δ differential; variation
∂ Italian differential
→ approaches limit of
∼ cycle sine
∽ horizontal integral
∮ contour integral
∝ variation; varies as
Π product

Signs and Symbols

Σ summation of; sum; sigma
! *or* ⌊ factorial product

See MATHEMATICAL NOTATION.

Measurement

℔ pound
ʒ dram
*f*ʒ fluid dram
℥ ounce
f℥ fluid ounce
O pint

Miscellaneous

§ section
† dagger
‡ double dagger
℀ account of
℅ care of
𝍸 score
¶ paragraph
þ Anglo-Saxon
℄ center line
☌ conjunction
⊥ perpendicular to
″ *or* “ ditto

∝ variation
℞ recipe
⊐ move right
⊏ move left
○ *or* ⊙ *or* ① annual
⊙⊙ *or* ② biennial
∈ element of
℈ scruple
f function
! exclamation mark
⊞ plus in square
♃ perennial
ϕ diameter
c̄ mean value of c
∪ mathmodifier
⊂ mathmodifier
⊡ dot in square
◬ dot in triangle
⊠ station mark
@ at

Money

¢ cent
¥ yen
£ pound sterling
₥ mills

Sex

♂ *or* ♂ male
□ male, in charts
♀ female
○ female, in charts
⚥ hermaphrodite

Weather

T thunder
⌈ thunderstorm; sheet lightning
< sheet lightning
↓ precipitate
● rain
← floating ice crystals
↔ ice needles
▲ hail
⊗ sleet
∽ glazed frost
⊔ hoarfrost
V frostwork
✱ snow or sextile
⊠ snow on ground
+ drifting snow (low)
≡ fog
∞ haze
⌂ Aurora

Slashes

Slashes (/) have several meanings:

And
Or
Both
To
Mathematical division
Per (mathematical division again)
End of a line in poetry

Be careful when you use a slash. Your readers might not understand the meaning of this apparently simple little symbol.

NOTE: The slash sometimes is called a solidus and sometimes a virgule.

1. Use a slash when a season or a time period extends beyond a single year:

winter 1989/1990

fiscal year 1989/90

425/424 B.C.

NOTE: A hyphen sometimes replaces the slash:

Winter 1989-1990

425-424 B.C.

2. A slash can replace *per*:

yards/mile

feet/second *or* ft/sec

3. A slash is used in mathematical expressions written on a single line:

$x/a - y/c = 1$ *for* $\frac{x}{a} - \frac{y}{c} = 1$

$(C/D)/(C+2D)^3$ *for* $\frac{\frac{C}{D}}{(C+2D)^3}$

See MATHEMATICAL NOTATION.

4. A slash separates lines of quoted poetry presented in prose form:

As Shakespeare so aptly noted: "There is a tide in the affairs of men, / Which, taken at the flood, leads on to fortune."

See QUOTATION MARKS.

5. A slash appears in *and/or*:

We asked for a rebate and/or an explanation.

NOTE: Some writers and editors object to all uses of *and/or*, arguing that the expression is ambiguous. In the above example, the meaning includes *a rebate and an explanation* as well as a *rebate or an explanation.* Many editors would prefer to rewrite the sentence:

We asked for a rebate or an explanation or both.

Spacing

Spacing decisions range from the arrangement of text and visuals on the page to the amount of space left after each paragraph and the number of spaces following the final period in a sentence. Proper, even creative, spacing can help guarantee that a final document looks professional and is easy to read.

Page Formats

Decide early in the writing process how you want your pages to look. Options, especially with word processing, include variable margins, a variety of typefaces, and variable line spacing. For important writing projects, you might consult professional designers before writing the text. Sometimes design considerations affect how much and what you write.

See MANUSCRIPT FORM, EMPHASIS, WORD PROCESSING, and DESKTOP PUBLISHING.

1. Leave ample white space on your pages, especially around important ideas or data.

Writers (and typists) often cram too much writing onto a page, trying to stay within page limits or adhering to custom, an arbitrary format, or just plain myth about how pages ought to look. Some writers and typists ignore the appearance of the document because they have never had to think about it.

Without careful and early attention to the desired page layout, the text might not fit within prescribed limits, and the tables, figures, and other visuals might not complement the text.

Although every page layout is different, here are some principles to follow as you work with available space:

—Adjust the margins in letters and memos so that the top and bottom margins are roughly equal and the left and right margins are also equal. Your goal is to center the letter or memo on the page. See LETTERS and MEMOS.

—In single-spaced text, double-space between paragraphs. Even triple-spacing might be desirable for extra space on a page or for highlighting key paragraphs.

—Avoid excessively long paragraphs or a series of short, choppy paragraphs. See PARAGARAPHS.

—Add lists, tables, figures, or other visuals to break up long stretches of text. See LISTS, TABLES, and NUMBERS.

—Design a system of headings that allows you to divide the text frequently and to highlight key ideas. See HEADINGS, EMPHASIS, WORD PROCESSING, and DESKTOP PUBLISHING.

NOTE: A rough mockup of your document is an excellent planning aid. A mockup typically consists of a series of blank pages, one for each page in the proposed document, with titles, headings, lists, visuals, and perhaps paragraphs sketched in. The mockup suggests where and how long each of the major textual units will be.

You should produce the mockup well before writing the actual text.

A variation of the mockup is to prepare a a style sheet prior to writing the text. A style sheet would contain guidance on the margins, the number of columns, the typefaces, and the spacing of all levels of headings. Such style sheets are especially valuable when teams of writers are working on a document.

See DESKTOP PUBLISHING and WORD PROCESSING.

Spacing and Punctuation

One sign of an inexperienced typist is erratic spacing before and after punctuation marks. The following list covers the basics of spacing around punctuation:

—Leave two spaces after any mark of punctuation that ends a sentence.

NOTE: In much typeset and printed material, only a single space follows punctuation ending a sentence. For this reason, some publishers suggest that manuscripts prepared with word processing use only a single space following punctuation ending a sentence so that excess spaces don't need to be removed during typesetting.

Spacing

—Place colons, semicolons, and dashes outside of quotation marks. Place question marks and exclamation marks inside or outside of quotation marks, depending on whether they are or are not part of the quotation.

—Always place commas and periods inside of quotation marks.

NOTE: British usage places commas and periods inside or outside quotation marks, depending on whether they are or are not part of the quotation. See QUOTATION MARKS.

—Leave no space before a semicolon and one space after it.

—Leave no space before or after dashes. On a standard typewriter, create a dash by typing two hyphens with no space between them. Most word processing programs have a code to allow for a solid dash, not two hyphens. Use this code whenever possible so that your dashes are solid and do not have a space before or after them:

The plan—a method for extracting iron ore—is cost effective.

See DASHES.

—Leave no space before a colon and two spaces after it within a sentence.

—Leave one space before an opening or left parenthesis within a sentence. Leave two spaces when the opening parenthesis follows another sentence; if it is a complete sentence, the parenthetical material opens with a capital and the final punctuation comes before the final parenthesis. See PARENTHESES.

—Leave no space before a closing or right parenthesis and one space after it within a sentence. When an entire sentence is enclosed within parentheses, the final parenthesis goes outside of the closing punctuation and two spaces follow the right parenthesis.

—Leave one space before and after each of the three periods in an ellipsis. If an ellipsis concludes a sentence, use three spaced periods followed by the end punctuation mark for a sentence. See ELLIPSES.

NOTE: Each of the punctuation marks discussed in this section has its own entry in this *Style Guide*. Refer to those entries if you have questions or wish to see additional examples.

Spelling

Spelling every word correctly is the final ingredient in any professional document—from formal report to everyday letter or memo.

Spelling is important for the sake of both clarity and credibility. Most misspellings do not cause readers to misinterpret the sentence in which the misspelling occurs. But the misspelled word draws attention to itself, which slows down readers and diverts their attention away from the ideas being expressed.

Language is a medium. When the medium draws attention to itself, it detracts from the message.

Misspelling words may also cause readers to question the writer's competence, intelligence, and credibility. How much confidence would you have in this writer's engineering abilities?

> Raw seewater has been considured as a posible alternet sorce for the consentrater principle water supply. However, bench scale tests indacate that the high consentration of disolved salts in seewater interfeer in the eficenct recovary of minaral from the ore.

Misspellings in a document make the writer and the writer's organization look incompetent, sloppy, careless, and potentially untrustworthy.

However, spelling in English is far from simple. Roughly 90 percent of the words in English are regular, but the other 10 percent are demons. Which words in the following pairs are correct?

accomodate/accommodate
committment/commitment
concientious/conscientious
changable/changeable
imperceptable/imperceptible
indispensible/indispensable
inevitible/inevitable
irresistable/irresistible
occurence/occurrence
offerred/offered
preceed/precede
prefered/preferred
prevalant/prevalent
privlege/privilege
seperate/separate
similiar/similar
transfered/transferred
truely/truly

If you are like most people, you had to pause on at least two or three of the above pairs. Perhaps you still aren't sure. Did you look up any of them in a dictionary?

English is a hybrid language. It evolved over centuries of influence from the languages of the armies that invaded England: the Romans, the Saxons, the Normans, the Vikings, and so on. English is "impure" in this regard and consequently has an inconsistent base system of words. That's why English pronunciation and spelling are inconsistent.

---

1. Challenge the spelling of every word in your document, especially those words you have difficulty with.

The best proofreaders and editors challenge every word, especially those that are known to be difficult (such as those listed above).

If the word is common enough, you can trust yourself to recognize correct spelling. If you are unsure, however, check a dictionary or spelling dictionary. See REFERENCES.

---

2. Use those spelling rules that you find helpful.

The spelling rules are difficult to remember, and most have many exceptions. If you take the time to memorize the rules, you should probably also memorize the exceptions. At some point, the exercise becomes tedious, and the rewards are questionable.

However, you should use those rules that you have found helpful and that you remember well enough to apply.

Probably the most well-known and most useful rule is "*i* before *e* except after *c*." Here are some of the exceptions:

counterfeit
foreign
freight
height
neighbor
sleigh
weigh
weight

Some of the other common rules are briefly summarized below:

- Change a final *y* to *i* before adding a suffix to a word, but keep the *y* before *–ing:*

activity	activities
deny	denies, denying
happy	happily, happier, happiest, happiness
likely	likelihood
study	studies, studied, studying

- Drop a silent final *e* before suffixes beginning with a vowel but not before suffixes beginning with a consonant:

age	aging
desire	desirable
mobile	mobility
notice	noticing
scarce	scarcity
care	careful
manage	management
safe	safety
wife	wifely

Exceptions

acreage
argument
changeable
courageous
judgment
lineage
mileage
ninth
truly
wholly

- Double a final consonant before a suffix beginning with a vowel (1) if the consonant ends a stressed syllable (or a single-syllable word) and (2) if the consonant is preceded by a single vowel:

bag	bagged
brag	bragged
gun	gunned
shop	shopped, shopper
stop	stopped
begin	beginning
occur	occurred
prefer	preferred
regret	regretting, regretted

3. Form plurals carefully. Many irregular forms exist:

man	men
ox	oxen
analysis	analyses
matrix	matrices
potato	potatoes
piano	pianos

See PLURALS for a discussion of these irregular forms as well as a list of the most common irregular plurals.

4. Keep a list of the words you have trouble spelling.

Remembering spelling rules and their exceptions is difficult. A simpler and nearly foolproof method for improving your spelling is to keep a list of the words you commonly misspell. Look up the correct spellings and list the words alphabetically.

When you see that you have misspelled a word, add it to your list. Then refer to the list when you need to use one of those words. Over time, your mind will come to recognize the look of the word with its correct spelling, and you will no longer need the list.

Until you no longer need it, keep the list in a convenient place: tucked inside your dictionary, on the wall in front of your desk or writing area, under the glass on top of your desk, or taped inside your notebook. Keep it where you can see it easily as you write.

A List of Common Spelling Demons

Below is a list of some of the most common spelling demons. These words, interestingly enough, are not technical ones because most of us learn to spell technical words as we learn our technical subjects.

Common words are the problem because their irregularities are often difficult to predict and almost impossible to remember. Also, we often see common words misspelled, so we remember the look of the misspelling, not the look of the correct spelling.

absorb
acceptable
accessible
accommodate
accompanied
accuracy
accustomed
acetic *(acid)*
achievement
acoustic
acquire
acreage
adapter
adsorb
aegis
affect *(usually a verb)*
affected
aggression
aging
aid *(help)*
aide *(assistant, helper)*
aisles
all ready *(all prepared)*
all right
all together *(all those in group)*
all ways *(by every means)*
a lot of
already *(previously)*
altogether *(entirely)*
aluminum
always *(all the time)*
amateur
analogous
announcement
anonymous
antibiotics
any one *(any specific person or object)*
anyone *(any person)*
appall, appalled
apparent
appearance
appraise *(estimate value)*
apprise *(inform)*
appropriate
aquatic
archaeology
artisan
ascetic *(austere)*
aspirin
athletics
attendance
authentic
a while *(noun)*
awhile *(adverb)*

bargain
basically
beneficial
benefited
beside *(next to)*
besides *(in addition)*
beveled
biased

Spelling

breath *(noun)*
breathe *(verb)*
bulletin
bureaucracy
business

caffeine
calendar
caliber
caliper
calk
calorie
canceled, canceling
cancellation
candor
canvas *(cloth)*
canvass *(solicit)*
capital *(city)*
capitol *(building)*
carat *(gem weight)*
caret *(arrow mark)*
category
cemetery
census
challenge
changeable
channel
characteristic
chisel, chiseled
choose *(present tense)*
chose *(past tense)*
coarsely
commitment
committee
competent
competition
complement *(complete)*
compliment *(praise)*
conceited
conceive
condemn
confidant *(person)*
confident *(sure)*
conscience
conscientious
consensus
consistent
continuous
controlled
controversial
councilor *(of council)*
counselor *(advisor)*
courteous
criticism
criticize
curiosity
curious

deceive
decision
definitely
descend
descendant
description
desirable
despair
desperate
despicable
device *(noun)*
devise *(verb)*
dietitian
disappoint
disapprove
disastrous
discipline
discreet *(prudent)*
discrete *(distinct or separate)*
disease
distill, distilled
distinct
doctor
dyeing *(coloring)*
dying *(death)*

easily
ecstasy
effect *(usually a noun)*
efficient
eighth
elaborately
elicit *(to draw)*
embarrass
emigrate *(go from)*
employee
enroll, enrolled
ensure *(guarantee)*
entirely
envelop *(verb)*
envelope *(noun)*
environment
equipment
equipped
especially
every day *(each day)*
everyday *(ordinary)*
evidently
exaggerate
except
exhaust
existence
experiment
explanation
eying

familiar
farther *(distance)*
fascinate
favorite
February
fiber
finally
financially
flammable *(not* inflammable)
fluorescent
fluorine
foreign
foresee
foretell
forgo *(relinquish)*
forego *(precede)*
forty
forward *(ahead)*
foreword *(preface)*
fulfill, fulfilled
further *(degree)*
fuselage

gauge
generally
glamour
government
governor
grammar
guaranteed
guerrilla

happened
harass
heard
height
heroes
hindrance
hoping
humane
humorous
hurriedly
hypocrisy
hypocrite

ideally
idiosyncrasy
ignorant
illicit *(illegal)*
illogical
imaginary
imagine
imitate
immediately
immensely
immigrate *(go into)*
incalculable
incidentally
incredible
indispensable
inequity
influential
initiative
innocuous
insurance
insure *(guarantee financially)*
integrate
intelligent
interference
interrupt
irrelevant
irresistible
irritated

jealousy
jewelry
judgment

kilogram
knowledge

laboratory
laid
lath *(wood)*
lathe *(machine)*
led

Spelling

leisure
length
lenient
leukemia
liable
library
license
lightning
likelihood
liquefy
liveliest
logistics
loose *(adjective)*
lose *(verb)*
luxury
lying

magazine
magnificent
maintenance
manageable
management
maneuver
mantel *(shelf)*
mantle *(cloak)*
margarine
marijuana
marriage
material *(goods)*
materiel *(military goods)*
mathematics
meant
medicine
meteorology
mileage
miniature
minor
mirror
mischievous
missile
morale
mortgage
mucous *(adjective)*
mucus *(noun)*
muscle
mysterious

naturally
necessary
nevertheless
nickel
niece
nineteen
ninety
ninth
noticeable
nowadays
nuclear
nuisance
numerous

occasion
occasionally
occurred
occurrence
occurring

off
offense
official
omission
omitted
omitting
oneself
opponent
opportunity
opposite
oppression
optimism
ordinance *(law)*
ordnance *(military)*
ordinarily
originally

pamphlet
parallel
paralleled
parole
particle
particularly
pastime
peaceable
peculiar
penetrate
perceive
performance
perhaps
permanent
perquisite *(privilege)*
personal *(individual)*
personnel *(employees)*
perspective *(viewpoint)*
persuade
pertain
phosphorous *(adjective)*
phosphorus *(noun)*
physical
picnicking
pigeon
poison
politician
pollute
possession
possibly
practical
practically
precede
precedence *(priority)*
precedents *(prior instances)*
predominant
preferred
prejudice
prerequisite *(requirement)*
prevail
prevalent
preventive (*not* preventative)
principal *(chief or main)*
principle *(theory or idea)*
prisoner
privilege
probably
procedure
proceed

processes
professor
programmed
programmer
programming
prominent
pronounce
pronunciation
propaganda
prophecy *(noun)*
prophesy *(verb)*
prospective *(expected)*
psychology
publicly
pursue
pursuing
pursuit

quandary
quarreled
quarreling
questionnaire
quiet
quite
quizzes

rarefy
rarity
rebel
receipt
receive
recession
recipe
recommend
reconnaissance
reconnoiter
recyclable
referring
regular
regulate
rehearsal
reinforce
relief *(noun)*
relieve *(verb)*
religious
remembrance
reminisce
repellant *(noun)*
repellent *(adjective)*
repetition
resemblance
resistance
restaurant
rhythm
ridiculous

sacrifice
safety
salvage *(save)*
satellite
scarcity
scenery
schedule
secede
secretary
seismology
seize

Spelling

selvage *(edging)*
separate
sergeant
sheriff
shining
shrubbery
signaled
signaling
significant
similar
sincerely
sizable
some time *(some time ago)*
sometime *(formerly)*
sometimes *(at times)*
souvenir
spacious *(space)*
specious *(deceptive)*
sponsor
stationary *(fixed)*
stationery *(paper)*
statistics
stepped
stopped
straight
strategy
strength
strenuous
stretch
studies
studying
subpoena
subpoenaed
subtlety
suburban
succeed
succession
suicide
sulfur
superintendent
supersede
suppress
surely
surreptitious
surround
surveillance
susceptible
suspicious
synonymous

technical
technique
temperature
temporary
their *(pronoun)*
themselves
there *(adverb)*
therefore
thorough
though
through
tie, tied, tying
tobacco
too
totaled, totaling
tragedy
transferable
transferred
traveled
traveling
tremendous
truly
twelfth
typical
tyranny

Unanimous
unconscious
undoubtedly
until
usage
usually

Vacuum
various
vengeance
villain
violence
visible
vitamins

Warrant
warring
weather
Wednesday
where
wherever
whether
whichever
whiskey
wholly
woman *(singular)*
women *(plural)*
writing
written

yield

Strong Verbs

Strong verbs shorten sentences and usually convey direct, memorable messages.

A common stylistic problem is using weak, rather than strong, verbs. Weak verbs are those simple verbs that occur so frequently in our language that they have little impact: *is, are, was, were, can, could, has, had, have, do, did, done, make, use, come.*

Obviously, these verbs are essential to English. Using them, either as primary or auxiliary sentence verbs, is inescapable. However, writers often use them unnecessarily to create wordy, weak sentences:

> The system has wide applicability for a variety of industrial cogeneration situations. *(12 words)*

In this sentence, the writer has transformed *apply*, a much stronger verb than *has*, into an awkward, bureaucratic noun, *applicability*, and used the weaker verb as the sentence verb. Using *apply* as the sentence verb creates a shorter, stronger sentence:

> The system applies to a variety of industrial cogeneration situations. *(10 words)*

See SCIENTIFIC/TECHNICAL STYLE.

1. Use strong verbs.

Strong verbs are less common; therefore, readers tend to pay more attention to them. They have more impact in a sentence, and they help writers avoid big, bureaucratic nouns:

this

Since 1965, our Basic Development Department has studied membranes for the separation and enrichment of gas mixtures.

not this

Membranes for the separation and enrichment of gas mixtures have been under study by our Basic Development Department since 1965.

---

this

We have vastly improved our reaction mechanisms.

not this

We have made vast improvements in our reaction mechanisms.

---

this

We would like to investigate further the pilot program before proposing a factory location.

not this

We would like to conduct further investigations into the pilot program before giving a proposed factory location.

---

this

We will especially emphasize evaluating plating techniques for depositing amorphous or glassy metal coatings.

not this

We will give special emphasis to the evaluation of plating techniques for the deposition of amorphous or glassy metal coatings.

---

this

Before developing the catalyst, we would assess the technical and economic advantages of the various source materials.

not this

Before proceeding with catalyst development, we would make technical and economic assessments of the advantages of the various source materials available.

Style

Style is the sum of the choices, both conscious and unconscious, that writers make while planning, designing, writing, and editing documents.

These choices include the type of document, the words chosen, the structure and length of sentences, the length and type of paragraphs, the document's organization, the use of emphatic devices (headings, lists, white space), the use and kind of visuals, the typeface and type size, the paper, and so on. See DESKTOP PUBLISHING.

Such choices give each document a unique style, tone, and feeling. Each fax, each field note, each business letter, each quick memo, each formal report—they are all unique because they differ in tone, attitude, perspective, and style from every other fax, note, letter, memo, and report.

Style and Tone

Style and *tone* are often confused. The terms are similar, and some speakers use them interchangeably. However, style is the cause and tone is the effect:

- **Style** refers to those choices writers make that create the tone conveyed to readers.
- **Tone** refers to the feeling or impression a document conveys to its readers. See TONE.

Style is often categorized as being either **formal** or **informal**. These distinctions typically depend on the type of document being written, the intended readers, the writer's relationship to the readers, the document's purpose, and the message being conveyed.

Formal documents, such as legal agreements, technical reports, and many letters, are written for readers with whom the writer has no personal relationship. Therefore, familiarity or levity is generally unacceptable. It would seem inappropriate to the circumstance and would interfere with the message. Formal documents are usually written to convey information objectively to readers who may not know (or care to know) the author.

The tone of formal documents tends to be impersonal, objective, restrained, deliberate, and factual. Formal documents that are intended to convince readers to do or accept something are often also forceful, dynamic, and perhaps intensive. Most documents that convey negative or unpleasant information are formal.

Informal documents, such as personal letters, newsletters, trip reports, and most memos, are generally written for people the writer knows or feels comfortable with, perhaps only through employment in the same organization. Familiarity, levity, and wit are often acceptable. The informality creates a more relaxed atmosphere, which makes the message warmer, more easily accepted. Informal documents are often informative, friendly, and subjective.

The tone of informal documents is generally relaxed, informative, helpful, casual, personal, positive, nonthreatening, and perhaps cheerful. Informal documents may be persuasive, but they are rarely forceful or aggressive. When writers need to be aggressive and when they need to convey negative or unpleasant information, they generally become more formal in their approach. See TONE.

Style also refers to styles associated with particular disciplines: geologic style, geophysical style, legal style, medical style, engineering style, auditing style, academic style, scientific style, social science style, bureaucratic style, and so on. See SCIENTIFIC/TECHNICAL STYLE.

In each of these styles, the writer uses jargon particular to the discipline and writes according to a long tradition of document preparation and appearance. We are perhaps most familiar with the legal and bureaucratic styles, but all disciplines have a set of standards and traditions that affect the way people communicate in writing. See JARGON.

Word Choice and Style

Each word you choose helps establish the style of your writing. Words are one of the most visible traits of style.

You may, for instance, wish to discuss the effects of a decision. The word *effects* is a fairly neutral choice. Instead of *effects,* you might speak of *impacts, consequences,* or *results.*

Impacts suggests some negative connotations, as does *consequences*, which is more formal sounding (perhaps because of its length) than *impacts*. *Results*, on the other hand, has a positive feeling to it: *We're going to get results.*

You have other less common choices: *aftermath, corollary, end product, eventuality, outcome, sequel, upshot. Aftermath* has definite negative implications, besides being almost dramatic in its tone. *Corollary* has limited usefulness, if for no other reason than its mathematical echoes (and hence almost too educated a tone). *End product* seems plain, yet still wordy when compared to *effects* or *results. Eventuality* implies some final or ultimate result; again, its length makes it sound more formal. *Outcome* is about as neutral as any of the words in this list, but it may have negative connotations, as in the outcome of a medical test. *Sequel* implies a second follow-up event, not a real effect. And *upshot* suggests surprise, even chaos. Even more words are possible: *development, fruit, outgrowth, ramification, repercussion, conclusion.*

Part of the richness of English is its large vocabulary, which offers multiple possibilities for expressing any idea. Yet no two words mean exactly the same thing, so when you choose one word rather than another, you change the style of the document, if only slightly. Within a few lines, then, you will make dozens of choices, all of which combine to establish the style (and resulting tone) of the document.

Obviously, some word choices make a bigger difference than others. Selecting *effects* rather than *results* changes the style very little. But if you use *impacts, consequences,* or *aftermath,* the document may shift in tone and effect:

> What is the effect of altering course in midflight?
>
> What are the consequences of altering course in midflight?

> What were the effects of the pipeline installation on the salmon in Little Middle River?
>
> What was the aftermath of the pipeline installation on the salmon in Little Middle River?

As you can see, some word choices are important stylistic signals. Others are inconsequential:

> What is the effect of altering course in midflight?
>
> What is the result of altering course in midflight?

Writers in various technical professions have a body of technical words that affect the style:

Legal

> tort, legatee, real property, contract, conveyance, *amicus curiae,* party, sue, brief, witness, jurisdiction, plaintiff, etc.

Medical

> curette, mamillary, uvulae, amoebic, gastric hernia, leucoplast, dermatitis, proboscis, etc.

Computer

> batch processing, cursor, default, field, file, logon, real time, sign off, etc.

Construction

> sill, head, transom, mullion, fascia, neoprene spaces, support mullion, jamb, seat board, glazing gasket, butt glazed, hopper sash, soffit, rowlock, etc.

Such specialized scientific and technical terms are unavoidable given today's complex technologies. See JARGON. The presence of this jargon is the most visible sign to readers that a document reflects a particular style.

Sentences and Style

Writers have virtually an infinite number of ways to express ideas. Even in an ordinary 15– to 30–word sentence, the possibilities run into the millions, both in terms of word choice and sentence structure. The sheer range of possibility means that every sentence except the shortest and most trivial is potentially unique (never having been written or said before).

Sentence options—**length** and **structure**—are the most important features of a writer's style. However, these options are often less obvious to readers than the choice of a particular word or technical term. Readers notice the style of sentences only when something goes wrong, as in an awkward sentence or one where something is deliberately unusual:

> That is something up with which I shall not put.
>
> *or*
>
> Turning into the wrong driveway, a tree was hit by me which I don't have.

Style

Sentence Length. Sentence length by itself normally will not establish a definite style, but it will contribute to style. Most sentences average anywhere from 12 to 25 words in length. Readers are accustomed to those lengths, so they are likely to notice only those sentences that are either extremely short or extremely long:

> We refuse.
>
> *or*
>
> Science is nothing but trained and organized common sense, differing from the latter only as a veteran may differ from a raw recruit: and its methods differ from those of common sense only as far as the guardsman's cut and thrust differ from the manner in which a savage wields his club. (from Thomas Huxley's *Collected Essays*)

An individual sentence, even if potentially noteworthy, won't be noteworthy unless it stands out from the sentences surrounding it. So **average sentence length** is probably more of a direct indication of style than the length of a single sentence. Readability formulas always include average sentence length as a measure of readability because length is a good indicator of the difficulty of a document. See SENTENCES.

Long sentences can reflect different styles (and tones), depending on other features within them. Long, well-structured sentences with a sophisticated vocabulary usually convey an educated or thoughtful quality. But if the sentence seems longer than necessary for the ideas being expressed, and if the vocabulary is more sophisticated than necessary, then the sentence may seem stuffy, extravagant, or pompous:

> If biological populations or habitats that may require additional protection are identified by the DCMOFO (Deputy Conservation Manager, Offshore Field Operations) in the leasing area, the DCMOFO will require the lessee to conduct environmental surveys or studies, including sampling, as approved by the DCMOFO, to determine existing environmental conditions, the extent and composition of biological populations or habitats, and the effects of proposed or existing operations on the populations or habitats that might require additional protective measures.

This sentence's length—some 77 words—is surely excessive, but other features contribute to its bureaucratic, stiff, faintly legal style:

- The use of the unfamiliar acronym *DCMOFO* gives the sentence a bureaucratic touch, especially with its repetitions of the acronym.
- The repetition within the sentence, especially of the phrase *populations or habitats,* reinforces the bureaucratic, even stuffy, tone.
- The delay of the main subject and verb *(the DCMOFO will require)* until after the long introductory *if* clause forces readers to absorb, comprehend, and remember too much information at once. Consequently, the sentence is more difficult to read than it should be.
- Some of the phrasing is clumsy and ill-placed. The phrase *in the leasing area* comes so late in the opening clause that its meaning is fuzzy. Is the DCMOFO in the leasing area? Are the populations and habitats in the leasing area? Have any or all of these been identified in the leasing area?

For an example of a well-structured long sentence, see SENTENCES.

Sentence Structure. Sentence structure—including grammatical structure, the sequence of ideas, and the various repeated word patterns—all contribute to the style of a sentence or passage. The following versions of the same basic sentence say much the same thing, but their different structures create different tones:

1. We considered how best to present the conflicting data and our interpretations of these conflicts.
2. How to present the conflicting data, as well as our interpretations of these conflicts, was under consideration.
3. Because of conflicting data and differing interpretations, we were considering different presentation strategies.
4. We were considering different strategies for presenting the conflicting data and our interpretations of the data.
5. It was difficult to decide on strategies for presenting the conflicting data and the differing interpretations of the data.

Sentences 1 and 4 are the most direct (and they happen to be the ones that follow most closely normal English word order). Sentence 2 is formal, even stuffy, because its opening clause is so long that the verb *was* is almost lost. Sentence 3 is fairly ordinary, even though it opens with the conditional *because* clause. Sentence 5 is perhaps the most stuffy; it opens with a false subject (see FALSE SUBJECTS), and it avoids all pronouns. See PRONOUNS.

The structural patterns for a single sentence present a broad range of possibilities. Putting sentences together increases the possibilities exponentially.

A string of formal, oddly structured sentences not only slows down readers but also conveys a tone of formality or stuffiness. A string of short, direct sentences can sound clean and efficient (or abrupt and efficient, depending on the context).

Other Stylistic Choices

Many other features in a document besides words and sentences can convey a particular style.

The basic format of a document is usually significant. A document with narrow margins, single-spaced text, and long paragraphs conveys a dense, information-packed but potentially dull image. Readers may consider the language heavy and ponderous. A document with generous margins and lots of open space makes readers feel that the writing is open and inviting, easier to read.

See DESKTOP PUBLISHING.

Besides format choices, many other features influence a reader's perception of a document:

- The typeface used for the text
- The type of paper—both weight and texture
- The number and quality of the visuals
- The care with which the proofreading and editing has been done
- The professionalism of the binding and the quality of the printing
- The presence or absence of color

Individual Style

We all have styles of speaking and writing that are unique to us, regardless of the circumstances in which we write. This fact reflects the basic and pervasive nature of style.

In speech, an individual's style is easy to identify. Most of us can recognize a close friend, not only from the sound of the friend's voice, but also from the structure and content of the speech, from the words chosen, and from the sentence patterns used. We know our friends as talkative, quiet, abrupt, cheerful, depressed, thoughtful, humorous, or tactful. In writing, an individual's style may be harder to identify, and yet it exists in each choice the individual has made to produce a document.

Style and Ineffective Writing

Ultimately, style **is** the writer. We can't describe a universally preferable style because the decisions writers make depend on the context: on the subject or content, the purpose of the document, the readers, previous or related documents, and the situation or climate in which the document is produced.

Nevertheless, good writing is distinguishable from bad writing, and you should never confuse bad writing with style.

Good writing is clear, emphatic, well organized, and concise. Bad writing is often vague or confusing, unemphatic, chaotic, and wordy.

Good writers obey the principles of effective writing—regardless of subject matter, purpose, readers, context, style, or tone.

For a review of those principles, see this *Style Guide*, particularly the sections on SENTENCES, PARAGRAPHS, ORGANIZATION, EMPHASIS, ACTIVE/PASSIVE, STRONG VERBS, FALSE SUBJECTS, and KEY WORDS.

For information on writing specific types of documents, see LETTERS, MEMOS, REPORTS, and SUMMARIES.

Summaries

Summaries are abridgments or compendiums of the important points in a document. Summaries are essential for readers who don't have time to read the entire document, are not interested in reading the entire document, or need to review the important points without reading the entire document.

Traditional summaries appear at the end of documents, especially those organized scientifically. See ORGANIZATION. These summaries present the main points from the preceding discussion.

Executive summaries appear at the beginning of documents, especially in documents organized according to the managerial format. See ORGANIZATION. These summaries preview the main points that will appear in the discussion that follows.

Traditional Summaries

These summaries briefly repeat the major ideas, especially conclusions and recommendations. They include little, if any, background information and no supporting data or detail of any kind. They are typically shorter than executive summaries, which may include some background and supporting information.

Traditional summaries should not be separated from the rest of the document. They are a final summation, so they depend on information presented earlier in the document. Everything in them must already have been stated earlier.

The writer of a traditional summary often assumes that readers will use the summary after having read the rest of the document.

Executive Summaries

Executive summaries—which are also known simply as summaries—appear at the beginning of documents. They usually include the following:

- **Background/introduction to the document.** Although very brief, this section gives readers enough information so that they'll understand the reason for the document, the key problems addressed, and any special conditions or situations that the reader should be aware of. See ORGANIZATION and INTRODUCTIONS.
- **Main conclusions.** These may be a little longer than in traditional summaries because they are not repeated from conclusions presented earlier. Therefore, in addition to the conclusion itself, you may need a little explanation or elaboration. Just keep it short.
- **Recommendations, if any.** Again, you are not repeating recommendations presented earlier, so each recommendation might require some explanation. If appropriate, tie each recommendation to the specific conclusion or conclusions that prompted it.
- **A review of data (optional).** This section is limited to pertinent items, not all the data. The complete data usually appear in an appendix. However, you may need to present key data in an executive summary so that readers are aware of the key supporting information that your document presents. Remember that readers may read only the executive summary, not the entire document. Give them enough detail to substantiate your conclusions, but not so much that the rest of the document becomes unnecessary.

In some instances, business and technical documents may consist only of an executive summary, with supporting or explanatory material located in appendices or attachments. Such documents reflect the attempt of many businesses to limit documentation to the essentials.

Summaries

Summaries vs. Abstracts

Scientific and technical writers often include abstracts with their reports. Abstracts are condensations of a document, usually written so that readers can preview the content of the document to determine whether they are interested in reading the entire document. In a sense, abstracts are extended titles.

Abstracts may contain much of the same information found in summaries, but abstracts are meant to be detached from their documents. Frequently, abstracts are published separately, in a catalog or list of abstracts. Sometimes, journals request that potential authors submit abstracts of their articles. The editors read the abstracts to determine which articles they want to read in full.

Summaries on the other hand, are an integral part of the documents they belong to, and they are not normally detached.

By convention, abstracts are rarely longer than one paragraph (about 200 words). Summaries have no conventional length restrictions. They should be concise, of course, but summaries may range from 50 to 5,000 words, depending on the length of the parent document. An extensive report or multivolume proposal could very well have an executive summary of 20 pages.

See REPORTS and ORGANIZATION.

How to Write Summaries

You may wish to produce a preliminary summary of a long or complicated document. A preliminary summary will help you organize your thoughts and determine your most significant points. However, the final summary (the one appearing in your document) should be written last. Here is a procedure for writing good summaries (especially executive summaries):

1. Read through the entire document. Ensure that you have a firm grasp of the document's purpose, scope, point of view, and major ideas.
2. Identify the major ideas and data. You can underline or circle major ideas, or put stars beside them, or highlight them with a highlighting pen. Identify all of the major statements: observations, conclusions, recommendations, key supporting data, key facts, etc.
3. Pull the major ideas together and note how they are developed sequentially throughout the document. If necessary, refer to details in the text to clarify any points not absolutely clear.
4. Condense by combining sentences, generalizing, eliminating unnecessary supporting information, and eliminating unnecessary words and phrases. Use simple, direct sentences, and eliminate all unnecessary jargon and big words. Keep your writing simple and straightforward.
5. Use transitional words and phrases to link ideas and provide a smooth flow of thought from one sentence to the next.
6. Test the result by challenging every word, phrase, sentence, and idea. If something isn't pulling its weight, get rid of it.
7. Challenge the overall summary. Does it accurately reflect the content of the whole document? Have you left out major ideas? Does the summary distort any facts, relationships, conclusions, or recommendations? Does the summary provide ample information for readers to comprehend the ideas without reading the whole document? Can the summary stand by itself? If readers read nothing but the summary, will they be adequately informed?

Remember that the purpose of the summary is not to convey everything. Summaries convey the essentials. If readers want additional support or proof, they should read the rest of the document. But make sure that the summary provides readers with a firm grasp of the major ideas.

Tables

Tables are information displays organized by rows and columns.

Tables are especially useful because they provide for very organized displays of precise data. Tabular information is usually more understandable than the same information presented in text.

Tables allow writers to present precise data: *3.1415, 9.8690, 31.0035,* etc. Such data cannot be presented as precisely in any other type of visual aid. See VISUAL AIDS. Tables allow for quick and accurate comparisons and can also depict trends and relationships, although not as well as charts and graphs. See CHARTS and GRAPHS.

Use tables when you must present a large amount of information, when you need to give readers the exact figures, or when you want readers to be able to compare figures or other information presented in different rows and columns.

For general information on using visual aids, see VISUAL AIDS. See also CHARTS, GRAPHS, ILLUSTRATIONS, MAPS, and PHOTOGRAPHS. For information on captions, see CAPTIONS.

For a much more elaborate discussion of tables, including printing considerations, see the *United States Government Printing Office Style Manual.* See REFERENCES.

Parts of Tables

The standard parts of tables are the following: the **table number** and **caption**, the **boxhead** (containing column headings), the **stub** (containing row headings), the **field (body), rules, footnotes,** and the **source line.** See figure 1 for a sample table layout.

Table Number and Caption

Number tables sequentially as they appear in the document, and number them separately from figures.

Unless you are presenting uninterpreted data, make the table caption an action caption (see table 1). The table caption

Figure 1. Sample Table Layout. *A clear, correct table layout assists readers to understand and interpret the data.*

Table Number — **No. 201.** **PERCENT OF POPULATION ENGAGED IN PHYSICAL EXERCISE, BY TYPE OF EXERCISE, SEX, AND AGE: 1975** — Caption

Boxhead:

SEX AND AGE	Total popula-tion (1,000)	Percent exercis-ing regu-larly[1]	PERCENT, BY TYPE OF EXERCISE[2]						
			Ride bicycle	Calis-thenics	Jog	Lift weights	Swim	Walk	All other
Total, 20 years and over	**135,655**	**48.6**	**10.9**	**13.5**	**4.8**	**3.4**	**11.8**	**33.8**	**6.8**
20-44 years	71,084	53.7	16.1	17.3	7.3	5.4	16.9	33.8	6.9
45-64 years	43,145	43.4	6.5	10.8	2.7	1.5	8.0	32.9	6.5
65 years and over	21,426	42.3	2.9	6.1	1.2	(B)	2.8	35.7	6.9
Male, 20 years and over	**63,665**	**48.5**	**10.8**	**13.5**	**7.2**	**6.3**	**13.3**	**32.5**	**6.4**
20-44 years	34,268	52.7	14.9	17.5	10.6	10.1	18.8	31.4	6.2
45-64 years	20,567	42.0	6.7	10.1	3.8	2.6	8.1	31.4	5.9
65 years and over	8,830	47.3	4.3	5.9	2.1	(B)	4.1	39.4	8.1
Female, 20 years and over	**71,990**	**48.7**	**11.1**	**13.5**	**2.7**	**.8**	**10.5**	**35.0**	**7.1**
20-44 years	36,816	54.6	17.2	17.1	4.1	1.1	15.0	36.0	7.5
45-64 years	22,579	44.6	6.4	11.4	1.6	(B)	7.8	34.2	7.1
65 years and over	12,595	38.7	1.8	6.3	(B)	(B)	1.9	33.0	6.0

Stub — Field

B = Base less than minimum required for reliability. [1]Regular exercise is any exercise done on a weekly basis. [2]More than one type of exercise can be reported per person. — Footnotes

Source: U.S. National Center for Health Statistics, *Health, United States, 1976-1977.* — Source Line

should clearly identify the table and tell readers how to read or interpret the table:

> Table 1. The industrial gas shipment decline since 1980.
>
> Table 2. Wood panel products (1975-84): Production has more than doubled in 10 years.
>
> Table 3. Increasing arsenic concentrations in groundwater, Sonoma County, California, 1985.

These captions indicate both what the tables are about and how readers should interpret them.

If you are presenting a large amount of uninterpreted data and your purpose is to present, not interpret, the data, then use shorter, title-like captions:

> Table 1. Industrial gas shipments (1976-84)
>
> Table 2. Wood panel product production (1975-84)
>
> Table 3. Arsenic concentrations in groundwater, Sonoma County, California, 1985

Unless the caption is too long (more than two full lines), place it above the table, just after or below the table number (see table 1). If you use lengthy captions for tables, place them below their tables. However, if you place captions below tables, use a short title with the table number and center the table number and title above the tables.

If a unit of measurement applies throughout the table, you may state the unit of measurement in the caption or within parentheses beneath the caption. If the unit of measurement appears below the caption, you can subordinate it by printing it in a smaller type size.

See CAPTIONS.

Boxhead

The boxhead contains the stub heading and the column headings (see figure 1). Place a rule (line) above and beneath the boxhead to separate it from the table number and caption and from the field. Make column and stub headings as concise as possible. Use more than one line, if necessary, to state a column heading, but try not to exceed three lines for any heading. Orient the headings horizontally.

If appropriate, include units of measurement in the headings or enclose the units of measurement within parentheses below the headings. If the column headings require more than one line and you place units of measurement below the headings, separate the headings and units with a thin rule (see tables 2 and 3). Use thicker rules around the boxhead itself.

Stub

The stub is the left column. Use it to label the rows. Make the row headings as concise as possible. As necessary, put row units of measurement either within parentheses following the row heading or in another column beside the stub (see table 4).

If the rows consist of major and subordinate items, place the major items flush left and indent the subordinate items (see table 1).

Field

The field consists of the data rows and columns below the boxhead and to the right of the stub. If necessary for clarity, use leaders (rows of periods) between rows to facilitate reading (see tables 2, 3, or 4). Align the data presented in each column by placing words left flush within columns, integers (e.g., *40*) right flush by digit, and real numbers (e.g., *40.0* or *40.068)* vertically by decimal point.

Rules

Rules are horizontal or vertical lines that separate parts of the table. Always place rules between the boxhead and the field. Also, place a rule above the boxhead to separate the boxhead from the table number and caption. If you use footnotes or a source line, place a rule between them and the bottom of the field.

If your table is large, you might need to place rules between groups of rows. Typically, the rules appear between groups of five. These rules help readers follow information down large tables.

The rules surrounding the boxhead should be thicker than those appearing within the field.

NOTE 1: Instead of placing rules between every fifth row, you may leave an extra line to separate groups of rows.

Tables

Table 1. U.S. Machine Tool Consumption. *Imports as a share of consumption increased more rapidly during 1980 and 1981 than during 1982.*

Item	1979	1980	1981	1982
Machining Centers				
Production	356.5	413.0	482.6	339.5
Exports	45.4	56.7	53.4	34.0
Imports	39.6	93.4	195.7	188.9
Consumption	350.7	449.7	624.9	494.4
Imports as share of consumption	11.3%	20.8%	31.3%	38.2%
Horizontal Spindle Turning Machines				
Production	284.4	321.7	346.6	238.6
Exports	NA	20.5	20.4	30.4
Imports	NA	159.8	278.0	194.1
Consumption	NA	461.0	604.2	402.2
Imports as share of consumption	NA	34.7%	46.0%	48.2%
Punching and Shearing Machines				
Production	82.5	110.6	97.1	59.0
Exports	NA	13.2	28.3	8.3
Imports	NA	16.5	32.5	25.5
Consumption	NA	113.9	101.3	76.2
Imports as share of consumption	NA	14.5%	32.1%	33.4%

Note: Data in this table differ from those in other tables due to different source of production data and exclusion of data on machine tool parts.

Sources: Bureau of the Census, "Current Industrial Report for Metalworking Machinery," MQ-35W; "U.S. Imports for Consumption," IM146; and "U.S. Exports," EM522.

NOTE 2: Some authorities also use vertical rules to separate the stub from the field and groups of columns from each other. The trend today is to eliminate all vertical rules.

Footnotes

Use footnotes to clarify the headings, to identify unfamiliar abbreviations and units of measurement, and to explain the data appearing within the field.

Use superscripted footnote numbers or letters (^{1}, ^{2}, ^{3} or ^{a}, ^{b}, ^{c}) or symbols (*, **, ***) to link the footnoted information in the table and its explanation (see tables 2 through 4). If the footnote applies to the entire table, you do not need a footnote symbol (see the note beneath table 1).

The footnotes should appear below the table, beginning flush left. If a footnote extends across the table and you have many footnotes, break the footnote references into two columns and print them in a smaller type size, if possible (see table 4).

Source Line

The source line identifies the source of the information presented in the table. Source lines always appear below footnotes and should be aligned with the footnote references (see tables 1 through 4).

Rules for Using Tables

1. Keep tables as simple as possible.

Tables can become complicated quickly, so simplify them as much as possible. If the information you are trying to present becomes too complicated, break it up into two or more tables.

2. Place important tables in the body of the document; place unimportant tables in appendices or attachments.

Tables conveying critical information must appear in the text. However, if you are presenting tables of uninterpreted data, consider placing them in an appendix or attachment. Do not force readers to ponder uninterpreted data unless they want to. See EMPHASIS and APPENDICES/ATTACHMENTS.

3. Use table numbers and captions to identify tables and to help readers understand the information presented.

Table numbers help readers track tables through a document and help them find important tabular information.

Captions label the information found in a table and can tell readers how to read the table. The caption is your opportunity to influence the reader's perception of the information you present. You should take advantage of that opportunity and write an action caption. See CAPTIONS.

4. Orient tables horizontally on the page.

Try to orient tables horizontally so that readers do not have to reorient the page to read the table. This means that most tables can be longer than they can be wider (that is, they can have more rows than columns). If you need to have more columns than rows, consider redesigning your table or breaking it into two tables. As a last resort, orient the table sideways with the boxhead toward the left side of the page.

Table 2. Production and Imports of Crude Oil—1960 to 1984. *The production and import of crude oil increased significantly from 1960 to 1970; however, the volume remained relatively level during the 1970s and the early 1980s.*

	Production				Gross Imports	
Year	Crude oil[1] (billions of barrels)	Natural gas[2] (trillions of cu ft)	Natural gas plant liquids (billions of barrels)	Total (quadrillions of Btu's)	Crude oil (billions of barrels)	Natural gas (trillions of cu ft)
1960	2.575	12.23	0.340	29.05	0.373	0.16
1970	3.517	21.01	0.606	44.58	0.482	0.82
1972	3.455	21.62	0.638	44.85	0.813	1.02
1973	3.361	21.73	0.634	44.25	1.183	1.03
1974	3.203	20.71	0.616	42.25	1.270	0.96
1975	3.057	19.24	0.596	39.74	1.497	0.95
1976	2.976	19.10	0.587	39.07	1.936	0.96
1977	3.009	19.16	0.590	39.35	2.413	1.01
1978	3.178	19.12	0.572	40.17	2.321	0.97
1979	3.121	19.66	0.578	40.47	2.380	1.25
1980	3.146	19.60	0.576	40.42	1.925	0.98
1981	3.129	19.40	0.587	40.15	1.605	0.90
1982	3.157	17.75	0.566	38.55	1.273	0.93
1983[3]	3.161	16.28	0.562	37.26	1.278	0.86
1984[4]	3.126	17.41	0.567	38.23	1.636	0.90

[1]Includes lease condensate.

[2]Net dry natural gas, including nonhydrocarbon gases.

[3]Estimated.

[4]Forecast.

Source: Energy Information Administration.

5. Clearly label tables that extend beyond one page, and use continuation headings on continued pages.

If you must continue a table from one page to another, write *continued* on the bottom right corner of the table on each page to be continued. Then on the top of each new page where the table has been continued, write, for instance, *Table 4, continued.*

Finally, repeat the boxhead on each continued page.

6. Use white space, boxes, or lines to separate tables from surrounding text.

Tables are visual aids and should be placed as thoughtfully as any other visual aids. Separate them from surrounding text by leaving three lines above and below tables (more white space on the page), by placing the tables within boxes (or frames), or by using thin rules above and below the tables to separate them from the text. See EMPHASIS and DESKTOP PUBLISHING.

7. Logically organize rows and columns so that they reflect the purpose of the table and make the table easy to read.

The arrangement of rows and columns depends on the information being presented and on the purpose of the table.

Use a chronological order for information presented by time, date, or sequence. Use a whole-to-parts pattern for major and subordinate items. Use logical grouping for items that should appear together because of type, size, or relationship. See ORGANIZATION.

Place information that you want readers to compare in adjacent rows or columns. As much as possible, avoid forcing readers to compare or contrast information separated by other rows or columns.

Place information that must be numerically tallied or compared in columns. Performing mathematical operations across rows is much more difficult than performing the same operations down columns.

Table 3. Prices and Price Indexes for U.S. Imported and Domestically Produced Crude Oil, 1972 to 1984. *The 7 to 9 percent cost increase of crude oil from 1972 to 1984 was passed on to consumers.*

Year	Refiner acquisition cost of U.S. imported crude		Refiner acquisition cost of U.S. produced crude		Wellhead price of U.S. produced crude	
	Price	Index	Price	Index	Price	Index
1972	3.22	100.0	3.67	100.0	3.39	100.0
1973	4.08	126.7	4.17	113.6	3.89	114.7
1974	12.52	388.8	7.18	195.6	6.87	202.7
1975	13.93	432.6	8.39	228.6	7.67	226.3
1976	13.48	418.6	8.84	240.9	8.19	241.6
1977	14.53	451.2	9.55	260.2	8.57	252.8
1978	14.57	452.5	10.61	289.1	9.00	265.5
1979	21.67	673.0	14.27	388.8	12.64	372.9
1980	33.89	1,052.5	24.23	660.2	21.59	636.9
1981	37.05	1,150.6	34.33	935.4	31.77	937.2
1982	33.55	1,041.9	31.22	850.7	28.52	841.3
1983	29.13	904.7	28.97	789.4	26.37	777.9
1984	29.00	900.6	29.00	790.2	27.15	809.6

NA = not available

Source: Energy Information Administration.

When time is one of the variables, you can arrange it along rows or columns. However, time is traditionally displayed on the horizontal or x-axis of charts, so display time across columns (see table 1). (Note, however, that tables 2 and 3 are also easy to read. Time is displayed in rows in these tables because displaying time in columns would create wider, rather than longer, tables. See rule 4 above.)

8. Use row headings (in the stub) and column headings (in the boxhead) to identify the information listed in each row and column.

Tables without adequate headings are often incomprehensible. Ensure that your headings are concise and yet descriptive. If necessary, use footnotes to explain or fully describe the headings.

9. Use rules to separate the boxhead from the field, and, as necessary, use rules to separate groups of data columns or rows from each other.

Complex tables are much easier to read and to follow when the information is separated by rules. Use thicker rules to separate the boxhead and the stub from the field and thinner rules to separate groups of rows and columns.

10. Where space is limited, use abbreviations.

Abbreviations are appropriate in tables (as well as other visual aids). Use them where space is limited. If the abbreviation is uncommon, explain it in a footnote. See ABBREVIATIONS.

11. Base comparable numerical amounts on the same unit of measurement, and convert all fractions to decimals.

Numbers that readers will want or need to compare must be presented in the same unit of measurement. Do not present some numbers in meters and similar numbers in centimeters, and some data in feet and comparable data in yards.

Further, convert all fractions to decimals and use real numbers (numbers with decimals) as necessary for accuracy. However, do not make numbers more precise than accuracy allows. In other words, do not give more than the significant digits in a real number. If you do, you will convey a false sense of accuracy.

See DECIMALS and FRACTIONS.

12. Align decimals vertically within columns.

Except where you are mixing types of numbers, ensure that decimals are aligned vertically. The exception occurs in columns containing different types of real numbers, as in table 1. The percentage figures are distinct from the production figures and should not be aligned, although both sets of data contain decimals. Note that the percent signs clearly distinguish the percentages from the production figures.

Table 4. Minimum Viable Population Levels for Management Indicator Species for the Targhee National Forest.

Species	Habitat Unit	Total Acres Habitat on Forest	Potential[1] Population	Minuimum[2] Viable Population
Grizzly Bear	Variable	340,000[3]	Undetermined	Undetermined
Bald Eagle	500 ac/nest site	25,000	50 pairs	Undetermined
Williamson's Sapsucker	20/ac/territory	467,000	23,350 pairs	9,340 pairs
Pika	1 ac/territory	53,000	53,000 pairs	21,200 pairs
Brewers Sparrow	5 ac/territory	121,000	24,200	9,680 pairs
Goshawk	15 sq mi/territory	870,000	90 pairs	36 pairs
Aquatic Invertebrates	per/sample[4]	25,000	Undetermined	Undetermined
Beaver	2 colonies/sq mi	46,000	144 colonies	58 colonies
Trout	lb/ac	25,000	Undetermined	18 lb/ac
Antelope	1/25 ac	77,000	4,000	1,000
Elk	6,000 ac	1,329,000	11,075	5,000[5]
Bighorn Sheep	Undetermined	77,000	600	150[6]
Mountain Goat	Undetermined	77,000	400	50[6]

[1]Within multiple use constraints and using currently available acres.

[2]40 percent of the potential is considered minimum viable population level on nongame species. Game species is the population at which a general hunt can be sustained.

[3]Situation 1 habitat and the occupied portion of Situation 2.

[4]Species diversity will be the measure of habitat quality.

[5]This level with about 40 bulls/100 cows preseason and 20 bulls/100 cows postseason.

[6]Idaho Fish and Game will begin to hunt a population at this level in any given herd area.

Source: *Final Environmental Impact Statement for the Land Management Plan for the Targhee National Forest.*

13. Use zeros, dashes, ellipses, or *NA* to indicate that information is missing or not applicable.

Do not leave entries in rows or columns blank where the information is unavailable or not applicable (NA). Readers will not know whether the blank entry was intentional.

Instead, indicate missing or inapplicable information by entering a dash, a zero, an ellipsis mark, the abbreviation *NA*, or a comment like *undetermined* (see table 4).

NOTE: Use the abbreviation *do* (for *ditto)* where a data entry in a column is the same as the data entry directly above it.

14. Use footnotes to explain or clarify table headings and entries.

Tabular information is governed as much by space limitations as it is by content necessity, and you may not be able to explain fully a table heading or entry in the space available. So use footnotes where necessary for clarification. See VISUAL AIDS.

Footnotes belong below the table and are usually flush left. Footnotes usually have the following format: superscripted reference number or letter indented, second or additional lines flush with the left margin, etc. See tables 2, 3, and 4.

If you are referencing numerical entries located within the field, use footnote letters or symbols rather than numbers, which some readers may confuse with the number being referenced. However, use a consistent system of reference. If you establish a system of footnote letters, then use that system throughout all of your tables.

See the example tables with this section. See also FOOTNOTES.

15. Identify all data sources.

For the sake of clarity, as well as substantiation, identify all data sources. The source line may follow the standard bibliographic format (see table 1) or may identify the source by name alone (tables 2 through 4). See BIBLIOGRAPHIC FORM and CITATIONS.

Whether you provide full source information depends on the nature of the source documents, the extent to which you have summarized from the original, the purpose of your document, and the purpose of the table. If readers will want to examine the original sources, then provide full source information. However, if you have gathered data from a variety of sources or documents, you might not be able to identify specific documents.

If you have examined a number of EPA documents, for instance, and collated data from many of those documents, your source line should not list every single source. Instead, you should simply indicate:

> Source: Environmental Protection Agency.

Begin source lines with the word *Source* or *Sources*, followed by a colon. End the source line with a period.

Tables of Contents

Tables of contents help readers in two ways: (1) They outline the structure of the document and thus provide insight into the document's organization, and (2) they provide the page numbers for all sections and subsections, thus helping readers to locate parts of the document.

Creating a preliminary table of contents is a useful writing technique because writers have to think carefully about the document's organization. Gaps, illogical order, and misplaced emphasis become more apparent when the writer is forced to clarify and complete a preliminary table of contents.

The final table of contents cannot be prepared until the document is finished and the pages numbered.

1. Use a table of contents for any report longer than 10 pages.

The 10-page figure is arbitrary, but remember that a table of contents helps readers to see the overall organization of the document as well as to find key sections. Documents under 10 pages are generally short and uncomplicated enough for readers to determine the structure by skimming through the document before reading. However, skimming through longer documents may not provide an adequate sense of structure because the reader's mind is being asked to comprehend too much information spread over too great a distance.

2. Include major divisions (often chapter headings) and the next level of subdivisions in the table of contents.

Major divisions and the next level subdivisions are essential if readers are to comprehend the document's structure. Make the division titles as specific as possible:

this

II. Testing for Flammability

  Temperatures
  Duration
  Flash Points

not this

II. Testing

NOTE: Ensure that all of the divisions and subdivisions that appear in the table of contents also appear in the body of the document.

See HEADINGS.

3. Use letters and numbers with division and subdivision titles in the table of contents only if you also use them in the text.

A table of contents can resemble an outline with page numbers, but such an outline structure *(I, A, 1, a,* etc.) is not necessary unless the chapter or section titles and the headings in the document reflect the same numbering system. Tables of contents often have a decimal numbering system *(1.1.1, 1.1.2, 1.1.3,* etc.) in place of the standard outline system. Either system is acceptable.

See OUTLINES and NUMBERING SYSTEMS.

4. Use blank lines, indentation, and leader dots to lay out the table of contents and help readers find page numbers.

Leave **blank lines** between major entries, and ensure that the spacing reflects the logical structure of the document. For instance, you may want to leave two lines between major divisions (first-level headings) and one line between major subdivisions (second-level headings). Readers should be able to tell where major divisions occur simply by noting the number of lines between entries.

Use **indentation** to show levels of subordination. Major divisions (first-level headings) should be flush left. Major subdivisions (second-level headings) should be indented five spaces. Minor subdivisions (third-level headings) should be indented 10 spaces, and so on. Note the table of contents example at the end of this section.

Finally, consider using **leader dots** (a row of spaced periods) to connect entries with their page numbers. Leader dots allow readers' eyes to trace the connection across the page.

To emphasize major divisions or subdivisions, you might also use all capital letters, boldface type, and other emphatic techniques. See EMPHASIS.

Tables of Contents

The table of contents example in figure 1 shows one method of displaying the organizational structure of a document and of providing page numbers to help readers locate the document's parts. For a further example, see the table of contents to this *Style Guide.*

5. Include preliminary material and appendices or attachments in the table of contents.

Some writers ignore the preliminary material and attachments when they construct their tables of contents. However, a table of contents should reflect the structure of the entire document, so include all of the document's parts.

TABLE OF CONTENTS

iii

Figure 1. Sample Table of Contents. *This table of contents includes second-level headings so that readers can easily find the relevant sections.*

6. If appropriate, supplement your table of contents with a matrix or checksheet showing how and where you have dealt with key requirements or issues.

Such matrices or checksheets do not replace the standard table of contents, but they can help guide readers to see how you have organized your document. They are especially valuable when you need to show readers that you have met all legal or procedural requirements.

These matrices or checklists have various formats, but as figures 2 and 3 on the next page show, most requirements or issues are usually listed vertically down the left with the document sections or chapters horizontally across the top. Page numbers (or subsection numbers) appear in the matrix.

Tables of Contents

Statement of Work Requirements	Section Numbers
3.0 Survivability	4.4, 8.2, and 9.0
3.1 Stress Resistance	4.4.1 and 8.2.2
3.2 Temperature Constraints	4.4.2 and 8.2.3
3.3 Humidity	4.4.3 and 8.2.4
3.4 Electromagnetic Pulse	4.5 and 9.0

Figure 2. A Matrix from a Proposal. *A two-column matrix may be sufficient to track the way the document responds to each requirement listed in a client's statement of work. An option would be to list all section titles and numbers across the top and then fill in the matrix with page numbers.*

Issues	Chapters (page numbers)						
	Summary	I. Purpose and Need	II. Alternatives	III. Affected Environment	IV. Environmental Consequences	Appendix A Public Involvement	Appendix B
1. Soil Stability	2	4-5	8, 10-11	18-21	49-52, 68	A-3, A-5, A-7, and A-15	B-6, B-11, and B-15
2. Water Quality	2-3	5	8, 11-12	21-24	53-57, 68-69	A-3, A-5, A-14, and A-20	B-5, B-8, and B-20
3. Wildlife	3	5-6	8, 13	27-30	60-64, 69-70	A-5, A-14, A-20, and A-24	B-1, B-2, B-7, and B-15

Figure 3. A Matrix from an Environmental Document. *The issues are crucial to the organization (and legality) of the document. By showing that each issue appears in each chapter, the writer is able to show readers that all issues have been consistently addressed. In a sense, a matrix like this could replace the index.* *See* INDEXES.

Titles

Titles of people, organizations, governments, and publications often require special capitalization, punctuation, and other format conventions. See NOUNS and CAPITALS.

1. Capitalize the first letter of titles when they immediately precede personal names, but do not capitalize the first letter when they follow personal names:

Mrs. Robert T. Evans

Mr. Edward Johnson

Miss Sylvia Smead

Ms. Josephine Kukor

President Amy Kaufmann

Assistant Professor Ned Davies

Mayor-elect Boon Hollenbeck

General Laswell Hopkins

Lieutenant Cynthia Wagner

the Reverend John Tyler

Rabbi Tochterman

Amy Kaufmann, the president of Union College, spoke to the press.

Ned Davies is an assistant professor at Columbia University.

We voted for Boon Hollenbeck, who is now mayor-elect.

Laswell Hopkins was our general for only 2 months.

Our lieutenant was Cynthia Wagner. *(Here* was *separates the title from the name.)*

NOTE 1: The titles of high-ranking international, national, and state officials often retain their capitalization, even when the name of the individual is either absent or does not follow the title:

The President spoke before the Congress.

We wrote the Vice President.

The Pope toured South America.

The Governor still had 2 years to serve.

The Prime Minister of Ghana was invited to the White House.

NOTE 2: Titles of company or corporation executives as well as titles of lesser federal and state officials are sometimes capitalized. Such capitalization is unnecessary, but you should follow company or agency practice:

The Mayor announced an end to the New York transit strike. *(or* The mayor)

The Vice President for Finance is resigning Monday, September 18.

The Superintendent refused to approve our budget request.

NOTE 3: Titles used in a general sense are not capitalized:

a U.S. representative

a king

a prime minister

an ambassador

2. Capitalize the first letter of names of companies, schools, organizations, and religious bodies:

the Johnson Wax Company

the University of Oregon

the Young Men's Christian Association

the Urban League of Detroit

the Republican Party

St. John's Lutheran Church

NOTE: The words capitalized are those normally capitalized in any title. See CAPITALIZATION. *The* in most such titles is not capitalized unless the company, school, organization, or religious body has established *the* as part of its legal name: *The Johns Hopkins University, The Travelers Insurance Company.*

3. Capitalize the first letter of names of government bodies:

the United Nations

the Cabinet

the Bureau of the Budget

the California Legislature

the Ohio Board of Education

the Davis County Commission

the House *(for* House of Representatives)

Titles

the Department *(for* Department of Agriculture)

the Court *(for* the U.S. Supreme Court)

the police department

the county council

the board of education

NOTE: Except for international and national bodies, shortened forms of these government bodies or common terms are not capitalized.

4. Capitalize and italicize (or underline) the titles of books, magazines, newspapers, plays, movies, television series, and other separately published works:

Oliver Twist (book or movie)

Newsweek

the *New York Times*

West Side Story

Superman

NOVA

See UNDERLINING and ITALICS.

5. Capitalize and use quotation marks for chapters of books, articles in magazines, news stories or editorials, acts within a play, episodes of a television series, or other sections of something separately produced or published:

The last chapter was called "The Final Irony."

"The Colombian Connection" was the lead article in last week's *Time.*

We supported his editorial, "A Streamlined Election System."

We watched "The Fatal Circle" last night on *Gunsmoke.*

See QUOTATION MARKS, UNDERLINING, and ITALICS.

Tone

Tone reflects your attitude toward your subject and your readers. Your writing may strike your readers as personal or impersonal, friendly or distant. You may sound warm and engaging or cold and abrupt.

Your style reflects your disposition as a writer and the choices you make while writing: the words you choose, the way you structure your sentences, whether you feel comfortable using personal pronouns, whether you lecture to readers or invite them to join you in considering ideas.

See STYLE.

Style and *tone* are often confused. Some people use the terms interchangeably, but one is the cause and the other the effect:

- **Style** refers to those writers' choices that create the tone readers perceive. Style is the writer's "manner of speaking," the way the writer uses language to express ideas.
- **Tone** refers to the feeling or impression a document conveys to its readers. It is one of the products of the writer's style.

Tone, then, is the impression readers receive from your writing, the attitude conveyed in your treatment of the subject. We usually describe the tone of a piece of writing with these words:

abrasive	formal
aggressive	forthright
assertive	friendly
authoritative	impersonal
blunt	informal
bureaucratic	informative
casual	objective
cold	officious
condescending	personal
courteous	polite
demanding	sincere
discourteous	stiff
distant	subjective
earnest	threatening
engaging	warm

Desirable Business Tone

Most of the time, your business documents should be:

courteous	informative
forthright	personal
friendly	polite
helpful	sincere
informal	warm

The extent to which your documents are personal will depend on your relationship with the reader. But never fail to be courteous, polite, informative, sincere, and helpful—especially when you don't know the reader.

If you need to convey negative information, as in a poor performance appraisal or reprimand, or in a document threatening legal action, your document may need to be:

assertive	impersonal
formal	objective

However, you should never write documents that are:

abrasive	blunt
discourteous	cold
bureaucratic	officious
condescending	

Good business documents—no matter how tough or adversarial they are—should **never** be discourteous.

Below are the stylistic choices that will help you write business letters and memos that have an effective tone. Not coincidentally, these are the same rules that make writing clear, concise, and easy to read.

---

1. Use pronouns to establish a personal, human tone in letters and memos.

Probably no single language choice is as effective in making business documents sound human and personal as well-chosen pronouns. Of the pronouns possible, *you* is the most important. You should always be aware of your readers and address them directly:

this

During the discussion of your April bill, you mentioned that you had called your local service representative at least three times during the month. Do you remember the representative's name and the dates when you called?

not this

Concerning the April bill, the local service representative may have been called, but these calls cannot be verified unless the representative's name and the dates when the representative was called are provided to this office.

The ineffective version has no personal pronouns; consequently, the reader is ignored. Omitting personal pronouns makes the letter cold and informal. The passive verbs contribute to the impersonal tone and make the letter sound unfriendly at best. See ACTIVE/PASSIVE.

Next to *you*, the pronouns *I* and *we* are essential for effective letters and memos. Some people argue that the writer should not be mentioned in documents.

Tone

They argue that documents should not reflect personal opinions or the personality of the author. This argument fails to distinguish between personal opinions and personal responsibility for one's actions. Contrast these two examples:

this

Based on the data, I (*or* we) conclude that MOGO should plug and abandon the Gilbert Ray Well 3.

not this

Based on the data, it is concluded that MOGO should plug and abandon the Gilbert Ray Well 3.

The second version is mechanical, almost robotic. No person seems to have acted. The conclusion simply occurred, like something out of the twilight zone. The result is a faceless, anonymous tone, one calculated to avoid responsibility and perhaps to confuse readers or keep them deliberately in the dark.

---

2. Make your letters and memos sound very much like the language you would choose if you actually talked with the readers.

Read your document aloud. Would you be comfortable saying those words to someone in person? If you delivered the message to readers orally, would you express yourself this way?

The tone of a good business document is a natural one. It isn't full of slang or homey conversational expressions *(Well shucks, I reckon we ought to drill anyways)*, but it should sound natural, not forced or contrived.

If the document does not sound natural, if it is stiff and complex, if it is formal and faceless, you should rethink your tone.

A business document is not a transcription of your actual words, pauses, corrections, and other verbal lapses *(Well, uh, I think that, uh, if we, uh . . .)*. It should, however, be similar to the way you talk. Even contractions are useful in letters and memos but not in more formal reports.

See APOSTROPHES.

The words, phrases, and sentences you use should be simple and direct, even though you have edited and revised them:

this

I recommend that we immediately replace the roof on the Bradley building.

not this

It is recommended that the roof on the Bradley building be replaced forthwith.

---

this

Before leaving the room, turn out the lights.

not this

Prior to evacuating the premises, ensure that the illumination has been terminated.

The simplest remedy for overly stiff, bureaucratic writing is to write like a human being. Don't write like an official, faceless bureaucrat. Just be yourself. Imagine that you're talking to other people in person. Try to sound human, not mechanical.

Using personal pronouns will help considerably. Here are some other suggestions:

- **Keep your sentences short and direct.** Challenge any sentence that is longer than 30 words, and try to limit average sentence length to about 20 words. You can often break a long sentence into two shorter sentences. Ensure that each sentence, whatever its length, is as clear and direct as possible. See SENTENCES.
- **Avoid long, unnecessarily complex words and unnecessary technical terms.** See GOBBLEDYGOOK and JARGON. Never use words because you think those words are impressive. The writer who struggles to sound intelligent and educated (often by using a thesaurus) often winds up sounding silly:

this

We think your water pipes have corroded so much that only a trickle of water can flow through them.

not this

Our hypothesis is that your water supply system has undergone severe corrosion and reached the debilitating point where water normally available is unavailable in the quantity and at the pressure provided for in the original specifications for your domicile.

Leaving aside the laughable words (*debilitating* and *domicile*), the second version still suffers from terminal wordiness. Isn't *pipes* better than *water supply system*? And *corroded* so much better than *undergone severe corrosion*? What do the inexact references to quantity and pressure accomplish that the word *trickle* doesn't do more vividly? The idea being expressed does not require technical terms, especially if the primary reader is a homeowner, not an engineer.

Legal documents often suffer from the same kind of wordiness and unnecessary complexity:

this

According to the procedure outlined above, please sign all three copies of the conveyance and have your signature notarized. Then return the completed forms to this office by Friday, May 23.

not this

In accordance with the provisions of the aforementioned procedure, the attached conveyance should be executed by you in triplicate, with the signature duly witnessed and attested to by a Notary Public, and the executed set of conveyance forms should then be returned to this office on or before, and no later than, Friday, May 23.

---

3. Choose sentence structures that reflect a friendly, conversational tone.

- **Avoid passive sentences:**

this

Our review of your claim indicates that you should receive a refund of $72. This refund would apply to 1988 charges.

not this

Your claim has been reviewed, and it has been determined that $72 should be refunded to you for the period January to December 1988.

---

this

We analyzed the drilling reports for the source of the discrepancies. Over 90 percent of the discrepancies turned out to be simple errors in daily recording.

not this

The drilling reports have been analyzed to determine the source of the discrepancies. It is concluded that over 90 percent of the discrepancies were caused by simple errors in daily recording.

See Active/Passive.

- **Avoid false subjects:**

this

Unless we address these issues during this quarter, they will distort our financial report for the entire year.

not this

There are certain issues that we should address during this quarter that will distort our financial report for the entire year.

---

this

Under MOGO's policies, we will not acquire additional drilling pipe until after the beginning of the new fiscal year.

not this

It is likely that, given MOGO's policies, it will be impossible to acquire additional drilling pipe until after the beginning of the new fiscal year.

See False Subjects.

---

4. Include personal information and personal references.

Readers like to know that you have addressed their needs. So, if appropriate, include information from previous letters, memos, or discussions in your document. Or include information they have either requested or will need:

I recommend that you file a complaint with the Federal Trade Commission. Your review of the relevant correspondence with the company persuaded me that you have a case.

A mechanical, yet easy, way to make a letter or memo personal is to include the reader's name in the body of the letter:

So, Beth, if you have any more suggestions, please call me at ext. 3578.

or

If we proceed, Cal, you should ask Product Research for a copy of their assessment form. I think you'd find it helpful.

Note: As in the preceding example, an occasional contraction (*you'd*) makes the tone conversational and informal. See Apostrophes.

---

5. Choose your paper, typeface, and format to reflect a personal, friendly tone.

Even physical concerns can affect the tone of a letter or memo.

Choose quality paper (usually 20–pound rag paper) and a pleasing typeface. Now with word processors and computers, the typeface options are growing. Know your options. Your goal is to capture the personal, friendly quality of the content of your letter (consider Helvetica or Optima). Some typefaces are too rigid and stark (American Typewriter). Others are too informal (Script, which attempts to look like cursive writing).

Next, design your document so that it has a lean and open look, one conveying a personal, friendly tone. This usually means using generous margins, short paragraphs (on the average), headings, lists, and lots of white space. See Emphasis and Desktop Publishing.

Transitions

Transitions are words or phrases that connect ideas and show how they are related. Occurring between two sentences or paragraphs, a transition shows how the sentences or paragraphs are connected, thus making the writing smoother and more logical. A transition creates a point of reference for readers, allowing them to see how the writing is organized and where it is heading.

Following is a list of transitions and their functions.

A List of Transitions

- Addition

  additionally, again, also, besides, further, furthermore, in addition, likewise, moreover, next, too, what is more

- Comparison or Contrast

  by contrast, by the same token, conversely, however, in contrast, in spite of, instead, in such a manner, likewise, nevertheless, otherwise, on the contrary, on the one hand, on the other hand, rather, similarly, still, yet

- Concession

  anyway, at any rate, be that as it may, even so, however, in any case, in any event, nevertheless, of course, still

- Consequence

  accordingly, as a result, consequently, hence, otherwise, so, then, therefore, thus

- Diversion

  by the way, incidentally

- Generalization

  as a rule, as usual, for the most part, generally, in general, ordinarily, usually

- Illustration

  for example, for instance

- Place

  close, here, near, nearby, there

- Restatement

  in essence, in other words, namely, that is

- Summary

  after all, all in all, briefly, by and large, finally, in any case, in any event, in brief, in conclusion, in short, in summary, on balance, on the whole, ultimately

- Time and Sequence

  after a while, afterward, at first, at last, at the same time, currently, finally, first (second, third, etc.), first of all, for now, for the time being, immediately, instantly, in conclusion, in the first place, in the meantime, in time, in turn, later, meanwhile, next, presently, previously, simultaneously, soon, subsequently, then, to begin with

See CONJUNCTIONS, ORGANIZATION, and PARAGRAPHS.

Punctuation and Transitions

1. Use commas to separate transitions from the main body of a sentence:

> However, uncontrolled R&D efforts that do not design quality into the product, process, or service may be of dubious value.

> Consequently, development areas will include high-performance ceramic seals and ceramic-plate material characterization.

> The regulator poppet is, however, normally held open by the regulating spring.

Transitions interrupt and are generally not part of the main thought of the sentence; therefore, you should separate them from the rest of the sentence. When a transitional word occurs where two complete thoughts are joined, as in the following sentence, use a semicolon where the two complete thoughts join (usually in front of the transition) and a comma after the transition:

> The scope of this study will not permit a review of all technologies; however, we believe our experience in advanced ship design will allow us to maximize the study of those areas with greater operation potential.

See SEMICOLONS and COMMAS.

2. If the transition interrupts the flow of a sentence, place commas on both sides of the transitional word or phrase:

> A lightweight airframe, for instance, partially offsets poor propulsion technology.

> The sensor probe, on the other hand, contains thermistor sensing elements.

3. If a transitional word occurs at the beginning of a sentence and is essential to the meaning of the sentence, do not separate it with a comma:

> However warm air enters the cabin, the conditioned temperature will not rise above the nominal range.

NOTE: Such sentences can be confusing, so you should consider rephrasing the sentence:

> Regardless of how warm air enters the cabin, the conditioned temperature will not rise above the nominal range.

Underlining

Underlining in typed text replaces italics as a tool for highlighting certain unusual words and phrases. See Italics. You can also underline words, phrases, and sentences to emphasize them.

Underlining is becoming less common because most word processing programs provide italics. So in rules 1 to 4 below, italics would be preferred if it is available. In rule 5 underlining, not italics, would still be preferred. See Italics and Word Processing.

Editors differ as to whether to underline words and the spaces between them or only the words. Given the influence of word processing, which allows writers to highlight a block of text and then underline it, the pattern of continuous underlining is more common and accepted:

> The Making of a President
>
> *not*
>
> The Making of a President

---

1. Underline words used as words:

> The words affect and effect are often confused.
>
> The contract stipulated that monitoring must be continuous, but during negotiation they stated that periodic monitoring would suffice. Should the contract read continual or periodic rather than continuous?

Note: Single letters, words, and even phrases should be underlined to separate them from the ordinary words within a sentence:

> The phrase come hell or high water has a long and interesting history.

Some editors prefer to use quotation marks for words and phrases used unusually within a sentence. However, quotation marks clutter up a sentence if several words are being talked about:

> The forms "am," "is," "are," "was," and "were" don't even resemble "be," which is the principal form of the verb.

---

2. Underline foreign words and phrases that have not been absorbed into English:

> After a coup d'oeil, the detective was ready to question the suspect. (Coup d'oeil means "a quick survey.")

Note: Contrast *coup d'oeil*, which is clearly not part of English, with *coup d'état*, which is now so familiar that no underlining is necessary. Many modern dictionaries fail to specify whether a word should be considered foreign or not, so you may have to use your own judgment.

---

3. Underline the titles of separate publications and productions:

> I bought a copy of The Wall Street Journal.
>
> Have you read the novel All Quiet on the Western Front?
>
> The Sunshine Patriot is a pamphlet being circulated by the Republican Party.
>
> We attended a preview of The Story of the Bell System.
>
> We have tickets for the opening night of Aida.

Note: Underline separately published or produced items, but use quotation marks for book chapters, articles in magazines, and sections of the separate works:

> The latest issue of the Oil and Gas Journal contained an article entitled "Shearing Problems with Sucker Rods."
>
> The Salt Lake Tribune had an editorial entitled "A Bold Proposal."

See Quotation Marks and Titles.

---

4. Underline the names of aircraft, vessels, and spacecraft:

> U.S.S. Constitution
>
> H.M.S. Bounty
>
> Gemini 4

---

5. Underline words and phrases for emphasis:

> Please send two copies to us by Friday, October 13, at the latest.
>
> Unscrew the fitting by turning it clockwise, not counterclockwise.

Note: Use underlining for emphasis sparingly. Underlined text is difficult to read, and the effect diminishes quickly if you overuse it. See Emphasis.

Units of Measurement

Units of measurement include either English units (also called the U.S. customary system) or metric units. Many U.S. firms still favor English units, but metric units, especially the SI system, are now widely used by scientists and engineers. See METRICS.

1. Use the following common English units to measure length and area:

NOTE: The abbreviations for these units of measurement usually appear only in tables, charts, graphs, and other visuals. See ABBREVIATIONS.

LENGTH

English Unit	U.S. Equivalents	Metric Equivalents
inch	0.083 foot	2.54 centimeters
foot	⅓ yard, 12 inches	30.48 centimeters
yard	3 feet, 36 inches	0.914 meter
rod	5½ yards, 16½ feet	5.029 meters
mile (statute, land)	1,760 yards, 5,280 feet	1.609 kilometers
mile (nautical, international)	1.151 statute miles	1.852 kilometers

AREA

English Unit	U.S. Equivalents	Metric Equivalents
square inch	0.007 square foot	6.452 square centimeters
square foot	144 square inches	929.030 square centimeters
square yard	1,296 square inches, 9 square feet	0.836 square meter
acre	43,560 square feet, 4,840 square yards	4047 square meters
square mile	640 acres	2.590 square kilometers

2. Use the following common English units for volume or capacity and weight:

VOLUME OR CAPACITY

English Unit	U.S. Equivalents	Metric Equivalents
cubic inch	0.00058 cubic foot	16.387 cubic centimeters
cubic foot	1,728 cubic inches	0.028 cubic meter
cubic yard	27 cubic feet	0.765 cubic meter
English Liquid Measure	**U.S. Equivalents**	**Metric Equivalents**
fluid ounce	8 fluid drams, 1,804 cubic inches	29.573 milliliters
pint	16 fluid ounces, 28.875 cubic inches	0.473 liter
quart	2 pints, 57.75 cubic inches	0.946 liter
gallon	4 quarts, 231 cubic inches	3.785 liters
barrel	varies from 31 to 42 gallons established by law or usage	
English Dry Measure	**U.S. Equivalents**	**Metric Equivalents**
pint	½ quart, 33.6 cubic inches	0.551 liter
quart	2 pints, 67.2 cubic inches	1.101 liters
peck	8 quarts, 537.605 cubic inches	8.810 liters
bushel	4 pecks, 2,150.420 cubic inches	35.239 liters

Units of Measurement

English Avoirdupois Unit	WEIGHT U.S. Equivalents	Metric Equivalents
grain	0.036 dram, 0.002285 ounce	64.798 milligrams
dram	27.344 grains, 0.0625 ounce	1.772 grams
ounce	16 drams, 437.5 grains	28.350 grams
pound	16 ounces, 7,000 grains	453.592 grams
ton (short)	2,000 pounds	0.907 metric ton (1,000 kilograms)
ton (long)	1.12 short tons, 2,240 pounds	1.016 metric tons
Apothecary Weight Unit	**U.S. Equivalents**	**Metric Equivalents**
scruple	20 grains	1.295 grams
dram	60 grains	3.888 grams
ounce	480 grains, 1.097 avoirdupois ounces	31.103 grams
pound	5,760 grains, 0.823 avoirdupois pound	373.242 grams

NOTE: Although the United States and the British Commonwealth both use the same names for units and their abbreviations, the two systems do differ, so be cautious in interpreting publications using these units. Here, for example, are the equivalents between the British Imperial units and the U.S. English or customary units:

British Imperial Liquid and Dry Measure	U.S. English Equivalents	Metric Equivalents
fluid ounce	0.961 U.S. fluid ounce, 1.734 cubic inches	28.413 milliliters
pint	1.032 U.S. dry pints, 1.201 U.S. liquid pints, 34.678 cubic inches	568.245 milliliters
quart	1.032 U.S. dry quarts, 1.201 U.S. liquid quarts, 69.354 cubic inches	1.136 liters
gallon	1.201 U.S. gallons, 277.420 cubic inches	4.546 liters
peck	554.84 cubic inches	0.009 cubic meter
bushels	1.032 U.S. bushels, 2,219.36 cubic inches	0.036 cubic meter

Verbs

Verbs are the key action words in most sentences. They tell what the subject has done, is doing, or will be doing, and they indicate the subject's relationship to the object or complement. Because verbs also signal time through their different tenses (forms), they are potentially the most important words in a sentence. For instance, varying only the verb in a sentence produces major shifts in the meaning:

She shows us her report.
She showed us her report.
She will show us her report.

She has shown us her report.
She had shown us her report.
She will have shown us her report.

She is showing us her report.
She was showing us her report.
She will be showing us her report.

These nine sentences only begin to illustrate all the possible verb forms. If we include more complex verb phrases, the possibilities multiply:

She is going to be showing us her report.

She must have been showing us her report.

Principal Verb Forms

Verbs commonly have several standard forms (called principal parts) from which all the other verb forms are built:

base form	call eat cut
–s form (3rd person singular present—he, she, it)	calls eats cuts
past form	called ate cut
–ed participle (past participle)	called eaten cut
–ing participle (present participle)	calling eating cutting

Regular verbs, like *call*, routinely require only an *–s*, *–ed*, or *–ing* to change the base form. If a dictionary does not supply any forms except the base form, the verb is regular, like *call.*

Irregular verbs, like *eat* and *cut*, are unpredictable, so writers have to know the different forms, not just follow the regular pattern. Dictionaries include these irregular forms in their entries for these verbs.

NOTE: Unfortunately, not all verbs are clearly regular or irregular. The following verbs, for example, have two different forms of the past participle, one regular, the other irregular:

mow, mowed, mown (*or* mowed)
show, showed, showed (*or* shown)
swell, swelled, swollen (*or* swelled)

---

1. Check a recent dictionary to determine the correct forms for any verb you are unsure of.

Here, for instance, are the main forms for some of the common irregular verbs:

buy, bought, bought
cost, cost, cost
drink, drank, drunk
freeze, froze, frozen
keep, kept, kept
lead, led, led
lie, lay, lain
light, lighted/lit, lighted/lit
rise, rose, risen
sell, sold, sold
sit, sat, sat
speak, spoke, spoken
spoil, spoilt/spoiled, spoilt/spoiled
take, took, taken
tear, tore, torn
think, thought, thought
wet, wet/wetted, wet/wetted
write, wrote, written

NOTE: Where two forms exist, the regular forms (with *–ed*) are becoming more common. Over time, many irregular verbs have changed and are changing into regular verbs.

Verb Tenses

Verbs have the following basic tenses or times:

Basic Verb Tenses

Present:	They study.
Past:	They studied.
Future:	They will study.
Present Perfect:	They have studied.
Past Perfect:	They had studied.
Future Perfect:	They will have studied.

Then a parallel set of progressive forms exists, which indicates that the action is continuing:

Progressive Verb Tenses

Present:	They are studying.
Past:	They were studying.
Future:	They will be studying.
Present Perfect:	They have been studying.
Past Perfect:	They had been studying.
Future Perfect:	They will have been studying.

Finally, a parallel set of passive verb tenses also exists:

Passive Verb Tenses

Present:	The report is studied.
Past:	The report was studied.
Future:	The report will be studied.
Present Perfect:	The report has been studied.
Past Perfect:	The report had been studied.
Future Perfect:	The report will have been studied.

NOTE: As in the above sentences, passive verb sentences highlight the object or thing receiving the action, not the person or thing performing the action. The passive sentences above do not identify the person who is, was, or will be studying the report. In most cases, you should prefer the active voice and avoid the passive. See ACTIVE/PASSIVE.

2. Vary your verb tenses to reflect the often complex data in your writing.

This rule contradicts what you may have learned in high school: "Don't mix your tenses." Actually, you can and should vary your tenses to reflect the often complicated time relationships of your subject:

> Yesterday, we analyzed *(past)* the samples for any traces of zinc ore. We found *(past)* none. Today, however, we were reexamining *(past progressive)* the sample when we found *(past)* two promising pieces of rock. They have *(present)* veins like zinc ore, although their color is *(present)* not quite right. Our report will therefore show *(future)* the potential presence of zinc.

Most writers choose their tenses unconsciously, but several basic conventions exist for selecting tenses in technical writing:

—Record in the past tense experiments and tests performed in the past:

> The second run produced flawed data because the heating unit failed. We failed to detect the failure until the run was almost over.

—Use the present tense for scientific facts and truths:

> Water freezes at 32°F, unless a chemical in the water changes its freezing point.
>
> Newton discovered that every action has an equal and opposite reaction.

—Use the present tense to discuss data within a published report:

> The slope of the temperature curve decreases sharply at 20 minutes. The figures in table 3-14 document this decrease.

—Shift from present to past tense as necessary to refer to research studies and prior papers. When you are discussing an author and his or her research, use the past tense:

> Jones (1976) studied a limited dose of the drug. He concluded that no harmful side effects occurred.

—When you are discussing different current theories, use the present tense:

> Jones (1976) argues that limited doses of the drug produce no harmful side effects. His data, however, is flawed because he failed to distinguish between the natural and synthetic versions of the drug.

Auxiliary Verbs

Auxiliary verbs are the most common verbs in English: *is, are, was, were, be, been, can, could, do, did, has, have, had, may, might, shall, should, will, would, must, ought to*, and *used to*.

Auxiliaries are crucial to many of the tenses presented above, but auxiliaries also can function by themselves as main sentence verbs:

> The tests are complete.
> He did the primary drawings.
> They have no budget.

See STRONG VERBS.

Verbs and Agreement

The verb should agree in number with its subject. So a plural subject requires a plural verb, and a singular subject requires a singular verb:

> The geologist has completed the tests. *(singular)*
> The geologists have completed the tests. *(plural)*
>
> A test was completed last week. *(singular)*
> Several tests were completed last week. *(plural)*
>
> The report analyzes the impact. *(singular)*
> The reports analyze the impact. *(plural)*

See AGREEMENT.

Verbs

3. Ensure that your verbs agree with your subjects.

The only circumstance in which verbs change their forms to adjust to different numbers is in the third person forms of the present tense:

She works every day. *(singular)*
They work every day. *(plural)*

She is the candidate. *(singular)*
They are the candidates. *(plural)*

He has the answer. *(singular)*
They have the answer. *(plural)*

It is broken. *(singular)*
They are broken. *(plural)*

Note 1: Third person singular verbs have an *–s* ending, as in *works* above. The third person plural verbs have no *–s*, as in *work.* So the rule for verbs is the opposite of nouns: the forms with *–s* endings are the singular forms.

Note 2: The verb *be* is exceptional because it changes in the present tense to agree with different pronouns:

I am studying.
You are studying. *(singular)*
He, she, it is studying.

We are studying.
You are studying. *(plural)*
They are studying.

Subjunctive Verbs

Subjunctive verbs are special verb forms that signal recommendations or conditions contrary to fact. Centuries ago, subjunctives were very common verb forms, but today they are limited to the instances covered in the following two rules.

4. Use a subjunctive verb in *if* clauses to state a situation that is untrue, impossible, or highly unlikely:

If I were (*not* was) the candidate, I would not agree to a debate.

If it were (*not* was) raining, we couldn't conduct the experiment.

If I were (*not* was) you, I would change banks.

Note 1: The above sentences require *were* rather than normal *was*, which would appear to agree with the subjects. This use amounts to a historical survival, so it doesn't fit our modern expectations. (Actually, other verbs in *if* clauses are subjunctive, but only the *were*/ *was* pattern looks or sounds exceptional.)

Note 2: Subjunctive verbs are especially useful when a writer has to make recommendations. The *if* clause presents the hypothetical condition and then the main clause indicates what would, could, or might happen:

If rainfall were 40 inches a year or more, most dirt roads would be impassable.

If the Accounting Department were reorganized, overall efficiency could increase by perhaps 50 percent.

See Would in Word Problems.

Note 3: If the *if* clause states something that is possible or likely, then do not use a subjunctive:

If he leaves this job, he'll get $500 in severance pay.

If it was an error, and I suspect it was, then we'll have to pay you damages.

5. Use subjunctive verbs in sentences making strong recommendations or demands, or indicating necessity:

I recommend that the case be settled by Tuesday.

He demands that the money be refunded.

The court has resolved that the witness be found in contempt of court.

It is essential that he leave by noon.

They urge that she return the money.

They resolved that Dan write the termination letter.

Note 1: As the first three sentences show, if the verb in the *that* clause would normally be *am, is,* or *are*, then its subjunctive form is *be.*

Note 2: As the last three sentences show, if the verb in the *that* clause is normally a third person singular verb, then its subjunctive form does not take the usual *–s* ending.

Visual Aids

Visual aids are one of the writer's best devices for emphasizing information. Because they are visual rather than verbal (as writing is), visual aids are much more emphatic than the written text around them.

Sometimes overhead transparencies, slides, and other visuals are called visual aids. For the following discussion, however, **the term *visual aids* refers only to graphics used within documents, not to graphics prepared for oral presentations.**

Visual aids stimulate the reader's interest in the topic, they focus the reader's attention, and they aid the reader's understanding of the information being presented.

Visual aids can emphasize important data and ideas in ways that text cannot. Visuals can be dramatic, revealing, stimulating, even surprising. To achieve these same effects, text would have to be written far better than most writers are capable of writing.

Visual aids show data in a concise and effective manner (in tables); they show how data compare or contrast (in charts); they show changing data relationships (in graphs); and they show configurations that would be difficult, if not impossible, to describe (in illustrations). Thus visuals enhance the reader's ability to understand, interpret, and remember the data visualized. See CHARTS, GRAPHS, ILLUSTRATIONS, and TABLES.

Because visuals are so powerful, writers sometimes overuse them. A text with inadequate visuals suffers, but so does a text with too many visuals. In an ideal document, the text and the visuals are balanced. They complement one another. The complete story is not told in either form; instead, the two forms work together in harmony to convey and emphasize the high points of the message being delivered.

Properly balancing visuals and the accompanying text is not difficult if you obey a few general principles.

---

1. Use visuals to emphasize your important ideas and data, and place the visuals for maximum impact.

Visuals should capture the key recommendation, the surprising trend, the unexpected financial problem, the most convincing data. Use visuals for the **highlights** of your message.

If your purpose is to recommend a new high-volume pump, then consider contrastive bar graphs showing volumes for the old and the new pump. If your purpose is to revise prior estimates of the effects of acid rain on New England lakes, design your visuals with clear before and after contrasts (perhaps a bar chart, a pie chart, or even contrastive photographs). You control your readers' minds by using appropriate visuals to control their eyes.

Beware, however, of using visuals for mere impact or decoration. By their very nature, visuals are highly emphatic, so reserve their use for important information that reinforces your message. If you waste visuals on unimportant or unnecessary information, you will be wasting a valuable opportunity, and you might distract your readers.

Place visuals as strategically and for as much impact as possible. Ideally, readers should encounter the visuals just after the ideas being visualized have been introduced and stated concisely but before lengthy explanation or elaboration.

The right visual should appear at the right moment. Do not let visuals come too early (before the reader can properly appreciate or comprehend them), and do not let visuals come too late (after the reader has already spent time reading and absorbing the information being visualized).

If possible, try to place visuals so that the visuals and the text concerning them are on the same page.

---

2. Create your visuals before you write the text.

Visuals should never be an afterthought. They are more emphatic than text and should therefore receive greater attention early in the writing process.

Create your visuals first; write your text last.

Visual Aids

As you generate ideas and begin to focus your message, list the important ideas that you will be conveying to your readers. Then ask yourself whether and how you could visualize those ideas. Do some rough sketches. For longer documents, create a mock-up (style sheet) for the document, which is simply a collection of projected pages, with potential visuals and accompanying text sketched in. See WORD PROCESSING and DESKTOP PUBLISHING.

Later, as you write the draft, return to your notes or the mock-up to check up on how and where the reader will be encountering your visuals.

3. Eliminate unnecessary visuals.

- If the visual duplicates information already in the text and if the visual will not significantly enhance the reader's comprehension, eliminate it.
- If the visual cannot present information more effectively than text, eliminate it.
- If the visual presents unnecessary, irrelevant, or unimportant information, eliminate it.
- If the visual was created for another document and does not exactly fit the information and circumstances of your document, eliminate it.
- If you are submitting a document to a journal or a publisher, eliminate all visuals that do not contribute substantially to your message, especially those visuals involving color, which is expensive to reproduce.

4. Select visuals that are appropriate for your readers.

The visuals you select should depend in part on the orientation and skill of your readers. For instance, you should not use logarithmic graphs with nontechnical readers (who will probably not understand them); conversely, you should not use simple charts to present complex technical data to highly technical readers.

Documents become difficult to write, however, when they need to be read by many readers, all of whom have different technical backgrounds and different uses for the information.

Remember that your visuals (and your text) are indirectly controlled by the least technical of your projected readers. Keep these readers in mind as you generate your visuals and your text. You might, of course, sometimes make a particular visual or a part of your text a little too difficult for such readers, but if you do this, you'll need to build in nontechnical explanations somewhere else in the text.

Some of the best writers and editors deliberately vary the readability of their text and visuals; they are assuming that different readers will read and interpret different sections of a document. Readers with much technical knowledge might survey only the key table or the most technical graph. Readers with less technical knowledge might stop after reading the introduction and the summary (or abstract).

So, writers need to analyze carefully their prospective readers—**all** of their readers. Once writers know just who their readers are and what their technical backgrounds are, they can begin to adapt their document to these readers.

5. Select visuals that are appropriate for your topic.

Visual aids come in many forms: charts, graphs, illustrations, maps, photographs, and tables. These forms—and all of the variations within them—give you many alternatives for transforming ideas and data into visual representations. Use table 1 to help you determine which visual aids to use in a given document.

Charts depict relationships between two or more variables, possibly at distinct points in time (bar charts). Charts can also display organizational relationships (organization charts), identify the relationship of parts to a whole (pie charts), and illustrate the flow and relationship of steps in a process (flow charts). See CHARTS.

Graphs depict the relationship of two or more variables and show how those variables change. Graphs allow for comparisons and show trends. See GRAPHS.

Visual Aids

Type of Visual	Document Purposes										
	Costs	Causes Effects	Trends	Organizational Relationships	Policies Procedures	Decisions Alternatives	Work Flow	Chronology	Design Parts Apparatus	Comparison Contrast	Advantages Disdadvantages
Tables	X	X	X	X	X	X		X		X	X
Line Graphs	X		X					X		X	
Bar Charts	X		X			X		X		X	X
Pie Charts	X		X			X				X	X
Schematic Diagrams									X		
Flow Charts		X		X			X	X			
Maps/Site Plans			X			X					
Photographs		X							X	X	X
Tree Diagrams				X	X	X	X				
Illustrations									X		
Blueprints									X		
Combination		X	X	X	X	X	X	X	X	X	X

Table 1. Visual Aids for Different Documents. *An X appears in a square to show when a specific type of visual aid would likely implement a particular document's purpose.*

Illustrations and **diagrams** show conceptual objects or assemblies and provide perspectives on existing objects or assemblies that photographs cannot capture. Illustrations can show exploded views that focus attention on smaller parts of a larger object or assembly. See Illustrations.

Maps show topographical relationships and indicate scale and distance. See Maps.

Photographs convey realism. They allow you to show readers exactly what something looks like. With photographs comes authenticity. See Photographs.

Tables display data in rows and columns. They allow for quick comparisons of precise data. See Tables.

The visual aid you select depends on your readers, but it also depends on what you are trying to achieve with the visual. Table 1 shows how various visual aids can be used to accomplish a writer's purposes.

6. Keep your visuals focused and keep them simple and uncluttered.

When you are designing and constructing a visual aid, ask yourself, What is the point? What is the most important idea that I am trying to convey visually? What is my central concept?

Focus on your key purpose or concept and then build your visuals around it.

Do not ask the visual to do two or more things. Keep it simple. Ineffective visuals typically fail because writers have not designed them with a clear concept in mind (which makes the visuals unfocused) or because writers have tried to make the visuals do too much (which makes them cluttered or too complex). Like a good paragraph, a good visual focuses on one idea—and conveys it sharply and purposefully.

Keep visuals uncluttered by eliminating all extraneous information. Your preliminary coordinate graph or the complete table of readings contains a lot of valuable information, but neither of these is likely to be effective unless you pare it down to its essentials.

A good visual contains nothing that is not directly related to its central concept.

Visual Aids

7. Introduce visuals in the text before the visuals appear.

Always introduce visuals in the text. A visual that suddenly appears without introduction or explanation generally confuses readers.

The introduction should come **before** the visual. Furthermore, the introduction should be informative and specific:

informative and specific

As figure 3 shows, produced water from the 2nd Langley is much more acidic than produced water from the 1st Langley.

This project is estimated to cost $356,200. The cost breakdown in table 15 shows that hardware costs account for nearly 65 percent of total costs, while labor costs constitute only 12 percent of the total.

not informative

See figure 3.

The total cost of this project is estimated to be $356,200. Table 15 provides a cost breakdown.

As these examples illustrate, a good introduction indicates not only what the visual is about but also, at least in part, what the reader should get from it.

A good introduction tells the reader how to interpret the visual aid. See CAPTIONS.

EXCEPTION: Sometimes a visual must appear in the text before you can introduce it. This occurs, for instance, when a small table or chart appears at the top of a new page and is followed by a column of text. Rather than break up the text, you might keep the table or chart at the top of the page. The introduction would then have to appear after the visual. See rule 12 below.

8. Number the visuals in the order of their appearance and use clear, active captions.

Figures include all visuals that are not tables, including graphs, charts, diagrams, illustrations, photographs, and maps. Traditionally, tables and figures are numbered separately. Therefore, table 5 could appear in a document after figure 20. However, a current trend is to name all visuals *figures*, regardless of their type, and to number them consecutively.

In a short document or a document with few visuals, number the visuals sequentially through the entire text. In a lengthy document with chapters or numbered sections, give the visuals hyphenated numbers, such as *figure 3-2*. The first number indicates the chapter or section, and the second number indicates the number of the visual within that chapter or section.

In longer documents, especially formal reports and publications (pamphlets, books, research studies, etc.), include in the table of contents a list of figures and, if appropriate, a list of tables.

A list of figures (and a list of tables) should provide, in sequence, each figure's number, caption (title), and page number. If the document has a large number of specialized figures, then create a separate list of each special type. For instance, a lengthy report containing a number of maps might include a list of maps. Another report, in which photographs play an important role, might include a separate list of photographs. If the document does not warrant such special listings, however, don't create them.

Lists of tables and figures appear immediately after the table of contents (usually on separate pages) and should themselves be listed in the table of contents. If you create both a list of tables and a list of figures, either list may appear first. See TABLES OF CONTENTS.

Include a figure/table number reference, a title, and an action caption for each visual. The action captions for your visuals should be informative and specific. Using only indicative titles (those that merely indicate what the visual is about) is not very helpful:

Figure 17. Pronghorn Population Trends in Montana

Table 2. Particulates in Sonoma Valley, California

Action captions are informative. They state not only what the visuals are about but also what readers should learn from them:

Figure 17. Pronghorn Population Trends in Montana. *The pronghorn antelope population in Montana has declined steadily since 1971.*

Table 2. Particulates in Sonoma Valley, California. *From May to October 1984, particulates in Sonoma Valley, California, have remained well below EPA emission standards.*

Action captions usually are one sentence. They should be informative without becoming too lengthy. In the list of tables or figures, normally include only the figure reference and the title. In proposals, whose main purpose is to sell a product or service, action captions usually are listed as well. See CAPTIONS for further examples.

9. Design visuals that are easy to read.

Design the visual so that the central concept is immediately apparent. Leave out extraneous elements that tend to draw attention away from the central concept. If your readers cannot tell you what the point is within 5 to 10 seconds, the visual is not effective.

Choose a simple typeface for the lettering on visuals, and use capitals and lowercase letters for all headings and labels. (Lettering all in capitals is hard to read, especially if it extends beyond two or three words.) Ensure also that the lettering is large enough so that if the visual is reduced, the lettering will still be readable.

Make the lines and lettering that indicate scales, axes, notes, and explanations lighter than the lines and lettering indicating data points, curves, areas, or bars. Ensure that the visual's features do not hide or detract from the central concept.

10. Use emphatic devices to emphasize important ideas in visuals.

Emphatic devices include underlining, italics, boldface type, larger type sizes, shading, line patterns, and color. Use these devices to highlight important words and data in visuals. Furthermore, use the same emphatic device each time to emphasize the same kind of word or data. Establish a typographical system (document style sheet) and be consistent throughout all of your visuals. See WORD PROCESSING and DESKTOP PUBLISHING.

Color is especially useful in helping readers understand the visuals, locate information, and distinguish between different phases, parts, or configurations. Color can also highlight special features, such as cautions (usually yellow) and warnings (usually red). Using color to highlight a line, row, column, slice, area, circle, or data point can focus the reader's attention on that item. See EMPHASIS.

As you select colors, try to establish a color scheme that makes sense: green for things that are prospering, yellow for things in transition, red for things that are failing. Or blues to indicate coolness, reds to indicate warmth. Use contrasting colors to show contrasting concepts or major changes; use variations of one color to show minor variations. Use the brightest colors to emphasize the most important ideas, the dullest colors to subdue the less important ideas. Finally, beware of using too much color at once and making the visual look kaleidoscopic.

11. Orient visuals horizontally on the page.

Text has a horizontal orientation, which means that it is comprehensible from left to right across the page (i.e., horizontally). If possible, visuals should be oriented the same way. Readers should be able to "read" visuals without turning the page sideways.

The standard page layouts for visuals are full-page, half-page, and quarter-page formats (see the models on the following pages).

Larger visuals (such as maps) may be printed on larger paper, folded, and inserted into a flap at the end of the document or bound into the document. Visuals that are bound into the document and that fold out for readers to view are called foldouts. Typically, foldout pages are 11 inches high and 17 inches wide (for a one-fold) or 25.5 inches wide (for a two-fold). (The widths might need to be adjusted to make room for the binding.)

Full- and quarter-page visuals are higher than they are wide. Half-page visuals and foldouts are wider than they are high. Separate visuals (such as those inserted into a flap) may have any dimensions.

As you design visuals, you must consider whether the information you wish to present in the visual is consistent with the size and the dimensions of the visual format that is most appropriate for the information.

Page Layout Models

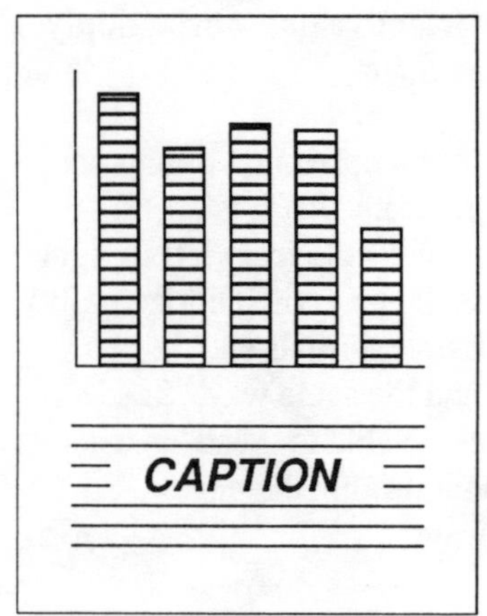

Model 1

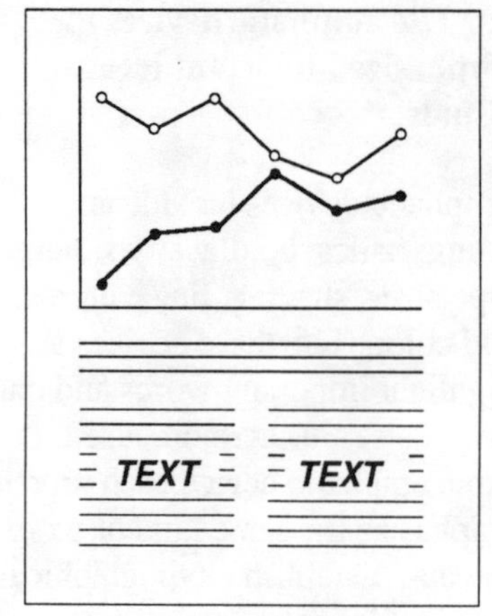

Model 2

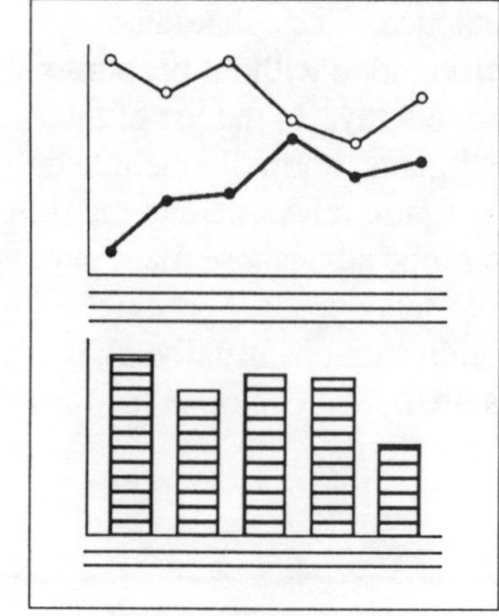

Model 3

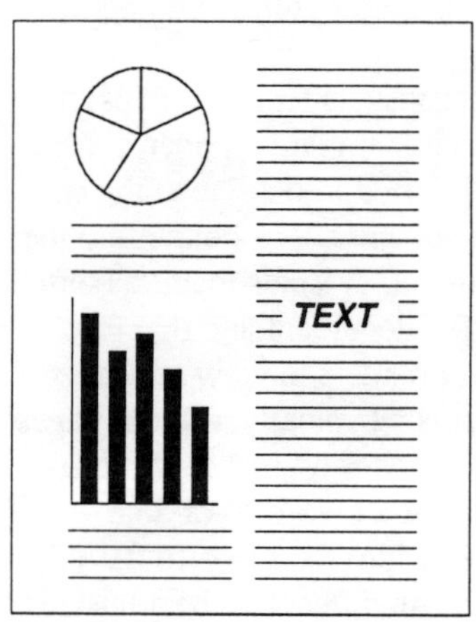

Model 4 Left-Facing

Model 5 Right-Facing

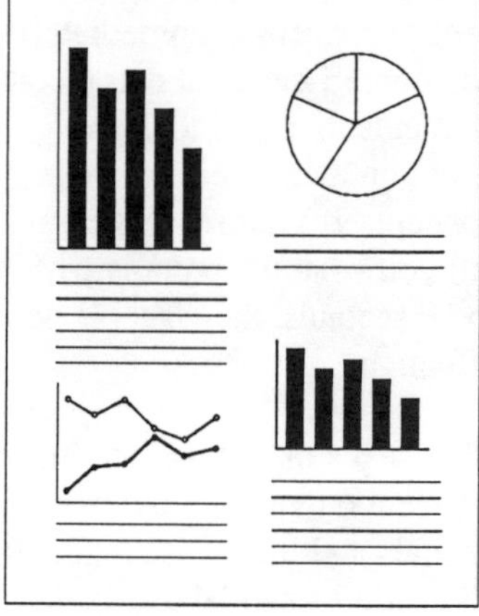

Model 6

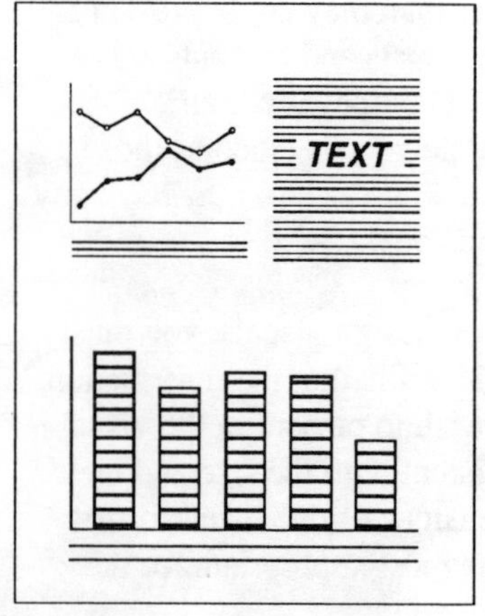

Model 7 Left-Facing

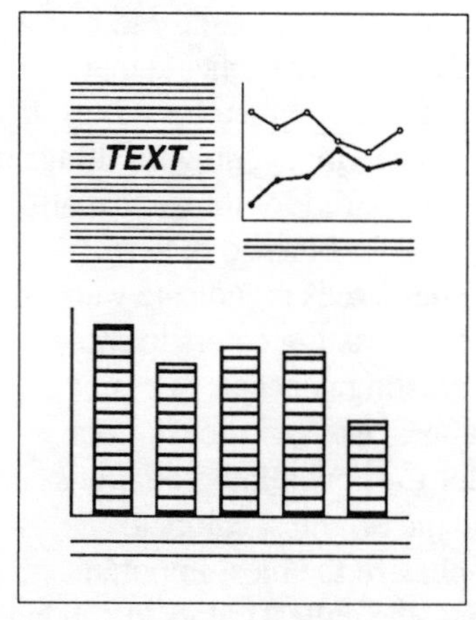

Model 8 Right-Facing

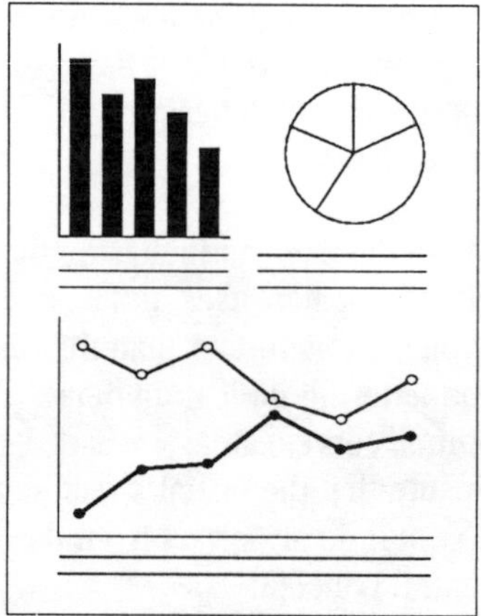

Model 9

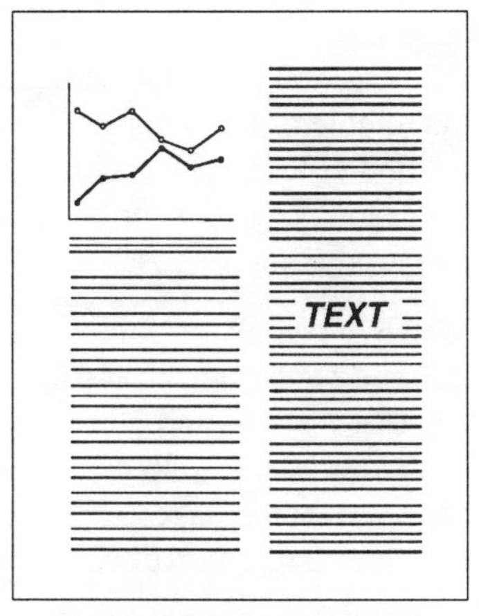

Model 10 Left-Facing

Model 11 Right-Facing

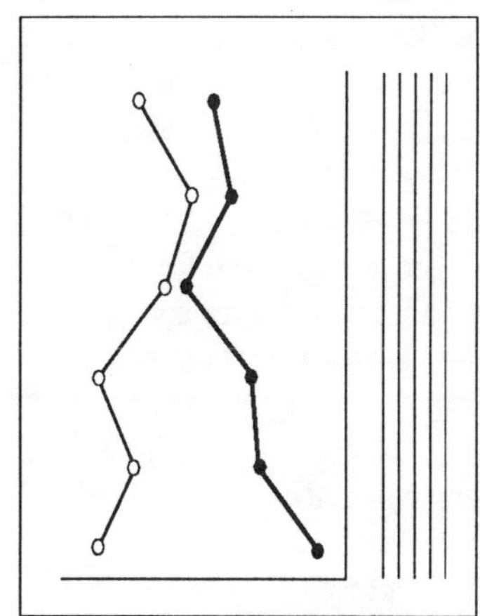

Model 12

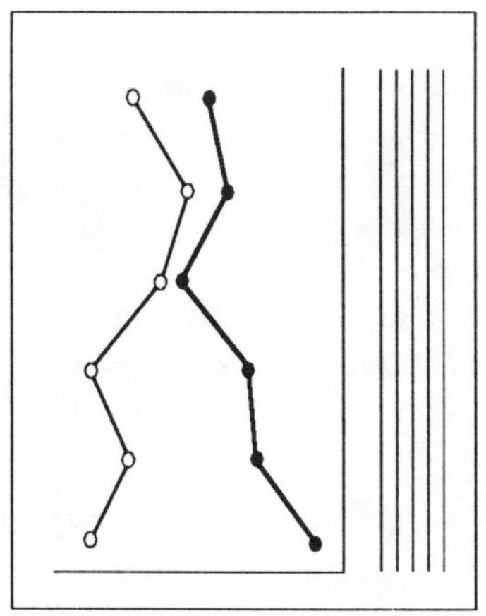

Model 13

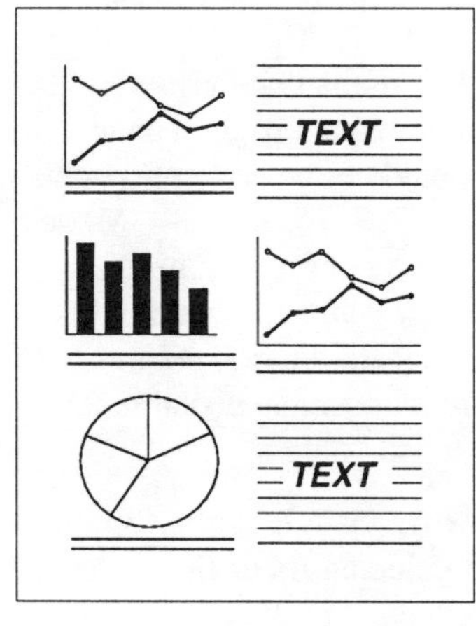

Model 14 Left-Facing

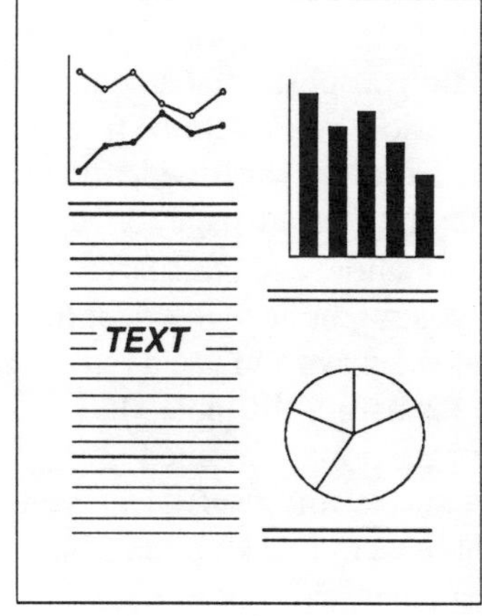

Model 15 Right-Facing

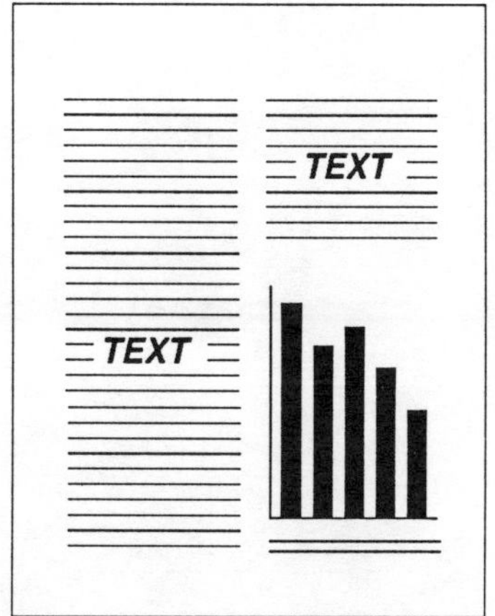

Model 16

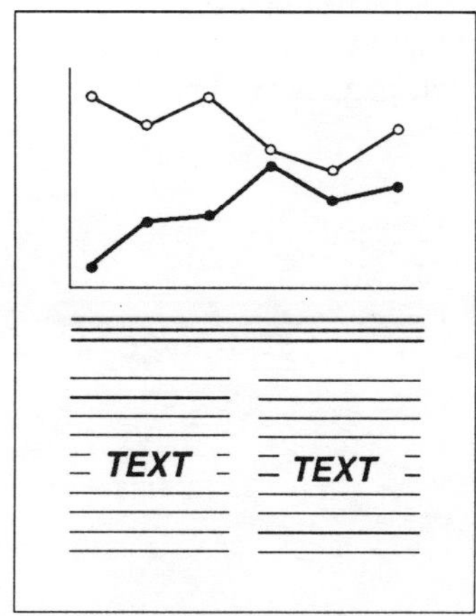

Model 17

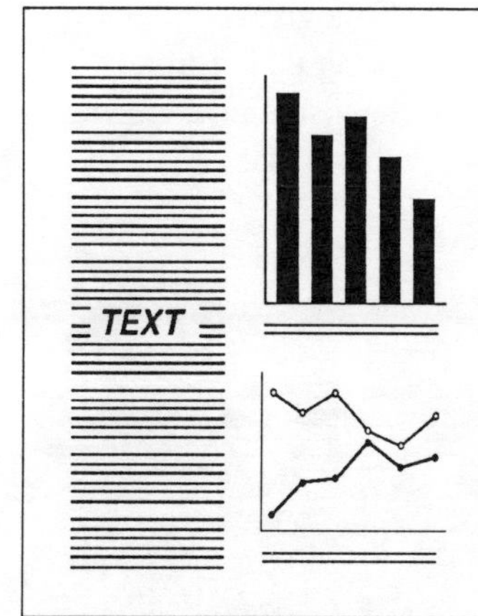

Model 18 Right-Facing

For instance, if you are designing a table and have twice as many columns as rows, you must use a format that allows for more width than height. Typically, you would select a half-page format. However, a half-page format might occupy too much space on a page. If the information is not critical, consider reorienting the table by switching the columns and the rows, thereby creating a table that is higher than it is wide, which might allow you to use a quarter-page visual.

On the other hand, if your tabular information requires more columns than rows, and if you are tabulating a substantial amount of information, you might be forced to use a format that is wider than it is high. If a half-page format does not allow enough space, then you might have to orient the visual sideways and use a full-page format for the table. If a full-page format (oriented sideways) is still insufficient, you might have to break up the table into smaller tables or use a foldout.

If you can, avoid orienting visuals sideways. If a visual will not fit within an acceptable format, redesign the visual or divide it into workable parts.

12. In double-sided text, avoid unnecessary breaks in the text, and, if possible, balance your pages so that the left pages complement the facing right pages.

The model page layouts shown in this section illustrate possible placements of visuals on a page. These layouts reflect the following guidelines:

—**Avoid unnecessary breaks in the text.** This guideline is easy to follow if only one visual appears on a page (models 2, 10, 11, 16, and 17). If more than one visual appears on a page, then text should not be broken (models 4, 5, 7, 8, 15, and 18). Model 14 is an exception; in it, the writer wants to separate the visuals in the first column from the single visual in the second column.

—**Move visuals to the top and outside edges of the page** (the left side of left pages and the right side of right pages). Models 2, 4, 5, 7, 8, 10, 11, 15, and 18 illustrate this guideline. Model 16, used as a left page, would be an exception; but the writer might choose this option if the reference to the visual came in the middle of the second column of text. The visual needs to appear as soon after its introduction as possible.

—**Balance visuals on facing left and right pages.** Models 4 and 5, 7 and 8, and 10 and 11 are the best examples of balanced facing pages. Balanced pages mirror each other, so if a left page opens with a visual in the upper left corner, the facing right page will have a visual in the upper right corner. Such balanced pages are difficult to achieve, especially given the normal variations in text as well as visuals of different sizes and types. Models 14 and 15, for instance, partially balance each other even though model 14 has an additional visual on it.

NOTE: These guidelines do not apply to single-sided pages. On single-sided pages, you should place visuals as close as possible to their introductions. See rule 7 above.

Word Problems

Words are symbols representing persons, places, things, actions, qualities, characteristics, states of being, and abstract ideas. Words are the substance of language.

To use words well, you must know what the words mean (both their **denotations** and **connotations**); you must select words that convey the right impression to your readers; you must use specific, concrete words whenever possible; and you must use the correct words for the context.

Denotations and Connotations

The denotation of a word is what that word signifies or stands for, what it explicitly represents. The connotation of a word is something suggested by the word, something implied.

The word *pig*, for instance, **denotes** an animal of certain characteristics, specifically, a swine. *Pig* also denotes an earthenware crock, a device used to clean out pipes (a *piggot*), and an oblong mass of metal (as in *pig iron*). *Pig* even came in the 1960s to denote a person in authority, particularly a police officer, but this sense has now become less common. As with the word *pig*, many words have multiple, often changing, denotations. *Pig* **connotes** any of those attributes commonly associated with swine that may be applied to persons: sloppiness, filthiness, gluttony, sloth, immorality, or unwholesomeness.

What a word explicitly stands for might constitute only a small part of the word's meaning. Thus connotations play an important role in English. They help our language expand, adapt to changing needs, and exercise the flexibility that makes it such an expressive language.

However, you must be aware that connotations affect word usage possibilities in ways that are sometimes difficult to predict. Words that meant (denoted) one thing years ago might today mean (connote) something different enough to be undesirable in your context. *Chauvinism*, for instance, denotes excessive patriotism and devotion to duty, which might or might not be favorable, depending on the prevailing political climate. The term originated with Nicholas Chauvin of Rochefort, whose devotion to Napoleon was at first celebrated and later criticized. Whether pro or con, the term meant excessive patriotism.

Today, however, *chauvinism* has been applied to persons, usually male, who exhibit favoritism toward men and a bias against women. This connotation has been used so widely that, today, labeling someone a chauvinist is to suggest sexual bias, not excessive patriotism, so the term is entirely negative.

If you are to use language well, you must be aware of the connotations of words, particularly in the minds of your readers. If your readers will assume that *effects* are favorable and that *impacts* are unfavorable, then your word choice will depend on which impression you wish your readers to have. The right word then is the precise word that conveys your intended meaning. See Tone.

Concrete and Abstract Words

The distinction between concrete and abstract words is similar to the distinction between specific and general. Concrete words are those words representing specific people, places, objects, and actions—all things that we can experience through our senses. So concrete words create a vivid mental image. Abstract words are usually more general. They represent ideas, qualities, actions, conditions, and other things that are removed from direct sensory experience. Here are some examples of concrete and abstract words:

Concrete	Abstract
apple	food
M-60 tank	transportation
Arthur Smith	coworker
Teledyne	corporation
Los Angeles	urban area
IBM Selectric	office equipment

Using specific, concrete terms is important because in doing so you narrow the range of possible interpretation. If you use an abstraction like *food* when you mean *apples*, the reader will probably not receive the message you intended to send. Here, from the *Guide for Air Force Writing*, is an example of an abstraction ladder:

weapon system
hardware
aircraft
bomber
B-52

Word Problems

The higher you go on the ladder, the more abstract the words become. The problem many writers have is that they use more general, abstract words than they should. Instead of B-52, some writers might say *strategic bomber, aircraft,* or even *weapon system.* A B-52 is certainly a strategic bomber, but so is a B-1. Therefore, *strategic bomber* is more abstract than B-52. Saying *bomber* rather than B-52 will not create the image of a B-52 in readers' minds, and they might not understand precisely what you mean. *Weapon system* is even further removed from the concrete reality of a B-52 bomber, so a writer mentioning a weapon system allows readers to imagine everything from a B-52 to the latest attack submarine.

Avoid this problem by using the most specific, concrete words you can. If you need abstractions, use them. But be as specific as you can with every word choice.

The Correct Word for the Context

A major writing problem can occur if you use the wrong word for the context. Which of the words within parentheses in the following sentences is correct?

> (You're, Your) supposed to call the manager before leaving.
>
> The (principal, principle) problem with this alternative is its reliance on a second wash cycle between chemical baths.
>
> The plan will (affect, effect) residents living south of the city.

In all three cases, the first word is correct. Using the wrong word might not prevent readers from understanding the sentences. But many readers might begin to wonder if you are literate. And if you seem illiterate, then even the facts in a letter might appear questionable. So using correct words is important.

You should be aware, however, that using incorrect or imprecise words in legal documents (or in any document that can potentially be subject to interpretation in a courtroom) is very dangerous. Courts tend to support the word on the page, not what the author claims to have intended.

Sometimes, using the incorrect word causes serious confusion and potential misinterpretation:

> Please ensure that the third production cycle is stopped continuously for quality assurance testing.

Continuously means "uninterrupted or constant." *Continually* means "recurring often." If the production cycle is stopped continuously, then it never runs. If the cycle is stopped continually, it is stopped frequently, but not constantly. (Some readers might not make this distinction. For the sake of clarity, the writer would be better off issuing a more specific order: *Please ensure that the third production cycle is stopped every half hour for quality assurance testing.*)

Some words are clearly correct or incorrect. You can't write *it's* when you mean *its*, and vice versa. However, some distinctions are more difficult to make. Even the dictionaries do not offer clear-cut distinctions in some cases:

> (Since, Because) we had not received payment, we decided to close the account.
>
> They proposed to publish a (bimonthly, semimonthly) newsletter for all employees.
>
> The proposal (that, which) you prepared has turned out to be very profitable.

In the first sentence, both choices do include the notion of causality and nothing else, while *since* primarily means "before now" or "from some time in the past until now." Only secondarily does *since* suggest causality. Thus, strict editors consider *because* less ambiguous.

In the second sentence, *bimonthly* is unclear because the ambiguous *bi-* can mean either twice within a time period (twice a month) or every other time period (every two months). *Semimonthly,* which has always meant twice a month, has suffered because of the confusion over *bimonthly.* Given the confusion between the two terms, you should avoid both terms and just say *twice a month* or *every 2 months.*

In the third sentence, both words are acceptable to many writers and editors. According to strict editors, however, *that* is more correct because the clause it introduces is essential to the sentence and cannot be removed; if the clause were nonessential, *which* would be the more correct word and the nonessential clause would be separated from the main clause by commas. Many educated writers and speakers violate this distinction, some using *that* and *which* almost interchangeably. So insisting that *that* is the only correct choice for the third sentence is difficult.

Word Problems

Language and usage rules cannot be and never have been independent from the living language they describe. The spoken and written language that people use is always the final arbiter in disputes over word correctness. And a living language is always changing, so today's correct choice might be tomorrow's error. Good writers must remain alert to changes in a word's meaning and their acceptability.

The following list of problem word choices reflects some of the main choices facing today's writers. You should supplement this list and update it as necessary to remain current.

For information about words not in the following list or if you want more detailed information, see *Webster's Dictionary of English Usage*. 1989. Springfield Massachusetts: Merriam-Webster, Inc.

Word Problems

Accent/Ascent/Assent. *Accent* means "to emphasize or stress." *Ascent* means "a going up or rising movement." *Assent* means "to agree":

> His accent on the word *demotion* betrayed his true feelings.
>
> His ascent up the corporate ladder has been rapid.
>
> The trustee's assent is necessary before we sign the agreement.

Accept/Except. *Accept* is a verb meaning "to receive." *Except* is a preposition meaning "to the exclusion of":

> Have you accepted our explanation for the overpayment?
>
> We completed everything except the two proposals for Acme, Inc.

A.D. and B.C. *A.D.* stands for the Latin *anno Domini* (in the year of the Lord). Using *A.D.* is simple—place it before a year and after a century:

> Pope Julius II, whose fertile partnership with Michelangelo produced many fine works of art, reigned from A.D. 1503 to 1513.
>
> Arabians borrowed coffee from the Abyssinians about the twelfth century A.D.

B.C. stands for "before Christ." Using *B.C.* is also simple—place it after the year and after the century:

> King Priam's Troy fell near the end of the Bronze Age, around 1200 B.C.
>
> The high point of ancient Greek civilization, the Periclean Age, was during the fifth century B.C.

Some writers, however, have qualms about using *A.D.* and *B.C.*, which are connected to the birth of Jesus Christ. They use other systems, such as *B.C.E.* (before the common era) or *B.P.* (before the present) and place them after the date.

Adapt/Adept/Adopt. *Adapt* means "to adjust to a situation." *Adept* means "skillful." *Adopt* means "to put into practice or to borrow":

> Within a week she adapted to the new billing procedure.
>
> She won the promotion because she was so adept at her job.
>
> Just last year we adopted a new method for maintaining inventory.

Adjacent/Contiguous/ Conterminous. *Adjacent* is the most general word, usually meaning "close to and nearby" and only sometimes "sharing the same boundary":

> Burger King is adjacent to the Cottonwood Mall.
>
> The adjacent lots were both owned by the same construction company.

Contiguous usually means "sharing the same boundary" even though it includes the notion of "adjacent" in most of its uses:

> The two mining claims turned out to be contiguous once the survey was completed; the owners had originally believed that a strip of state land separated the claims.

Conterminous (also *coterminous*) is the most specific of the terms and also the rarest. Its most distinctive meaning is "contained within one boundary" even though it also includes the senses of "sharing the same boundary" and quite rarely of being "adjacent." Its most distinctive use, however, is as follows:

> The conterminous United States includes only 48 of the 50 states.

These three words are a problem because they share a common meaning: "close to or nearby each other." At the same time, they each have more specific meanings, as illustrated. As with any confused words, writers should choose other phrasing if they wish to be as precise as possible:

> *better*
>
> Our two lots shared a common boundary on the north.
>
> *or with a different meaning*
>
> Our two lots fell entirely within the city boundary.
>
> *not*
>
> Our two lots were adjacent. (*neither* contiguous, *nor* conterminous)

Word Problems

Adverse/Averse. *Adverse* is an adjective meaning "unfavorable." *Averse* is an adjective meaning "having a dislike or a distaste for something." The two also contrast in how they are used in sentences. *Averse* appears only after the verb *be* or occasionally *feel*:

> We studied the adverse data before making our decision to plug and abandon the well.
>
> An adverse comment destroyed the negotiations.
>
> The President was averse to cutting the Defense budget.
>
> We felt averse to signing for such a large loan given the adverse economic forecasts.

Advice/Advise. *Advice* is a noun meaning "recommendations." *Advise* is a verb meaning "to make a recommendation":

> My advice was to meet with the client about the service problem.
>
> Did someone advise you to hire a lawyer?

Affect/Effect. *Affect* is usually a verb meaning "to change or influence." *Effect* is usually a noun meaning "a result or consequence":

> Temperature variations will affect the test results.
>
> The technician analyzed the effects of the new sample on the data.

NOTE: *Affect* can also be a noun meaning "the subjective impression of feeling or emotion," and *effect* can also be a verb meaning "to bring about or cause":

> His strange affect (*noun*) caused the psychiatrist to sign the committal order.
>
> The general manager's directive effected (*verb*) an immediate restructuring of all senior staff operations.

All right/Alright. *All right* is the standard spelling; *alright* is an informal or nonstandard spelling and is not considered correct. Never use *alright*.

Allusion/Illusion/Delusion. *Allusion* means "a reference to something." *Illusion* means "a mistaken impression." *Delusion* means "a false belief":

> His allusion to Japanese management techniques was not well received, but he made his point.
>
> Like the old magician's illusions of the floating lady, the bank manager created an illusion of solvency that fooled even seasoned investors.
>
> The patient had delusions about being watched by the FBI.

Alternate/Alternative. Confusion comes from competing adjective uses. *Alternate* as an adjective means "occurring in turns" or "every other one." *Alternative* as an adjective means "allowing for a choice between two or more options":

> Winners were chosen from alternate lines rather than from a single line.
>
> The alternative candidate was a clear compromise between the two parties.

Sometimes these two adjective meanings almost merge, especially when an alternative plan is viewed as a plan that replaces another:

> An alternate/alternative plan provided for supplementary bank financing. (*Either is correct.*)

NOTE: Strict editors attempt to restrict *alternative* (in its noun and adjective uses) to only two options:

> Life is the alternative to death.

Actual (correct) usage, however, has broadened *alternative* to include any number of options:

> The planning commission analyzed five alternative sites. (*or* The planning commission analyzed five alternatives.)

Altogether/All together. *Altogether* means "completely or entirely." *All together* means "in a group":

> We had altogether too much trouble getting a simple answer to our question.
>
> The spare parts lists are all together now and can be combined.

a.m./p.m./m. The abbreviations *a.m., p.m.,* and *m.* sometimes appear in printed text with small caps: A.M., P.M., and M. In most word processing text, lowercase versions are preferred.

Use *a.m.* for times after *midnight* and before *noon:*

12:01 a.m.	(1 minute after midnight)
6:00 a.m.	(early morning)
11:59 a.m.	(1 minute before noon)

Use *p.m.* for times after *noon* and until *midnight*:

12:01 p.m.	(1 minute after noon)
6:00 p.m.	(early evening)
12:00 p.m.	(midnight)

Noon remains a problem. Some guides continue to list *12 m.* as *noon.* However, using *m.* for *noon* with readers who do not know this abbreviation is unwise. They might well read *m.* as *midnight. Noon* and *midnight* will never be misinterpreted; use them in place of *12 m.*:

> The conference will be at noon on July 25.

Among/Between. *Among* refers to more than two choices. *Between* usually refers to two choices only, but it can refer to more than two:

> We had difficulty deciding among the many options—over 200 colors.

> The contracting officer has eliminated three bidders, so the Source Selection Authority must choose between us and Universal Data.

Strict editors do try to restrict *between* to two choices only. But occasionally, you can use *between* instead of *among*, especially where *among* would not sound right:

> The research group analyzed the differences between the five alternatives.

See PREPOSITIONS.

And/or, Or, And. Avoid using *and/or*. This term is usually difficult and sometimes impossible to read with surety. See SLASHES.

In one court case, three judges ruled three different ways as to the meaning of *and/or*. Courts in different cases have ruled that *and* means *or*, that *or* means *and*. Be careful when using these three troublesome words. See CONJUNCTIONS.

To repeat, avoid using *and/or*. If you do use it, make sure that the situation you describe has at least three possibilities:

> The road will be made of sand and/or gravel.

This road could be (1) an all-sand road (2) an all-gravel road, or (3) a road made from both sand and gravel.

You can make reading even more difficult by adding other possibilities:

> The road will be made from asphalt, concrete, sand, *and/or* gravel.

The road now has far more construction combinations. Rather than using the shorthand *and/or*, change the sentence to explain to your readers your exact meaning:

> The road will be made from asphalt, concrete, sand, and gravel. *(Implies a combination of all four—with the percent composition variable.)*

> The road will have an asphalt and concrete surface, with fill being a mixture of sand and gravel. *(More specific and less ambiguous.)*

Or has two meanings: inclusive and exclusive. For the most precise use of this word, use only the **exclusive** meaning:

> Use the blue pen or the black pen.

> Use either the blue pen or the black pen.

Do not use *or* in its **inclusive** sense:

> Limestone or calcium carbonate is used to neutralize the effects of acid rain.

Readers who do not know that limestone is calcium carbonate might think that two substances can be used. They cannot tell whether *or* is being used in its inclusive or its exclusive sense. See CONJUNCTIONS.

Readers who know that limestone is calcium carbonate know that *or* is being used in its inclusive sense, but these knowledgeable readers do not need the reminder that limestone is calcium carbonate.

Write the sentence, eliminating *or* and using parentheses:

> Limestone (calcium carbonate) is used to neutralize the effects of acid rain.

See PARENTHESES.

Anyone/Any one. *Anyone* means "any person." *Any one* means "a specific person or object":

> Anyone who wants a copy of the Camdus report should receive one.

> We were supposed to eliminate any one of the potential mine sites.

As regards. See In regard to/As regards/In regards to.

Assure/Insure/Ensure. All three words mean "to make certain or to guarantee." *Assure* is limited to references with people:

> The doctor assured him that the growth was nonmalignant.

Insure is used in discussing financial guarantees:

> His life was insured for $150,000.

> The company failed to insure the leased automobile.

Much of the time, *insure* and *ensure* are confusingly interchangeable. For example, in one Federal document in the late 1970s, *insure* and *ensure* both appeared numerous times with the same meaning; chance seems to have guided which spelling appeared in which sentence. To try to end such confusion, the *U.S. Government Printing Style Manual* (March 1984) defines *insure* as "protect" and *ensure* as "guarantee":

Word Problems

Your life insurance will insure (protect) your family from financial ruin.

To ensure (guarantee) that the drill bit does not overheat as it penetrates through the rock layer, keep the drilling fluid flowing at a maximum rate.

Reality suggests that despite such tidy distinctions, *insure* and *ensure* will continue to be confused. Try, however, to be consistent within a single document by choosing *insure* or *ensure* and then sticking with your choice.

Bad/Badly. Originally, *bad* was the adjective form, and *badly* was the adverb form. Now, however, *badly* has begun to function in sentences the same way *bad* has. This overlap is a problem when you use the verbs of the senses (*feel, look, smell,* etc.):

Originally

Harold felt bad (*adjective*) all day from the blow on his head.

The machine worked badly (*adverb*) despite the overhaul.

Currently Acceptable

Harold felt badly all day from the blow on his head.

NOTE: Only the verb *feel* allows for either *bad* or *badly*, as in the preceding sentence. Other confusions between the adjective and the adverb are not acceptable, especially in written English:

Not Acceptable

He looked badly after the bachelor party. (*correct form:* bad)

The lab smelled badly after the drainage samples arrived. (*correct form:* bad)

B.C. See A.D. and B.C.

Between. See Among/Between.

Biannually/Biennially. *Biannually* means "two times a year." *Biennially* means "every two years":

Because we meet biannually, we will have 10 meetings over the next 5 years.

Our long-range planning committee meets biennially—on even-numbered years.

Bimonthly/Semimonthly. *Bimonthly* can mean either "every 2 months" or "twice a month." *Semimonthly* means "twice a month." Because of the potential confusion surrounding *bimonthly*, you should avoid the word and write *every 2 months* or *twice a month*. *Semimonthly* has only one meaning and should not be confusing. Still, it has suffered from the ambiguity of *bimonthly*:

Our bimonthly newsletter appears in January, March, May, July, September, and November. (*better:* Our newsletter appears every 2 months, beginning in January.)

We proposed semimonthly meetings of the legislative committee. (*better:* We proposed meetings twice a month of the legislative committee.)

Can/May. *Can* means (1) "ability," (2) "permission," and (3) "theoretical possibility." *May* means (1) "permission" and (2) "possibility":

Ability

She can speak German, but she can't write it very well.

Permission

Can I help you with your project?

May I help you with your project?

NOTE: *May* sounds more formal than *can*, so if you wish to sound formal, use *may*.

Possibility

George can make mistakes if he's rushed. (*or* may)

The project can be stopped if necessary. (*or* may)

The trail may be blocked, but we won't know until later.

Your objection may be reasonable, but we still don't agree.

Capital/Capitol. *Capital* means "the central city or site of government," "invested money," and "an uppercase letter." *Capitol* means "the main government building":

Paris is the capital of France.

The necessary capital for such an elegant restaurant is $1.5 million, but I doubt that investors will put up that much.

THIS SENTENCE IS WRITTEN IN CAPITALS.

The legislature authorized a complete renovation of the capitol dome.

Carat/Caret/Karat. *Carat* means "the weight of a gem." *Caret* means "a mark showing an insertion." *Karat* means "a unit for the purity of gold":

The ring had a 2.2 carat diamond.

I've used a caret to indicate where to insert the new sentence.

The ring is made of 18-karat gold.

Cite/Sight/Site. *Cite* means "to quote." *Sight* means "vision." *Site* means "a location":

During the trial, our attorney cited earlier testimony.

Most of the tunnel was out of sight, so we could not estimate the extent of the damage.

The contractor prepared the site by bulldozing all the brush off to the side.

Complement/Compliment. *Complement* means "completing or supplementing something." *Compliment* means "an expression of praise":

> The report's recommendations complement those made by the executive committee last year.

> The manager passed on a compliment from the vice president, who was impressed with the proposal team's efforts.

Comprise/Compose. Strict editors carefully distinguish between these two words—that is, *comprise* means "to include or contain" and *compose* means "to make up from many parts":

> The U.S. Congress comprises the House of Representatives and the Senate.

> The House of Representatives and the Senate compose the U.S. Congress.

Such sentences, especially those with *comprise*, are beginning to sound stiff and overly formal, and passive alternatives are more and more common, although not accepted by all editors:

> The U.S. Congress is comprised of the House of Representatives and the Senate.

As with other disputed word uses, choose an alternate version whenever possible:

> The House of Representatives and the Senate constitute the U.S. Congress.

Contiguous. See Adjacent/Contiguous/Conterminous.

Continual/Continuous. *Continual* means "intermittent, but frequently repeated." *Continuous* means "without interruption":

> Because the pipes are so old, continual leaks appear despite our repair efforts.

> Because of a short in the wiring, the horn sounded continuously for 10 minutes.

Contractions. Do not use contractions (*don't, couldn't*) in formal documents. However, when you want to create a personal tone, do use contractions in informal documents such as letters and memos:

> John, don't forget that you must finish this work by Tuesday; otherwise, Bill can't get your figures into his report, which must be done for Vice President Stern by Thursday.

See STYLE.

Council/Counsel/Consul. *Council* means "a group of people." *Counsel* means "to advise" (verb), "advice" (noun) or "an attorney." *Consul* means "a foreign representative":

> The safety council passed a motion to ban smoking in shaft elevators.

> The consultant counseled us in ways to improve our management of ID team efforts.

> His counsel was to rewrite the proposal.

> MOGO's counsel made the opening statement in the hearing.

> The French consul helped us obtain an import license.

Councilor/Counselor. *Councilor* means "a member of council." *Counselor* is "an advisor or lawyer":

> The councilors decided to table the motion until the next meeting.

> Our staff medical counselor has a PhD in clinical psychology.

Could. See Would/Probably would/Could/Might/Should.

Credible/Creditable/Credulous. *Credible* means "believable." *Creditable* means "praiseworthy." *Credulous* means "gullible":

> His revised report was more credible, chiefly because the manpower estimates were scaled to match the price.

> In spite of some short cuts, the proposal team wrote a creditable proposal; in fact, they won the contract.

> He was so credulous that anyone could fool him.

Data. *Data* (the plural of *datum*) is now often used as both the singular and plural forms of the word. In some technical and scientific writing, however, *data* is still traditionally plural only. If the convention in your discipline or organization is to use *data* as a plural, then be sure that your sentences reflect correct agreement of subject and verb:

> Our production data are being examined by the EPA because a citizen complained about excessive emissions from our plant.

> The data have been difficult to analyze, chiefly because of sloppy recordkeeping.

These sentences may sound strange or awkward to many readers. Consequently, some technical writers avoid phrasing that calls attention to the plural meaning of *data.* The two sentences above, for instance, could read as follows:

> EPA is examining our production data because a citizen complained about excessive emissions from our plant.

> We found the data difficult to analyze, chiefly because of the sloppy recordkeeping.

Word Problems

Delusion. See Allusion/Illusion/Delusion.

Different from/Different than. These two forms can and should be used interchangeably. Strict editors, however, may insist that *different from* is somehow better than *different than.* Actually, well-educated writers and many editors have used both forms for well over 300 years. The argument over these two forms is an example of a preference being mistaken for a rule. In fact, no clear distinction between the two forms has ever existed:

> The results were far different from those we expected. (*or* different than)
>
> The study is different than we had been led to expect. (*or* different from the one we had been led to expect)

Disburse/Disperse. *Disburse* is the verb meaning "to pay out." *Disperse* is the verb meaning "to scatter":

> The payroll clerk disburses the petty cash funds as needed.
>
> The reserved top soil was dispersed over the site after the project was completed.

Discreet/Discrete. *Discreet* means "tactful or prudent." *Discrete* means "separate or individual":

> The counselor was so discreet that no one learned we had been meeting with him.
>
> The testing included three discrete samples of the ore body.

Disinterested/Uninterested. Originally, *disinterested* meant "neutral or unbiased," and *uninterested* meant "without interest." Careful writers and editors still maintain this distinction:

> The judge was appointed because he was clearly disinterested in the dispute.
>
> The President was so uninterested in the problem that he failed to act.

Effect. See Affect/Effect.

Elapse/Lapse. *Elapse* is a verb meaning "to pass by or to slip"; it usually refers to time. *Lapse* is a verb with many meanings, most derived from sense of "to drift, to discontinue, or to terminate":

> Two weeks elapsed before we heard from the Internal Revenue Service.
>
> The speaker lapsed into silence after the embarrassing question.
>
> Our contract lapsed before we could negotiate its renewal.

Eminent/Imminent. *Eminent* means "outstanding or prestigious." *Imminent* means "very near or impending":

> Only eminent researchers will win Nobel prizes.
>
> The dam's collapse was imminent, so we evacuated downstream communities.

Ensure. See Assure/Insure/Ensure.

Envelop/Envelope. *Envelop* is the verb meaning "to enclose or to encase." *Envelope* is the noun meaning "something that contains or encloses":

> They proposed to envelop the storage tank with the fire-retardant foam.
>
> We placed in the envelope both the final report and the backup surveys.

Except. See Accept/Except.

Farther/Further. As far back as Shakespeare these words have been confused, and in some contexts they are clearly interchangeable—e.g., *farther/further from the truth.*

Strict editors still maintain that *farther* should be restricted to senses involving distance, while *further* includes other senses:

> The assembly site was farther from the testing area than we wished.
>
> A further consideration was the inflation during those years.

Fewer/Less. *Fewer*, the comparative form of *few*, usually refers to things that can be counted. *Less*, one comparative form of *little*, refers to mass items, such as sugar or salt, which cannot be counted, and to abstractions:

> We analyzed fewer well sites than the government wanted us to analyze.
>
> Less sodium chloride in the water meant that we had fewer problems with corrosion.
>
> Fewer teachers, less education.

See NOUNS and ADJECTIVES.

Forward/Foreword. *Forward* is an adjective and an adverb, both meaning "at or near the front." *Foreword* is the noun meaning "the introduction to a book":

> The hopper moves forward when the drying phase is nearly finished.
>
> The foreword to the book was two pages long.

He/she, s/he, (s)he. Avoid these created new words. If possible, recast your sentence so that it is plural:

this

All engineers must bring their reports to the meeting. (*plural*)

All new employees should complete the health forms before beginning work. If they have not done so, their insurance will not be in effect.

not this

Every engineer must bring his/her report to the meeting. (*singular*)

Each new employee must complete the health forms before beginning work. If (s)he has not done so, his/her insurance will not be in effect.

These newly coined words, which have not been widely accepted, are attempts to create a singular, neuter pronoun other than the word *it* because *it* in many sentences is too odd and too impersonal to refer to people.

See SEXIST LANGUAGE.

Illusion. See Allusion/Illusion/Delusion.

Imminent. See Eminent/Imminent.

Imply/Infer. *Imply* means "to suggest or hint." *Infer* means "to draw a conclusion or to deduce":

The report implies that the break-even point may be difficult to reach, but it fails to give supporting data.

Based on our comments, she inferred that we would not give our wholehearted support to her project.

Infinitives. See Split Infinitives.

In regard to/As regards/In regards to. The first two forms are acceptable. By convention, the third form (*in regards to*) is unacceptable. Do not use *in regards to.*

In regard to your report, our firm is still busy analyzing it.

As regards your second question, we have taken all of the steps necessary to acquire mineral rights on the Bruneau lease.

A better choice in most sentences is to use the shorter and simpler *regarding*:

Regarding your second question, we have taken all of the steps necessary to acquire mineral rights on the Bruneau lease.

Insure. See Assure/Insure/Ensure.

Irregardless/Regardless. *Irregardless* is an unacceptable version of *regardless.* Do not use *irregardless* in either speech or writing:

We decided to fund the project regardless of the cash flow problems we were having.

Its/It's. *Its* is the possessive pronoun. *It's* is the contraction for *it is*:

Its last section was unclear and probably inaccurate.

It's time for the annual turnaround maintenance check.

See PRONOUNS.

Karat. See Carat/Caret/Karat.

Lapse. See Elapse/Lapse.

Later/Latter. *Later*, the comparative form of *late,* means "coming after something else." *Latter* is an adjective meaning "the second of two objects or persons":

Later in the evening a fire broke out.

In our analysis of the Lankford and Nipon sites, we finally decided that the latter site was preferable.

NOTE: *Latter* (and its parallel *former*) are sometimes confusing, so rewrite to avoid them:

We finally decided that the Nipon site was preferable to the Lankford site.

Lay/Laid/Laid. These three words are the principal parts of the verb *lay.* The verb itself means "to put or to place." It must have an object:

The contractor promised to lay the sod before the fall rains began. (*object:* sod.)

The manager laid his plan before his colleagues. (*object:* plan)

Our recent talks with the Russians have laid the groundwork for control of nuclear weapons in space. (*object:* groundwork)

Less. See Fewer/Less.

Lie/Lay/Lain. These three forms are the principal parts of the verb *lie. Lie* means "to rest or recline." In contrast with *lay, lie* cannot have an object:

The main plant entrance lies south of the personnel building.

The new access road lay on the bench above the floodplain.

That supply has lain there for over a decade.

May. See Can/May.

Maybe/May be. *Maybe* is the adverb meaning "perhaps." *May be* is a verb form meaning "possibility":

Maybe we should analyze the impacts before going ahead with the project.

Whatever happens may be beyond our control, especially if inflation is unchecked.

Might. See Would/Probably would/Could/Might/Should.

Word Problems

Or. See And/or, Or, And.

p.m. See a.m./p.m./m.

Practical/Practicable. These two words mean much the same thing, and dictionaries disagree on their distinctions. Given this confusion, writers should stay with the common form *practical* and avoid *practicable.*

Strict editors do maintain that the difference between *practical* and *practicable* is similar to the difference between *useful* and *possible. Practical* means "not theoretical; useful, proven through practice." *Practicable* means "capable of being practiced or put into action; feasible":

> Despite the uniqueness of the problem, the contractor developed a practical method for shoring up the foundation.
>
> Although technically practicable, the solution was not practical because it would have put us over budget.

The last sentence says that we were technically capable of achieving the solution but that this solution was not feasible because of financial constraints.

Similarly, building a house on top of Mt. St. Helens is probably possible (it is practicable), but doing so is not feasible (it is not practical) for obvious reasons.

Precedence/Precedents. *Precedence* is the noun meaning "an established priority." *Precedents* is the plural form of the noun meaning "an example or instance, as in a legal case":

> The Robbins account should take precedence over the Jackson account; after all, Robbins gives us over 50 percent of our business.
>
> The Brown decision was the precedent for many later decisions involving racial issues and education.

Principal/Principle. *Principal* is a noun or adjective meaning "main or chief." *Principle* is a noun meaning "belief, moral standard, or law governing the operation of something":

> The principal technical problems we faced were simply beyond current technologies.
>
> The principles of electricity explain the voltage drop in lines.
>
> If we act according to our principles, we will not allow the transaction to proceed.

Note: Some writers are confused by *principal* because it also means "the head of a school" and "the money borrowed from a bank." These are noun forms of a word that used to be only an adjective. The noun forms of *principal* come from noun phrases: *the principal teacher* and *the principal amount.* Over time, the nouns *teacher* and *amount* were dropped, and *principal* assumed the full meaning of the original phrases. Now, *principal* is a noun as well as an adjective.

Probably would. See Would/ Probably would/Could/Might/ Should.

Raise/Raised/Raised. These three forms are the principal parts of the verb *raise. Raise* means "to move (something) upward." *Raise* always requires an object:

> They will raise the funds by January 1, 1990. (*object:* funds)
>
> We raised the water level some 20 feet to accommodate the changing use patterns. (*object:* water level)
>
> They had raised the amount to cover the travel costs. (*object:* amount)

Regardless. See Irregardless/ Regardless.

Respectfully/Respectively. *Respectfully* means "with deference and courtesy." *Respectively* means "in the sequence named":

> Our representatives were not treated very respectfully.
>
> According to production data for March, May, July, and September, the number of cases were, respectively, 868, 799, 589, and 803.

Note: *Respectively* often makes sentences difficult to interpret, so avoid *respectively* whenever you can.

Rise/Rose/Risen. These three forms are the principal parts of the verb *rise. Rise* means "to stand up or move upward." *Rise* does not take an object:

> The balloon rises/will rise once the air heats up.
>
> Because the water rose, we had to evacuate the ground floor.
>
> The moisture level in the gas has risen substantially over the last week.

Said. The word *said* often becomes a shorthand term for a document or item previously mentioned:

> We have examined said plans and can find no provisions for the clay soils on the site.

Such uses of *said* are not appropriate in normal business and technical writing. Only in legal writing (and maybe not even there) should writers ever use *said* in this way. The above sentence could be rewritten as follows:

We have examined the plans and can find no provisions for the clay soils on the site. (*Readers will usually know from the context what plans the writer is referring to.*)

Semimonthly. See Bimonthly/ Semimonthly.

Set/Set/Set. These three forms are the principal parts of the verb *set*. *Set* means "to put or to place (something)." *Set* must have an object:

They set the surveying equipment in the back of the truck. (*object:* equipment)

Yesterday we set up the derrick so that drilling could start at the beginning of today's shift. (*object:* derrick)

After we had set the flow, we began to monitor fluctuations from changes in pressure. (*object:* fluctuations)

Shall/Will. Use *will* for the simple future with all of the personal pronouns:

I/We will leave.
You will leave.
He/She/It/They will leave.

Shall is rarely used for simple future, at least in American English, but it does retain some sense of extra obligation or force, as in legal contexts:

The vendor shall provide 24-hour security at the site.

Shall (or *should)* is also used for some questions:

Shall/Should I stop by your office tomorrow?

Shall/Should I sign the document now?

Neither *will* nor *would* can replace *shall/should* in these questions.

Some grammarians, beginning in the 17th century, formulated a supposed rule for *shall* and *will:*

> For simple future, use *shall* with *I* and *we*; *will* with *he, she, it,* and *they*. For obligation and permission, reverse the choices: *will* with *I* and *we; shall* with *he, she, it,* and *they*.

This rule was not accurate in the 17th century, and it has never been true of actual English sentences. British English does use *shall* somewhat more frequently for the simple future than American English, but even in England, the 17th-century rule is not consistently followed.

She. See He/she, s/he, (s)he.

Should. See Would/Probably would/Could/Might/Should.

Sic. *Sic*, from the Latin, means "thus." Use *sic* when you are quoting something and want to show that, yes, I have copied this ungrammatical or odd language as it was originally written or spoken:

The computer experts in their memorandum stated: "We took for granite [sic] that everyone knew about their [sic] weekend changes to the system."

The stationary bus was coming from [sic] the opposite direction.

Do not use *sic* to embarrass someone by highlighting harmless mistakes, which we all make.

Sight/Site. See Cite/Sight/Site.

Sit/Sat/Sat. These three forms are the principal parts of the verb *sit*. *Sit* means "to rest or to recline." *Sit* does not take an object:

The well sits at the foot of a steep cliff.

The committee sat through the long session with very few complaints.

The oil drums must have sat on the loading dock all weekend.

Split Infinitives. Many people who often can't even recognize a split infinitive still believe a split infinitive is a grammatical crime. Perhaps because of its memorable name, a split infinitive has become part of the folklore about what good writers should avoid.

Actually, split infinitives have been acceptable in English for hundreds of years. Only in fairly recent times have editors even worried whether sentences like the following should be accepted because they contain split infinitives:

The company's goal was **to rapidly retire** its investment debt before moving into new markets.

To totally avoid splitting infinitives, the writer decided to eliminate all infinitives from the document.

In the first of these examples, rephrasing to move *rapidly* before or after the infinitive *to retire* is easy: *rapidly to retire* or *to retire rapidly.* Strict editors would choose one of these rephrasings and thus eliminate the split infinitive, but the sentence is actually correct with or without the split inifinitive.

In the second example, however, moving *totally* behind the infinitive *to avoid* changes the sentence:

Word Problems

> To avoid totally splitting infinitives, the writer decided to eliminate all infinitives from the document. *(Is the splitting being done totally or does* totally *continue to modify* avoid?)

In this second example, a writer would have to either retain the split infinitive or recast the entire sentence.

To conclude, split infinitives are not worth worrying about. Leave them in your document when the context seems to require a split infinitive.

Stationary/Stationery. *Stationary* is an adjective meaning "fixed in one spot, unmoving." *Stationery* is a noun meaning "paper for writing on":

> Because the boiler was bolted to the floor, it remained stationary despite the vibration.

> The new letterhead on our stationery made our company seem more up to date.

Than/Then. *Than* is used in comparisons. *Then* is an adverb meaning "at that time":

> George's report was shorter than Mary's.

> We then decided to analyze the trace minerals in the water samples.

That/Which. After centuries of competition (and confusion), the two words continue to be often interchangeable:

> The connecting rod that failed delayed us for two days.
>
> *or*
>
> The connecting rod which failed delayed us for two days.

In both of these correct sentences, the clauses *that failed* and *which failed* identify which specific rod—that is, the rod that failed, not the other rods. So these clauses are both identifying (restricting) the meaning. As in these two sentences, the restrictive clause is not set off by commas. When *that* and *which* introduce restrictive clauses, the choice between them is merely stylistic—that is, choose the one that sounds the best.

Which is the proper choice, however, for nonrestrictive clauses:

> The Evans report, which took us several months to finish, is beginning to attract attention.

> The U.S. Senate, which many consider the most exclusive club in the world, does follow some quaint rules of decorum.

In both of these examples, the *which* clauses provide additional but unnecessary information about the Evans report and the Senate. Both *which* clauses are thus nonrestrictive because neither helps to identify the report or the Senate. An informal test is if the *which* clauses were deleted, the basic meaning of each sentence would not change. Note, also, that such nonrestrictive clauses are enclosed with commas. See COMMAS.

Strict editors argue that because *which* is clearly the choice to introduce nonrestrictive clauses, *that* should be used for all restrictive clauses. The tidy distinction is not true of spoken English, and many careful writers continue to use *that* and *which* interchangeably for restrictive clauses.

This is another case where a supposed rule (actually part of a rule) is best ignored. To summarize, use either *that* or *which* to introduce restrictive clauses (with no enclosing commas). Use *which* for nonrestrictive clauses (with enclosing commas).

Their/There/They're. *Their* is a possessive pronoun. *There* is an adverb meaning "at that place." *They're* is the contraction for *they are*:

> The engineers turned in their reports for printing.

> The well site was there along the base of the plateau.

> They're likely to object if we try to include those extra expenses in the invoice.

To/Too/Two. *To* is the preposition. *Too* is both an adverb meaning "excessively" and a conjunctive adverb meaning "also." *Two* is the numeral:

> The proposal went to the Department of the Interior for approval.

> The design was too costly considering our budget. (too = *excessively*)

> The issue, too, was that technology is only now beginning to cope with these low-temperature problems. (too = *also*)

Toward/Towards. *Toward* and *towards* are merely different forms of the same word. *Toward* is the preferred form in American English. In British English, *towards* is more common than *toward.*

Uninterested. See Disinterested/Uninterested.

Which. See That/Which.

Word Problems

While. *While* is best used as only a time word to show simultaneity—"at the same time as another event":

> While the wash water flows over the screening plates, measure the water's temperature.
>
> Check the level of the car's transmission fluid while the engine is running.

In other instances, *while* can mean "though," "although," "even though," "but," or "and." These meanings are particularly common in spoken English. In written English, however, replace *while* with its equivalent word:

> *this*
>
> Although windmills are economical, they are too often destroyed by severe storms, and in calm weather, they produce no electrical power.
>
> At some places the coal layer is 4 feet wide; at other places it narrows to 10 inches.
>
> *not this*
>
> While windmills are economical, they are too often destroyed by severe storms, while in calm weather, they produce no electrical power.
>
> At some places the coal layer is 4 feet wide, while at other places it narrows to 10 inches.

Who/Whom. See the discussion of interrogative and relative pronouns in PRONOUNS.

Who's/Whose. *Who's* is the contraction for *who is. Whose* is the possessive form of the pronoun *who*:

> Who's the contractor for the site preparation work?
>
> She was the supervisor whose workers had all that overtime.

Will. See Shall/Will.

Would/Probably would/Could/ Might/Should. Today these words are usually used as one form of the subjunctive mood, stating future probability. Long ago, *would* and *could* were used as past tense verbs.

These words, except for *would*, never convey an exact probability. The context in which these words are used gives the reader a sense of the probability:

- Would = certain, 100 percent

  If we were to drill the well, we would get 100 barrels of oil per day.

- Probably would = very high, 80 percent

  If we were to drill the well, we probably would get 100 barrels of oil per day.

- Could = reasonably high, 50 percent

  If we were to drill the well, we could get 100 barrels of oil per day.

- Might = moderate, 30 percent

  If we were to drill the well, we might get 100 barrels of oil per day.

Do not use *should* for "high probability." Use *should* in its principal meaning—"an ethical or moral obligation":

> You should not allow your graph to have an appearance of precision greater than your data allow.
>
> This final part of the president's speech should not be quoted out of context.

See the discussion of subjunctives in VERBS.

Your/You're. *Your* is the possessive form of *you. You're* is the contraction for *you are:*

> Your letter arrived too late for us to adjust the original invoice.
>
> If you're interested, we can survey the production history of that sand over the last decade or so.

Word Processing

Word processing is the writing, editing, and printing of documents using either automated editing typewriters or computers and computer printers. Workers using word processing equipment type (input) text, move it around, revise it at will, paste in pieces of other documents, and file and retrieve their work—all electronically.

Word processing is different from typing—so much so that the term *typing* now seems old-fashioned. In the world of word processing, typing is now called keyboarding or inputting, which includes the original writing of text as well as the typing in of existing text. Once text has been input, word processing allows the inputter to experiment freely with different formats and to revise and edit the text easily.

Format options include margins, type faces, line lengths, tabs, boxes, shaded areas, italics, boldface, and graphics. These format options used to be available only in professionally typeset documents.

Now, a sophisticated word-processed document can be very professional appearing. Word-processed documents are especially sophisticated if they have been prepared using software with desktop publishing features. See DESKTOP PUBLISHING.

Revising with word processing equipment is especially easy. All word processing programs have a menu (list) of commands: SAVE, PRINT, DELETE, SEARCH, REPLACE, CUT, COPY, PASTE, SORT, etc. With these commands, inputters (writers and editors) can rearrange sentences, paragraphs, or whole sections; can delete single words or whole sentences; and can replace with a single command a specific word or phrase throughout an entire document.

Word processing makes writing and editing easier and more flexible than it has ever been.

This ease and flexibility can, however, be a trap. Clients, supervisors, and editors begin to believe that everything can be changed and made better within a few seconds by pushing a single key. To them, change is easy, and it is, but it is also time-consuming, even frustrating to the person doing the changes. In the workplace, efficient word processing means knowing when the document is okay as it is—when enough changes are enough!

Part of learning to use word processing involves becoming comfortable looking at a computer monitor. Many of today's writers and editors are more comfortable with a hard (printed) copy of a document than with a document on a monitor. To them, the computer monitor prevents them from perceiving the overall organization and structure of a document—the "feel" of the document. They find it hard to proofread on a monitor.

But change in the word processing environment has been rapid. Many workers, especially those who have grown up using computers, are now accustomed to seeing documents or data on the computer monitor. They find it easier to work on a monitor than to proofread and edit on a hard copy.

Such differences in background and experience mean that no single set of rules (suggestions) about word processing techniques will work for everyone.

Whatever your own comfort level with computers, take time to learn how to use your computer's word processing features. It will be time well spent.

Short classes are more and more available either at schools and colleges or even from computer retailers, who include training as part of their customer support. Don't overlook the individual computer tutorial that likely came with your word processing software. Also, review the software documentation manual so that you'll know where to find answers quickly when problems occur. If nothing else helps, try calling the software company's Customer Service Department (usually an 800-number).

When Problems Occur

1. Learn to SAVE often and, for important documents, to SAVE on a second (backup) disk.

Remember that the computer's memory is temporary and will vanish whenever electric power vanishes or the hardware or software fails. Therefore, the cardinal rule of word processing is to save your writing often.

When you command your machine to SAVE, everything you have written up to that point (including all corrections, changes, and even errors) will be recorded on a diskette or hard disk.

Certain word processing programs or networks are programmed to save your copy automatically every few minutes—assuming you want it saved! Usually, the automatic save function can be set to save your work at whatever interval you choose. Some systems signal you with a bell or a flashing light to remind you to save your work.

For important documents, save your work on a second (backup) disk in case problems develop with the main disk or disk drive. Some word processing programs and networks automatically back up (save) everything that has been written on a given day so that nothing will be lost if the whole network fails (crashes).

In any case, if you lose something, don't panic. Your work might have been preserved somewhere on a network system that provides backup possibilities. Many word processing programs also permit you to "undo" inadvertent erasures if you act quickly. Be sure to check your word processing program for such an "undo" command.

2. Be flexible (and patient!) when your computer refuses to respond to a command.

Even the most sophisticated computer system has its quirks and lapses. Sometimes problems develop within hardware or software, but more often, you are asking the machine to do something it isn't programmed to do.

Occasionally, such problems cause computers to freeze, crash, or come down. When this happens, you have probably lost all of the text you have written since you last asked the computer to SAVE.

In other instances, your system doesn't freeze (crash), but your command is simply not obeyed. Usually, this problem is the result of "toggle trouble." The computer functions by means of an incredibly elaborate series of microscopic electrical switches (toggles). If something interferes with this extremely fast switching process—a random static charge, a dust particle—then the "toggling" may not happen.

Repeating a command will sometimes overcome a problem. If not, **copy your work to a new file** and then try the command again.

If after trying everything you still can't get a command to work, call the Customer Service Department for your word processing software program; usually they have an 800-number. They can usually tell you how to check out your hardware and software to see if something is really wrong.

As You Are Getting Started

3. Plan ahead to save your work using intelligible file names.

As rule 1 above suggested, SAVE often. Almost as important is how you name your files so that material saved will be accessible days, weeks, even months later.

Electronic word processing files are similar to the files in a filing cabinet. Well-organized and clean files are a pleasure to work with; messy, chaotic files are a disaster.

Each word processing file should have its own name (code), including, as appropriate, alphabetical or numerical indications of its subject, its writer, and the version saved. For example, you might choose to label a file on *Word Processing* with the abbreviation *WP* or perhaps *Word Pro.* If different writers work on the same subject, you could add the writer's initial: *Word Pro-RL.*

Most software programs have a feature that indicates the date and time when the file was last opened, but this information might not always help you, especially if you have multiple versions of the same document with the same title. After all, you may have opened an early version of a document while you were trying to find the current version; this early version will automatically carry the most recent date. Consider, therefore, some system for identifying the version or draft—A, B, C, etc. or 1, 2, 3, etc.

Word Processing

[Date]

[Customer's name]
[Customer's address]

Dear [customer's name]:

Thank you for taking time to write us about service problems you have been having at [dealer and and city and state]. We are naturally concerned that you have not received better service on your WAM [model year] [model].

As a result of your letter, we have contacted [the dealer] for your service record. From that record we have determined that [explanation and conclusions].

Because your [model] is still covered under warranty, we recommend that you continue to work with your dealer. We also will follow up with you by phone to see if the dealer's service has been more satisfactory.

Again, thank you for writing to us. Please let us know if we can be of any further help.

Sincerely,

[Name]
Customer Service Representative

cc: [Dealer]

Figure 1. A Typical Template for a Customer Service Letter. *This template can be kept in a computer and updated each time a writer wants to use it. Each time it is used, it needs a new file name to avoid copying over the template itself.*

File Names for a Team Document. File names are crucial if a number of writers and editors are working as a team on a document. Teams usually share electronic drafts for review and revision. The more sharing, the more a recent revision is likely to be lost or replaced with an earlier version. Remember also that computers are very literal; they will save (replace) a recent draft with an early draft if the two drafts have the same title.

Also, agree as a team on how to manage access to the files. Consider privacy issues and the problems of handling client and proprietary information. Decide beforehand who will know passwords and have access privileges.

4. Decide on a format for your document before you begin writing.

The simplest format is usually the one that is already set for your computer by your software program. This basic format will have certain defaults (standard settings)—for example, standard margins, a standard type face, and standard tabs. Use this standard format for routine documents.

The more sophisticated your document, however, the more you will want to develop your own format—perhaps with wider margins, a two-column format, a different type face, etc. Word processing systems allow you to program such style variations so that you can insert them with a single key stroke.

Consider also using available templates (boilerplate) instead of always generating a new document. A template is a standardized document or preset form (e.g., memo, sales letter, proposal, customer service letter, invoice, manual, procedure, report) that you have to change or update frequently. See figure 1 for the template of a customer service letter. To update such a template, you set "insert codes" in your master file. These codes permit you to jump immediately to your preselected points of insertion (names, addresses, dates, particular responses or new text, personalized closings).

Remember to save the changed text under a new file name to avoid confusion when retrieving the standardized document.

Format Decisions for a Team. If a team is working on a document, the earlier members can agree on a format, the more efficient will be the writing.

A simple team technique is to develop a single printed style sheet for everyone to use. A style sheet can be as complex as you wish to make it. In essence, it shows how your page will be laid out (margins, spacing, etc.), which type face to use, and when to use special features (boxes for visuals, shaded quotations, etc.). Figure 2 presents a simple style sheet, which would be easy to construct using most word processing software. See DESKTOP PUBLISHING for an example of a more complex style sheet.

If You Write on Your Computer

Writing a new document directly on your computer has become easier and easier because word processing tools have become more user-friendly and accessible.

Word processing equipment now represents a fourth or even fifth generation of electronic equipment for writing. In less than a generation, writers and writing have moved from manual typewriters to electric typewriters with interchangeable type balls, and finally to computers using updated word processing software. Of course, some hold-outs still argue that nothing helps the writer more than sitting down with a yellow legal pad and a favorite pen or pencil.

The changes in writing technology have even changed how we write.

The most obvious change is that writers can write much faster. If your fingers unconsciously know the keyboard, you can now input (write) your text probably two or three times faster than you could type on a manual typewriter and four or five times faster than you could scratch your text on a legal pad. You can now write your text with a speed that more closely mirrors the speed of speech. Your thoughts will still run ahead of the words your fingers are typing, but the faster you write, the better your chance of catching an insight or an implication before your mind moves on.

Writing is still, however, a mystery. Even the computer cannot reveal just how someone comes up with a particular organization or a certain train of logical thought.

The following rules are suggestions about how to write using word processing. As suggestions, they are necessarily provisional and tentative. You need to ask yourself what works for you and what doesn't. You might still need, for example, to plan on paper before turning to the keyboard. Or you might decide that you can only proofread effectively if you have a hard (printed) copy in front of you.

As you write using word processing, test the following suggestions. Be alert for shortcuts. Try to make your writing efficient, even pleasant.

5. Plan your document before you begin to write (input).

Planning is important to avoid false starts or dead ends. Try to identify a few of the givens about the document before you begin to write.

Do you have your task or assignment clearly in mind?

- What is your main purpose?
- Who will read your document and what are their goals and priorities?
- What sort of document (length, format, content) do you expect to write?

These and similar questions will surely be in the back of your mind as you are writing. Do you need to write them down before beginning—perhaps on a pad or on a whiteboard?

Will writing down some of these givens help you focus your efforts? Do what you must to make your writing as efficient as possible.

6. Brainstorm your content.

Your word processor can be a valuable brainstorming tool. After all, anything you write can vanish with the touch of a key, and you can move ideas around at will. So you needn't be afraid of writing down something stupid or something that you think won't fit.

First-level headings will be 14-point bold Times, centered.

Second-level headings will be 12-point bold Times, flush left.

Third-level headings will be 10-point bold Times, and will lead into paragraphs. Ordinary text will be 10-point Times. Paragraphs will be ragged right.

Double-space after 1st- and 2nd-level headings and to begin a new paragraph.

1. Wherever possible, we will use numbered lists. Indent text so that successive lines line up with the first line.

- Where numbering is not crucial, lists will begin with bullets. Indent text so that successive lines line up with the first line.

Figure 2. A Typical Word Processing Style Sheet. *For many documents, writers need to develop a style sheet so that as they write they will be consistent with themselves throughout the document and with other writers (assuming a team effort).*

Experiment with a brainstorming phase before you actually begin to write the text—that is, **before** you try to write complete sentences and fleshed-out paragraphs.

Such a brainstorming phase might be a rapid inputting of key words and phrases without any order or sequence. Let your mind race as fast as it will, and don't block even the dumb ideas. Don't worry about spelling.

Brainstorming is most applicable to documents that are not regular and routine. For routine documents, you already know much of the content, and you may even have a format (template) to start with. See rule 4 above.

After you finish brainstorming, you have to choose what you want to do next. You might, for example, print a copy of your brainstorming and use it as a guide for writing your draft. Your software may even display your brainstorming notes in a window on the screen while you are writing your text.

7. Organize your content.

The more complex the document, the more you will need to organize your brainstorming notes.

This process might be merely a sequencing or tidying up of your brainstorming notes. Or, you might decide to work up a fairly complete outline.

Many word processing programs have an outlining function. This function usually gives you a standard outline format to work with, and once you finish your outline, you usually can view the outline in a window on your screen while you are writing your text. See OUTLINES and ORGANIZATION.

If you have always liked to outline before writing, you will probably want to continue using an outline as part of word processing. If you never liked writing from an outline, you might want to move directly from your brainstorming notes to the writing of your draft.

8. Use word processing techniques to simplify your drafting of a document.

Writing rough drafts used to be a more daunting task before the word processor. Now you can write, tinker, move text around, insert, and delete ideas at any point in the writing process.

The computer can help you overcome "writer's block." If you write quickly, not trying to be perfect the first time, the computer can cut your writing time. You also can avoid anxiety about having something with errors, misspellings, and other warts.

Nevertheless, ease of editing on the word processor means you will be tempted to rework sections or whole drafts before you finish writing the initial version.

Try not to allow such revision work to interrupt your thinking or cause you to forget ideas you should record.

Keep these things in mind while writing on a word processor:

- Remember, you can always change text later, so avoid tinkering with grammar, spelling, and punctuation before you have all of your ideas on the screen.
- Make notes on-screen of ideas that occur to you but may not be relevant to the passage you're working on. Some word processing programs permit you to make "text notes," i.e., text that is invisible to the printer but appears on-screen.
- Code or mark points in the text where missing data needs to be inserted or more work needs to be done. For example, you can insert a non-word symbol like ??? or XXX. Then with your SEARCH feature, you can tell the computer to search for places where this symbol appears.

Team Writing of a Draft. Recognize that rough drafting is not a group activity. Instead, assign each team member a section to write, and remind them of the style they should follow. See rule 4 above. When team members finish with their drafts, assign a single person to integrate the drafts so that the team can review the whole document.

9. Make revision (editing) efficient by setting priorities and sticking to them.

Take care of the big issues such as purpose, content, and emphasis before you begin to polish sentences and mold your paragraphs.

Proofreading comes last.

Setting priorities makes sense because it forces you to address the more global issues rather than spending too much time on trivial details when the document has failed to achieve its main purpose.

Revision (editing) begins when you reread what you've written. Decide, first, if you need to see the document in hard copy. If so, print a copy, preferably with double-spacing and wide margins.

Next, review the whole document with these major questions in mind:

- Is my main purpose clear and up front?
- Have I emphasized my key ideas?
- What else should I tell my readers?
- Is my tone and approach appropriate and effective?

After you have asked these hard questions (and fixed any problems), begin working on your paragraphs and sentences.

Here is where the word processor is a boon. You can rewrite, move, or delete text so easily that you can experiment with different ways to say the same thing. For example, you might make a second copy of a paragraph and rewrite the copy. After rewriting, you can return to the original to see if you have improved it. Finally, you can delete the version you decide not to use.

To help with rewriting, some word processing programs have an electronic thesaurus. Consider using it if you are stumped for an appropriate word or phrase.

Also, during rewriting, you might want to code words or phrases that you wish to appear in your index or in a table of contents. Then when you finish editing, you can command your word processor to sort the words and phrases and to prepare the table of contents or the index. See INDEXES and TABLES OF CONTENTS.

A Final Caution About Revision. No text is ever finished or perfect, at least in the minds of most writers. Word processing often lures writers into spending excessive time revising and polishing their drafts. The secret is to know when to quit revising.

Decide when the draft is adequate, even good, but not necessarily perfect, and then stop.

---

10. Use word processing techniques to help you proofread your document.

Although the word processor makes writing and especially editing much more flexible and easier than ever before, it also adds new possibilities for errors. The ease of changing things makes consistency of content, data, grammar, and spelling a major problem.

Proofreading becomes even more essential after a writer has tinkered with a text for hours and hours because for every change the writer has made, probably 10 others should have been made for consistency with the single change.

Follow these general suggestions for proofreading on a word processor:

- **Proofread on the Screen.** An advantage of the word processor is that you don't have to print a hard copy to proofread or to review your text. But even experienced editors have trouble proofreading using only the screen. The text is often too small, and it is sometimes awkward to check the document for overall consistency when you can see only a dozen or so lines of text at a time.

  If you do proofread on the screen, consider changing the text to larger, more readable type and adjusting the line spacing to double spaces. Both of these changes will help you identify proofreading problems.

- **Proofread a Hard Copy.** Some people find it difficult to proofread on a screen because screens do not always show entire pages and the visual resolution of characters on a screen is not always clear and sharp. Actually, reviewing a hard copy will give you a second chance to catch things you've already missed on the screen.

- **Check for Consistency.** When you change your text at some point, odd problems may appear elsewhere in the text. Some subjects no longer agree with verbs, spellings become inconsistent, and pronouns no longer agree with their antecedents.

  Be particularly careful about global search and replace commands; if you order all the *threes* in your document to become *fives*, you had better be sure that you mean **all** the *threes*. When you insert new information or update boilerplate, be careful that the old text is consistent in every way with the new.

- **Run a Spelling Check.** Most word processing programs are equipped with spellcheck features. When you command the computer to check your spelling, it matches every word in your text with words in its internal dictionary, flagging those it doesn't recognize. Then the machine gives you the option of changing the questionable word or leaving it as is.

  Spellcheckers are wonderful for finding typographical errors and plain old misspellings—but be careful. The spellchecker may overlook words that are spelled right but are wrong for the context (e.g., **there** instead of **their**), so proofreading is still necessary. Often, you can add words from your professional vocabulary to the computerized dictionary; make sure you spell them correctly when you do.

- **Run a Grammar Check.** Grammar checkers are designed to catch grammar and punctuation errors by comparing your writing with lists of common phrases that often present problems.

  For example, most grammar checkers can identify whether you have used a passive or an active verb in a sentence. The checker cannot, however, tell you whether the passive is the correct choice or whether you should change it to an active verb. See ACTIVE/PASSIVE. As this example illustrates, grammar programs are not very advanced in their ability to point out errors in grammar, punctuation, or word usage. They may flag only a small percentage of the errors in your copy, and what they flag may not even be errors.

Some grammar checkers also purport to analyze style. Such style checkers measure sentence length and word length to determine a "reading level" for your text. These levels may be expressed in terms of an index of readership or grade level in school terms. Often, style checkers can help you gauge whether your sentences are short enough and your word choice simple enough to make your point effectively. See SENTENCES and GOBBLEDYGOOK. Style checkers will not really identify basic problems of inconsistent or incoherent sentence structure.

Special Word Processing Features for Writers

Bibliographic Databases. Scientific and technical researchers who must work with or provide reference lists in reports may find bibliography programs helpful. These programs permit you to enter information about references and then to format the information according to any bibliographical style you choose (e.g., for formal reports, catalogs, journals, conference proceedings, or dissertations). Professionals who use on-line databases can transfer reference information directly into the bibliographic database.

Remember to proofread reference lists just the same as you proofread text.

Mathematical Expression Checkers. Aimed at technical professionals who present mathematical proofs in their writing, these programs enable them to pull mathematical symbols into their copy; to highlight equations, making editing easier; and to work within templates that provide preset mathematical structures for many common equations.

Graphics Programs. Professional-looking graphics are becoming standard in business and technical reports. Many sophisticated, easy-to-use programs exist for generating graphics. You can create your own graphs, diagrams, and charts with a painting or drawing program, and then paste them into your copy. Or you can use one of the many programs that contain predesigned graphics and just plug them into your copy (be careful here—the quality of these images ranges widely). Finally, you can transfer an image printed on paper into your computer by using a scanner, which turns a picture into digital codes and then displays it on the computer screen. You can then manipulate its size, orientation, and position on the page.

If you need to use colored or complex and eye-catching graphics, you may want to step from word processing to desktop publishing, which involves more sophisticated page layout and graphics opportunities. See DESKTOP PUBLISHING.

Wordy Phrases

Wordy phrases are phrases that use too many words to express an idea. Many of them are similar to or incorporate redundancies, and many wordy phrases have been overused so much they've become cliches:

all of a sudden
at a later date
beyond a shadow of a doubt
in light of the fact that
in the environment of
in the neighborhood of
kept under surveillance
on two different occasions
reported to the effect
the fullest possible extent

None of these phrases is necessary, but many writers use them habitually, so they seem "natural" somehow. In informal speech and writing, these phrases may in fact be preferable, depending on your audience. In technical and business writing, however, you should avoid them.

See Redundant Words, Cliches, Gobbledygook, and Scientific/Technical Style.

---

1. Eliminate wordy phrases.

A fundamental of good writing style is to eliminate unnecessary words. Do not say *all of a sudden.* Just say *suddenly.* Instead of *at a later date,* say *later. In light of the fact that* simply means *because of.*

The shorter, simpler words or expressions make your writing more concise and, consequently, make it look and sound more professional.

A List of Wordy Phrases

The following list of wordy phrases will help you identify those you habitually use. The wordy phrase appears in the left column; in the right column are possible substitutes:

according to the law	legally
add an additional	add
add the point that	add that
afford an opportunity	permit/allow
a great deal of	much
a greater number of	more
a great number of times	often/ frequently
a large number of	many
a little less than	almost
all of a sudden	suddenly
along the lines of	like
a majority of	most
a number of	several/ many/some
any one of the two	either
a period of several weeks	several weeks
as a general rule	usually/ generally
as a matter of fact	in fact
a small number of	few
as of now	now
as of this date	today
as regards	about
as related to	for/about
assuming that	if
as to	about
a sufficient number	enough
at a later date	later
at all times	always
at an early date	soon
at hand	here
at present	now
at regular intervals of time	regularly
at that time	then
at the conclusion of	after
at the present time	now
at the rear of	behind
at the same instant	simulta- neously
at this time	now
at which time	then
based on the fact that	due to/ because
beyond a shadow of a doubt	doubtless
brought to a sudden halt	halted
by means of	by
by the time that	when
by the use of	by
by way of illustration	for example
called attention to the fact	reminded
came to a stop	stopped
cannot be possible	impossible
come to an end	end
cost the sum of	cost
despite the fact that	although
detailed information	details
draw to a close	end
due to the fact that	because
during the course of	during
during the time that	when/while
during which time	while
estimated at about	estimated at
estimated roughly at	estimated at
exactly alike	identical
except in a small number of cases	usually
exhibit a tendency to	tend to
expose to elevated temperature	heat
few in number	few
for a short space of time	for a short time
for the purpose of	for/to
for the reason that	because/since
for this reason	so
from now on	in the future
from the point of view of	for
from time to time	occasionally
having reference to this	for/about
if and when	if/when
if at all possible	if possible
if that were the case	if so
in accordance with	by/under
in addition (to)	also/besides
in a number of cases	many/some
in a position to	can/may
in a satisfactory manner	satisfactorily
inasmuch as	because/ since/as
in back of	behind
in case of	if
in close proximity	near
in conjunction with	with
in consideration of the fact	because
in excess of	more than
in favor of	for
in few cases	seldom
in few instances	seldom
in lieu of	instead of/in place of

Wordy Phrases

in light of the fact that	because
in many cases	often
in most cases	usually
in order to	to
in other words	or/that is
in rare cases	rarely
in (with) reference to	about/concerning
in regard to	about/concerning
in relation to	with
in respect to	about/concerning
in short supply	scarce
in terms of	according to
in the absence of	without
in the amount of	of/for
in the case of	for/by/in/if
in the course of	during
in the environment of	around/near
in the event of	if
in the event that	should
in the first place	first/primarily
in the instance of	for
in the majority of cases	usually
in the matter of	about
in the nature of	like
in the near future	soon
in the neighbor-hood of	about/near
in the proximity of	near/nearly/about
in the vicinity of	around/near
introduced a new	introduced
in view of the fact that	considering
involve the necessity of	requires
is/are in the possession of	has/have
is defined as	is
is in the process of making	is making
is of the opinion that	believes
is representative of	typifies
it is apparent that	apparently
it is clear that	clearly
it is evident that	evidently
it is obvious that	obviously
it is often the case that	frequently
it is plain that	plainly
it is unquestionable that	unquestion-ably
it would appear that	it seems
kept an eye on	watched
kept under surveillance	watched
last of all	last
leaving out of consideration	disregarding
made an investigation of	investigated
major portion of	most of
make application to	apply
make a purchase	buy
make contact with	meet/contact
more and more	increasingly
notwithstanding the fact that	although
of considerable magnitude	big/large/great
off of	off
of no mean ability	capable
of small diameter	fine/thin
of very minor importance	unimportant
on account of	because
on a few occasions	occasionally
on a stretch of road	on a road
on behalf of	for
once in a great while	seldom/rarely
one after another	alternately
one by one	singly
one part in a hundred	1 percent
on the basis of	by
on the grounds that	because
on the part of	by
on two different occasions	twice
ought to	should
outside of	except
owing to the fact that	since/because
period of time	interval/period
pertaining to	about
possibly might	might
prior to	before
probed into	probed
proceed to investigate, control, study,	analyze/study/investigate
provide a continuous indication of	show continuously
pursuant to	following
range all the way from	range from
reduced to basic essentials	simplified
refer back	refer
relative to	about
repeat again	repeat
reported to the effect	reported
revise downward	lower
Seldom if ever	rarely
separate into two equal parts	halve
since the time when	since
started off with	started with
subsequent to	after/following
take appropriate measures	act
take this factor into consideration	therefore
that is to say	that is
the foregoing	the/this/that/these/those
the fullest possible extent	mostly/fully/completely
the only difference being that	except that
there is no doubt that	doubtless/no doubt
there is no question that	unquestion-ably
through the use of	by
to be cognizant of	to know
to summarize the above	in summary
total operating costs	operating costs
turn up	turn
two by two	paired/in pairs
Until and unless	unless
until such time as	until
up to now	formerly
Went on to say	added/continued
when and if	if
with a view to	intending to
with full approval	approved
within the realm of possibility	possibly/possible
without variation	constant/stable
with reference to	about
with regard to	about/regarding
with respect to	about/respecting
with the exception of	except
with the object of	to
with the result that	so that

Reference Glossary Index

Reference Glossary Index

Reference Glossary Index

Reference Glossary Index

Reference Glossary Index

Reference Glossary Index

Reference Glossary Index

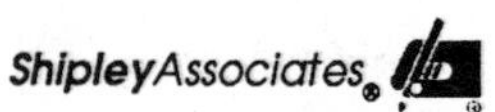

Reference Glossary Index

Reference Glossary Index

Reference Glossary Index

Reference Glossary Index

Reference Glossary Index

Reference Glossary Index

Reference Glossary Index

Contents (Section 2)

Letters

Memos

Others

Reports

Using Model Documents

The following model documents represent the best in current business and technical English. Their subjects are typical of those that today's writers must write about. Their formats are emphatic and visual. Their language is concise, direct, and conversational.

These model documents should guide, not intimidate users of this *Style Guide*. Study the models, practice using the techniques and formats illustrated, but don't try to follow the models too closely. If you do, your own document may have words or phrases that are not applicable or appropriate. Don't worry if you find your own words and phrases straying from the language in a particular model. Most documents will be effective if they represent your personal approach and style—if they sound like you, not like someone else.

The best, most useful models are simply points of departure.

Response Letter

With Information and Directions

The set-up is short but essential. It explains why John Smythe isn't writing. See ORGANIZATION.

The response comes early in the letter and is clear and straightforward.

Listing the requirements emphasizes them. Using a bulleted list makes every item equally important. See COLONS, LISTS, EMPHASIS, and PARALLELISM.

The listed items do not end in periods because none of them is a complete sentence. See LISTS.

The closing is social and informative. See LETTERS.

BCC
BOUNTIFUL CHEMICAL COOPERATIVE, INC.
139 Sequoia Park Way
Suite 303
Oakland, California 90022
(415) 451-7561

February 16, 1990

Mrs. Louise Lantham
12039 Plaza Drive
Tallahassee, FL 32303

Dear Mrs. Lantham:

**How to Add Your Husband as a Dependent
Under Your Group Insurance Plan**

John Smythe asked me to write to you to explain how you can add your husband as a dependent under the group insurance plan underwritten by the Savannah Life Insurance Company.

To enroll your husband, simply complete the enclosed enrollment card and medical information sheet and send them, along with a medical report from your physician, to me at the above address, M/S 258. The medical report should be up to date and complete and should include the following information:

- Current illnesses or injuries, including your physician's prognosis
- Illnesses and injuries within the past 5 years
- Diagnoses and dates of treatments for all illnesses or injuries listed above
- Types and dosages of medications, including whether he is still taking them, and, if not, when he stopped
- Any other information your physician believes might help us to evaluate your husband's physical condition

As soon as we receive the enrollment card, the medical information sheet, and the medical report, we will be able to process your application. If you have further questions, please call me at (415) 451-7582.

Sincerely,

Walt Cavanaugh

Walt Cavanaugh
Assistant Manager
Personnel Department

WC/ght
Enclosures

A brief set-up is essential, but the response itself must appear as early as possible. The list enhances readability and emphasizes the requirements. See LISTS.

The tone of the letter is businesslike but courteous. The writer tries to establish warmth and cooperation in the response. The writer also includes the appropriate mail stop number (paragraph 2) and personal phone number (closing paragraph). See TONE.

This letter illustrates the semiblock format with standard punctuation. See LETTERS.

Response Letter
To a Concerned Customer

The opening paragraph establishes the context of the response and is a courteous acknowledgment of the customer's concern.

This paragraph attempts to develop rapport with the reader. The tone is informal and personal. See TONE and LETTERS.

This paragraph states FFFF's position and leads into the summary of the testing—which provides evidence validating FFFF's position.

A displayed list highlights the test results, which are presented in everyday language. See SCIENTIFIC/TECHNICAL STYLE and TONE.

FARMLAND FROZEN
FAMILY FOODS

January 16, 1990

Ms. Josephine Lambert
1667 Willow Avenue
Seattle, WA 96508

Dear Ms. Lambert:

Thank you for your recent inquiry about the use of mozzarella cheese substitute in our FFFF lasagna.

I, too, am worried about the increasing presence of artificial products and additives in our food, so I can sympathize with your concern over finding a mozzarella cheese substitute as an ingredient in FFFF lasagna.

Let me assure you, however, that the mozzarella cheese substitute and all other ingredients in our lasagna are as wholesome and safe as we can make them. We decided to use the mozzarella cheese substitute only after extensive testing. Here are the results.

Advantages of Mozzarella Cheese Substitute

—**Mozzarella cheese substitute has no cholesterol** but does have all of the vitamins, minerals, and protein found in natural mozzarella. Many of our customers have asked for lower cholesterol levels in our products.

—**Our consumer test panel, in extensive blind testing, could detect no difference in taste**, smell, or appearance between the mozzarella cheese substitute and natural mozzarella.

—**Ingredients in natural mozzarella and the substitute are almost identical:** water, milk protein, and fat. Natural cheese has animal fat, which contributes the cholesterol, while the substitute has soybean oil. Both products have similar minor additives to enhance the flavor, prevent spoilage, and guarantee consistent quality.

303 Blossom Avenue Des Moines, Iowa 50321 (515) 521-4911

Letters responding to customer complaints should be as personal and direct as possible. The writer must address all questions or grievances in the reader's earlier letter and must do so in a friendly, sympathetic, and courteous manner.

In responses to complaints or negative inquiries (as in this letter), beware of repeating the negative events or details verbatim. Instead, summarize the complaints. Don't force readers to relive the circumstances that made them angry enough to write in the first place.

Response Letter
To a Concerned Customer

Ms. Josephine Lambert
January 16, 1990
Page 2

—**Using mozzarella cheese substitute helps us lower the cost of FFFF lasagna**, especially given the recent increase in the price of natural cheese. This economic advantage also allows us to put more mozzarella into our lasagna—something many of our customers want.

The opening sentence begins with a dependent clause and delays its major point (our lasagna is high quality); however, the introductory clause mentions *cheese substitute*, so it forms an effective transition from previous thoughts. See TRANSITIONS.

Even with the mozzarella cheese substitute, we believe that our lasagna is a very high-quality product. It is both delicious and nutritious.

I hope this letter has answered your questions about our use of a cheese substitute and will make you feel comfortable about purchasing our lasagna. You mentioned that you enjoy a variety of FFFF products, so I am sending you several complimentary coupons. Thank you for your concern and for your interest in FFFF products.

Sincerely,

Martha Frampton

Martha Frampton
Public Relations

MF:sj
Enclosures

The personal pronoun *I* is appropriate even though the writer is speaking for FFFF. She shifts to the collective *we* when she speaks for the company as a whole. Such shifts in pronouns are natural and acceptable. See TONE, LETTERS, and PRONOUNS.

This letter illustrates the semiblock format with standard punctuation. See LETTERS.

Response Letter
Answer to a Complaint

June 25, 1990

Mr. Wiley G. Elkins
1456 Jackson Avenue
Jordan, MO 64833

Dear Mr. Elkins:

Thank you for your recent letter about Potato Ripples. The blackened material you found is not harmful although I can appreciate your dissatisfaction at finding it.

What you found was a small chunk of burned potato. These blackened chunks occur when particles break loose from potatoes and collect in our deep-fat frying system. To prevent these chunks from being packaged, we continuously filter the oil in our fryers, and we periodically clean the fryers. In addition, our inspectors visually check all Potato Ripples before packaging. Despite these precautions, a chunk of blackened potato occasionally finds its way into a package of Potato Ripples.

We do value the quality of our products and will continue to make every effort to prevent chunks of burned potato from being packaged with our Potato Ripples.

I am enclosing a coupon for a free package of Potato Ripples, Potato Crisps, Zucchini Fritters, or Eggplant Gems. We hope you will use the coupon to try Potato Ripples again or to try one of our other products. Again, thank you for your letter and for your interest in FFFF's products.

Sincerely yours,

Jackson Blaine

Jackson Blaine
Quality Control

JB:mm
Enclosure

303 Blossom Avenue   Des Moines, Iowa 50321   (515) 521-4911

The opening is courteous, personal, and reassuring. See INTRODUCTIONS and TONE.

The explanation is simple and nontechnical. See JARGON and GOBBLEDYGOOK.

This single-sentence paragraph establishes a key idea: quality.

The closing (and the coupons) further customer relations. The last sentence repeats the opening. See REPETITION.

Tact and a personal touch are crucial in letters to disgruntled customers. Personal pronouns help establish a tactful tone, and the details include specific references to Mr. Elkins' letter. See TONE.

The writer avoids technical complexity and jargon (he might have called the chunk of potato a "carbonized carbohydrate particle"). See JARGON, GOBBLEDYGOOK, and SCIENTIFIC/TECHNICAL STYLE.

The letter follows the modified block format with standard punctuation. See LETTERS.

Reprimand Letter

The first sentence sets up the major idea in the second sentence. See ORGANIZATION, LETTERS, and TONE.

This paragraph presents details. Listing these details is optional, but the list might create too formal an impression in this letter. See LISTS and PARAGRAPHS.

The closing paragraph is personal and hopeful while reiterating the seriousness of the situation.

Sky Aviation
822 Ocean View Drive
Long Beach, California 90802
(714) 332-3978

March 28, 1990

Mr. Fred Benson
7654 Laguna Boulevard
Long Beach, CA 94986

Dear Fred

I regretted having to talk to you last Wednesday about your failure to call in before being absent from work on March 22. Based on our discussion and your prior attendance problems, the company has decided to give you 2 days off without pay on April 1 and 2.

I have enrolled you in the Long Beach Alcohol and Drug Abuse program, which is a confidential service open to all of our employees. The program coordinator, John Hughes, has made an appointment at 10:30 a.m. on April 1 for you to see Roberta Crenshaw, an alcoholism counselor. Roberta is located in the main office at our Alameda facility. John also requested that you begin attending AA meetings each Thursday evening at the Paloma Community Church.

We hope, Fred, that this counseling will help you solve your problems. If further unannounced absences occur, the company will have to take more stringent disciplinary actions, including possible termination.

Sincerely

Terry Nielsen

G. Terry Nielsen
Director of Personnel

GTN:fg

Reprimand letters are hard to write, especially when the reader is a valuable employee. The best strategy is to soften the tone by being friendly and direct. Using the reader's name and using the pronouns *I* and *you* help make the tone friendly and personal. Consequently, this letter will be easier for the reader to accept. See TONE.

As in any effective letter, each of the paragraphs has a clear and definite purpose. Clear organization helps readers read and understand the content. See ORGANIZATION and PARAGRAPHS.

This letter illustrates the modified block format with open punctuation. See LETTERS.

Complaint Letter
With a Tactful Request for Aid

The opening paragraph establishes the problem and its seriousness. See LETTERS.

This description of a delay is concise yet specific. Note the paragraph structure—each sentence leads into the next, and the paragraph ends with a strong statement. See PARAGRAPHS.

This paragraph actually states the request. Then the second sentence repeats the financial problems caused by the delays. See PARAGRAPHS and REPETITION.

These paragraphs make two distinct requests. The short paragraphing helps highlight the requests. See EMPHASIS and PARAGRAPHS.

MIDLAND OIL AND GAS OPERATIONS, INC.
7000 Jalapeno Boulevard
Dallas, Texas 75234
(214) 735-9600

November 15, 1990

District Director
U.S. Immigration and Naturalization Service
2645 St. Anne Street
Houston, TX 77004

Dear Director:

Subject: Request to Resolve Unnecessary Shipping Delays Caused by INS Officials

During the past year, MOGO ships delivering crude oil to our Houston refinery complex have been unnecessarily delayed by immigration officials who have not arrived as scheduled for boarding. These delays cost MOGO Oil (and ultimately consumers) an average of $2,745/hr.

The most recent delay occurred on September 28, 1990, when the MV *Seaworthy* docked in Gulfview. Boarding was scheduled for 0400 that morning, but immigration officials did not arrive until 0930. When the officials finally arrived, they apologized for being late by saying, "We forgot." As you know, dock workers cannot unload a foreign vessel until immigration officials have cleared it, so unloading was delayed for over 5 hours. That delay cost MOGO over $15,000.00.

We would appreciate whatever you can do to help eliminate or at least reduce these delays. Occasional delays are inevitable, but we cannot sustain financial losses like the one above and remain competitive unless we increase the price we charge consumers for our oil products.

Please clarify for us the regulations regarding unloading of a vessel prior to boarding by immigration officials. In particular, can dock personnel unload a vessel that has cleared Customs but has yet to clear Immigration?

We would also appreciate having an after-hours telephone number to call when immigration officials do not arrive on schedule.

Complaint letters have to be tactful yet firm. They are usually based on one or more incidents, which must be established before you can request a remedy. The first two paragraphs of this letter provide background information that establishes the nature and seriousness of the problem. The request in the third paragraph is therefore understandable and reasonable. See ORGANIZATION and LETTERS.

Tone in complaint letters is important. Such letters should not sound shrill, angry, or unreasonable. In this letter, the author writes calmly but directly. He presents a specific case and then makes several understandable requests. The letter ends with a plea for cooperation. See TONE.

Complaint Letter
With a Tactful Request for Aid

The telephone number strengthens the pleasant, yet direct closing. See LETTERS.

U.S. Immigration and Naturalization Service
November 15, 1990
Page Two

Please call Jack Severenson or me at 886-2233 to discuss solutions to this problem. We want to do everything we can to cooperate with the Immigration and Naturalization Service.

Respectfully,

Frank Whitaker

Frank W. Whitaker
Shipping

FWW:dfe

The letter illustrates the block format with standard punctuation. See LETTERS.

Complaint Letter

With a Request for Action

FARMLAND FROZEN
FAMILY FOODS

August 8, 1990

Ms. Patricia Goodway
Customer Support Manager
The Pacific Baking Company
9924 West Pacific Way
San Francisco, CA 97521

Dear Ms. Goodway:

Request for Adherence to Breader Specifications

Recent samples of your breader contain more fines than our specifications allow. Please investigate the problem and let me know as soon as possible what you can do to solve it.

On August 5, our Medford plant inspectors noticed excessive carbon specks on breaded products, so they checked the breader lots on hand (codes 341X and 345X). According to our specification, fines through a U.S. Standard Sieve No. 80 must fall within these limits: 1 percent $\pm$ 1 percent (or a maximum of 2 percent). The breader lots on hand gave these results:

341X—3.30%

345X—4.10%

As you can see, the fines in these two lots exceeded our specification by 1.3 and 2.1 percent. These levels are not yet serious, but they do cause excessive carbon specks in the frying oil and on the finished product.

We have enjoyed a long relationship with Pacific Baking and hope to continue doing business with you. We are therefore anxious to solve this problem and will appreciate your prompt action.

Sincerely,

James Van Prooven

James Van Prooven
Plant Manager

JVP:qw

303 Blossom Avenue Des Moines, Iowa 50321 (515) 521-4911

The lead sentence sets up the problem, and the second sentence asks for a solution. See LETTERS and ORGANIZATION.

The test results are highlighted by the additional space around them. See EMPHASIS.

The closing paragraph establishes how serious the writer considers the problem to be and applies some pressure; yet the tone is not blunt or negative. See TONE.

Complaint letters, even if written in anger, should not sound angry. The tone should be positive and constructive. The writer should present clear evidence of dissatisfaction but should strive to balance the complaint with positive solutions. See TONE and LETTERS.

As in this letter, complaint letters usually start with a concise statement of the problem followed by a request for action or resolution. The problem statement should be as brief as possible but long enough to make the request understandable. See the discussion of set-ups in ORGANIZATION.

This letter illustrates the semiblock format with standard punctuation. See LETTERS.

Letter Soliciting a Bid

This single-sentence opening paragraph concisely states the letter's purpose. It states the "What's new?" portion of the message. See PARAGRAPHS.

The second paragraph provides essential detail and indicates that the letter has enclosures.

This paragraph is an effective—though not entirely subtle—appeal to the reader to keep the bid price low.

The closing paragraph provides final details. It constitutes the "What's next?" portion of the message.

Sky Aviation
822 Ocean View Drive
Long Beach, California 90802
(714) 332-3978

April 24, 1990

Mr. James Quirk
Wizard Machine Tools, Inc.
568 Flatbush Boulevard
Montrose Island, IL 44572

Dear Mr. Quirk

Subject: Invitation to Bid for Delta Q Indicators

Sky Aviation is soliciting bids for delta Q indicators for our Foxx 175 business jets.

After examining the enclosed drawing and specifications, you are invited to submit a quote by Friday, May 14, for producing 1,980 of these indicators—delivered at a rate of 55 per month for 36 months beginning November 1, 1990.

I understand that the indicators you already provide for our Windstream 88 fixed wing aircraft are very similar to the proposed delta Q indicator. This similarity should make design and fabrication of the new indicators relatively easy and should therefore reduce development and manufacturing costs.

Please send your quote to Mrs. Ernestine Gonzales in our Purchasing Department. The bids should arrive no later than Friday, May 14. If you have any questions, please call me or Jim Booth at (714) 332-3984.

Sincerely

Arnold Madsen

Arnold Madsen
Manager, Engineering

AM:mm
Enclosures

This letter features classic letter design: a concise opening that clearly indicates the letter's purpose (to solicit bids); a crisp middle with details appearing in short, well-designed paragraphs; and a courteous closing that provides final administrative details and ends with an offer of assistance. See LETTERS and ORGANIZATION.

This letter illustrates the block format with open punctuation. See LETTERS.

Sales Letter
With a Soft Sell

The opening is positive yet low-keyed, and the writer establishes the purpose of the letter within the first three short paragraphs.

RFP (Request for Proposal) is an abbreviation that will be familiar to the readers. Therefore, the writer does not have to spell it out. See ABBREVIATIONS.

The run-in heading highlights key technical points. See HEADINGS and LETTERS.

Sky Aviation
822 Ocean View Drive
Long Beach, California 90802
(714) 332-3978

June 18, 1990

International Aeronautics
P.O. Box 1149
Galveston, TX 41504

Attention: Mr. Boon Hollenbeck

Subject: Proposal to Assist in Designing the Cabin Pressurization System for the K–38

Gentlemen:

We were delighted to hear that International Aeronautics won the contract to develop the K-38 Heavy Cargo Helicopter.

As you know, Sky Aviation has done much of the pioneering work in cabin pressurization. Our pressurization systems are the state of the art in aircraft cabin pressurization, largely because of our patented flowback valve, the VA-321-E.

As you initiate detail design studies for the K-38, we hope you will consider basing cabin pressurization on our VA-321-E and allowing us to assist in cabin pressurization design.

The RFP indicates that the K-38 will require an 8-lb/min valve capable of maintaining a delta P of 0.3 to 0.5 psi. Valve VA-321-E meets these requirements and is more efficient than any of the other valves currently used in aircraft pressurization systems.

The enclosed drawing (DRA-321-E) shows the standard Sky Aviation configuration for the VA-321-E valve, including the outflow, check, and solenoid subsystems. Here are the control modes within this configuration:

> Minimum Differential Pressure Mode. In a 2-psi vacuum with the solenoid valve energized, the outflow valve will be fully open. With an 8-lb/min through-flow, this will result in maximum differential pressure of 0.75 inches of water.

A sales letter is a blend of fact and sales pitch. Thinking positively is essential, but sincerity and reality are also necessary ingredients of successful sales letters. This letter opens and closes with a soft sales pitch. The technical information in the middle is emphasized by headings and underlining. The writer's goal is to make the technical information seem substantial and convincing. See EMPHASIS, LETTERS, TONE, and SCIENTIFIC/TECHNICAL STYLE.

Sales Letter
With a Soft Sell

Mr. Boon Hollenbeck -2- June 18, 1990

Positive Differential Pressure Control. With the solenoid valve deenergized, the outflow valve will move toward the closed position and regulate the differential pressure to 0.6 psi. The regulation point is achieved by the correct sizing of the main poppet return spring.

Negative Differential Pressure Control. As presently configured, the proposed system incorporates negative differential pressure control, i.e., if the cabin pressure becomes less than the ambient air pressure, the outflow valve opens and admits ambient air into the cabin at approximately 0.4 psi. If you do not want this feature in your application, we can eliminate it through a minor change to the valve.

Leaving an extra blank line here helps distinguish the control mode discussion from the continuation of the text.

Valve VA-321-E is currently not in production. Before initiating production, we would have to size the outflow valve return spring. This design and test phase would take no more than 4 weeks.

This paragraph presents relevant past performance information—justification for selecting Sky Aviation.

If you decide to use our valve, you will have all of the technical resources of Sky Aviation at your command, including the engineers who have designed the pressurization systems for over 8,000 aircraft flying today. We now manufacture 25 percent of the pressurization systems for commercial aircraft and 15 percent of the systems for military aircraft.

For further information, please call Fred Huber or me at (714) 332-3973.

Sincerely is a good complimentary closing to a business letter. *Very truly yours* is too effusive. See LETTERS.

Sincerely,

Howard Patterson

Howard C. Patterson
Vice President

HCP:cv
Enclosure

This letter illustrates the modified block format with standard punctuation. See LETTERS.

Recommendation Memo

With a Political Delay

The subject block is very specific. Even though the reader will be averse to the request, the subject block should not be coy, misleading, or vague.

The opening paragraph sets up the request by providing sound support for it. The reader is being asked to do something he does not want to do; therefore, the writer must validate the request before actually stating it. See LETTERS and ORGANIZATION.

Note how the sentences lead from one to the other. See PARAGRAPHS and TRANSITIONS.

Repeating the 20 percent figure is helpful because it reinforces one of the writer's major points. See REPETITION and EMPHASIS.

To: Bob Conners

From: Denise Van Horn

Subject: **Recommendation to Lower the Toggle Testing Requirement on the Nose Landing Gear Transducer**

Date: June 10, 1990

We feel confident that our production of nose landing gear transducers has improved to the point where 100 percent toggle testing is no longer necessary. As I told Tom Rogers on the phone yesterday, 31 of 32 transducers in the second lot passed the test, and the only reject was just barely out of specification. Consequently, we request that you lower the toggle testing requirement to 20 percent.

Toggle testing delays production considerably and is both time consuming and extremely expensive. We hope to eliminate the testing procedure and rely on quality assurance checks, which is our standard practice. For now, however, we believe that 20 percent testing will guarantee quality assurance.

By return memo, please authorize us to lower the toggle testing requirement so that we can improve our production efficiency. If I can provide further information, please let me know.

Normally, writers should open their memos by clearly stating their request. Sometimes, however, politics forbids such directness. In this case, Bob Conners has been adamant about 100 percent toggle testing, so Denise knows that she cannot open the memo with a blunt request for him to change his mind. She has to prepare him to change his mind, so she leads off with a two-sentence set-up that introduces the idea and provides solid evidence to support it. See MEMOS, LETTERS, and ORGANIZATION.

This organization is most effective when, for political reasons, writers cannot open with a direct statement of the request. If politics are not an issue, however, writers should open with the request itself.

Recommendation Memo

With Technical Content

The references are complete enough to facilitate document retrieval and are numbered to facilitate citation in the text of the memo. See MEMOS and LETTERS.

The opening paragraph states the author's position and lists three key reasons for that position.

The summaries of the references are optional, but they should appear somewhere in the memo. They inform readers not familiar with the references and remind readers who are familiar with the references. See MEMOS.

To: F. Winters

Date: December 7, 1990

Subject: **Recommend Priming Windstream Fuselage with Rivlin 680 (NOT 780) to Avoid Increased Production Costs**

Reference: (a) Memo 5870-5-113 (10-25-84), R. Trent to D. Birdwell, "Long Beach Paint Hangar Requirements to Support Windstream Airplane Programs"

(b) Memo 3281-6-98 (11-18-84), S. Blaine to R. Trent, "Painting the Windstream Fuselage in the Long Beach Paint Hangar"

Rivlin 780 should not be used to prime the Windstream airplanes painted at the Foxx facility in Long Beach. We recommend continued priming with Rivlin 680 for these reasons:

- More cost effective
- Easier to apply
- Cleaner, more appealing to customers

Reference (a) stated that Long Beach would have the capacity to apply exterior paint to the Windstream by early 1991. However, Long Beach capability will depend on the ground rules attached to reference (a).

Reference (b) stated that the Windstream airplanes will require Rivlin 780 instead of Rivlin 680. The memo requested adjusting the applicable rules to accommodate Rivlin 780.

Though the authors of both memos argued persuasively for Rivlin 780, we continue to support Rivlin 680 as the primer for the Windstream.

Recommendation memos should either open with the recommendation (as above) or with a brief set-up that prepares readers for the recommendation. Only in exceptional cases should a memo lead up to the final sentence or paragraph that reveals the recommendation. See ORGANIZATION and MEMOS.

The references are often extensive, especially in technical discussions. They should follow the order they are mentioned in the memo, and all references listed at the beginning of the memo should be mentioned in the text.

Recommendation Memo

With Technical Content

Numbering this list emphasizes the extra steps necessary.

F. Winters -2- December 7, 1990

Rivlin 680 More Cost Effective

Unnecessary disposal costs for a single Windstream run around $650 when we use Rivlin 780. Rivlin 780 contains about six times as much chromium as Rivlin 680 and must therefore be disposed of via a tank truck instead of the sewer.

Rivlin 680 Easier to Apply

Labor and production delay would equal at least one 8-hour shift for each Windstream treated with 780. The whole painting process now takes only 3 days, so we would be adding another day's costs.

Using Rivlin 780 in the areas to be painted does not eliminate the need for Rivlin 680 on the unpainted areas of the fuselage. Therefore, we would need to perform **five extra steps** to apply the 780: (1) Mask the skin area to remain unpainted, using metal-foil tape to prevent contact with Rivlin 680; (2) Apply Rivlin 780; (3) Rinse; (4) Allow to dry; (5) Remove metal-foil masking tape. After taking these steps, we would still need to apply Rivlin 680 to unpainted areas as usual.

Rivlin 680 Leaves Cleaner Surfaces, More Appealing to Customers

Customers have rejected airplanes with unremovable Rivlin 780 stains. Rivlin 780 is impossible to mask; it seeps under even metal-foil tape and stains adjacent skin surfaces. Removing these stains requires hand or mechanical polishing, especially in critical areas. Often, such polishing is unsatisfactory, and customers notice it.

Summary: Continue to Prime with Rivlin 680

In brief, the performance benefits of Rivlin 780 (an insignificant 2-3 percent increase in durability and corrosion protection) do not warrant its use. We should consider staying with a uniform application of Rivlin 680 mainly to avoid increased manufacturing costs.

Harry Roterman

H. Roterman, Manager
Long Beach Production
Supervisor

dfg

Deliberate repetition is a valuable technique. The opening paragraph on page 1 establishes three key reasons for adopting the writer's recommendation. These reasons are discussed and restated in the fifth through eighth paragraphs and in the closing summary. See REPETITION.

The initial *we* and the *our* in the summary paragraph indicate that H. Roterman and the staff in Long Beach Production are making the recommendation. Using personal pronouns is much better than a common approach (*It is recommended that . . .*) using false subjects and passive verbs. See FALSE SUBJECTS, ACTIVE/PASSIVE, and TONE.

Request Memo
With Informal Instructions

A set-up is unnecessary, so the writer opens with the major idea: a request. The word *please* is courteous, and it adds a personal touch. See ORGANIZATION and LETTERS.

The opening sentence captures the gist of the paragraph. See PARAGRAPHS.

The NOTE (all in capitals) emphasizes a key point. See EMPHASIS.

Each item in the list begins with an infinitive verb; therefore, the list is parallel. See VERBS, LISTS, and PARALLELISM.

To: All Managers and Supervisors

From: Jacqueline Burrows

Date: April 7, 1990

Subject: **Request for Monitors of the Air Conditioning Survey and Removal of Vent Blockages**

Please appoint someone from your department to monitor the effectiveness of the air conditioning system between now and May 1. During this period, Constant Air, Inc., will be reviewing and balancing the systems in Buildings 3 and 4 to guarantee that all departments can independently maintain the temperatures appropriate for their areas.

Please ask all employees to remove cardboard, styrofoam, tape, and other material from the ventilation grills before Constant Air's visit. Many employees have tried to control the temperature in their office by blocking the vents. However, Constant Air will not be able to draw valid conclusions about the current system unless the vents are clear.

Duties of the Air Conditioning Monitor

1. To contact Constant Air with questions and reports. Constant Air's number is 976-3421. NOTE: Neither the monitor nor any other employee should call Building Services with requests related to the air conditioning.

2. To keep an hourly log of temperatures at selected points in your department. Constant Air will identify these points for you during its initial visit to your department on April 9 or 10.

3. To survey employees at least once a day to determine their satisfaction with room temperatures.

BCC
BOUNTIFUL CHEMICAL COOPERATIVE, INC.

Although a request, this memo is very neutral both in content and in tone. The writer minimizes the use of *I*, *my*, and *me*. Instead, she follows the *you* approach. Note how often and how directly she addresses the readers. See TONE.

The paragraphs and sentences are short and direct, and the list allows readers to scan the memo for key points. See EMPHASIS, LISTS, and SENTENCES.

Request Memo
With Informal Instructions

This single-sentence paragraph emphasizes and repeats a key point. See REPETITION, PARAGRAPHS, and EMPHASIS.

Often handwritten initials as a full signature validate the writer's personal attention. As an option, initials or a signature can be added to the opening block following the writer's name.

All Managers and Supervisors -2- April 7, 1990

4. To prepare a weekly report summarizing survey results. Constant Air will bring sample forms for this report to your department when they visit on April 9 or 10.

Only Constant Air, not Building Services, should adjust the air conditioning system during this survey.

Please call me (Ext. 456) or Ned Trent (Ext. 459) if you or your monitor have any questions about this survey.

J.B.

asd

Request Memo

For Clarification of a Problem

The specific subject line simplifies cross-referencing and filing. See HEADINGS.

The opening paragraph establishes the topic and conveys the purpose of the memo.

The second paragraph sets up the list and leads into the details. See ORGANIZATION.

Displayed lists are naturally emphatic, so the BW recommendations are highlighted. Note that both listed items begin the same way. See PARALLELISM, LISTS, and EMPHASIS.

Compound modifiers, such as *1-inch*, must be hyphenated. See NUMBERS, HYPHENS, and MODIFIERS.

Apparently and *instead* are conjunctive adverbs that introduce a sentence; therefore, they are followed by commas. See TRANSITIONS and COMMAS.

To: Howard Deedy   Date: November 24, 1990

From: Charlotte Smart

Subject: **Request to Investigate Improper Repairs on the Barrett-Woodward Rotary Car Dumper and Positioner**

I understand that the recent repairs on the BW (Barrett-Woodward) rotary car dumper and positioner did not follow the recommended procedure and are therefore inadequate. I would appreciate your investigating and clarifying this situation.

Here are the facts as I understand them. Please inform me if these facts are incorrect.

Recommended Repairs

Early in November, we discovered many problems with the BW rotary car dumper and positioner and called the BW Customer Service Engineering Group. They analyzed the problems and recommended the following:

1. Replacing the 3/8-inch steel rails with 1-inch rails. The positioner rides on these rails. An AR (abrasion resistant) plate caps the steel, and both rest on a concrete pedestal. The concrete is spalling, and the rail welds are beginning to crack.
2. Installing the 1-inch rails by grouting under them and continuously welding the AR plate to the rails.

Repairs Improperly Completed

Management authorized the repairs on November 9. Before they were completed, the BW consulting engineer discovered that the AR plate had been stitch welded, not continuously welded. He claims that he reported this to Howard Beale. However, I learned of the improper welding only after John Sturgees conducted a safety inspection and discovered it more or less by accident.

Apparently, the improper welding was not replaced. Instead, the repairs were covered with grout. BW believes that the AR plate will eventually curl up and become loose because of the improper welding.

We seem to have ignored BW's advice and potentially wasted BCC maintenance funds, especially if we have to redo these repairs a year or two from now.

BCC
BOUNTIFUL CHEMICAL COOPERATIVE, INC.

While basically a request for information, this memo is potentially critical of the reader or people working for the reader. In such politically or humanly sensitive matters, tone is important. The writer must be forceful without being aggressive, direct but not blunt, businesslike but not inhuman.

Clearly, this memo is written to someone who already knows a lot about the subject. The abbreviations *BW* and *AR* are explained, but some terms, such as *spalling*, are not defined. The writer has assumed a knowledgeable audience. See SCIENTIFIC/TECHNICAL STYLE.

Request Memo
For Clarification of a Problem

The closing is direct but not harsh. *Please* makes the closing more courteous, and *shed whatever light*, which is a cliche, makes it more colloquial and therefore personal. See TONE and CLICHES.

Howard Deedy -2- November 24, 1990

I would like to know why the repairs were not made according to BW's recommendations and who was responsible. Please shed whatever light you can on this issue.

C.S.

rw

Transmittal Memo
With Attachment

Both the subject line and the opening line of the first paragraph focus on the key point—a new field test. The word *attached* appears after the key point. See LETTERS and ORGANIZATION.

The parenthetical comment separated by commas could have been separated by parentheses or dashes. See DASHES and PARENTHESES.

Long introductory clauses should be separated by a comma from the sentences they introduce. See COMMAS.

Courteous writers give their telephone or extension numbers when they offer to provide more information. See LETTERS.

To: Production Supervisors   Date: February 28, 1990

From: Clarence Hough

Subject: **Recommendation of a Simple, Fast New Field Test of Effluents for Sulfides**

A new field test for determining the presence of sulfides in the effluents that we release into the county water system is attached. This test is simpler and faster than our current tests and is the one that the Dade County Sanitation District currently uses.

The new test, commonly called the Alka-Seltzer test, uses half of an Alka-Seltzer tablet in one cup of the sample. The liberated gases pass through a test paper, which turns brown if sulfides are present (a positive reaction).

The test is simple and fast, but it does not reveal the concentration of the sulfides present. Samples with a positive reaction must go to the laboratory for further testing.

If the Alka-Seltzer test is positive, then the Hamilton test will usually give a positive reading. When the Hamilton tests and the Alka-Seltzer test disagree, use the Alka-Seltzer results to determine whether to release effluents into the county water system.

Please call Steve Hankin (Ext. 589) or me (Ext. 591) if you need further information about this new test.

C.H.

nm

MIDLAND OIL AND GAS OPERATIONS, INC.

This routine transmittal memo properly starts with its point—the new field test. Thus the memo follows a managerial format (see ORGANIZATION); the writer wisely avoids a recital of the history of sulfides testing.

The paragraphs are short and direct. These, plus the short sentences, contribute to the readability of the memo. See PARAGRAPHS and SENTENCES.

Safety Memo
With a Mild Reprimand

The specific subject captures both issues raised in the memo. See HEADINGS.

The first paragraph combines good and bad news—thus softening the impact of the reprimand. The contractions make the memo sound less formal, more personal.

This detail paragraph presents information simply and directly. The logical pattern is cause to effect. See PARAGRAPHS.

The tone of the reprimand is professional, not personal or harsh. The last sentence, with its inclusive *we*, softens the impact of the memo while reinforcing its message.

To: Jerry Falmouth — Date: January 6, 1990

From: Wally Velder

Subject: **Your Accident on December 23 and the Prevention of Accidents**

Jerry, I'm pleased that you weren't seriously injured in your accident on December 23, but I'm also disappointed that this accident happened to one of our foremen. Managers and supervisors must be especially safety conscious in our business.

I understand that you were working as a substitute foreman on the Acid Line and that you stepped on a steel meter cover, slipped, and twisted your knee. It had been raining earlier in the afternoon, and the plate was wet. You were wearing safety shoes, but apparently your shoes are old and the tread is worn smooth.

As a foreman, you should be especially alert to hazardous conditions, such as wet flooring and worn treads on safety shoes. You set an example that those people working for you should follow. If we, as management, are to prevent accidents, we must anticipate them.

Please be more cautious in the future.

W.V.

mm

BCC
BOUNTIFUL CHEMICAL COOPERATIVE, INC.

Personnel memos (or letters) are often difficult to write, especially as in this case, when the letter contains even a mild reprimand. A proper tone, therefore, is essential. As in the above example, tone comes from several things: (1) positive information—as in the opening comment about Jerry's not being seriously injured, (2) a personal tone—as in the pronouns and use of Jerry's name in the opening, and (3) a firm but courteous closing—both with reasonable and honest requests for improvements and with the use of *please*. See TONE, MEMOS, LETTERS, and PRONOUNS.

Personnel Memo
With Suggested Procedures

Although more humorous than informative, the subject does fit the light tone of the memo.

The opening sentence states the point of the memo. Beginning with a contraction creates an informal, conversational tone. See TONE, MEMOS, and LETTERS.

The bulleted list is a good way to highlight the suggestions. Note that each listed item is parallel in structure. See LISTS and PARALLELISM.

The use of the run-in headings (in all capitals) visually highlights each suggestion.

To: All Employees of the Sales Department

From: James Haworth

Date: May 30, 1990

Subject: **Your "Home Away from Home"**

Let's all try to do everything we can to make our offices as pleasant, comfortable, and well maintained as possible.

Offices should reflect our personalities, but they also should convey a professional impression to visitors. So please take time to consider ways to ensure that your office reflects our excellent products.

<u>Suggestions</u>

- NAILS. Please use low-impact nails for hanging pictures. They will support most pictures, and they do less damage to the walls. My secretary has these if you need them.
- SCOTCH TAPE. Please do not use it. Tape is a quick and easy way to get that poster, map, or note up on the wall, but when it is removed, it removes paint and sometimes plaster.
- POSTERS, MAPS, PICTURES. Please frame any that you intend to hang. Several inexpensive frame shops around town can make a $2.98 print look like a $200 lithograph. Family pictures likewise get special attention if attractively framed.
- MACRAME AND OTHER PLANT HANGERS. The secret to hanging things from ceilings is a little gadget called the "handi-hook," which is designed for suspended ceilings. It hooks over the metal separators and is easy to install or move. However, it can't support very heavy plants. My secretary has a supply of handi-hooks.

Personnel notices often require a light touch. Employees rightly object to personnel notices that are too serious, impersonal, or even critical in tone (and content). Managers and supervisors sometimes have to send reminders and requests that are potentially negative (as this notice could be). The lighter tone helps writers convey negative information in a manner that readers will not find objectionable. See MEMOS, LETTERS, and TONE.

Personnel Memo
With Suggested Procedures

The social closing (beginning with *please*) is also conversational in tone.

- GENERAL HOUSEKEEPING. Neatness and organization take a lot of effort, but they are worth it. We'll all be able to walk the halls without glancing into offices and wincing. Even more importantly, we'll be able to locate information more easily if the information is carefully labeled and filed.

Please give some thought to making your office as attractive as possible. We have a beautiful facility, and with a little effort from us all, it will remain so.

J.H.

mm

Proposal Memo
To a Negative Audience

The arrangement of these items varies from memo to memo. See MEMOS.

Because the readers are antagonistic, the memo proposes a meeting, not a solution, and the language is deliberately conciliatory. Note the inclusive *we*. See TONE.

To highlight a paragraph list, the numbers are enclosed within parentheses. See PARENTHESES and LISTS.

The opening sentence to this paragraph is a topic sentence: It states the point of the paragraph. See PARAGRAPHS and COLONS. The sentences are short and active. See ACTIVE/PASSIVE and SENTENCES.

MEMO Date: August 23, 1990

To: Jack Ladda and Harvey Smith

From: Charles Percival

Subject: **Invitation to Discuss Upgrading Testing and Maintenance**

OSAGE GAS AND ELECTRIC COMPANY, INC.

Let's explore ways to upgrade substation testing and maintenance. As we found out in Tuesday's meeting, we can agree on a number of the current problems; now we need to discover ways to solve these problems. If you are available, let's meet at 2 p.m. on Wednesday, September 6, in my office to discuss our ideas and solutions.

Maintenance as a Priority Responsibility

During Tuesday's meeting we identified many specific test and maintenance areas needing improvement: (1) maintenance intervals, (2) tests between maintenance, and (3) adherence to maintenance procedures. Even more important is our overall commitment to maintenance as a priority responsibility, especially given the complex and expensive equipment in the OG&E electrical system.

Inadequate Maintenance at Substations

Yet the signals are clear: Maintenance is not a high priority in many substations. Many substations have inadequate maintenance personnel, and many of the personnel are not properly trained. Some maintenance crews spend too much time on ordinary construction. Finally, maintenance personnel who leave are not being replaced. Obviously, management needs to address these problems if we are going to improve our maintenance situation.

Suggestions for Improving Test and Maintenance Procedures

As a starting point, here are a few preliminary suggestions for improving our test and maintenance procedures:

1. Use contract or construction personnel, not maintenance personnel, for all construction work.

Because of the antagonistic audience, the writer deliberately makes his memo more tentative than it would ordinarily need to be. The opening paragraph is conciliatory, and the six listed items are called suggestions, not proposals; the six are also listed well into the memo rather than at the beginning. See ORGANIZATION, LETTERS, and MEMOS.

Proposal Memo

To a Negative Audience

The displayed list highlights the suggestions. Note that the items listed are parallel and begin with imperative verbs. See PARALLELISM, SENTENCES, and VERBS.

Repeating the meeting time reinforces the central message of the memo and solicits the reader's cooperation. See REPETITION and EMPHASIS.

Jack Ladda and Harvey Smith -2- August 23, 1990

2. Make comprehensive manpower and equipment forecasts based on present maintenance needs. Use these to hire additional maintenance personnel.

3. Train existing personnel to meet the above forecasts.

4. Contract with Noble Engineering to perform key testing and to inspect and maintain power circuit breakers. Noble personnel should be on call 24 hours a day but should be used only to catch up during crises.

5. Establish a trouble-shooting maintenance crew in the Central Office. This crew would have special responsibility for extra high-voltage equipment.

6. Make Engineering, not Operations, responsible for maintenance and testing.

Can you meet at 2 p.m. on Wednesday, September 6, in my office to discuss these and other suggestions? Let's do what we must to arrive at constructive solutions to our test and maintenance problems.

C.P.

uio

Summary Memo
For an Executive Audience

The set-up is brief and informative. The recommendation immediately follows it. See LETTERS and ORGANIZATION.

Headings signal key divisions in the executive summary. They highlight the document's organization and allow readers to locate information easily. See HEADINGS and SUMMARIES.

Attachments should always be referred to in the body of the document. See APPENDICES/ ATTACHMENTS.

MEMO Date: June 12, 1990

To: Steward Pollack
From: Brenda Hamilton
Subject: **Recommendation for Osage Gas Plant Compressor Engine and Cylinder Overhaul, Contract MR-789-65**

OSAGE GAS AND ELECTRIC COMPANY, INC.

The following mechanical overhaul contractors have submitted time and material bids to perform the compressor engine and cylinder overhauls at the Osage Gas Plant:

Martin Energy Services
J & L Incorporated
Efficiency Production Services
White River Maintenance, Inc.

Recommendation: Contract with White River Maintenance

Based on the attached bid summary and the related analysis, I recommend contracting with White River Maintenance, Inc., to perform this work. All bidders, except J & L Incorporated, appear to be equally qualified, but White River was the lowest bidder by an estimated $50,000.

Bid Calculation: Total Labor Costs Added to Time and Material Estimates

Bids included only time and material, so we had to analyze the bids by developing a hypothetical crew size and calculating a composite man-hour rate. From these calculations, we were able to determine the total labor costs for each contractor. We also calculated probable transportation costs as an add-on amount to labor costs. Finally, we built in an 85 percent contingency amount based on the uncertainty of the parts needed to complete the overhaul. For further details, see the attached bid calculations.

Many memos are actually summaries of attached materials. Such summary memos are similar to executive summaries, which open longer, more involved reports. Readers of summaries are often managers and supervisors who already know something about the subject but who do not need extensive background information before making a decision. See SUMMARIES and REPORTS.

Summary Memo

For an Executive Audience

The paragraph division parallels the heading. See HEADINGS and PARAGRAPHS.

One-sentence paragraphs emphasize key points. See PARAGRAPHS and EMPHASIS.

Steward Pollack
Page Two
June 12, 1990

Scope of Work and Specifications

The scope of the work includes the overhaul of 5 Hall-Burke HB-76 gas engines and 12 compressor cylinders. White River will unload all equipment and will handle all procurement through their office. They will also pay for all transportation costs and for the complete installation of necessary replacement parts. Finally, they will be responsible for aligning and grouting the final crankshaft.

A copy of the specifications is available from Sven Nordstrom of Engineering Services.

Implementation: Weekly Report and Onsite Quality Assurance

Either J. K. Barnes or I will submit a weekly progress report and budget update. J. K. Barnes will be onsite at the White River shop to guarantee the quality of the work.

B.H.

gsp
Attachments

In this memo (as in most executive summaries), a brief set-up orients readers as to the subject and then the main point (the recommendation, in this case) follows immediately. Limited supporting information or detail comes next. Extensive background data, calculations, supporting documents, and references should remain as attachments. See ORGANIZATION.

Procedure Memo

The opening sentence establishes the purpose of the memo. See LETTERS and ORGANIZATION.

Parentheses enclose supplemental information. See PARENTHESES.

Each procedure opens with an imperative verb. See PARALLELISM, SENTENCES, and VERBS.

Each item in the subordinate list begins with a dash. The format and indentation differences between the major (or outer) list and the subordinate (or inner) list help readers tell them apart. See LISTS.

The reason for the procedures is less important than the procedures themselves, so the rationale comes last.

The paragraphs are short, which aids readability. See PARAGRAPHS.

To: All Department Heads

From: Susan Hall

Date: December 28, 1990

Subject: **Procedures for Storing Records at Trolley Street Warehouse**

Please comply with the following procedures when you store records at the Trolley Street Warehouse:

1. Use a standard records transmittal box and a records transmittal slip. (Call 287-9009 to order these boxes. Each empty box will contain a blank records transmittal slip.)

2. Include the following information on each records transmittal slip:

   —Description of the contents

   —Destruction date according to policy R-23 (Duplicate copies of this policy are available from Susan Jameson in Corporate Services.)

   —Name of responsible supervisor

   —Department number (and extension)

3. Enclose the white and yellow copies of the records transmittal slip inside each box of records. At the Trolley Street Warehouse, the number and location of each box will be recorded on the yellow copy, which will be returned to the department sending the records. Each department should maintain a file of the yellow copies.

These procedures result from the recent reorganization of the records retention area. This reorganization was necessary because too many records were being lost and too many out-of-date records were being retained.

A clear format is essential in procedures. In this memo, the numbered and dashed lists are crucial if the procedure is to be clear and readable. See EMPHASIS and LISTS for options; also see the more formal procedures illustrated elsewhere in these model documents.

The imperative verbs are also essential in procedures. They highlight actions the reader should take, and they allow writers to condense their directions. For the sake of parallelism, state **all** directions or steps using imperative verbs. See SENTENCES.

Procedure Memo

Giving the extension number is courteous. Writers should do so even when they know the readers well.

The writer's initials (either typed or signed) are optional.

All Department Heads -2- December 28, 1990

Under this new procedure, all departments should know what is and is not stored. Periodically reviewing the records transmittal files should enable departments to determine what stored materials can be destroyed.

If you have any questions about these procedures, please call me at extension 2344.

S.H.

bip

Memo Reporting on Training

The subject is specific. See HEADINGS and MEMOS.

The first paragraph summarizes the assessment and makes a recommendation. See ORGANIZATION, MEMOS, and LETTERS.

The displayed list highlights what the writer learned from the school, including potential changes in Gulfport procedures. This is more important than the course content. See ORGANIZATION and LISTS.

To: James MacWhortle

From: Seymour Hirschfield

Date: December 18, 1990

Subject: **Assessment and Recommendation of the Applications Engineer School, Dallas, November 5-27**

The Dallas school for applications engineers was both effective and worthwhile. I recommend that all of our applications engineers attend this school. The training should more than pay for itself in reduced maintenance expenses.

Based on what I learned, here are some general recommendations that apply to our situation at Gulfport:

1. **Develop Documentation Standards**

   We should develop documentation standards for applications engineers. We spend far too much time tracing and flow charting existing programs. These inconsistent and ad hoc documentation efforts lead to excessive maintenance time, needless repetition of maintenance, and frequent errors during installations.

2. **Work from Standard Logic Flow**

   All Gulfport applications engineers should be given a master copy of the standard logic flow. The standard logic flow lists steps in the proper order, thus helping to ensure efficient adjustments to the program. Working from the standard logic would minimize omissions and mistakes, especially those resulting from ad hoc decisions. This standard logic would also help to improve our documentation. (See attachment for an example of a standard logic flow.)

3. **Attend Dallas Engineer School**

   All Gulfport applications engineers should attend the Dallas 3-week school. This school is just as valuable as the basic school for control engineers. The optimum arrangement would make the Control Engineer School a prerequisite for the Applications Engineer School.

MIDLAND OIL AND GAS OPERATIONS, INC.

This memo deliberately opens with the "bottom line" so that busy supervisors or managers do not have to read beyond the first paragraph unless they want more information. The key applications follow immediately. Everything else is optional (depending on whether readers wish to know more of the details). See ORGANIZATION.

Memo Reporting on Training

The course content should be no longer than necessary. If readers want detail, give it to them; if not, summarize.

Parentheses enclose additional but nonessential information. See PARENTHESES.

The headings divide content into identifiable areas, making it easier for readers to understand how the document is organized and where to find particular information. See HEADINGS.

James MacWhortle -2- December 18, 1990

Course Content: Computer Systems, Utilities, Programming Basics

The school provides the applications engineer with enough background knowledge for understanding the computer system and utility programs, as well as the basics of computer programming. We also reviewed the fundamentals of process dynamics.

During the first week (the lecture week), the instructors gave us reading assignments. Each day's instruction ended with a question-and-answer period, with plenty of time to review essential concepts.

During the second and third weeks (the laboratory weeks), we used a computer simulation of a real process at our East Chicago plant. The goal was to build, tune, and document a control scheme to control the process. Inherent in the simulation were process noise, nonlinear valve characteristics, and dead time. To test the process, we subjected it to large load upsets.

The first assignment was to build all variables and to write supervisory logic for the control scheme. Trial-and-error tuning was not effective, so we used SLEUTH to obtain tuning constants. When documentation was complete, we subjected the loop to large load upsets and then observed and recorded the responses. We learned that ordinary supervisory control was not fast enough for an acceptable response.

Next, we used DDC programming with two feed-forward algorithms. The first was a simple ration controller, and the second included dynamic lead/lag terms. East Chicago's Shut Blocks (preprogrammed, shared, or common general blocks) were used for the feed-forward algorithm. We determined the feed-forward constants using SLEUTH and PFTUNE. This control scheme caused significantly less deviation in the control variable, and response time was significantly faster.

Course Presentation: Practical and Engaging

Both the instructors and the materials were excellent. The laboratory simulations were the high point of the school. Such practical experience guarantees that students

The recommendation about other engineers attending the school is the memo's most important idea; therefore, it appears very early in the memo.

Memo Reporting on Training

This recommendation about rental cars is less important and would detract from the memo's purpose if it came first, so the author subordinates it by putting it at the end of the memo.

James MacWhortle -3- December 18, 1990

retain the skills and concepts learned and know how to apply them in actual plants and facilities.

The instructors had all had field experience as applications engineers, so they were well versed in the content. Moreover, they were excellent presenters and knew how to involve students throughout the 3 weeks of training.

Final Recommendation: Rent Cars for Trainees

Some of us attending the school felt isolated during the weekends, so I would recommend either making several rental cars available or holding the course at a less isolated site. The training took place at the downtown Holiday Inn, where much happens during the week. But over the weekend, everyone leaves for the suburbs. The town seemed deserted, and walking around after dark was not advisable.

S.H.

mm
Attachment

The tone of the memo is conversational. The writer's use of the pronouns *I* and *we* is appropriate because he is relating a personal experience. See ACTIVE/PASSIVE and TONE.

Resume Cover Letter

With a Traditional Format

Always use the person's name in the salutation if the advertisement gave the name. See LETTERS.

Make your opening direct, and refer to the position and the source for your information. See LETTERS and ORGANIZATION.

Focus on the need you can fill.

Organize for readability and emphasis. See LISTS and EMPHASIS.

Include related experience.

Use a strong closing statement with positive language. SEE LETTERS.

1862 South Elm Avenue
Lincoln, NE 48298
October 11, 1989

Ms. Carolyn Myers
Human Resources Director
Healthtronics, Inc.
500 Research Parkway
Denver, CO 80014

Dear Ms. Myers:

My qualifications closely match your advertisement in today's *Wall Street Journal* for a **Regional Human Resources Manager**.

According to your job profile, you need a human resource generalist in the electronics industry. As the current personnel supervisor for Western Electronics, I have a broad experience in human resource activities:

- Wage and salary administration
- Benefits administration
- Labor contract negotiation and administration
- Hiring and outplacement
- Affirmative action and EEO Guidelines

My prior work at Lesco, Inc., provided me with practical experience in design, performance measurement, and succession planning. In addition, I have held positions in local ASPA and ASTD chapters.

As this letter and my resume indicate, I am a dedicated professional with the skills and experience necessary for a human resource generalist in a growing industry. I am available to discuss this position; please call me at (302) 531-2468.

Sincerely,

Douglas A. Bowen

Douglas A. Bowen

The cover letter should expand or amplify the information contained in the resume. Your letter should also mention specific qualifications or requirements from the advertisement for the position.

Be creative and be direct about your qualifications and suitability for the job. Always follow any interviews with a thank-you letter.

Resume

With a Traditional Format

Always include an accurate address and telephone number. See LETTERS.

A statement of your career goal is helpful.

Position first the information you want to emphasize most. See ORGANIZATION.

Arrange chronologically beginning with the most recent.

List information applicable to the position. Avoid lengthy lists of interests or outside activity.

Douglas A. Bowen
1862 South Elm Avenue
Lincoln, NE 48298
(302) 531-2468

Objective

A challenging, responsible position in human resource management

Experience

- Supervise currently the Human Resource Department in a 1,500-employee facility. Responsible for all personnel activities including labor/management relations.
- Coordinated a plant-wide Total Quality Management (TQM) program in a manufacturing environment. Member of President's Quality Council.
- Designed a Performance Planning and Review system for all hourly and exempt workers, including a Career Enhancement program for clerical employees.
- Developed and conducted management skills training courses for 200 mid-level managers.

Work History

- 1986 to present Personnel Supervisor for Western Electronics, Lincoln, Nebraska
- 1982 to 1986 Human Resource Coordinator, Lesco, Inc., Kansas City, Kansas
- 1979 to 1982 Benefits Administrator, Lincoln General Hospital, Lincoln, Nebraska

Education

- M.A. Human Resource Management, University of Nebraska, 1982
- B.S. Sociology (major), Accounting (minor), Kansas State University, 1980

Other Qualifications

- Member, American Society of Personnel Administrators (ASPA)
- Member, American Society for Training and Development (ASTD)

Interests

- Water skiing, snow skiing, camping, wood working

***References** (available on request)*

Keep your resume short and concise—a single page if you can. The above content is standard, but you might include military service, personal interests or special skills (e.g., facility with a foreign language), and licenses or accreditations. Avoid personal information, such as age, marital status, national origin, religion, or physical features.

Layouts for resumes may vary, but spacing should always be neat and uncluttered. Readability and the ease of finding important information are critical. See EMPHASIS.

Resume Cover Letter
With a Less Traditional Tone

Be sure to refer to the position you want and to the source of your information.

Use a list or other emphasis techniques to highlight key points. See EMPHASIS and LISTS.

1862 South Elm Avenue
Lincoln, NE 48298
October 11, 1989

Ms. Carolyn Myers
Human Resources Director
Healthtronics, Inc.
500 Research Parkway
Denver, CO 80014

Dear Ms. Myers:

Please consider my application for the position of **Regional Human Resources Manager**, as described in the October 11 *Wall Street Journal.*

My qualifications, as summarized in my resume, fit your advertisment point for point:

- **Experience in electronics.** My current employer is Western Electronics.

- **Human resource generalist.** My broad education and experience have covered all human resource specialities.

- **Supervisory experience.** I have been a supervisor at both Western Electronics and Lesco, Inc.

Besides complying with your stated qualifications, I am a dedicated team player, as my current supervisor will verify. You would find me to be a valuable addition to your human resources team.

I am available for an interview, at your convenience. Please call me at (302) 531-2468 (my home) or (302) 531-5589 (my office).

Sincerely,

Douglas A. Bowen

Douglas A. Bowen

The cover letter should address points from the advertisement for the position. Do not rely on a stock, generic letter that is merely an announcement that the resume is attached.

Be sure your letter is accurate and without grammatical errors; proofread it carefully.

Resume

With a Less Traditional Format and Tone

Resume for Douglas A. Bowen
1862 South Elm Avenue
Lincoln, NE 48298
(302) 531-2468

Major Accomplishments

The bulleted points are like headlines, with the explanations (in smaller type) giving positive results or benefits.

- **Supervise currently the Human Resource Department in a 1,500-employee facility at Western Electronics.**

  I am responsible for all personnel activities, including labor/management relations, wage and salary administration, hiring, and Affirmative/EEO requirements. My staff and I have been credited with avoiding two threatened strikes during the last 3 years.

- **Coordinated a plant-wide TQM (Total Quality Management) program for Western Electronics.**

  Member of the President's Quality Council. Our TQM program is credited with reducing our in-plant rejects from 12 percent to 8 percent and our customer returns from 4 percent to 0.2 percent.

- **Designed a Performance Planning and Reviews system for all hourly and exempt workers, including a Career Enhancement program for clerical employees.**

  This program at Lesco, Inc., has reduced significantly the legal challenges of disciplined and terminated employees.

- **Developed and conducted management-skills training courses for 200 mid-level managers.**

  These training courses at Western Electronics are now a regular part of the curriculum. The course materials have been separately printed and are being used under contract by other companies.

List jobs chronologically beginning with your current one.

Job History

- 1986 to present — Personnel Supervisor for Western Electronics, Lincoln, Nebraska
- 1982 to 1986 — Human Resource Coordinator, Lesco, Inc., Kansas City, Kansas
- 1979 to 1982 — Benefits Administrator, Lincoln General Hospital, Lincoln, Nebraska

Education and Professional Memberships

- M.A. — Human Resource Mangement, University of Nebraska, 1989
- B.S. — Sociology, Kansas State University, 1982
- Member of ASPA (American Society of Personnel Administrators) and ASTD (American Society for Training and Development). Program chair in 1987-1988 for ASTD.

Prepare a separate list of references for use at the interview or for sending later to an interested prospective employer. (Only use people's names after you've gotten their permission.)

References (available on request)

A resume need not follow the traditional format (as illustrated in the previous example). Instead, resumes can be designed to highlight (sell) the person's qualifications, as the above resume does in its list of accomplishments. You should still keep your resume short; one page is ideal.

Do not include information on your religion, national origin, marital status, age, or physical features.

Job Description

These initial facts will vary from company to company, but job codes and the date of the last revision are usually desirable pieces of information.

The opening section (and its heading) highlights those general personnel traits usually valued in any employee (not just an entry-level auditor).

The traits are listed beginning with a verb. This eliminates much needed repetition—for instance, "the employee will . . . ." In essence, this approach is an action one. See PARALLELISM.

The numbering system (and the lists) will allow for easy references to a particular duty or responsibility. See LISTS and NUMBERING SYSTEMS.

Job Description

Job Title	
Internal Auditor	
Job Level	**Pay Range**
101-Au	5
Department	**Group or Area**
Internal Auditing	Production

General Requirements

A. Works effectively as a member of the Audit Department

1. Maintains the highest standards of professionalism
2. Cooperates with coworkers to improve both the quality of the work and the morale of the department
3. Works diligently to improve the department's audit processes and procedures
4. Assists in making audit reports and other departmental documents as professional as possible

B. Maintains good job behavior

1. Is punctual and conscientious about work hours, and makes appropriate arrangements for vacations and special leave
2. Is properly groomed at all times
3. Performs tasks cheerfully and without complaint
4. Accepts responsibility for all properly assigned tasks
5. Accepts criticism well and makes sincere efforts to improve

Last Revised August 1990 Page 1 of 3

Job descriptions are difficult to write because they should be as specific as possible, and writers (often the employees themselves) don't want to be very specific about the duties. Also, many employees think job descriptions are a waste of time and effort. (Actually, they may be a waste if they are only written for the files or if they are misused by supervisors.)

The specific duties and responsibilities are organized almost chronologically—from the beginning of the audit to the end. Other organizations would be possible. See ORGANIZATION.

The parentheses set off an extra piece of information. See PARENTHESES.

The numbering of the main subheadings (A, B, C, etc.) continues sequentially throughout the job description (despite different major headings). This sequential numbering also permits good cross-referencing.

Job Title Internal Auditor

Specific Duties and Responsibilities

C. Analyzes upcoming audit situations

1. Reviews relevant prior audits (including working papers)
2. Solicits help (if appropriate) from auditors who worked on prior audits
3. Prepares the individuals being audited—either in person or through correspondence
4. Coordinates upcoming tasks with other auditors participating in the audit

D. Conducts efficient and professional audits

1. Maintains an objective and unbiased attitude toward those being audited; is conspicuously fair
2. Briefs those being audited as to goals, procedures, and purposes
3. Creatively plans and projects necessary audit tasks and procedures
4. Devises appropriate strategies for tracking key tasks
5. Prepares orderly working papers and other records of the facts discovered during the audit
6. Consults with other auditors (including the audit supervisor) to guarantee that the audit is proceeding properly and according to SOP
7. Maintains good personal relations with those being audited
8. Conducts (or participates in) an effective exit interview

Page 2 of 3

The description covers two areas: (1) general requirements and (2) specific duties and responsibilities. General requirements by themselves may be too general—hence, the need for some specific job-related duties and responsibilities.

Job Description

Job Title Internal Auditor

E. Prepares a high-quality, professional audit report

1. Submits draft materials by assigned deadlines
2. Assists colleagues during reviews of the overall audit report
3. Writes clear and effective audit summaries, findings, and recommendations
4. Coordinates the preparation of audit reports with secretaries and word processing personnel

F. Assists in transmitting the audit report to appropriate managers and supervisors

1. Prepares individual oral briefings, if necessary
2. Arranges for follow-up investigations and reports

Page 3 of 3

Some organizations would prefer, of course, to have a proposed rating scale as part of the job description. So each duty or task would have some sort of scale: *Exceeds expectations*, *Meets expectations*, etc. Some personnel specialists even argue for evaluations tied to percentages or production: *Has fewer than 5 percent errors* or *Produces 185 widgets per day*. Such scales are not applicable to all types of jobs, so the above job description does not attempt to incorporate them.

Performance Review
Positive

The initial sentence (and the following paragraph) summarize the positive nature of the review. See ORGANIZATION.

The review uses third person (*she*) because it goes into the personnel file and not directly to Judith (although she would see this statement). See PRONOUNS.

The discussion opens with strengths—a good strategy in any review.

The run-in headings are keyed to specific duties listed in Judith's job description. See the model job description given on the preceding pages.

Each strength is illustrated by an example, even proof.

Performance Review

Name	
Judith Hirsch	
Job Level	**Department**
101-Au	Internal Auditing
Evaluated by	**Date**
Sidney Jenson	February 11, 1990

Written Commentary

Judith Hirsch has been a credit to the Auditing Department during her first 6 months with us. She has learned a lot about our company; she has learned to work well with her colleagues in the Auditing Department; and, most importantly, she has become an excellent auditor.

The following comments support the numerical ratings in the attached department performance checklist.

<u>Strengths</u>

<u>Duty D2</u>. Judith did an excellent job preparing the Shipping Department for the audit we conducted for them in February. She initially met with their department manager, who commented that she made a good impression on everyone, especially those who were intimidated at the thought of an audit.

<u>Duty D5</u>. Judith's working papers are excellent. She takes accurate notes, and her marginal commentary will aid future auditors in tracking the basis for her findings.

<u>Duty E3</u>. Judith promises to be one of the most able writers in our department. While she is still learning to use our format and organization, her writing is clear and concise. I found it satisfying not to have to rewrite her sections of the final audit report.

Sidney Jenson
Evaluator Signature

Page 1 of 2

The positive performance review should be almost a pleasure to write. Resist, however, the temptation to skip the positive review because "everything's going fine." Even the most eager of workers needs the praise of an honestly earned review.

Reviews are usually part of a checklist, where actual numerical ratings have to be recorded. These ratings are not sufficient, however, so always add written comments. While you should always comment on low ratings, don't forget to mention the positive examples.

Performance Review

Positive

These suggestions should be as specific as possible, but they are often based only on general impressions.

The summary repeats in different language the points made in paragraph 1. See REPETITION and ORGANIZATION.

Name: Judith Hirsch

Job Title Internal Auditor Date 2-11-90

Areas Needing Improvement

Duty D3. Judith needs to be more aggressive in challenging questionable practices discovered during an audit. Given her newness to the company, she was concerned with establishing good relationships with personnel from other departments, but she can still be personable while challenging questionable practices.

Duty D6. Judith needs to work more closely with the other auditors in the department. She seems reluctant to reveal uncertainties, but newly hired auditors must ask questions about procedures and about departments scheduled for upcoming audits.

Summary

Except for the above duties, where Judith's evaluations were either lower or higher than expected, her evaluations were typical of promising new hires. She is, therefore, an asset to the Auditing Department. I look forward to following her career with us.

Page 2 of 2

Written comments should be as specific as your time and knowledge allow. Someone reading your comments should believe that you had a firm basis for the different ratings you have given. Also, specific comments (even proof) are the most memorable features of a review.

Performance Review
Negative

The initial sentence opens with something positive despite the negative nature of the review. The positive point should be an honest one.

The promotion issue is also valuable background for what is to follow. See LETTERS and ORGANIZATION.

The initial points should explain Judith's strengths in very specific terms. These points help to put the negative comments into perspective.

The run-in headings correspond to the duties listed in the job description. See the model job description given earlier in this section.

The direct quotation is an excellent piece of evidence (positive or negative). See QUOTATIONS and QUOTATION MARKS.

Performance Review

Name	
Judith Hirsch	
Job Level: 101-Au	Department: Internal Auditing
Evaluated by: Sidney Jenson	Date: February 11, 1990

Written Commentary

Judith Hirsch continues to improve as an auditor, but she still has some serious weaknesses. Unless these weaknesses are corrected, Judith will not be eligible for promotion within the Auditing Department.

The following comments support the numerical ratings in the attached department performance checklist, which is based on the job description for an internal auditor.

Strengths

Duties B3 and B4. Judith accepts assignments cheerfully and attacks them with enthusiasm. When I asked her to fill in for Steve Broom (who suddenly quit), she immediately agreed and energetically began to assume his role in the auditing team for the Production Department.

Duties D2, D7, and D8. Judith seems to relate very well with the field personnel we often deal with. Last month, for instance, she participated in an audit of the Maintenance Department. According to the senior auditor who managed that audit, Judith was a "strong, likable representative of the Auditing Department." I suspect this is due to Judith's mechanical abilities, as well as her solid one-on-one skills.

Sidney Jenson
Evaluator Signature — Page 1 of 2

Negative reviews are always a problem. Face-to-face meetings are bad enough, but having to put negative judgments into writing is even worse. To make such written reviews as painless as possible, bring in some positive traits and keep your discussion as specific as possible. After all, the employee needs to know exactly why you are dissatisfied with the job performance.

Positive points are essential so that the employee can't argue that you have not even tried to be fair. Managers should also reinforce positive behaviors whenever possible.

Performance Review
Negative

Besides being specific, the negative comments should, if possible, suggest ways to improve. Here Judith is asked to develop a "plan of attack."

Name Judith Hirsch

Job Title Internal Auditor Date 2-11-90

Areas Needing Improvement

Duty D5. Judith's working papers are not acceptable. They need to be carefully planned and cross-referenced so that all findings have clear supporting data. This is a skill related to general writing ability. I suggest that Judith prepare a detailed written outline or mockup of future working papers and that she check this outline with either a senior auditor or me.

Duty E3. Judith's writing skills are still below average. She works hard to make her writing correct, but correct writing is not necessarily adequate. Judith's writing is usually "thin," often unsupported. She seems to have trouble expanding on or supporting her findings. I suggest that she develop a plan of attack to work on this deficiency; we can involve several of our more seasoned auditors in the plan. Perhaps they could review draft materials and give specific feedback on a variety of writing tasks.

Duties C1 and D6. Judith still needs to be more willing to ask for help within the Auditing Department. Her good one-on-one skills need to extend to areas of professional activity. Judith needs to avail herself of department resources if she intends to continue to improve.

The summary is as upbeat as possible but still as honest as necessary. It does partially repeat paragraph 1. See REPETITION.

Summary

Judith could have a bright future with our department, but as I have explained to her, her advancement will be slow if she is unable to grow in the areas discussed above. The three deficiencies mentioned above are critical to this growth, so these will be the basis for the next performance review in 6 months.

Page 2 of 2

Candor, while difficult, is essential, especially if some negative personnel action (firing, demotion, or a transfer) is likely. Without candor, the employee has no idea of how to improve, and ultimately you have no written record on which to base the firing, demotion, or transfer.

Despite being part of a preprinted form (usually including a checklist), the review should still use the basics of good writing: emphasis, a clear organization, specific examples, clear and concise sentences, etc. See EMPHASIS, ORGANIZATION, and STYLE.

Procedure

With a Traditional Format

The heading, title, procedure number, and date permit easy updating and quick reference.

The purpose is brief yet specific and informative.

The outline format uses decimal numbering. This allows for easy cross-referencing. See NUMBERING SYSTEMS.

Responsibilities are written in sentences, but these are usually not imperative in form. See SENTENCES.

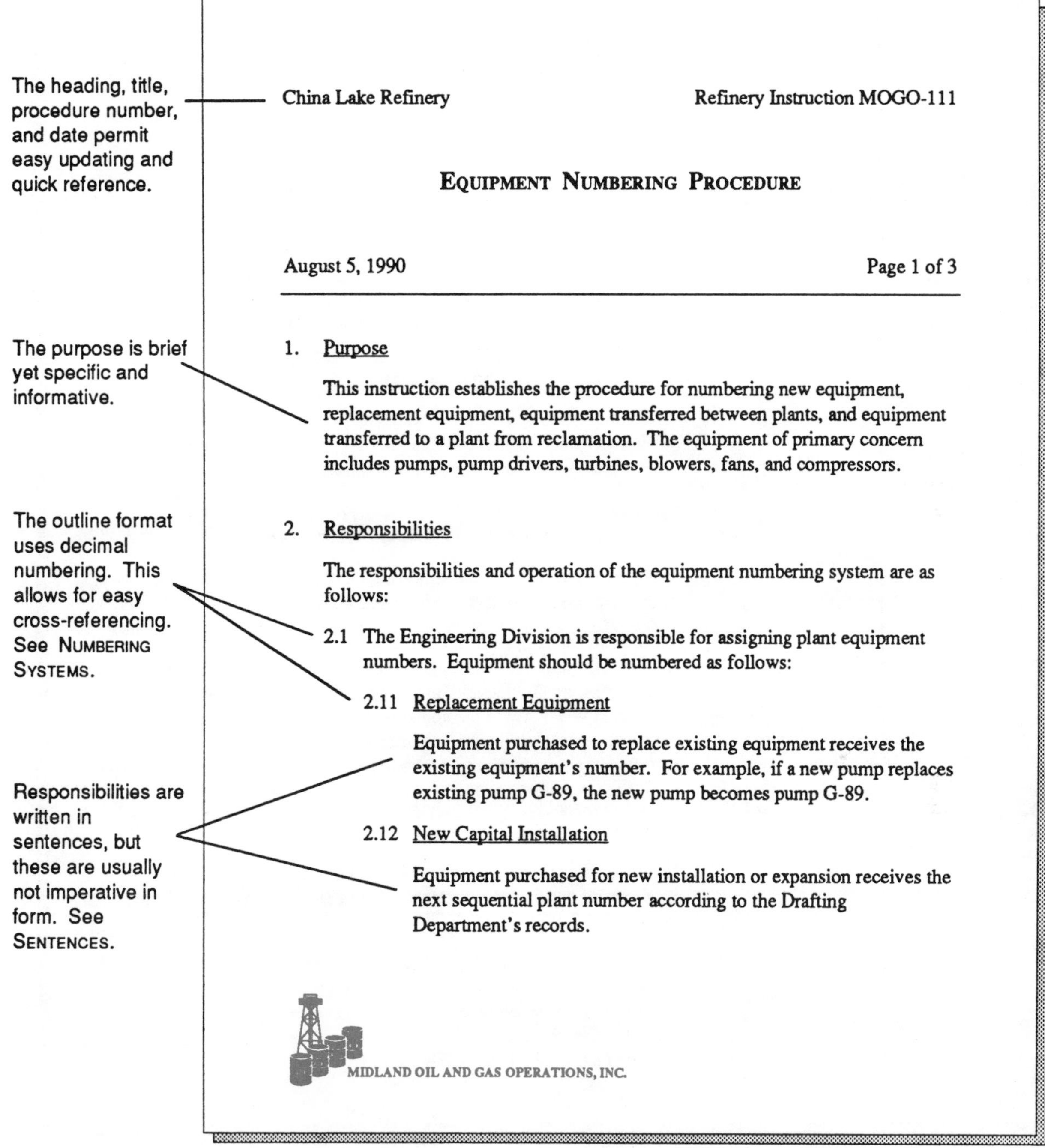

China Lake Refinery — Refinery Instruction MOGO-111

EQUIPMENT NUMBERING PROCEDURE

August 5, 1990 — Page 1 of 3

1. Purpose

This instruction establishes the procedure for numbering new equipment, replacement equipment, equipment transferred between plants, and equipment transferred to a plant from reclamation. The equipment of primary concern includes pumps, pump drivers, turbines, blowers, fans, and compressors.

2. Responsibilities

The responsibilities and operation of the equipment numbering system are as follows:

2.1 The Engineering Division is responsible for assigning plant equipment numbers. Equipment should be numbered as follows:

2.11 Replacement Equipment

Equipment purchased to replace existing equipment receives the existing equipment's number. For example, if a new pump replaces existing pump G-89, the new pump becomes pump G-89.

2.12 New Capital Installation

Equipment purchased for new installation or expansion receives the next sequential plant number according to the Drafting Department's records.

Traditional procedures use some techniques to make reading easier, but they also more closely follow the patterns of ordinary business and technical language. Procedures using an action format (as in the next model document) are usually more telegraphic or skeletal in their format and their language. The action format is often easier for readers to read and to use.

Procedure
With a Traditional Format

Headings on all pages repeat the key information from the first page. This allows quick identification of the procedure if the pages become separated.

Examples are essential for clarity.

The responsibilities under this section are phrased in parallel *-ing* forms. See PARALLELISM.

China Lake Refinery — Refinery Instruction MOGO-111

EQUIPMENT NUMBERING PROCEDURE

August 5, 1990 — Page 2 of 3

2.13 Used Equipment Transferred Between Plants or Equipment Transferred to a Plant from Reclamation

This equipment receives an existing equipment number if it replaces equipment (under paragraph 2.11) or the next sequential number if it is for new installation or expansion (under paragraph 2.12).

2.2 For Engineering filing and record purposes only, the following modification to the above numbering system is necessary:

2.21 Equipment that replaces existing equipment receives the existing equipment's plant number, as described above.

To indicate the number of replacements occurring in a particular service, the equipment number will receive a suffix. For example, a pump replacing G-89 would be numbered G-89-1. A pump replacing G-89-1 would be numbered G-89-2. Due to present computer system limitations, maintenance equipment records will reflect only the plant number, as discussed in paragraph 2.1.

2.3 The engineer assigned to monitor equipment numbers is responsible for the following:

2.31 Ensuring that new equipment receives proper numbers and that Engineering has recorded the correct numbers, according to paragraph 2.2 above.

2.32 Ensuring that drawings, data sheets, performance curves, installation, operating and maintenance procedures, and other associated information on equipment being replaced are removed from the plant file and photostat books and are transferred either to the reclamation or idle equipment files.

Other organizations of this procedure would be possible. For instance, the general subsection entitled "Responsibilities" is unnecessary. So a writer could convert subsection 2.1 to 2; subsection 2.2 to 3; and subsection 2.3 to 4. Of course, all the other numbering would change.

Procedure

With a Traditional Format

Comments in parentheses often emphasize points. Boldface type is another option. See EMPHASIS and BOLDFACE.

Paragraph lists are less visible than displayed lists, but they still visually emphasize points. See EMPHASIS and LISTS.

China Lake Refinery | Refinery Instruction MOGO-111

EQUIPMENT NUMBERING PROCEDURE

August 5, 1990 | Page 3 of 3

Further, ensuring that new equipment information is placed in the appropriate plant file. (Plot plans do not require updating because the plant number does not change.)

2.33 Providing maintenance coordinators with the following information: (1) appropriate equipment numbers; (2) installation, operation, and maintenance instructions; (3) complete parts lists including suggested spare parts; (4) performance curves; (5) data sheets; (6) wiring diagrams and electrical information; and (7) outline drawings. Maintenance coordinators are responsible for updating their records to reflect the new equipment.

2.34 For equipment transfers between plants or from reclamation, ensuring that equipment drawings and other equipment information are transferred to the appropriate plant files and photostat books, and that those files and books reflect the new equipment numbers.

Procedure
With an Action Format

The heading block provides the title, SOP number, date, and the number of pages. This format allows easy updating and quick reference.

BEDROCK MINING & MILLING CORPORATION

Administrative
Standard Operating Procedure

SUBJECT: DISTRIBUTION OF WEEKLY PAYCHECKS — DATE: 8 SEP 90 — S.O.P. 24, page 1 of 5

The scope defines the applicability of the procedure.

The policy statement describes the intent behind the procedure and establishes the policy's basic goals.

The contents description previews the rest of the procedure and functions as a table of contents.

Each step in the procedure opens with the person or department responsible for the step. Next comes the action associated with the step. Note that the action is stated in imperative sentences. See SENTENCES.

PURPOSE

To establish a procedure for the security and distribution of weekly paychecks.

SCOPE

This procedure applies to Bedrock Mining & Milling Corporation locations in the Billings, MT and Rock Springs, WY areas.

POLICY

Payroll checks will be distributed in such manner as to ensure their prompt delivery to maintain good management/employee relations and provide sound internal controls.

CONTENTS

Section A.	Check Custodians
Section B.	Distribution of First Shift Paychecks
Section C.	Distribution of Second and Third Shift Paychecks
Section D.	Distribution of Paychecks Before Payday
Section E.	Audit of Paycheck Distribution

SECTION A. CHECK CUSTODIANS

RESPONSIBILITY	ACTION
Each Department Head	A-1. Appoints check custodian for his or her department by signed memo to the CDS (Check Distribution Section), giving name, dept. number, and signature of check custodian.

Procedures using an action format are as schematic as possible, with headings, lists, and imperative statements. This format enhances readability and allows readers to find their particular responsibilities and actions.

The most common problem with procedures is the passive voice. Writers list actions passively, and readers often don't know who is supposed to do what. A procedure that

SUBJECT: **DISTRIBUTION OF WEEKLY PAYCHECKS** DATE: 8 SEP 90 S.O.P 24

page 2 of 5

		Informs CDS by memo of changes in check custodians. In no instance appoints a supervisor/manager who approves time cards as the check custodian.
Check Distribution Office	A-2.	Assigns a specified time for each check custodian to pick up checks at the Check Distribution Office.
	A-3.	Forwards checks to outlying check custodians via BMM courier, using locked bags.
Check Custodian	A-4.	Picks up checks at the assigned time, signing the pick-up log for the checks. If he or she misses the assigned time, picks up checks as soon as possible.
	A-5.	Prepares Form C82-974, "Notification of Personnel Transfer" (see attachment A), whenever employees are transferred to other departments or locations, and forwards it to the CDS no later than noon on the Wednesday before payday.

Quotation marks enclose titles. See QUOTATION MARKS.

says "Checks must be examined before delivery" does not indicate who is supposed to do the examining. Therefore, all steps in procedures **must** identify not only the action but also the person or department responsible. See ACTIVE/PASSIVE.

Inevitably, procedures must be updated, so the numbering system, date of creation, and any revision date need to appear on each page.

Procedure
With an Action Format

Underlining and capital letters emphasize key warnings and cautions. See EMPHASIS and UNDERLINING.

SUBJECT: **DISTRIBUTION OF WEEKLY PAYCHECKS** DATE: 8 SEP 90 S.O.P 24

page 3 of 5

	A-6.	Delivers paychecks to payees only. UNDER NO CIRCUMSTANCES GIVES PAYCHECK TO ANYONE OTHER THAN THE EMPLOYEE WHOSE NAME APPEARS ON THE CHECK.

SECTION B. DISTRIBUTION OF FIRST SHIFT PAYCHECKS

RESPONSIBILITY		ACTION
First Shift Check Custodian	B-1.	Picks up checks each Friday at the assigned time.
	B-2	Delivers checks to employees after pickup and safeguards undelivered checks. Returns checks not picked up by employees by 2:30 p.m. to the CDS by 2:45 p.m. DOES NOT HOLD CHECKS UNTIL THE FOLLOWING DAY.
First Shift Employee Who Did Not Receive a Paycheck	B-3.	Picks up undelivered check at the Check Distribution Section on the following work day.

NOTE: This procedure would have two more pages. These other pages would add little to the model, so we have omitted them.

Minutes

With a Traditional Format

The title or subject is specific. See HEADINGS.

The displayed list highlights the criteria. Each item is parallel with the others. See LISTS and PARALLELISM.

Short paragraphs enhance readability. See PARAGRAPHS.

September 16, 1990

MINUTES OF THE SEPTEMBER 15 MEETING ON THE SHUTTLE SYSTEM FROM GREEN BRIAR TO LAKEVIEW CENTER.

Attending: G. L. Benson, Frank Houck, Martha Memmert, and Jeanne Skorut.
Absent: Fred Householder.

AN OVERVIEW OF THE SHUTTLE SYSTEM CRITERIA

George Benson reviewed the working criteria for the proposed shuttle system:

1. One round trip every 2 hours (two buses in rotation), with trips starting at 7 a.m. and ending at 6 p.m. (Travel time is estimated to be about 50 minutes one way.)

2. Buses must be comfortable and attractive; they must convey a good image for our company.

3. Buses must carry at least 12 passengers.

4. Buses must be economical to operate and maintain.

MLT BUS SYSTEM'S PRELIMINARY BID

Frank Houck reviewed the preliminary bid from MLT Bus System. They proposed using two vehicles at $37.00/hour (including buses, drivers, and maintenance).

If we run the buses 11 hours a day, our weekly, monthly, and yearly fees would be as follows:

Weekly	$ 2,035
Monthly	$ 8,954
Yearly	$107,448

George Benson suggested that we look at other arrangements, given the costs of MLT Bus System. We should also develop comparable figures on costs should we decide to lease our own vans and hire drivers. Martha Memmert volunteered to get

BCC
BOUNTIFUL CHEMICAL COOPERATIVE, INC.

Traditional minutes usually attempt to record a good deal of what happened during the meeting, and they usually follow the events chronologically. The above minutes begin with a review of the proposed criteria and end with the report to Fred Householder. See ORGANIZATION.

Minutes

With a Traditional Format

Minutes of the September 15 Meeting Page 2

competitive bids from several other companies. Jeanne Skorut is going to develop an estimate of what it would cost us to lease our own vans and hire drivers. Both Martha and Jeanne will report on their findings at the October 1 meeting with Fred Householder.

Possible Changes to the Criteria

At Frank's suggestion, we discussed where and how our criteria could be more flexible. Martha made a motion that we use a single bus for most round trips, with double buses on the trips at 7 a.m. and at noon. The motion passed, so Martha and Jeanne will get estimates as they investigate the financial arrangements.

The standard paint for MLT vans is "school bus" yellow, and the initial criteria called for the buses to be painted blue and white, in keeping with our corporate colors. However, MLT estimated that painting the vans would add a one-time cost of $1,000 per van. After some discussion, we decided that the costs of painting exceeded the value of blue vans.

Frank suggested eliminating air conditioning on the buses. MLT's proposal also recommended eliminating air conditioning, which costs $2,500 per bus in initial charges and $250 per bus per week in additional operating expenses (because of fuel and maintenance costs). Jeanne pointed out that a 50-minute bus ride in the August heat and humidity would be detrimental to anyone's sanity, but the costs are astronomical. Frank suggested studying the problem further, perhaps by contacting local bus companies and the weather bureau to try to determine the feasibility of eliminating the air conditioning. The motion passed, and Frank was elected to study the problem. He will report on his findings by October 5.

George Benson will discuss our suggestions for revising the criteria with Fred Householder, who developed the initial criteria. George will inform the rest of us of Fred's decisions regarding changes.

Respectfully submitted,

Jeanne Skorut

Jeanne Skorut

Each paragraph summarizes a different motion, with some details about the discussion. The writer is following a chronological pattern: The results of the motions come late in the paragraphs.

The headings, lists, short paragraphs, and brief sentences all contribute to the overall readability, but motions and action items are potentially lost. For this reason, we recommend the action format for minutes (see the following example). See also Emphasis.

Minutes

With an Action Format

The subject line is quite specific. See HEADINGS and MEMOS.

An accurate record of attendees is essential.

Action items emphasize the people (with names boldfaced), their responsibilities, and the due dates. See BOLDFACE, EMPHASIS, and ORGANIZATION.

This overview supplies necessary background information (much as corrections to prior minutes would do).

The numbered list helps to highlight key information. See LISTS.

September 16, 1990

MINUTES OF THE SEPTEMBER 15 MEETING ON THE SHUTTLE SYSTEM FROM GREEN BRIAR TO LAKEVIEW CENTER

Attending: G. L. Benson, Frank Houck, Martha Memmert, and Jeanne Skorut
Absent: Fred Householder

ACTION ITEMS

Martha Memmert Obtain bids from several other transportation companies. (Due October 1)

Jeanne Skorut Develop an estimate of what it would cost for us to lease our own vans and hire drivers. (Due October 1)

Frank Houck Study the feasibility of eliminating air conditioning from the buses. (Due October 5)

George Benson Discuss our work with the criteria with Fred Householder, who originally drafted the criteria. (Due October 1)

AN OVERVIEW OF THE SHUTTLE SYSTEM CRITERIA

George Benson opened the meeting with a review of the criteria:

1. Buses must make one round trip every 2 hours (two buses to operate simultaneously), with trips starting at 7 a.m. and ending at 6 p.m. (Travel time is estimated to be about 50 minutes one way.
2. Buses must be comfortable and attractive—ones that convey a good image for our company.
3. Buses must carry at least 12 passengers.
4. Buses must be economical to operate and maintain.

BCC
BOUNTIFUL CHEMICAL COOPERATIVE, INC.

Action minutes highlight (1) actions during the meeting being recorded and (2) actions needed in the future (usually before the next meeting). Action minutes do not attempt to capture everything that was discussed, and they deliberately do not record the meeting in strict chronological order. See ORGANIZATION.

Some repetition is inevitable, especially if the meeting is long and the issues complex. As above, the action items duplicate items mentioned elsewhere in the minutes. See REPETITION.

Minutes

With an Action Format

The bid information is necessary background to the following motions.

This motion highlights the name of the person making the motion, but the heading could identify the issue: Other Busing Systems. See HEADINGS.

These headings highlight the content of the motion, but the person's name is included in parentheses.

Minutes of the September 15 Meeting Page 2

MLT BUS SYSTEM'S PRELIMINARY BID

Frank Houck reviewed the preliminary bid from MLT Bus System. They proposed using two vehicles at a cost per hour of $37.00 (including the buses, their drivers, and all maintenance).

If we maintained the proposed schedule of 11 hours a day, our weekly, monthly, and yearly rates would be as follows:

Weekly Fee	$ 2,035
Monthly Fee	$ 8,954
Yearly Fee	$107,448

George Benson's Motion: That we investigate other arrangements, given the costs of the MLT Bus System. Martha volunteered to investigate other companies, and Jeanne will develop an estimate of costs for leasing buses and hiring drivers.

POSSIBLE CHANGES TO THE CRITERIA

Number of Trips (motion by Martha Memmert): That we use a single bus for most trips, with double buses on the trips at 7 a.m. and at noon. The motion passed, so Martha and Jeanne will include this new criterion in their reports.

Painting of the Buses (informal motion): That we not paint the yellow MLT buses blue (BCC's corporate color). Motion passed, saving a one-time cost per van of $1,000.

Elimination of Air Conditioning (motion by Frank Houck): That we eliminate air conditioning (also recommended in the MLT proposal). Initial installation costs would be $2,500 per bus, with weekly costs of $250 per bus (because of fuel, maintenance, etc.) Frank will investigate the problem and report no later than October 5.

Report to Fred Householder: George Benson agreed to report recommended criteria revisions to Fred, who originally developed the criteria. George will report on Fred's response by October 1.

Respectfully submitted,

Jeanne Skorut

Jeanne Skorut

The format above, although not mandatory, does allow for visual openness and impact, thus making the minutes easy for readers to review. See EMPHASIS.

Action minutes still record enough information for them to be useful as a record of what the participants discussed. This information is important in case someone besides an attendee has to review the minutes.

Safety Alert

The subject line is specific enough to inform readers of the problem.

The actual alert is the point, so it opens the document. See ORGANIZATION.

The investigation revealed certain findings: These appear in short paragraphs, but a numbered list would also be possible. See LISTS and PARAGRAPHS.

Note that similar ideas are grouped together. See ORGANIZATION.

The parentheses enclose additional but nonessential information. See PARENTHESES.

This opening sentence is deliberately passive in order to highlight *alert*. See ACTIVE/PASSIVE.

ALERT RESPONSE

Alert No.:	P5 G-81	Alert Response:	TM-678-BB
Date Received:	July 11, 1990	Response Date:	August 1, 1990

Subject: **Follow Safety Procedures for Asbestos in Rivlin RK 786 Adhesive**

Alert

All personnel should use extreme caution when working with Rivlin TK 786 adhesive. These precautions include wearing dust respirators and wet sanding areas that are bonded with the adhesive (see Safety Procedure SP-56). For further information, see the attached safety notice.

Investigation

Rivlin TK 786 adhesive is used by Sky Aviation and our suppliers. This epoxy-based adhesive contains asbestos as an inert filler.

Our Production group uses the adhesive to bond flight hardware (both electrical and nonstructural) and to conduct some test operations. Our suppliers use the adhesive to bond fiberglass epoxy cable tray supports.

Although sanding and abrading is not always required, situations such as spillage can demand sanding and abrading. Sanding releases asbestos in the dust, so wet sanding is a standard precaution.

Actions Taken

This alert (and the accompanying safety notice) has been issued to all Production floor personnel. Procurement will circulate the alert and safety notice to our suppliers so they can warn their employees. Future procurement packages will contain the safety notice.

Sky Aviation

This document—called an "Alert Response"—is typical of many special documents developed to notify readers of a problem or to document an investigation. Documents such as this generally have a prescribed format that the writer must follow. The headings in the document reflect that format and indicate where readers can find particular types of information (e.g., investigative findings under "Investigation"). In keeping with the nature of the subject, the tone is formal and factual. See TONE.

Safety Alert

The final warning note uses all capital letters to emphasize the point. See EMPHASIS and HEADINGS.

Alert Response TM-678-BB -2- August 1, 1990

Materials Engineering is consulting with NASA to determine whether we can replace TK 786 with TK 780, which is a nonasbestos version of the adhesive.

<u>Actions Pending</u>

None

NOTE: THE ALERT ON TK 786 IS A PERSONNEL SAFETY PROBLEM AND DOES NOT AFFECT SKY HARDWARE.

Kitsie Gelb
RELIABILITY MANAGER

Attachment

Field Notes

The information in these blanks should be as complete as possible.

Some data, such as the date, may need to be added to printed forms.

Although telegraphic, comments should not be too brief or too cryptic.

Avoid symbols—for instance, the " for *inches* and ' for *feet*.

Be sure items in one column line up with the parallel information in other columns.

DRILLING AND SAMPLING LOG

HOLE NO. 5-4

ELEV. 4900 ±

FEATURE Irrigation Well — DEPTH 75 ft

LOCATION Sec. 18 T 17 N R 15 E — COUNTY Jasper

LOGGED BY L.H. Freyman — DATE DRILLED 7/18/90 and 7/21/90 — WATER LEVEL 16 ft (approx.)

DRILLING CO. Acme — DRILLER J. Stevens — DRILL RIG Glaser HD300

8 in. hammer bit — Starting time 3:52 — Air Rotary Drill Master

	ELEV. (DEPTH)	CLASS.	DESCRIPTION FIELD IDENTIFICATION	SAMPLE NUMBER	MODE	REMARKS
7/18	0-15		Glacial debris & collurium		Started up 12:00 noon	Set conductor 5-6 ft Dampness at start but no free water.
	15-25		Added Argo foam at 25 ft	Sample # 1 at 25 ft	Water at 15 ft 1:23 p.m.	
	25-47		Chips of Olivine basalt			35 ft—stopped to add Argo foam—to hold back caving
	47 ft		Drill rate 1 ft/min.	Sample # 2 47 ft	Down 2:48-3:10	Resume drilling 3:10
	47-50		Drilling going well			
	50-60		" " "	Sample # 3 50 ft		
	60-75				Down at 4:45	Broken air valve
			Caving—attempted to clean out—high use of Argo foam		Shut down 6:30 p.m.	
			Set 40 ft of slotted casing		Started up at 8:30 a.m.	
7/21			Water level 8 ft 4 in.			

SHEET 1 OF 1

Field notes or logs contain essential technical (even legal) information. As such, they need to be carefully written and systematically filed. Writers should use ink (or, at least, a dark lead pencil), and they should attempt to print or write as clearly and neatly as possible. If possible, writers should review their notes at least once a day and correct any obvious errors or sloppy writing (such as dotting *i*'s or connecting loops on *o*'s).

Newsletter Item

The headline captures the key idea.

The opening paragraph summarizes the who, what, where, when, how, and why.

The paragraphs are short because newsletters usually appear in narrow columns. See PARAGRAPHS.

Actual quotations help make the story more vivid and readable. See QUOTATIONS.

The dash emphasizes Joan's final summary comment. See DASHES.

Highland Wins 1989 Safety Award; Jason is Runner-up

The Highland Plant in Rimrock, Texas, has won the 1989 BCC Safety Award. This is the third straight win for Highland, which posted no lost-time accidents during 1989.

As winners, the Highland workers will all receive their choice of the following: a Coleman camp stove, a set of Oneida stainless steel dinnerware, or a Black and Decker shop vacuum with attachments.

According to Joan Tyree, Highland plant manager, "Everyone at Highland contributed to the success—it was a real team effort."

Highland supervisors conducted weekly safety meetings, and the plant offered its own $50 safety award. Jack Henderson won the award for his suggestion that the badly worn nonslip flooring in the men's shower room be replaced.

The Jason Plant in Yarrow, Oklahoma, was the 1989 runner-up for the BCC Safety Award. Yarrow employees will each receive their choice of a Norbest frozen turkey or a Swift Premium ham. The Jason Plant had only one lost-time accident during 1989.

Newsletters should be as specific and informative as possible. Thus writers should use direct quotations as well as other specific facts (such as the award prizes in the above example). Newsletters should follow the inverted organization, with the main point in the opening paragraph; this is similar to the managerial organization used in many letters and memos. See ORGANIZATION.

Newsletters should be as readable as possible, with short sentences and simple, direct words. See STYLE.

Technical Report

The title and associated data allow for careful cross-referencing and document storage and retrieval. The page notation (*1 of 4*) helps readers keep track of pages.

The one-page summary, although not asking for executive action, is almost an executive summary. See REPORTS and SUMMARIES.

The first paragraph establishes the purpose as well as the original line of investigation. See MEMOS, LETTERS, and ORGANIZATION.

The listed findings are concise. The sentences are deliberately short. See SENTENCES and SCIENTIFIC/TECHNICAL STYLE.

The recommendations and their potential cost savings conclude the summary.

RESEARCH AND DEVELOPMENT DEPARTMENT

TITLE			RDD No.
DRILLING OF THE G-175 STRUT FITTING WITH AN ACME 570			8795-3
ROUTING STATUS	CHARGE NUMBER	MODEL NUMBER (S)	PAGE NO.
Routine	3-T3743-8042-286444	G-175	1 of 3

SUMMARY

The purpose of this investigation was to determine the cause of the hole elongation in the drilling of the G-175 strut fitting. Three Acme Model 570 drills are currently used for this operation. We originally thought that improper sequencing of the feed and clamp-up system caused the elongation problem. In investigating this problem, we did the following:

1. Laboratory tests showed that one drill motor was unclamping with the drill still in the hole. We rebuilt the feed and clamp-up system to remedy this problem.

2. Further tests showed that the area of the clamp foot was too small to prevent the motor from rocking on its axis during drilling, so we designed a larger clamp foot.

3. Tests indicated that the drill motor feed rates were excessive. We corrected the feed rates on all three Acme drills.

4. The drill motors tended to stall right at the breakout of the drill, so we fabricated a Skylube application system. This modification prevents stalling.

We issued Memo 5698-4-76 recommending the larger clamp foot (CF-8765-54-A) and the new Skylube application system (LA-5767-87) for use with all Acme 570 drills now being used. We estimate that these changes will save approximately $6,000 per year by eliminating the need to rework poorly drilled holes.

Diane Metcalf	*5/30/90*
PREPARED BY	DATE
Wallace Petersen	*6/10/90*
APPROVED BY	DATE
Robert Hogge	*6/12/90*
APPROVED BY	DATE

Sky Aviation

The summary (likely limited to one page) is a powerful technique for limiting documentation and for making technical reports more accessible. Many readers will not want or need to read more than the summary. If the summary contains a few of the important details, these readers will be able to determine whether they need to read further. See REPORTS, SUMMARIES, and ORGANIZATION.

Technical Report

The brief introduction establishes the reason for and purpose of the investigation. As appropriate, relevant prior work and other background information might also appear in the introduction. See INTRODUCTIONS and REPORTS.

The displayed list highlights the proposed test and redesign program. This list actually repeats information covered under *Tests*. See REPETITION and LISTS.

The headings are not specific, but they are probably standard. All research/ investigation reports in this company have the same headings. The consistent format helps readers of many similar reports find information easily. See HEADINGS and ORGANIZATION.

Introduction

The Acme 570 drills were drilling many unsatisfactory holes in the strut fittings for the G-175 airplanes. The holes were often elongated or bell-mouthed, requiring reworking of the holes to an oversized diameter. Production Research initiated a program to determine the cause of these unsatisfactory holes.

Program Approach

To determine the cause of the problem, we developed a test and redesign program as follows:

1. Observe the Acme 570 drills in actual operation on a G-175.
2. Observe the clamp-drill cycle with a high-speed TV camera.
3. Redesign the clamp foot to increase the clamp area and reduce flexing.
4. Prepare a recommendation for Production, including a revised drilling procedure and accompanying drawings.

Tests

To determine the cause of the hole elongation, we brought one of the Acme 570 drills from the Production line to the laboratory for testing. We used a high-speed TV camera to observe the clamp-drill cycle of the drill motor. The camera showed that this motor was unclamping with the drill still in the hole. We sent this drill to Small Tool Repair for the overhaul of the clamp feed system.

The repaired Acme 570 was again tested and observed with the high-speed camera. The drill functioned well this time, but the clamp foot seemed to cover an insufficient area. The drill motor was able to move slightly during drilling. Apparently, vibration causes the drill to "migrate" during high-speed drilling, even though the bit tends to hold the drill in place. Pressure on the inside of the drill hole causes minute imperfections in the drilling circumference, which becomes exaggerated when the drill bites into one of these imperfections and causes it to elongate.

No. 8795-3
Page 2 of 3

The body of the report follows a scientific format rather than a managerial format. Thus the conclusions and recommendations appear at the end rather than at the beginning. In most cases, the sequence and specificity of the headings in the body are almost irrelevant. Most readers will not read carefully beyond the summary, and readers familiar with the report format will already understand the content and organization of ideas appearing in the body. See ORGANIZATION.

The tests are explained in the chronological order in which they were performed. The chronological pattern helps readers to follow the test sequence and therefore its logic. Note that each step ends with a conclusion or recommendation for further study.

Most paragraphs are organized chronologically, from problem to result or finding. This pattern is common in technical and scientific reports. See PARAGRAPHS.

The conclusions and recommendations can be so brief because they have already been covered—first in the summary and later in the Tests section. See ORGANIZATION and REPORTS.

To solve this problem, we designed a new clamp foot (CF-8765-54-A) with 57 percent greater surface area. Then we subjected the new clamp to 140 drill tests. During these tests, the drill did not "migrate" as before, nor did the hole elongate significantly, although some imperfections in the drilling holes were observable to the naked eye. (See attached figure 1.)

We next checked the feed rate on the drill motor for drilling the 0.309 holes. The standard rate (4,300 rpm) produces a uniform drilling shaft so long as the drill bit is aligned precisely in the drill. But if the bit is not aligned precisely, the bit produces excessive vibration and hole elongation.

To determine an optimal drill speed, we tested the drill at five speed ranges: 2,000; 2,500; 3,000; 3,500; and 4,000 rpm. Rates below 3,000 rpm were unsatisfactory because the reduced speed created more friction and thus more heat. Rates above 3,500 rpm produced excessive vibration and hole elongation with drill bits not precisely aligned. So we repeated this test using another four speed ranges: 3,100; 3,200; 3,300; and 3,400 rpm.

Of these ranges, 3,400 rpm proved to be optimal. Further adjusting revealed that 3,460 rpm ($\pm$ 30 rpm) is the best compromise rate. Accordingly, we adjusted the drilling speed to 3,460 rpm. (See Ref. 5Y114-87, Drilling and Reaming Feeds and Speeds.)

Finally, we noticed that the drill tended to stall just before the drill finished the hole. We designed a Skylube application system (LA-5767-87) to lubricate the bit (see attached figure 2). This system eliminated stalling problems. For further information on this application system, see RDD NO. 8799-6.

Conclusions and Recommendations

The Acme 570 drill was returned to the Production line in mid-September. It had a new clamp foot, a correct feed rate, and the Skylube application system. We are continuing to monitor the performance of this drill, but preliminary results are promising.

We sent a recommendation memo (5698-4-76) to B. Worth recommending that all Acme 570 drills be modified with a larger clamp foot (CF-8765-54-A) and the new Skylube application system (LA-5767-87).

Descriptive Abstract

The opening sentence identifies the what, where, and why of the study. No actual results should appear.

The pronoun *we* softens the impersonal tone and removes the need for passive sentences. See ACTIVE/PASSIVE.

The closing mention of the "guidelines" does not summarize the content of the guidelines.

Abstract of the Stimuflo Tests

After inconclusive laboratory tests,we conducted field tests in the Lubbock, Texas, area to determine if Stimuflo (from Fluid Engineering Company) is cost effective in enhancing acid stimulation. These tests, conducted from April 1988 to October 1989, contrasted oil and gas production from 14 wells stimulated with Stimuflo with production from 11 control wells stimulated using conventional acid techniques. We analyzed the results in light of Stimuflo production costs as well as differences in the average payout for all wells tested. Based on this analysis, we developed guidelines for the potential use of Stimuflo in future stimulations.

Descriptive abstracts describe the general content of a study or report, but they do not get into the actual results. As such, they are primarily useful for bibliographic cross-referencing, where someone wants to know the what, the why, and the how, but not the actual conclusions or recommendations. A descriptive abstract will, of course, mention enough specific key words to flag its content during a computer search. Key words in the above abstract would be *acid stimulation, Stimuflo, oil and gas, production*, and so on.

Informative Abstract

The opening sentence gives the key result—the cost-effectiveness of Stimuflo, under certain conditions.

The scope of the study is briefly summarized.

The results are specific enough that most readers would not need to read the actual report.

The dashes highlight a key qualification—Stimuflo's lack of success on mature wells. See DASHES.

Abstract of the Stimuflo Tests

Field tests indicate that Fluid Engineering Company's Stimuflo is a cost-effective method of enhancing acid stimulation of wells with attractive recoverable reserves. Despite inconclusive laboratory tests, field tests in the Mountain View Field (Lubbock, Texas) have demonstrated this cost-effectiveness. Over a 5-month period, 14 Mountain View wells were stimulated using Stimuflo. Another 11 wells were stimulated using conventional acid techniques. The results indicate an average recovery increase of 17.65 BOPD with Stimuflo rather than with conventional acid techniques. We predicated average payout with Stimuflo to be 14.3 months, depending on a well's production history and reservoir type. Mature wells—ones with prior stimulations—did not respond well enough to Stimuflo to warrant its use, especially given the 30 to 50 percent additional costs of using Stimuflo.

Informative abstracts give the actual information discovered—the results and any pertinent conclusions or recommendations. Primary readers for informative abstracts would be those already very familiar with the subject field and thus able to use the content of the abstract in place of ordering the whole report. As with a descriptive abstract, informative abstracts do contain many of the key words used in computer searches. Informative abstracts mention research methods and other techniques only if they are likely to be unknown to knowledgeable readers.

Scientific Report

The introduction states the problem that generated the research. See INTRODUCTIONS and REPORTS.

This abstract is informative because it presents actual conclusions. See REPORTS and SUMMARIES.

The purpose comes as early in the introduction as possible.

The scope of the tests—both their sites and dates—follows the statement of purpose. The chemicals tested could be listed here, but they already appear in the Abstract, and they will appear under METHODS AND MATERIALS.

The key words identify other words useful for computer searches based on the key words.

The first footnote, including the CAUTION, is a standard disclaimer used by many Federal and State agencies as well as some private research groups.

Termite Control Studies in Panama

ABSTRACT

Subterranean termite control studies in a tropical area (Panama) are described. Testing began in 1943 on Barro Colorado Island, which was formed when the Panama Canal was completed in the early 1900s.

Materials tested included DDT (various concentrations and formulations), BHC (benzene hexachloride), trichlorobenzene, sodium arsenite, pentachlorophenol, sodium flurosilicate, copper ammonium fluoride, aldrin, chlordane, dieldrin, and heptachlor. Dieldrin (1.0 percent), applied to the soil as a water emulsion, was still 100 percent effective after 27 years, when the tests were terminated. Tests with concentrations of 0.25 percent of aldrin, chlordane, and heptachlor were initiated in 1963, and all three chemicals were still 100 percent effective after 16 years.[1]

Additional key words: Field studies, soil treatments, test procedures, tropics.

INTRODUCTION

Termites have been damaging facilities of the Panama Canal ever since it was constructed in the early 1900s. Termites have also severely damaged nearby military facilities in the Canal Zone.

To evaluate various chemicals for their effectiveness in preventing termite damage in a tropical environment, a series of long-term field evaluations began in 1943 and were continued in 1946.

These initial tests were conducted on Barro Colorado Island, Panama. The island, formed by canal construction, is in the Canal about 18 miles from the Atlantic outlet. Since 1924 it has been under the jurisdiction of the Smithsonian Institute.

From 1951 to 1953, termite-control studies were considerably expanded in an area known as the Curundu Jungle Test Site at Fort Clayton on the Pacific side of the Isthmus. In 1963 more tests were initiated at a site adjacent to Curundu.

---

[1]This publication reports research involving insecticides. It does not contain recommendations for their use, nor does it imply that the uses discussed here have been registered. All uses of pesticides must be registered by appropriate State and Federal agencies before they can be recommended.

CAUTION: Pesticides can be injurious to humans, domestic animals, desirable plants, and fish or other wildlife—if they are not handled or applied properly. Use all pesticides selectively and carefully. Follow recommended practices for the disposal of surplus pesticides and pesticide containers.

This scientific report is based on a technical paper published by the U.S. Department of Agriculture.

The report follows the scientific pattern—the discussion leads down to the conclusions. Note, however, that the abstract summarizes key conclusions. See ORGANIZATION and REPORTS.

The sponsor of the research is optional if the title, the publication name, or footnotes do not clearly identify the sponsor.

The figures use action captions and are clearly labeled. See VISUAL AIDS and CAPTIONS.

The introduction ends with a brief note suggesting value or applications.

METHODS AND MATERIALS should be no longer than necessary. The actual test methods should be described, but some of the detail about the chemicals tested might be left for tables or appendices. See REPORTS and APPENDICES/ATTACHMENTS.

The U.S. Tropical Entomology Laboratory of the United States War and Navy Departments originally sponsored these tests; in 1951, however, sponsorship passed to the Pesticide Service of the Department of Agriculture.

All tests ceased in 1979 when jurisdiction of the test areas reverted to the Republic of Panama.

Although many of the test chemicals did not satisfactorily prevent termites from damaging test materials, the test results should provide baseline data for interpreting the results from future termite control tests in tropical environments.

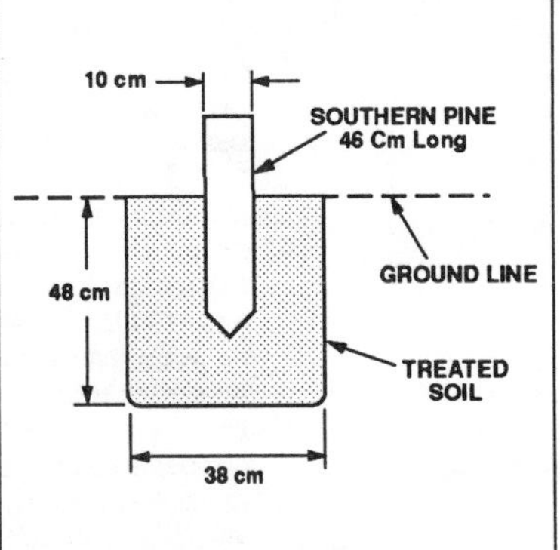

Figure 1. Stake Test Method. *The method evaluates insecticide protection for wood that is underground.*

METHODS AND MATERIALS

Two standard test methods were used during these studies. The test methods were altered slightly in later tests because of lessons learned in the early tests.

Standard Test Methods

Method 1. The stake test, illustrated in figure 1, consisted of digging a hole 38 cm in diameter and 48 cm deep, removing approximately 0.057 m^3 of soil, and then treating the soil before replacing it. A wooden stake (5 x 10 x 46 cm) was driven 31 cm deep in the center of this treated soil to serve as bait for the termites.

This bait stake was either southern pine or some other termite-susceptible wood that indicated at annual inspections whether termites had penetrated the treated soil around the stake.

Each stake site was placed a minimum of 1.5 m away from other sites. Each concentration of each chemical was repeated 10 times in a randomized test block. When termites had penetrated the soil in 5 of the 10 identical sites, the chemical treatment was considered a failure.

The 1943 Barro Colorado stake tests, which used 39 different chemical treatments, were the first termite studies conducted under tropical conditions. Treatments included sodium arsenite as a dry powder and as a 10 percent solution in water; creosote in various oils; 5 percent pentachloro- phenol; orthodichlorobenzene in oil, in creosote, and in creosote plus diesel oil; and diesel oil controls.

The tone of the report is formal and generally impersonal. Few pronouns appear, and some sentences are deliberately passive to avoid using personal pronouns. See SCIENTIFIC/TECHNICAL STYLE.

The amount of detail in reports is always open to debate. This report might well have been little more than a research note—with findings limited to the final studies and their results. Such abbreviated reports would probably reduce or eliminate the METHODS AND MATERIALS

Scientific Report

The reference to the figure is specific and falls on the same page as the figure. See CAPTIONS and VISUAL AIDS.

The hyphen is necessary because *43-cm²* is a compound adjective modifying *area*. See HYPHENS.

The paragraphs giving the different test materials open with dates and sites because the dates and sites are used as subheadings in the RESULTS section. This logical tracking helps to improve readability. See HEADINGS, PARAGRAPHS, and KEY WORDS.

The 1946 Barro Colorado stake tests included different dosages of 16 chemicals and methods for a total of 54 treatments. Dosages were 1.69, 3.38, and 6.76 liter/m^3 of soil for plots with the standard 38-cm diameter x 48-cm deep hole (0.057 m^3). Some of the more recognizable formulations included 5.0 percent DDT in water; 5.0 percent DDT in acetylenetetrachloride; 0.8 percent benzene hexachoride (BHC) in kerosene; copper naphthanate (2 percent copper in kerosene); lead arsenate, as dry powder at 227-g dosage and in water, 227 g in 0.94 liter at a 0.94 liter dosage; 5 percent monochloronaphthalene in kerosene; kerosene controls; and untreated controls.

In 1951 and 1952, a new series of standardized stake tests was installed at Curundu in a new test area. The 1952 group included the following emulsions and fuel oil solutions:

— 5.0 percent DDT in oil

— 5.0 percent DDT plus 2.0 percent chlordane in oil

— 20.0 percent DDT in Xylene

— 0.50, 1.0, and 2.0 percent dieldrin in water

— 0.4 percent gamma BHC in oil

— Trichlorobenzene in diesel oil (3:1 ratio)

— Untreated controls, both oil and water

Dosages were 6.76 and 10.1 liters/m^3 for the emulsions and oils, and 0.94 and 1.88 liters for the DDT concentrate.

Method 2. The ground-board test, as illustrated in figure 2, was designed to test conditions when wooden military equipment had to be laid on the jungle floor. However, the test also evaluated wooden construction materials used beneath slab-type houses.

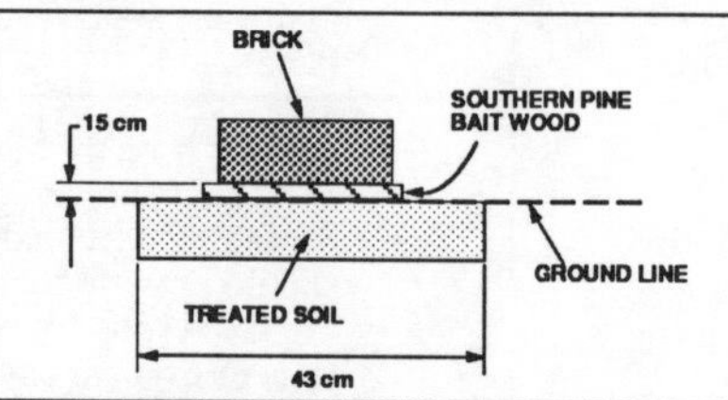

Figure 2. Ground-Board Test Method. *This method evaluates insecticide protection for wood that will be on or above the ground.*

The method consisted of removing the duff and debris from a 43-cm² area of soil to expose the surface soil. The chemical to be evaluated was then sprinkled on the soil and a wooden pine board (30 x 30 x 2.5 cm) was placed in the center of the treated area. A rock or brick was then laid on the board to hold it in place.

The board was examined annually for termite damage, which, if found, indicated that termites had penetrated the treated soil. Ten duplicate sites for each test material were also used in this method, and randomizing was complete within blocks. Again, when termites had penetrated 5 of the 10 identical sites, the treatment was considered a failure.

In 1946, a series of ground-board treatments were established on Barro Colorado Island not only to determine the chemical effectiveness in controlling termites but also to compare the results with earlier stake test results (method 1).

discussion and omit discussion of those chemicals that were ineffective. However, this data may be very significant because it tells other researchers what not to consider in future studies.

The two-column format is standard for many research reports. For this format to be effective, paragraphs must be shorter than normal because long single-column paragraphs become excessive in a two-column format. See SPACING, PARAGRAPHS, and VISUAL AIDS.

Scientific Report

The numbers are not spelled out because some of them are greater than nine. See NUMBERS.

The displayed list, introduced by dashes, helps make the dense technical names and amounts more readable. See LISTS.

Test boards were placed on 10 tilled sites and on 10 untilled sites in this heavily shaded jungle area. The 43 materials tested included 3 dosages each of 13 chemical formulations and 4 untreated controls. The formulations consisted of the following:

— Acetylenetetrachloride

— 5.0 percent DDT in diesel oil

— 5.0 percent DDT in waste motor oil

— 5.0 percent DDT in kerosene

— 5.0 percent DDT in gasoline

— 10.0 percent sodium arsenite in water

— Diesel oil, waste motor oil, kerosene, and gasoline

Dosages were 2.5, 5.1, and 10.1 liters of formulation/m^2 area of soil surface.

In 1951 and 1952 and again in 1953, groundboard surface tests, using 0.37 m^2 of treated soil and 2 x 15 x 15-cm bait boards, were initiated at the Curundu Jungle Test Site. The 1951-52 tests used the following materials:

— 0.5 percent pentachlorophenol in fuel oil and water

— 0.5 percent gamma BHC in oil

— 0.4 percent gamma BHC in water

— 5.0 percent DDT in oil and water

— 2.0 percent chlordane in oil and water

The oil formulations were put in at dosages of 0.47 and 0.94 liters; the water emulsions were at 0.94 and 1.41 liters. Additional formulations included:

— 5.0 percent pentachlorophenol plus 0.5 percent gamma BHC in oil

— 5.0 percent DDT in oil

— 5.0 percent sodium flurosilicate dry powder (113- and 170-g dosages)

— 0.5 percent copper ammonium fluoride in water

— Tetrachlorobenzene mixture with fuel oil

— Trichlorobenzene mixture with fuel oil

— Orthodichlorobenzene mixture with fuel oil

In 1953, tests of 10 dieldrin emulsion treatments of 1.0 and 2.0 percent, and 3 oil solutions of 0.5, 1.0, and 2.0 percent were initiated at 0.47 and 0.94 liters each.

In 1963, tests with a much wider range of previously proven insecticides were initiated in a jungle site close to the Curundu Jungle Test Site. This site was carefully selected to include as many species of subterranean termites as possible. The purposes were (1) to determine the lowest effective rate and dosage of emulsifiable concentrate of aldrin, chlordane, dieldrin, and heptachlor in a tropical exposure, and (2) to determine the efficacy of granular forms of insecticides when applied to the soil surface.

Scientific Report

The RESULTS AND DISCUSSION section presents information based on site and test data. This pattern reflects the pattern established in METHODS AND MATERIALS. See REPETITION and ORGANIZATION.

The boldfaced subheadings enhance readability and allow for quick cross-referencing and skimming. See HEADINGS and EMPHASIS.

The reference to table 2 becomes part of the actual discussion of results. See VISUAL AIDS.

The 48 separate treatments included chlordane and dieldrin at 0.03, 0.06, 0.12, 0.25, 0.50, 1.0, and 2.0 percent and aldrin and heptachlor at 0.06 and 0.25 percent. The application rates were 946 and 1982 mL/929 cm^2. Aldrin, dieldrin, and heptachlor granules were applied to the soil to give equivalencies of 0.12, 0.25, 0.50, and 1.0 percent applied at the rate of 10.12 liters/m^2. Chlordane granules were applied at only 0.25 and 0.50 percent.

RESULTS AND DISCUSSION

Barro Colorado - 1943—Stake Tests

By 1952 (9 years), all treatments except those that included sodium arsenite had failed to prevent termites from attacking the wood-bait stakes. When the tests ended in 1954, the arsenite treatments of 810, 1620, and 2430 g/m^3 of dry chemical and 4.73 mL of 10 percent solution in water/m^3 were providing termite protection under the severe tropical exposure.

Barro Colorado - 1946—Stake Tests

By 1952 (6 years), all treatments except 2 DDT formulations, 2 BHC, 4 monochloronaphthalene, 4 copper naphthanate, and 1 lead arsenate had failed to prevent termite attacks. The 1954 (8-year) inspection showed that only the 8.0 percent DDT in acetylenetetrachloride treatment still had limited effectiveness. In the DDT treatment, soil in 6 of the 10 sites had not been penetrated by termites—60 percent protection.

Barro Colorado - 1946—Ground-Board Tests

When the test was closed in 1954 (8 years), only 2 formulations continued to provide control: 5.0 percent DDT in diesel oil and 10 percent sodium arsenate in water. They were giving 80 percent protection, which, by today's standards, would not be acceptable for recommendation as subterranean termite control. The results of the new method were so similar to those from the more difficult and time-consuming stake tests that the new ground-board method was selected for future studies.

Curundu - 1952-53—Stake Tests

As table 1 indicates, dieldrin and chlordane were the most effective test materials; DDT was the next most effective, and BHC was the least effective.

The recorded attacks during the second and third test years to the test sites with the highest concentrations of dieldrin and chlordane might have been anomalies because few or no further attacks occurred at sites with these concentrations.

In soil treated with BHC, attacks were noted at the end of the fifth year. By the end of the ninth year, multiple attacks throughout the treated soil had occured.

Curundu - 1951-1953—Ground-Board Tests

As table 2 indicates, the only chemical concentrations that remained 100 percent effective for the entire 26 years were 1.0 percent dieldrin at 15.18 liters/m^2 and 2.0 percent dieldrin at 10.12 liters/m^2.

Scientific Report

The table is clear and easy to read despite the mass of data presented. See Tables.

This first table provides actual and essential results; earlier tests are summarized in the text, not in fully developed and unnecessary tables. See Tables.

The table is oriented horizontally so readers do not have to turn the page. See Tables.

The table caption is an action caption. See Captions and Tables.

Table 1. Evaluation of Insecticides Using Standard Stake Tests. *The 1952 to 1953 tests at Curundu, Panama, show that dieldrin and chlordane were the most effective insecticides.*

Treatment designation and material	Rate of application liters/m²	Percentage of stakes undamaged by termites after exposure for indicated years															
		1	2	3	4	5	7	9	11	13	15	17	19	21	23	25	27
5.0% DDT in fuel oil	6.76	100	100	100	100	100	100	100	80	70	70	50	...	...	...	...	...
5.0% DDT in fuel oil	10.1	100	100	100	100	100	100	90	70	50	...	...	...	...	...	...	...
5.0% DDT in water	6.76	100	90	80	80	80	60	50	...	...	...	...	...	...	...	...	...
5.0 % DDT in water	10.1	100	100	100	100	100	100	80	80	80	80	80	70	70	70	60	50
2.0 % chlordane in fuel oil	10.1	100	100	100	100	100	100	100	100	100	100	100	100	90[1]	90	90	90
2.0% chlordane in water	10.1	100	90	90	90	90	90	90	90	90	90	90	90	90	90	90	90
5.0% DDT + 2% chlordane in fuel oil	6.76	100	100	100	100	100	100	100	80	80	80	80	80	80	80	80	80
5.0% DDT + 2% chlordane in fuel oil	10.1	100	90	90	90	90	90	90	80	80	80	80	70	70	70	70	70
5.0% penta in fuel oil	6.76	100	100	100	70	70	70	70	30	...	...	...	...	...	...	...	...
5.0% penta in fuel oil	10.1	100	100	100	100	100	90	70	50	...	...	...	...	...	...	...	...
0.5% gamma BHC in fuel oil	6.76	100	100	100	100	100	80	70	60	50	...	...	...	...	...	...	...
0.5% gamma BHC in fuel oil	10.1	100	100	100	100	90	70	50	...	...	...	...	...	...	...	...	...
0.4% gamma BHC emulsion	6.76	100	100	90	90	80	70	50	...	...	...	...	...	...	...	...	...
0.4 gamma BHC emulsion	10.1	100	100	100	100	90	90	70	60	60	60	60	50	...	...	...	...
Fuel oil control	10.1	100	100	80	60	40	20	...	...	...	...	...	...	...	...	...	...
20% DDT concentration in Xylene	3.38	100	100	100	100	90	80	80	70	60	60	60	60	60	60	60	60
20% DDT concentration in Xylene	6.76	100	100	100	100	90	90	80	80	80	80	70	60	60	50[1]	...	...
Untreated control	......	50	20	0	0	0	80	30	40	30	40	40	20	30[1]	20	10	0
25% trichlorbenzene in fuel oil 1:3	6.76	100	90	90	80	70	60	50	...	...	...	...	...	...	...	...	...
0.5% dieldrin in fuel oil	6.76	100	100	100	100	100	100	100	100	100	100	100	90	90	70[1]	60	50
0.5% dieldrin in fuel oil	10.1	100	100	100	100	100	100	100	90	90	90	90	80	80	70[1]	40	...
1.0% dieldrin in fuel oil	6.76	100	100	100	100	100	100	100	80	80	80	80	80	80	80	80	80
1.0% dieldrin in fuel oil	10.1	100	100	100	100	100	100	100	90	90	90	90	90	90	90	90	90
2.0% dieldrin in fuel oil	6.76	100	100	100	100	100	100	100	100	90	90	90	90	90	90	90	90
2.0% dieldrin in fuel oil	10.1	100	100	100	100	100	100	100	100	100	100	100	100	100	100	100	100
1.0% dieldrin emulsion	10.1	100	100	100	100	100	100	100	100	100	100	100	100	100	100	100	100
2.0% dieldrin emulsion	10.1	100	100	90	90	90	90	80	80	80	80	80	80	80	80	80	80

[1] These attacks were made by *Heterotemes* sp.

Table 2. Evaluation of Insecticides Using Ground-Board Tests. *The 1952 to 1953 tests at Curundu, Panama, show the dieldrin was an effective insecticide for 26 years.*

Treatment designation and materials	Rate of application liters/m²	Percentage of ground boards undamaged by termites after exposure for indicated years															
		1	2	3	4	5	6	8	10	12	14	16	18	20	22	24	26
MOGO Oil Co. #1 Termicide Oil	5.06	100	50	...	...	...	...	...	...	...	...	...	...	...	...	...	...
Same as above plus 5% penta	5.06	90	50	40	...	...	...	...	...	...	...	...	...	...	...	...	...
Same as above plus 2% copper naphthanate	5.06	90	50	50	...	...	...	...	...	...	...	...	...	...	...	...	...
MOGO Oil Co. #6 Weed-Death	5.06	100	70	60	60	50	...	...	...	...	...	...	...	...	...	...	...
Same as above plus 5% penta	5.06	90	50	...	...	...	...	...	...	...	...	...	...	...	...	...	...
Same as above plus 2% copper naphthanate	5.06	90	60	50	...	...	...	...	...	...	...	...	...	...	...	...	...
1.0% Dieldrin in water	5.06	100	100	100	100	100	100	100	100	100	89	89	89	89	89	75	75
1.0% Dieldrin in water	7.59	100	100	100	100	100	100	100	100	100	100	100	100	100	100	100	100
2.0% Dieldrin in water	5.06	100	100	100	100	100	100	100	100	100	100	100	100	100	100	100	100
2.0% Dieldrin in water	7.59	100	100	100	100	100	100	100	100	89	89	89	89	89	89	89	89
0.5% Dieldrin in fuel oil	2.53	100	100	100	100	100	100	100	100	100	90	90	90	70	50[1]	...	...
0.5% Dieldrin in fuel oil	5.06	100	100	100	100	100	100	100	100	100	100	80	80	80	30[1]	...	...
1.0% Dieldrin in fuel oil	2.53	100	100	100	100	100	100	100	90	90	90	90	90	80	50[1]	...	...
1.0% Dieldrin in fuel oil	5.06	100	100	100	100	100	100	100	80	80	80	80	80	70[1]	70	70	70
2.0% Dieldrin in fuel oil	2.53	100	100	100	100	100	100	100	100	100	100	100	100	100	100	100	75[1]
2.0% Dieldrin in fuel oil	5.06	100	100	100	100	100	100	100	100	100	100	100	100	89	89	89	89
Untreated control	......	50	60	50	70	50	50	40	50	50	70	70	30	20	40	40	40[1]

[1] These attacks were made by *Heterotemes* sp.

Scientific Report

In fuel-oil mixtures, the 2.0 dieldrin sustained some attacks after 26 years, the 1.0 dieldrin after 20 years. Both concentrations gave excellent protection, but since oil is no longer used as a carrier for termiticides except in special cases, these formulations are not suggested for use.

Dieldrin at both 0.5 percent and 1.0 percent at 5.06 liters/m^2 of soil surface area failed (less than 50 percent effective) at 22 years.

Even though this is excellent long-term protection, it did not protect as long as dieldrin installed in tests in Mississippi.[2]

[2] Jason B. Kline and Josephine Everett, "Termite-Resistant Woods," *Southern Agricultural Studies*, 11 (February 1972), 35-37.

Table 3. Evaluation of Granular Insecticides Using Ground-Board Tests. *In the 1963 granular-insecticide test, aldrin proved the most effective, but some attacks occurred in the ninth year and failed in the fifteenth year.*

Formulation (approx % by wt.)	Rate of application liters/m^2	Percentage of ground boards undamaged by termites after exposure for indicated years															
		1	2	3	4	5	6	7	8	9	10	11	12	13	14	15	16
Aldrin (actual)																	
0.067	5.06	100	100	100	100	100	100	100	100	90	80	80	70	60	60	30	...
	10.12	100	100	100	100	100	100	100	100	100	100	100	100	90	70	70	60
0.25	5.06	100	100	100	100	100	100	100	100	100	100	100	100	100	100	100	100
	10.12	100	100	100	100	100	100	100	100	100	100	100	100	100	100	100	100
Dieldrin (actual)																	
0.033	5.06	100	100	100	90	90	90	80	70	50	...	...	...	...	...	...	...
	10.12	100	100	90	90	80	80	80	80	50	...	...	...	...	...	...	...
0.067	5.06	100	100	100	90	90	90	90	80	60	50	...	...	...	...	...	...
	10.12	100	100	100	100	100	100	90	80	80	80	50	...	...	...	...	...
0.125	5.06	100	100	100	100	100	100	100	100	100	100	90	70	50	...	...	...
	10.12	100	100	100	100	100	100	100	100	100	100	100	100	100	70	60	60
0.25	5.06	100	100	100	100	100	100	100	100	100	100	100	100	100	100	100	90
	10.12	100	100	100	100	100	100	100	100	100	100	100	100	100	100	100	100
0.50	5.06	100	100	100	100	100	100	100	100	100	100	100	100	100	100	100	100
	10.12	100	100	100	100	100	100	100	100	100	100	100	100	100	100	100	100
1.0	5.06	100	100	100	100	100	100	100	100	100	100	100	100	100	100	100	100
	10.12	100	100	100	100	100	100	100	100	100	100	100	100	100	100	100	100
Heptachlor (actual)																	
0.067	5.06	100	100	100	100	100	100	100	100	100	100	90	70	60	...	...	...
	10.12	100	100	100	100	100	100	100	100	100	100	100	100	80	80	50	...
0.25	5.06	100	100	100	100	100	100	100	100	100	100	100	100	100	100	100	90
	10.12	100	100	100	100	100	100	100	100	100	100	100	100	100	100	100	100
Chlordane (technical)																	
0.033	5.06	100	100	100	80	70	60	60	60	50	...	...	...	...	...	...	...
	10.12	100	100	100	70	70	70	40	...	...	...	...	...	...	...	...	...
0.067	5.06	100	90	90	90	80	80	80	70	40	...	...	...	...	...	...	...
	10.12	100	100	100	100	100	90	90	80	70	70	50	...	...	...	...	...
0.125	5.06	100	100	100	100	100	100	90	90	80	80	70	50	...	...	...	...
	10.12	100	100	100	100	100	90	90	90	80	80	80	70	50	...	...	...
0.25	5.06	100	100	100	100	100	100	100	100	90	60	60	40	...	...	...	...
	10.12	100	100	100	100	100	100	100	100	100	100	100	100	100	100	100	100
0.5	5.06	100	100	100	100	100	100	100	100	100	90	80	80	80	80	80	80
	10.12	100	100	100	100	100	100	100	100	100	100	100	100	100	100	100	100
1.0	5.06	100	100	100	100	100	100	100	100	100	100	100	100	100	100	100	100
	10.12	100	100	100	100	100	100	100	100	90	90	90	90	90	90	90	90
2.0	5.06	100	100	100	100	100	100	100	100	100	100	100	100	100	100	100	100
	10.12	100	100	100	100	100	100	100	100	100	100	100	100	100	100	100	100
Untreated control	0	50	50	70	40	60	50	40	50	10	0	10	0	0	40	10	10

Paragraphs (for the 1963 ground-board results) are each focused on a single type of result. SEE PARAGRAPHS.

Besides dieldrin (the only true pesticide), the tested chemicals included mainly different oils, which were ineffective. As table 2 indicates, only a MOGO Oil Company[3] weed killer gave 50 percent control for more than 4 years.

The results of these 1951-53 tests apply especially to *Heterotermes convexinotatus* Snyder and *Heterotermes tenuis* Hagen because these were the predominant species found in the study areas.

Ground-Board Series - 1963

At concentrations of 0.25 percent or more, aldrin, heptachlor, chlordane, and dieldrin all provided excellent protection until the tests ended in the sixteenth year (1979). As table 3 indicates, aldrin was slightly more effective than the others, all of which had at least some attacks by the sixteenth year.

At concentrations of 0.067 percent (see table 3), aldrin was also the most resistant, although some attacks did occur as early as the ninth year, with failure in the fiteenth year. Heptachlor was the next most resistant, with attacks occurring in the eleventh year and failure in the thirteenth year. At this concentration, dieldrin and chlordane both failed in the ninth year. (Concentrations were considered failures when termites attacked over 50 percent of the test sites with those concentrations.)

Table 4 presents the results of the granular insecticides applied directly to the soil. Only 5 treatments (0.50 percent and 1.0 percent aldrin, 0.50 percent and 1.0 percent dieldrin, and 1.0 percent heptachlor) remained 100 percent effective for the duration (16 years) of the study. The earliest attack occurred in the fifth year on 0.125 percent and 0.25 percent

---

[3]MOGO has neither financed nor sponsored this research. All results and conclusions are the responsibility of the authors.

Table 4. Evaluation of Granular Insecticides Applied Directly to the Soil

Formulation (approx. % by weight)	Weight of toxicant applied[1] (g/932 cm²)	Percentage of ground boards undamaged by termites after indicated years															
		1	2	3	4	5	6	7	8	9	10	11	12	13	14	15	16
Aldrin (actual)																	
0.125	1.19	100	100	100	100	100	90	90	90	90	90	90	80	70	70	30	...
0.25	2.37	100	100	100	100	100	100	100	100	100	100	100	100	90	90	90	80
0.50	4.73	100	100	100	100	100	100	100	100	100	100	100	100	100	100	100	100
1.0	9.46	100	100	100	100	100	100	100	100	100	100	100	100	100	100	100	100
Dieldrin (actual)																	
0.125	1.19	100	100	100	100	100	100	100	100	100	100	90	80	80	80	80	70
0.25	2.37	100	100	100	100	100	100	100	100	100	100	100	100	100	100	100	90
0.50	4.73	100	100	100	100	100	100	100	100	100	100	100	100	100	100	100	100
1.0	9.46	100	100	100	100	100	100	100	100	100	100	100	100	100	100	100	100
Chlordane (technical)																	
0.25	2.37	100	100	100	100	100	100	100	100	80	80	80	50	...	...	...	...
0.50	4.73	100	100	100	100	100	100	100	100	100	100	100	100	100	90	90	90
Heptachlor (actual)																	
0.125	1.19	100	100	100	100	90	90	90	90	80	80	70	60	60	40	...	...
0.25	2.37	100	100	100	100	90	90	90	90	90	80	80	70	60	50	...	...
0.50	4.73	100	100	100	90	90	90	90	90	90	90	90	90	90	90	90	90
1.0	9.46	100	100	100	100	100	100	100	100	100	100	100	100	100	100	100	100
Untreated control	......	50	50	70	40	60	50	40	50	10	0	10	0	0	40	10	10

[1] The amounts shown in this column are equivalent to amounts of toxicant that are applied for each percentage of 946 mL/932 cm² in water emulsion.

Scientific Report

Italics is used for the names of the different species of termites. See ITALICS.

The numbered list of conclusions emphasizes their importance even though they come last in the report. See LISTS, ORGANIZATION, and REPORTS.

heptachlor. Generally, these granular treatments did not perform as well as the emulsions, but this was expected because the granular materials were more subject to washing by rainfall than emulsions.

The species of termites penetrating the soil (either *Coptotermes* sp. or *Heterotermes* sp.) were recorded but in many cases, the wooden monitoring baits were destroyed and no termites were present. Based on the termites that could be identified, the predominant termites in the study area were *Coptotermes niger* Snyder, H. *convexinotatus* and H. *tenuis*. *Nasutitermes corniger* Motsch, and *Microcerotermes arboreus* Emerson were also found in the area.

CONCLUSIONS

1. Aldrin is the best chemical to use. No attacks occurred on any soil treated with 0.25 percent solution or higher.
2. Heptachlor is slightly more effective than dieldrin. Both were 90 percent effective at 0.25 percent after 16 years, but 0.067 percent dieldrin was attacked earlier than 0.067 heptachlor.
3. All granular materials at 0.50 percent appear equally effective; however, use labels are not available for granules at this time.

Model Documents Index

Model Documents Index

NOTE: This index does not include page numbers from the Reference Glossary. See the Reference Glossary Index if you need more information about a specific topic.

Model Documents Index

Please give us your comments and suggestions.

We are dedicated to making this *Style Guide* the finest of its kind. You can help by telling us what you like or don't like about it.

Have you found the *Style Guide* easy to use? Has it been helpful? Has it answered your questions? Are the rules and examples clear? Is our coverage of topics relevant to your work and the kind of writing you do?

Please write your comments and suggestions in the space below. Then fold this postage-paid mailer as indicated and staple it closed. If you need additional space for comments, simply fold a separate sheet of paper inside the mailer.

Use the **Order Form** on the reverse side of this page to order additional copies of the *Style Guide*. You may also wish to check the **Request for Information** form to receive more information about Shipley Associates training programs and services.

Thank you for your comments and suggestions.

First Fold

Fold

Fold

Put an end to uncertainties about writing—order your copy of the Shipley Associates Style Guide, Revised Edition, today!

The *Style Guide* costs $34.95 plus $2.00 a copy for shipping and handling. Allow 6-8 weeks for delivery.

Please indicate your order below. Enclose your check, money order, or PO# ____________. If you prefer, order at (801) 295-2386 or FAX (801) 292-3983.

_____ For Business and Industry

_____ For Oil and Gas Professionals

SAVE! Order in bulk.

☐ Please check if you want information about bulk orders. (Reduced prices are available if you want to order more than 20 *Style Guides*.)

☐ Please check if you want information on tailoring the *Shipley Associates Style Guide, Revised Edition,* for your company.

Name ________________________

Title ________________________

Company/Agency ________________________

Address ________________________

____

City, State, Zip ________________________

Phone (   ) ________________________

NO POSTAGE NECESSARY IF MAILED IN THE UNITED STATES

BUSINESS REPLY MAIL

FIRST CLASS PERMIT NO. 136 BOUNTIFUL, UTAH

POSTAGE WILL BE PAID BY ADDRESSEE

Shipley Associates
Writing in the World of Work
P.O. Box 460
Bountiful, Utah 84011

The Shipley Associates Style Guide is so full of relevant facts and examples, you'll reach for it every day!

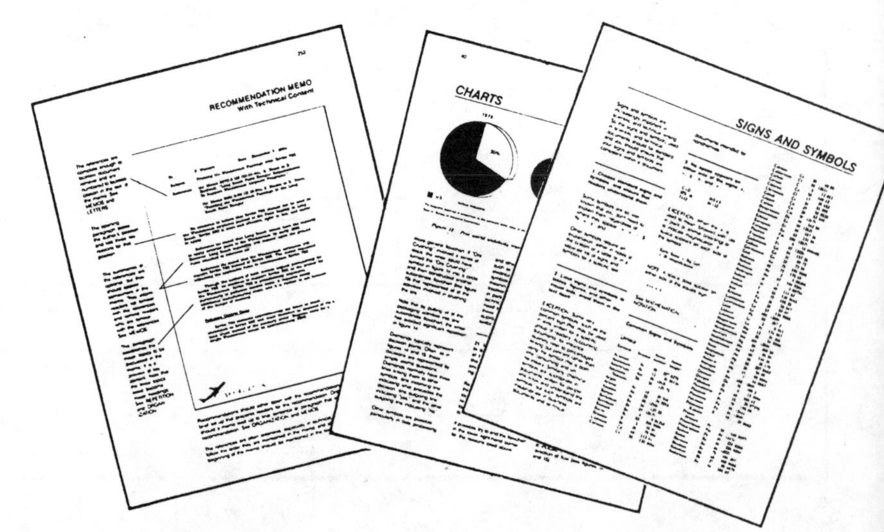